Moffett Field on May 21, 1940. City of Mountain View (upper left). Beginning of NACA construction. Flight research building in foreground. Existing Army buildings at left.

Ames Research Center on December 14, 1965.

Dr. Smith J. DeFrance, Director of Ames Research Center from 1940 to 1965.

NASA SP-4302

ADVENTURES IN RESEARCH

A HISTORY OF AMES RESEARCH CENTER 1940-1965

Edwin P. Hartman

NASA Center History Series

Scientific and Technical Information Division
OFFICE OF TECHNOLOGY UTILIZATION   1970
NATIONAL AERONAUTICS AND SPACE ADMINISTRATION
Washington, D.C.

BM
2-88

For sale by the Superintendent of Documents,
U.S. Government Printing Office, Washington, D.C. 20402

Library of Congress Catalog Card Number 78-601606

To Smitty DeFrance

The laboratory he founded bears
the stamp of his integrity

FOREWORD

NASA's Ames Research Center completed its first 25 years and experienced its first change of leadership in 1965. That juncture suggested that the story of those eventful years should be written.

We were especially fortunate to engage Edwin P. Hartman to write this story. During most of the period covered, his principal official duty had been to observe and report to NACA and NASA management the whole spectrum of aeronautical and space activities and developments in the western United States in industry, government, universities, and the Ames Research Center. He had been in an ideal position to evaluate Ames activities and relate them to contemporary events. His written reports in that period had attracted attention to his skills as a keen observer and perceptive reporter.

Hartman's academic training was as an engineer. At Marquette University he earned a professional mechanical engineer degree, and later at California Institute of Technology, a master's degree in mechanical engineering.

From 1930 to 1940 Hartman engaged in aeronautical research as an engineer at NACA's Langley Memorial Aeronautical Laboratory. There he worked with the men who were sent to California in 1940 to establish the Ames Research Center. In 1940 he was appointed NACA Western Coordination Officer in charge of the NACA's fledgling Western Coordination Office. Though it was never a part of Ames, Hartman's office was at first housed in the temporary building from which initial construction of Ames facilities was being supervised. Later, his office was moved to the Los Angeles area. In 1960 Hartman undertook what was to become a four-year tour of duty as NASA Senior Scientific Representative in Australia. A few months after he returned to the United States in 1964, retirement gave him freedom to accept the writing commission.

Ed Hartman's qualifications for writing this book were complemented by those of his wife. Miss Jean Kinsley, a fellow employee at the Langley Laboratory as editor of NACA reports, became Hartman's wife in 1939. When Hartman undertook his west coast assignment, Jean became his secretary. Ed Hartman's staff was small, so his wife-secretary served as an assistant. Thus, Jean, too, was constantly alert to aeronautical and space activities and to the fortunes of the Ames Research Center. Her career prepared her well to serve as her husband's secretary, critic, and assistant in writing this book.

The author's close, professional, personal observations of the events and developments as they took place strongly influenced what he has written. The opinions and judgments expressed in this book are wholly those of the author and were curtailed by NASA in no significant degree. He was given freedom to choose the content, style, format, and organization of the material presented and to make his own interpretations. The manuscript has been reviewed for factual accuracy by some 30 NASA personnel familiar with various phases and aspects of the history.

We, at Ames, feel that this book reflects accurately and sensitively the Center's first quarter-century. We feel that this true story is a tribute to Ames' Director throughout that period, Dr. Smith J. DeFrance.

H. JULIAN ALLEN,
Director, Ames Research Center
1968

PREFACE

DURING the past few decades the pace of research has been such that the story behind important research developments often has been lost—inundated and rendered quaint by the outpourings of more recent and more sophisticated research activities. It is not, of course, the research results that are lost, for these facts are safely recorded in technical journals. What is lost is the connective tissue of background conditions, motivating influences, and human experiences that tie the cold facts together and invest them with additional dimensions of warmth and meaning. Research scientists, a forward-looking lot, show a remarkable indifference to this loss and appear quite content as long as their work is brought to the attention of their scientific peers through the normal professional channels. Research management, on the other hand, takes a somewhat more humane view of the situation. Out of consideration for the public interest, and with a certain pride of accomplishment, the management of a research agency will, in some instances, go to some trouble and expense to ensure that the story of the agency's past activities is told—and recorded for posterity. Such motivational factors are responsible for the present work.

The present document, which I have called a history—though it certainly was not written for historians—was prepared for and at the request of the NASA Ames Research Center which, in sponsoring the project, acted with the encouragement of NASA Headquarters. It is an account of the establishment, evolutionary development, and activities of the Ames Research Center covering a period characterized by unprecedented scientific and technological revolution. The writing of this book about the Ames Research Center was undertaken with considerable pleasure by one who for many years was employed by the Center's parent organization NASA and, before that, NACA; who had closely followed the Center's growth from the beginning; and who was personally acquainted with, and who held in some affection, the members of its founding staff. These facts are given to alert readers to the presence of bias and the inaccuracies stemming therefrom.

It should be emphasized that this work is a history only of the Ames Research Center. It is not a history of the U.S. Government, of NACA or NASA, of other research centers, of the military services, of industry, or of world events. Information on these peripheral subjects is introduced

xi

merely to provide the reader with a generalized feeling for the local and world environment in which the formation and subsequent activities of the Ames Research Center took place. The background material provided is notably incomplete and in some instances reveals the bias of the NACA/NASA community at the time the events took place. Frequently, also, it reflects the personalized viewpoint of the author who was a close observer of many of these events.

In writing the Ames story, I have tried to convey the correct impression of prevailing conditions, influences, and associated events, but I am aware that, with respect to details, many unintended inaccuracies arising from omissions or from erroneous inferences or implications may have crept in. Owing to the secondary, impressionistic role played by the background material, these suspected faults have been tolerated and documentation has, for ease of reading, been held to a minimum. Indeed a major effort has been made to restrict the physical bounds of the book without sacrifice of essential material.

The preparation of the Ames history required the close cooperation of many people. In NASA Headquarters I would like to cite Dr. Frank Anderson, Jr., NASA Deputy Historian, and Mr. John L. Sloop, of the Office of Advanced Research and Technology, for their tolerance of an engineer-author who appeared bent on flouting every rule of conventional history writing and for their great help in preparing the manuscript for publication. At Ames the contributors were too numerous to be listed; nevertheless I would like to acknowledge the tremendous support provided by Manley Hood, the calm and understanding history-project monitor. Other notable contributors were Gerald Nitzberg, John Parsons, Russell Robinson, Colleen Garcia, Mildred Emel, Carol Tinling, and Mildred Macon.

Of great value, also, was certain information about the early days of NACA received from Dr. John F. Victory, first employee and eventually Executive Secretary of that organization. In the preparation of the sections on general environment, reference was frequently made to two documents: one, *Aeronautics and Astronautics 1915–60,* by Dr. Eugene M. Emme, NASA Historian; the second, *An Administrative History of NASA, 1958–1963,* by Robert L. Rosholt.

In particular I would like to acknowledge the invaluable assistance of my wife, Jean, without whose skillful and sustained effort in matters pertaining to editing and manuscript preparation this book would never have been completed.

EDWIN P. HARTMAN

CONTENTS

Part I

INITIATIONS: 1936–1945

Part II

A NEW WORLD OF SPEED: 1946–1958

1946–1949

CONTENTS

CONTENTS

Part I

INITIATIONS

1936–1945

1

The Nation's Aeronautical Research Agency

SINCE the founding of the National Advisory Committee for Aeronautics in 1915, this unique Government agency had fostered the development of aviation through scientific research. By 1936 the value of the Committee's work had become quite apparent. As a result of technical advances coming from NACA and other research organizations, the performance and reliability of the airplane had been greatly improved. Its role in domestic and international commerce was looming and its further development appeared to provide a means whereby a nation might exert influence abroad. The military value of the airplane had, of course, been sensed rather early and was probably the primary reason for such support of aeronautical research and development as the U.S. Government had given.

Despite the obvious potentialities of aviation, the Government's support of aeronautical research had been modest. Although the Wright Brothers had produced the first successful airplane, the United States had shamefully allowed itself to slip far behind the major European powers in the production of both airplanes [1] and aeronautical research facilities. The U.S. Government, by establishing NACA in 1915, took belated notice of the Nation's backward position in research but its appropriations for the new agency up to 1936 had been scarcely munificent. This was a period when the Nation was very peace minded; moreover, times were hard—in 1936 we were recovering from a long and painful depression and Congress was understandably imbued with a keen sense of frugality.

Despite its late start and lean fare, NACA had accomplished much. It had in 1917 established the Langley Memorial Aeronautical Laboratory at Langley Field, Va., and had pioneered in the development of advanced research facilities. In the world community, it had brought the United

---

[1] "When World War I erupted in 1914 it was reported that France had 1,400 airplanes, Germany 1,000, Russia 800, Great Britain 400 and the United States 23!"—*Forty Years of Aeronautical Research*, by Jerome C. Hunsaker (Smithsonian Report for 1955. Washington: Smithsonian Institution, 1956), p. 243.

Dr. Joseph S. Ames, Chairman of National Advisory Committee for Aeronautics from 1927 to 1939.

States to a position of leadership in aeronautical research.[2] This accomplishment resulted as much from wise management as from the technical competence of the NACA research staff which at Langley numbered, all told, about 400. The management arrangement was unique. The Committee (NACA) itself was a group of 15 (originally 12) eminently qualified men selected by the President. Of these the law required that two be selected from the War Department (Army Air Corps), two from the Navy Department, and one each from the Bureau of Standards, the Weather Bureau, and the Smithsonian Institution, the last of which had been very influential in aviation matters since the days of its early Secretary, Samuel Pierpont Langley. The remaining members of the Committee were to be persons "acquainted with the needs of aeronautical science, either civil or military, or skilled in aeronautical engineering or its allied sciences."

From the beginning the persons selected to serve on the Committee were men of great ability and high repute. Some had belonged to the National Academy of Sciences. The members served without pay and elected their own chairman. Thus the agency was relatively free from political influence and was allowed, within its budgetary limitations, to pursue a course of maximum effectiveness in advancing the aeronautical interests of the Nation.

In 1936 the Chairman of NACA was Dr. Joseph S. Ames, president of Johns Hopkins University. Dr. Ames, a member of the Committee since its formation and Chairman since 1927, was a man of the highest integrity and ability, respected—indeed revered—by his colleagues and friends.

Inasmuch as the Committee met only at monthly intervals, it required a permanent headquarters staff. This staff was headed by Dr. George W. Lewis, Director of Aeronautical Research, and John F. Victory, Secretary to the Committee. It was to these able and dedicated individuals that a substantial share of the credit for the success of NACA was due. NACA was a tiny Government agency serving the vital interests of much larger and more powerful bodies such as the Army, the Navy, and the Department of Commerce. Its staff had to exercise the greatest care and discretion to maintain the agency's independence. Either the Army or the Navy could easily have swallowed up NACA; and Herbert Hoover, both as Secretary of Commerce in 1925 and as President in 1932, had actually recommended that it be absorbed by the Department of Commerce.[3] The suggested move was strongly

---

[2] *Ibid.*

[3] Report by Charles D. Walcott, Chairman of NACA: "The National Advisory Committee for Aeronautics, Its Organization and Functions, and Reasons Why Its Present Independent Status Should Be Continued," Jan. 21, 1925. Also: House Doc. No. 493, 72d Cong., 2d sess., Dec. 9, 1932: "A Message from the President of the United States to Congress," a recommendation to group, coordinate, and consolidate executive and administrative agencies of the Government, including transfer of NACA to the Bureau of Standards in the Department of Commerce.

Dr. George W. Lewis, NACA Director of Aeronautical Research from 1924 to 1947.

Dr. John F. Victory, first (1915) NACA employee and later Executive Secretary.

and successfully opposed by the two services[4] who perhaps themselves were the greatest threat to NACA; but Lewis and Victory aimed to be of such value to each service that neither would allow the other to take over NACA. Dr. Lewis, in councils with his staff, declared that NACA must be so alert that it would anticipate the needs of the military even before the military became aware of those needs. Under such astute management, NACA maintained its independence while becoming an extraordinarily efficient and competent organization.

---

[4] Letter, George H. Dorn, Secretary of War, to President Franklin D. Roosevelt, Apr. 19, 1933, and letter, Claude A. Swanson, Secretary of the Navy, to President Franklin D. Roosevelt, Apr. 13, 1933.

2

Portents and Requirements of Aviation

THE necessity for keeping in touch with the world's aeronautical activities and literature was obvious to Chairman Ames, and he arranged quite early in the history of NACA for the establishment within the agency of an Office of Aeronautical Intelligence. As part of its operation, this Office maintained a liaison post in Paris—a post which from the beginning was occupied by John J. Ide. During the mid-1930's, Ide reported on the buildup of aeronautical research and development in Europe. In 1936 these reports were confirmed by evidence gained during a visit by Dr. Lewis to certain European research centers. In particular, Lewis was impressed by the progress being made by the Germans in the construction of aeronautical facilities and not a little concerned over the possibility that the accelerated activity abroad would leave NACA and the United States at a disadvantage. NACA's lead in aeronautical research was certainly disappearing and the intentions of Germany's leader, Adolf Hitler, were a source of worry.

NACA WARNING

On his return from Europe, Lewis attempted, with some success, to convey his apprehensions to Dr. Ames and the Committee.[1] At the end of the year, in transmitting NACA's Annual Report to the President, Dr. Ames urged a gradual expansion of NACA research effort and noted that—

> increased recognition abroad of the value and of the vital necessity of aeronautical research has led to recent tremendous expansion in research programs and to multiplication of research facilities by other progressive nations. Thus has the foundation been laid for a serious challenge to America's present leadership in the technical development of aircraft.

This warning, if noticed at all by Congress, produced no startling results.

[1] *NACA 22d Annual Report 1936*, p. 3. What Dr. Lewis learned about German aviation was shortly confirmed by Dr. Clark B. Millikan, Maj. Lester Gardner, and other Americans who attended the first formal meeting of the new German society for aeronautical research (*Lilienthal-Gesellschaft für Luftfahrt-forschung*) in Berlin on Oct. 12–15, 1936. For an account of this meeting and visits of Americans to German aviation centers, see the *Journal of the Aeronautical Sciences*, vol. 4, no. 1, Nov. 1936, pp. 19–27.

AGGRESSION RAMPANT

The world at this time was quite uneasy. Militancy was rampant and definitely in the ascendancy. Japan had invaded Manchuria in 1931; and in 1935 Italy had invaded Ethiopia, bombing Ethiopian cities from the air. That same year Germany openly admitted that it had built an air force in direct defiance of the Versailles Treaty. In March 1936 Hitler seized the Rhineland without resistance, and a little later the Spanish civil war was providing tests of new German, Italian, and Russian weapons. Then in 1937 Japan seized Peiping and bombed Chinese cities from the air. The military potentialities of the airplane were becoming all too evident. Hitler had recognized these potentialities from the first and, very soon after acquiring control of Germany, had given the "go ahead" signal for both aeronautical research and airplane construction.[2]

George Lewis saw some of the results of Hitler's actions in 1936; Germany's neighbors soon felt the results. Hitler made a bloodless conquest of Austria in March 1938 and later in the summer applied pressure on Czechoslovakia. In September at Munich, in a futile attempt at appeasement, the European nations sacrificed Czechoslovakia to his rapacious appetite. Hitler's hunger for power seemed insatiable and the peace of the world was in serious doubt. At this stage, NACA's research effort, as a logical first step in expanding the Nation's military airpower, took on an air of real urgency.

WESTOVER REPORT

In 1938 NACA had formed a Special Committee on the Relations of NACA to National Defense in Time of War, under the chairmanship of one of its members, Major General Oscar Westover, Chief of Air Corps.[3] The actions of the Special Committee were reported by General Westover at a meeting of the main Committee on August 19, 1938. Among other things, General Westover suggested that the Committee plan an additional research center somewhere in the interior of the country or on the West Coast to relieve the "congested bottleneck" at Langley Field. He asked that his Special Committee be authorized to make a study of long-range planning for such a research center.[4]

The "congested bottleneck" to which General Westover referred was

---

[2] As stated in NACA memorandum, "Some Major Considerations Underlying the Extension of Research Facilities at Langley Field and the Establishment of a Second Major Research Station for NACA at Sunnyvale, California," distributed to newspapers and magazines on Mar. 10, 1939.

[3] Mentioned in *NACA 25th Annual Report 1939*, p 38. Committee members, other than Westover, were Dr. W. R. Gregg, Chief of the U.S. Weather Bureau, and Rear Adm. Arthur B. Cook, USN.

[4] *Ibid.*

the lack of space at Langley for any further expansion of NACA's activities and the shortage of available electric power in that area to satisfy the demands of NACA's new high-speed wind tunnels. The Army Air Corps rather flatly told NACA that it could not spare any more space at Langley; and NACA, to gain only a small amount of badly needed land, was planning to go to the expense of building a seawall on its Back River border and filling in behind the wall.[5] This expedient had limited possibilities for future expansion.

The power shortage, moreover, appeared nearly as critical as the land shortage. Up to that time, NACA in designing new equipment had been limited to the use of 8000 horsepower at one time. To get even this amount of power, at off-peak rates, operation had to be limited largely to the period from midnight to 6 a.m.[6] The local power company, the Virginia Public Service Corp., had no links which tied Langley Field in with major power sources in Norfolk, Richmond, or elsewhere. A temporary expedient undertaken by NACA was the construction of a 10,000-horsepower diesel-powered generating plant at Langley, but this action apparently aroused the opposition of Senator Carter Glass of Virginia. The ultimate hope was that a tie-in with other power sources could be effected. The Virginia Public Service Corp. had no objection to such a tie-in but wanted the U.S. Government to pay for it. In any case, the bottleneck referred to by General Westover seemed very real.[7]

Special Committee on Future Research Facilities

Soon after the Committee's meeting on August 19, 1938, General Westover was killed in an airplane crash, and the membership of the Special Committee was further diminished by the death of Dr. Willis Ray Gregg. At its meeting in October, NACA decided to discharge the existing Special Committee and form a new Special Committee on Future Research Facilities to study the new research center proposed earlier by General Westover. The new Special Committee appointed by Dr. Ames was made up of Rear Admiral Arthur B. Cook, Chief of the Navy Bureau of Aeronautics (Chairman); Major General Henry H. Arnold, Chief of the Army Air Corps; The Honorable Edward J. Noble, Chairman of the newly formed Civil Aeronautics Authority; Dr. Edward P. Warner; and Dr. George W. Lewis.[8]

The Special Committee on Future Research Facilities wasted no time in carrying out its mission and was able to make its report to Dr. Ames on

---

[5] Space and power problems stated in "Memorandum for Rear Admiral Cook, USN, Chairman Special Committee on Future Research Facilities," from J. F. Victory, Secretary NACA, Nov. 4, 1938.

[6] *Ibid.*

[7] *Ibid.*

[8] *NACA 25th Annual Report 1939,* p. 38.

December 30, 1938. It seemed clear that considerable staff work had been accomplished ahead of time by Dr. Lewis and Mr. Victory.

The Special Committee made three strong recommendations:

(1) The establishment of a second major aeronautical research station by NACA on the present Army field known as Sunnyvale, California, the necessary land to be set aside for the Committee's use by the Secretary of War.

Estimated cost _____ $11,000,000

(2) The construction of certain additional research facilities (including a new power line) at the Committee's present single research station at Langley Field, Virginia, and the immediate expansion of the research staff to meet present needs and to provide a nucleus of trained research workers for the Sunnyvale station.

Estimated cost _____ $2,440,000

(3) A plan for the more effective coordination of applied aeronautical research in industry and for the stimulation of research in educational institutions.[9]

Estimated cost _____ $52,000

What was being proposed by the Special Committee was an expansion of NACA facilities to the tune of about 120 percent. Beyond that, the concept of multiple NACA research centers was one that would certainly give pause to economy-minded legislators. People wary of proliferating Government agencies might feel that little NACA was getting too big for its britches. But the Special Committee provided some solid supporting evidence for its recommendation. It pointed out that—

Aeronautics is more vital to national defense than ever before. Present plans of the Army and Navy contemplate a material expansion in aircraft procurement and in the development of air strength. To be of maximum value for military purposes, aircraft must have the highest attainable performance. In the light of world events, and particularly in the light of emphasis that is being placed on the development of aircraft in foreign countries, it is of the greatest importance that the United States excel or at least equal other nations in the technical development of aircraft. The United States has led in the technical development of both military and commercial aircraft during the past decade. This has been made possible largely by reason of the sound organization and effective prosecution of scientific laboratory research under the cognizance of NACA.

The Special Committee also noted that—

In the last four or five years, Germany has multiplied its aeronautical re-

<hr>

[9] Mentioned in *NACA 25th Annual Report 1939*, p. 38. Report with several appendices transmitted with letter to Dr. Joseph S. Ames from Special Committee on Future Research Facilities, Dec. 30, 1938.

search activities at least tenfold. It is known that whereas the United States has one major research center at Langley Field, Germany has five research centers, one of which [at Adlershof] has four times the staff of the NACA laboratories at Langley Field.

The Special Committee spoke of Italy's new city of Guidonia, entirely devoted to aeronautical research, and of Russia's Central Aero-Hydrodynamical Institute in Moscow, where 3500 employees were engaged in aeronautical research and development. It also referred to progressive countries which were extending their commercial and political influence abroad through air trade routes and of the necessity for improving airplane design to accomplish this purpose. The main burden of the Committee's argument, however, concerned the tremendous emphasis being placed by Germany on the development of air power supported by a concentration of much of its scientific resources on aeronautical research. "To meet this scientific challenge," the Committee said, "the United States must more than redouble its efforts and the NACA should be authorized to establish without delay a second research center and to proceed immediately with the construction of the most advanced wind tunnels and other aeronautical research equipment."

These recommendations presented a sobering picture and one which, combined with the truculent attitude of Hitler, flashed an imperative warning. But two of the men on the Special Committee were from the military services, and might this be just another case of overzealousness on the part of professional soldiers in preparing for dubious military threats? Was this new research station really needed, or was it a bit of empire building?

3

Pressures for Expansion of Research

THERE was no question that NACA took the report of its Special Committee seriously. It was immediately approved and, despite year-end holidays, was passed on within 10 days to the President and the Bureau of the Budget for executive action. In submitting the report to the President and the Bureau of the Budget, NACA made one addition to the recommendations of the Special Committee: $500,000 was requested for special research investigations in educational and scientific institutions on problems supplementary to the research programs of the Government. The purpose of this addition was to allow NACA to utilize more fully the research talent and facilities existing in universities and other scientific institutions.

Dr. Ames closed his letter of transmittal to the President with the paragraph, "In view of the gravity of the world situation and of the vital relation of scientific research to the military effectiveness of aircraft, the National Advisory Committee for Aeronautics is unanimous in strongly recommending the earliest possible execution of the program."[1]

President Roosevelt and his Bureau of the Budget acted on the recommendation with commendable speed and, on February 3, 1939, transmitted the request to the Congress for incorporation in the second deficiency bill. The only significant change which the Bureau of the Budget made in NACA's request was to reduce the amount specified for the new research center from $11 to $10 million.[2]

HOUSE COMMITTEE TURNDOWN

In March, the second deficiency bill came up for consideration by a House Appropriations Subcommittee headed by Congressman Clifton A. Woodrum of Virginia, who had generally acted favorably on NACA requests to expand Langley facilities. His actions on this occasion were consistent.

---

[1] Letter, Dr. Joseph S. Ames, Chairman NACA, to President Franklin D. Roosevelt, Jan. 10, 1939.

[2] *NACA 25th Annual Report 1939*, p. 38.

His subcommittee approved the funds requested for Langley and also the funds required to provide more effective coordination of aeronautical research in industry and the universities. But the funds requested for the new research center at Sunnyvale, California, as well as the $500,000 for research in educational and scientific institutions, were denied. Woodrum was reported, in the newspapers of the day, to have said that pending further study the Government's present facilities at Langley Field ought to be sufficient.

The House action was a severe blow to those who felt the Nation's safety was at stake. Of course it was also a blow to Californians who wanted the proposed research center established in their locality. On March 23, the day after the House subcommittee had acted, General Arnold and Admiral Cook jointly addressed a letter to Dr. Ames urging him to take immediate steps to have the deleted item of the Sunnyvale center reinstated in the second deficiency bill by the Senate. They pointed out that—

(1) The Army and Navy are dependent upon NACA for fundamental scientific data which make possible the improved performance of aircraft.

(2) The Army and Navy will spend about $225 million for aircraft for the coming year alone and such aircraft would not be worth all they cost unless our aircraft are at least equal in performance to the best produced abroad. America does not want second-best aircraft.

(3) It is absolutely impossible to expand adequately at Langley Field as the Army cannot provide more room without impairing the military efficiency of its own operations.

(4) A second major research station is necessary and, to be of maximum value to the Army and Navy, should be on the West Coast —near the aircraft factories.

(5) The Sunnyvale research project is emergency in character and of vital importance to the success of our whole program of strengthening the air defense of the United States.[3]

But Dr. Ames was not well. He was 75 years old and illness of one kind or another had sapped his strength. Yet from his sickbed he penned an eloquent letter to Congressman Woodrum on May 23 asking for reconsideration of the Sunnyvale station. He not only transmitted a copy of the letter prepared by Admiral Cook and General Arnold but also reviewed in general and in detail the urgent need for the new research facility. In the course of his letter he brought in a personal note:

For nearly twenty years I have been appearing before the Appropri-

---

[3] Letter, Rear Adm. Arthur B. Cook USN, Chief Bureau of Aeronautics, and Maj. Gen. Henry H. Arnold USA, Chief of Air Corps, to Dr. Joseph S. Ames, Chairman NACA, Mar. 23, 1939.

ations Committee. I have supported what at times appeared to be bold plans for development of research facilities in the United States. I have never supported a padded or extravagant estimate. I have never supported a project that Congress refused to approve. . . .

Now, through impairment of my health, I am nearing the end of my active career. I have served as a member of the National Advisory Committee for Aeronautics for nearly twenty-five years without compensation. . . . My compensation has been the tremendous satisfaction that has come to me from the realization that the work of the National Advisory Committee for Aeronautics has been successful over a long period of years, enabling American manufacturers and designers to develop aircraft, military and commercial, superior in performance, efficiency, and safety to those produced by other nations. Now I regret to say the picture has changed. I still, however, have faith in our ability, with your support and the support of Congress, to regain for America the leadership in scientific knowledge which will enable our designers and manufacturers again to produce superior aircraft.[4]

Woodrum could hardly have helped being moved by Dr. Ames' touching and persuasive letter but if he was he concealed his emotions very well. His reply, though not unkind, was brief, perfunctory, and noncommittal.[5]

SENATE COMMITTEE TURNDOWN

Dr. Vannevar Bush, then a member of NACA, was acting in behalf of the ailing Dr. Ames when he sought and, in early April, was granted a hearing by the Senate Appropriations Subcommittee. He was accompanied to the Senate chambers by John Victory and others. The purpose of their mission —to seek a restoration of the Sunnyvale item in the second deficiency bill— was known in advance to the Senate subcommittee. The senators were generally unsympathetic toward the mission of the NACA representatives and were, it appeared to Victory, prepared to freeze out Dr. Bush by any means at their command, including sheer bluff and rudeness. Dr. Bush asked for five minutes to present his case, but the subcommittee members, by their interruptions, interjections, and diversions, denied him this privilege. Dr. Bush was not the man to accept this kind of treatment from anyone, even senators. According to Victory, he beat on the table and forcefully asserted his claim to speak. And to this show of spirit the senators yielded, but Dr. Bush's remarks were to no avail; the subcommittee had obviously made up its mind ahead of time.[6]

---

[4] Letter, Dr. Joseph S. Ames, Chairman NACA, to the Honorable Clifton A. Woodrum, Chairman House Appropriations Subcommittee, May 23, 1939.

[5] Letter, Woodrum to Ames, Mar. 29, 1939. Contained three sentences, two of which dealt with the subject matter of Ames' four-page letter.

[6] Victory's impressions appear to be supported by congressional records—U.S. Congress, Senate, Subcommittee of the Committee on Appropriations, *Second Deficiency Appropriation Bill for 1939*, Hearings on H.R. 5219, 76th Cong., 1st sess., Wednesday, Apr. 5, 1939, pp. 75–94. Of the 10 members of the subcommittee present, seven were from the East.

Things looked black indeed at this point, and some in NACA were about ready to give up the struggle, but not John Victory. No tyro in Washington politics, Victory thought he knew a way to get the Sunnyvale project back into the deficiency bill. John Victory was a born fighter thoroughly devoted to NACA, and he had an armorplate that was never dented by the arrows of misfortune. In looking out for the welfare of NACA and its staff, he never took "no" for an answer, never was cowed by pomp or power, and never let false modesty prevent him from accomplishing his mission. He fought with a no-holds-barred vigor that sometimes embarrassed his colleagues, particularly Dr. Lewis who, though a more sensitive individual, was equally effective in his own, but different, way. A formidable opponent, John Victory was a good man to have on one's side.

SENATE APPROVAL

Victory knew that, despite the inaction of the Senate Appropriations Subcommittee, it was possible to get the Sunnyvale project reintroduced into the deficiency bill at the time the bill was brought up before the whole Senate. All it took was to get one of his senatorial friends who sympathized with NACA's needs (and there were many such, including Senator Hiram Johnson of California) to bring the matter up for a vote at the proper time. Once the matter had been properly presented to the whole Senate, Victory felt sure it would be approved. Unlike the House and Senate Appropriations Committees, which were loaded with easterners and dominated by Virginians, the Senate as a whole represented all the States and thus might be expected to exercise a more detached judgment in the matter.

Victory was right. He prevailed on a friendly senator to introduce the subject and on April 14 the Senate restored the Sunnyvale research center to the Deficiency Bill, appropriating $4 million to get the laboratory started.

JOINT COMMITTEE TURNDOWN

Although hope was thus restored, Victory knew that NACA was a long way from winning its case, for when the House and Senate disagree on an appropriations item, the matter is referred for settlement of differences to a joint appropriations committee of the House and Senate. Thus the Sunnyvale station matter would be reconsidered by the same people who had turned it down in the first place. But since the whole Senate had approved it, would the senators on the joint committee turn it down again? Perhaps they would not. This was the slim hope to which John Victory and others in NACA clung. The hope was in vain: the joint committee, meeting on April 26, struck the item from the bill. The Second Deficiency Bill as passed provided $2,140,000 for an expansion of Langley, but nothing for the new Sunnyvale laboratory.

The need for the new center had been very well established. Whence, then, came the opposition? Virginia's Congressman Clifton Woodrum and Senator Carter Glass, chairmen, respectively, of the House Appropriations Subcommittee and the main Senate Appropriations Committee, apparently felt that it would diminish the importance and restrict the growth of the NACA laboratory at Langley Field, Va. Evidence also existed of an east-west factionalism of a more general character.[7] There was a feeling that some Eastern congressmen and senators were not happy about having NACA, born and raised, so to speak, in the East, extend its operations to the West Coast. And there was also a rather solid impression in some NACA circles that at least one eastern aircraft manufacturer had prevailed upon his congressman to block this measure which would give aid to his competitors on the West Coast. The western aircraft industry had grown rather rapidly and at this time accounted for something like 60 percent of the airplane-manufacturing business. This fact, of course, was an important reason for building the Sunnyvale station. In view of the actions of Congress, NACA was now painfully aware that it had made a strategic error in the presentation of its request for the new station. The error lay in specifying the location of the station in the original proposal, a bit of political naiveté for which John Victory accepted the blame.

THE NEED GROWS

While Congress was busy appropriating funds for new airplanes and denying funds for an expansion of aeronautical research, the world situation was growing worse. In April, Italy seized Albania and in May, Germany and Italy formed an alliance—their famous Axis. The results of Germany's aeronautical research efforts were also appearing. Germany established two world speed records in April with its new Messerschmitt and Heinkel airplanes. And in June the growing importance of commercial aviation was emphasized by Pan American's inauguration of transatlantic passenger service. Transpacific service had been established even earlier (1936).

Early in 1939 Dr. George Lewis was honored by being elected president of the Institute of the Aeronautical Sciences and a little later was extended the further honor of being asked to deliver the Wilbur Wright Lecture before the Royal Aeronautical Society in London. He sailed for Europe on May 17 and, after delivering the lecture on May 25, spent several weeks visiting aeronautical research and development institutions in England, France, and Germany. In Germany, he visited Berlin (Adlershof), Goettingen, and the Heinkel plant in Oranienburg.

---

[7] Senate Hearings (see footnote 6). Senator McCarran of Nevada, the only member of the Senate subcommittee who seemed to favor the west coast laboratory, implied that the eastern senators were guilty of "sectionalism" (geographic factionalism).

What Lewis saw during his European visit confirmed the impression he had gained in 1936 about the buildup of German aeronautical research and production facilities. He was much impressed by what he saw and was also surprised by the supreme confidence of the Germans in the strength and destiny of the Third Reich. Although Lewis represented a country which Germany recognized as a strong potential enemy, the Germans appeared perfectly willing, if not eager, to show him their latest aeronautical developments, particularly their new aeronautical research facilities. Far from concealing anything, they seemed to gloat over their accomplishments in a manner of complete self-assurance, although possibly with the intent of discouraging U.S. intervention in Germany's aggressive activities. Dr. Lewis had opportunities to ask several of the German scientists with whom he had developed some acquaintance what they thought about the prospects of war. The answer he got, also very frank, was that war would come "before the snow flies this fall."[8]

Returning on the airship *Hindenburg* from his European trip, Lewis carried a grave message to his Government. Would they heed it? The justification for a major expansion of the country's aeronautical research was clearly growing, and many people in this country were not prepared to allow the needed expansion to be crippled or killed by narrow factionalism. When the joint House-Senate conference committee deleted the Sunnyvale station from the Second Deficiency Bill, a great hue and cry arose. Some of the cries were of course those of Californians, particularly Senator Hiram Johnson and Congressman Jack Anderson; but criticism of the congressional action also came from eastern sources. The *New York Times* had earlier editorialized about the gravity of the mistake the Congress would make if it did not restore the funds for Sunnyvale, and other eastern newspapers spoke in favor of the station. The Army and the Navy were, of course, backing it to the hilt, as was the Civil Aeronautics Authority. Another strong proponent who spoke far and wide in favor of the Sunnyvale station was Colonel Charles A. Lindbergh, an important national figure and, at that time, a member of NACA. He also, during a trip to Europe, had been dazzled by German aeronautical developments. How long could Congress resist these pressures?

---

[8] G. W. Lewis: "Report on Trip to Germany and Russia September–October 1936." The statements about German supreme confidence and war predictions represent recollections by R. G. Robinson and J. F. Victory of what Lewis told them on his return from Germany.

4

The Tide Turns

THE growing weight of evidence in favor of the Sunnyvale station began to have some effect. On June 22, 1939, Congressman Woodrum agreed to a rehearing of the case—a rehearing which Dr. Ames had requested a month earlier, shortly after Congress had struck the measure from the Second Deficiency Bill. The NACA, which met on June 23, was considerably heartened by this small sign of yielding by Woodrum and immediately authorized Acting Chairman Vannevar Bush to appoint a Special Survey Committee on Aeronautical Research Facilities—

> to examine into the aeronautical research facilities now available in the country and their best interrelationship, and to prepare a comprehensive plan for the future extension of such facilities with especial attention to facilities of the NACA and the universities, including the training of necessary research personnel.

From the actions of the Committee at the June 23 meeting, it was clear that NACA's concepts regarding the expansion of the Nation's aeronautical research had broadened considerably and now went well beyond the addition of a single new station at Sunnyvale. Also, certain members of the Committee had felt for some time that the research talent and facilities in universities should be utilized more effectively in the Nation's aeronautical research effort.

Lindbergh Committee

Acting Chairman Bush immediately implemented the authorization given to him and appointed a Special Survey Committee headed by Lindbergh and including General H. H. Arnold, Admiral J. H. Towers, and Robert H. Hinckley (Chairman of CAA).[1] The Special Survey Committee shortly began a tour of universities and aeronautical research laboratories in pursuit of its mission.

---

[1] Letter, Dr. Vannevar Bush, Chairman Executive Committee NACA, to Col. Charles A. Lindbergh, Air Corps, June 30, 1939.

The granting by Woodrum of one more opportunity for NACA to present its case relative to the proposed Sunnyvale station was not taken lightly. With Drs. Ames and Bush either sick or unavailable, NACA decided that Dr. Charles Abbot, Vice Chairman of the NACA Executive Committee, assisted by Colonel Lindbergh and Dr. Lewis, should make the crucial presentation. Lindbergh was well known and anything he said received wide press coverage. Besides, he was completely sold on the urgent need for the new station. Dr. Lewis had, of course, just returned from his second trip to Europe with convincing evidence concerning the German threat. In addition to these active participants, John Victory and Edward Chamberlin of Lewis's staff were in the hearing room, and within the congressional halls there were sympathetic congressmen and senators at work as well as lobbyists of one kind or another including Gen. W. E. Gilmore (Ret.), former member of NACA, who according to a press report, was sent to Washington by the *San Francisco Chronicle*. The stage was thus set for a showdown battle.

The hearing began on July 10. The House Appropriations Subcommittee, then reviewing items in the third deficiency bill for the year, was in an economy mood even blacker than usual. NACA was asking for $10 million for the new Sunnyvale center, $4 million to be immediately available and $6 million in contract authorizations. NACA had also requested additional funds for Langley, as well as $250,000 to support research in universities.

All three NACA representatives at the hearing made very strong statements as to the need for the Sunnyvale station, and Lindbergh's statement was felt by Lewis to be particularly effective. Lindbergh spoke forcefully not only in behalf of the new station but also in support of NACA's request for funds with which to sponsor research work in scientific and educational institutions. The matter of NACA-university relations was indeed one in which Lindbergh had taken a very personal interest for the past few years.

THE STRATEGY AND THE VICTORY

The attitude of the Woodrum subcommittee toward the proposed new station was not readily apparent at the time of the meeting, and only when the Third Deficiency Bill was reported out of the House Appropriations Subcommittee would NACA or the general public know the fate of Sunnyvale. But John Victory sensed that the Woodrum subcommittee had reacted less favorably than expected to the arguments of Lindbergh, Lewis, and Abbot. He thought that NACA's selection of California for the station might still be a major obstacle in Woodrum's mind and that a favorable psychological effect might be produced in the subcommittee if it could be provided with some means for justifying a new vote in favor of a measure which the subcommittee had recently turned down very flatly. Perhaps the desired end could be achieved if the site were not specified in the bill but were left open for later selection. This step would also please Congressman Louis Ludlow, high-ranking subcommittee member from Indiana, whose overwhelming desire was to have the new station placed in Indianapolis.

Of course a concession of the kind conceived by Victory was of somewhat dubious significance in view of NACA's stated site preference, and it would invite all kinds of political pressure and importuning from Chambers of Commerce and other city and state groups who wished to garner this plum. But the main thing was to get approval for the station; the site-selection issue could be dealt with later. Acting on this analysis, Victory slipped a note to Woodrum suggesting that the Sunnyvale site specification be deleted from the proposal and that the location of the new station be left for later decision by NACA.

The hearings ended and now came the anxious wait until the bill was reported out of committee. The answer came early in August when the third deficiency bill emerged from the Appropriations Subcommittee and was quickly passed by the House. The bill which the House had passed included an item of $10 million for a new research station. Of this amount, $1,890,000 was to be made available immediately and the remainder was a commitment to the later payment of contracts. A major change had been made in the wording of the bill. The site specification "Sunnyvale" had been replaced by the statement that the site for the new research station would be selected by the members of NACA within 30 days after passage of the bill. The urgent need for the new station was thus recognized and the time allowed for a reevaluation of the site-selection matter was happily limited to 30 days.

The bill also included $1 million for expansion of Langley Field facilities as well as an item of $109,020 for Langley to train men for the new station. Unhappily, the $250,000 that NACA had requested for the support of research in universities and other scientific institutions was deleted. Nevertheless NACA had been more fortunate than some other agencies; of the $215 million total requested in the Third Deficiency Bill, only $53 million had been appropriated.

The House action broke the logjam that had for so long held up action on the new station. The bill was passed by the Senate on August 4 and, after further consideration by Congress, it was enacted into law on August 9, 1939.[2] In less than a month, Hitler would launch his ferocious attack on Poland and World War II would begin. Although many in this country thought that the United States could remain aloof from the impending conflict, the need for strengthening our defenses and our preparedness was no longer questioned. The approval given for the new NACA station was heartening evidence that our congressmen had risen worthily, if somewhat tardily, to the occasion.

---

[2] *NACA 25th Annual Report 1939*, p. 1.

SITE SELECTION

The site for the new NACA station was to be selected within 30 days of the passage of the bill. Within a very few days of that event, NACA had received applications from a number of different communities which wanted the station. In all, more than 50 sites were recommended: among them were such places as Buffalo, New York; Dismal Swamp, Virginia; Indianapolis, Indiana; Menunketesuck Point, Connecticut; Chicago, Illinois; Fort Worth, Texas; Spokane, Washington; and, within California, Los Angeles, San Diego, Sacramento, and Sunnyvale.

Dr. Ames turned over the site-selection matter to the Lindbergh committee, but that committee was quite thoroughly occupied with its primary mission and was forced to leave the burden of the site-selection analysis to the NACA staff. Since the 30-day limitation did not allow time for hearings of applicants, as desired by Congressman Ludlow, the decision had to rest largely on specifications and qualifications which the applying communities had submitted in writing. Some additional evidence was available, however, from site inspections made by NACA members and staff.

NACA's original selection of Sunnyvale the year before had not, of course, been made by any simple arbitrary process. It was the result of a careful, objective study carried out in the absence of political pressures[3]. Moreover, it took advantage of an exhaustive survey by the Navy in 1930 of 104 sites considered for the location of a rigid-airship base. The requirements for the airship base had much in common with those for the NACA station and it is not surprising that the site selected by the Navy for its base had also turned out to be the best choice for the NACA station.

Among the more important site criteria established by NACA for its new station were the following:

1. The station should if possible be on an Army or a Navy Base.
2. The site should have, or allow for, the construction of a flying field of about one mile square and should not be in an area of high air-traffic density. Moderate temperature and good flying weather through most of the year were desirable.
3. Adequate quantities (50,000 kva) of electric power should be available on site at reasonable rates.
4. The site should be readily accessible to the aircraft industry on the West Coast. NACA wanted to be near the big western aircraft

---

[3] The report of the Special Committee on Future Research Facilities, relative to site selection, was transmitted in a letter dated Dec. 21, 1938, to the special committee chairman, Rear Adm. Arthur B. Cook, from two of its members—General Arnold and Dr. Lewis. This report indicated that Sunnyvale had been selected from a group of runner-up sites which included Mather Field, near Sacramento; March Field, near Los Angeles; the Ordnance Depot at Ogden, Utah; and Lowry Field, Denver. The second choice, Ogden, was felt to be less vulnerable to air attack than the first choice, Sunnyvale, but poorer because of climate and distance from the aircraft industry.

companies but not so near that it would be under pressure from industry to divert its attention from basic research to routine test work.

5. The site should be near an industrial center capable of providing labor, supplies, communications and transportation facilities, and other logistic support.

6. The site should be in an area providing attractive living conditions, schools, etc., and, if possible, should be near a university of recognized standing.[4]

Sunnyvale satisfied these conditions very nicely and when, back in 1938, John Victory proposed Sunnyvale as the site for the new NACA station, the military grasped the idea with alacrity. Dr. Lewis, it should be mentioned, neither then nor later made any attempt to influence site selection. At the time that Victory made his proposal, the Sunnyvale base was under the Army. General Hap Arnold said to John, "You can have the whole damn Sunnyvale base!" John said he didn't want it all—just 50 acres or so. Arnold replied, "Oh! You want the Army to mow the grass for you!" Later, when the threat of war had grown darker, General Arnold was probably glad that NACA had not taken seriously the offer he had made in jest.

Although NACA had earlier selected Sunnyvale as the site for its proposed new station, it nevertheless made a fair review of the many sites that were suggested both prior to and following the passage of the Third Deficiency Bill. It is not surprising, however, that the answer came out the same: Sunnyvale. A West Coast location had obviously been favored. In addition to Sunnyvale, such sites as San Diego, Los Angeles, Santa Ana, and Sacramento had received very serious consideration. The staff work on site selection was presented at a meeting of the Committee on September 22. Dr. Ames was too ill to attend but, before the meeting was over, the assembled members, with little argument, agreed that Sunnyvale was to be the site for the new NACA station. An official announcement of the selection was made at 11 a.m. that day.[5]

Dr. Ames Retires

With his health failing, Dr. Ames could no longer fulfill his duties as a member of NACA. He submitted his resignation on October 7.[6] It was a time of sorrow for the members of NACA because he was loved and respected by them all. A charter member of NACA appointed by President Wilson, he had worked with great zeal and effectiveness, and without pay, for 25 years. For more than 20 years, Dr. Ames had served either as Chairman of NACA or as Chairman of its Executive Committee. He was a man of

[4] Report of Special Committee on Future Research Facilities, Dec. 30, 1938. app. D.
[5] NACA memo for the press, Sept. 22, 1939, 11 a.m.
[6] Letter, Dr. Joseph S. Ames to President Roosevelt, Oct. 7, 1939.

the highest integrity, moral fortitude, and ability. On retirement, Dr. Ames received attestations of respect and appreciation from many people, including President Roosevelt[7] and the members of the Committee.

Dr. Vannevar Bush was chosen to succeed Dr. Ames as Chairman of NACA[8].

ENGINE RESEARCH LABORATORY

At a meeting of NACA on October 19, the Special Committee on Aeronautical Research Facilities (Lindbergh committee) reported on the results of its mission activities. Its principal finding was "that there is a serious lack of engine research facilities in the United States, and that it is of the utmost importance for the development of aviation in general, and for our defense program in particular, to take immediate steps to remedy this deficiency."[9]

The weakness in NACA's research program pointed out by the Lindbergh committee had been recognized even earlier and the main Committee (NACA) was unanimous in feeling that prompt action should be taken. Accordingly, Dr. Bush immediately appointed a Special Committee on New Engine Research Facilities headed by Dr. George J. Mead.[10] This committee, which was instructed to make recommendations as to the scope of the proposed new engine research laboratory, submitted its report to NACA on February 7, 1940. The report recommended, among other things, that the new engine research laboratory be built in a place readily accessible to the manufacturers of aircraft engines. Congress was asked for funds for the new engine laboratory and with little ado they were authorized on June 26, 1940. Cleveland was later selected as the site.

The selling job in the case of the engine laboratory was relatively easy. No specific site had been mentioned when the proposal was made to Congress; and, in any case, it was obvious that the new laboratory would have to be in the East since the engine companies were located there. More importantly the developing war situation in Europe spoke convincingly of the need for the proposed engine research laboratory.

For 25 years Langley had been NACA's only laboratory and then, in the course of a year, two more were authorized. A great surge of effort by NACA would be required to get the new laboratories underway. Both had been needed for years and, with war clouds building up, their construction was pursued with all speed. Another sign of the times was that the Army changed its mind about giving NACA more space at Langley Field; thus a further increase in the Committee's capabilities through an expansion of the Langley laboratory was made possible.

---

[7] Letter, President Roosevelt to Dr. Ames, Oct. 10, 1939.
[8] By action of NACA at its meeting on Oct. 19, 1939.
[9] *NACA 25th Annual Report 1939*, p. 2.
[10] *NACA 25th Annual Report 1939*, p. 3.

5

···

The Beginnings of a Laboratory

MOFFETT FIELD

THE scene now shifts from Washington, D.C., to California. What, and exactly where, was this Sunnyvale site over which there has been so much argument? In 1939 it was an Army air training base located on a thousand acres of boggy land at the foot of San Francisco Bay, six miles from the university (Stanford) town of Palo Alto and about 38 miles from the city of San Francisco. A few miles away was the town of Sunnyvale after which it was originally named.

The Sunnyvale site had in June 1933 been named Moffett Field in honor of Rear Adm. William A. Moffett who had much to do with its establishment and who, on April 4, 1933, was killed when the giant dirigible *Akron* which he was commanding crashed into a stormy Atlantic Ocean off the New Jersey coast. At that time, the rigid airship was thought to hold much promise for both commercial and military usage and the United States had built three—the *Shenandoah*, the *Akron,* and the *Macon*. The *Shenandoah* in 1925 was destroyed by violent air currents encountered over Ohio. For the operation of the *Akron* and the *Macon,* a West Coast base was required; and thus it was that, in 1930–1931, after an extensive survey conducted by Admiral Moffett and his staff, the site which was named Sunnyvale was selected.[1] Actually, the new base might more appropriately have been named after the nearest town, Mountain View, but "Sunnyvale" presented a more pleasing image for an airfield and seemed less likely to elicit critical questions about site selection. One result of the naming was that, since mail to the new base was routed through Mountain View, incoming letters bore the awkward address, "U.S. Naval Air Station, Sunnyvale, Mountain View, California."

Like the dinosaurs of old, the rigid airships of the 1930's met with rather sudden extinction. America's rigid-airship program came to a halt when, on February 12, 1935, the *Macon*, then based at Sunnyvale, crashed into the Pacific Ocean off Point Sur. But hopes for the gas-filled behemoths

---

[1] See U.S. Navy publication: *Moffett Field, 1933–1958 Silver Anniversary.*

Moffett Field location.

of the sky were kept alive by the successful transatlantic operations of the German airship *Hindenburg* under the command of the veteran airship pilot Hugo Eckener. These hopes went up in flames, however, when on May 6, 1937, the *Hindenburg* burned at the landing dock at Lakehurst, New Jersey.

The Navy's need for the Sunnyvale base largely disappeared with the crash of the *Macon*. The huge Sunnyvale hangar, 198 feet high, 1133 feet long, and covering about eight acres, now seemingly useless, remained a landmark mocking honest men for plans gone awry. Thus the Navy was not unhappy when an opportunity arose to trade Sunnyvale to the Army for a number of assets, among which, reportedly, was the Army's North Island base in San Diego Harbor. The transfer officially took place on October 25, 1935, and Sunnyvale became a U.S. Army air training base.[2] The Army's

---

[2] *Ibid.*

24

little training planes, housed in a hangar so huge that the weather was rumored to be different at the two ends, looked like ants in an empty sugar barrel. This was the situation when the first NACA contingents appeared at the base.

At the time of NACA's arrival at Moffett Field in 1939, the commanding officer was Lieutenant Colonel George L. Usher; he, however, was shortly replaced by Lieutenant Colonel Robert E. M. Goolrick, USA. The land originally assigned to NACA by the Army was a parcel of about 62 acres located at the western border of Moffett Field, to which NACA added about 39 acres purchased from private owners at a cost of approximately $20,000. The Army's land contribution was not a gift to NACA. Rather, NACA was merely allowed to use the land for the construction and operation of a research laboratory.[3]

SITE PROBLEMS

While the use of Moffett Field was generally advantageous to NACA, the site nevertheless introduced a number of specific technical problems. The plot of land assigned to NACA was of a rather odd, boot shape, offering difficulties in the layout of roads and facilities. Another problem was the question of earthquake hazard: the great San Andreas Fault lay in the range of mountains only a few miles to the west. To withstand the twitches of earth along this famous rift line, all buildings would have to be designed to resist a lateral acceleration of about 0.2 g. A third problem concerned the stability of the land itself. In past years, so much water had been pumped from the ground to irrigate the orchards of the Santa Clara Valley that the surface of a large region near Moffett Field was known to have settled several feet. To prevent further lowering of the subsurface water table, and further land subsidence, percolating reservoirs had been built in the foothills surrounding the valley, but at the time NACA arrived at Moffett Field, there was some question as to whether subsidence had actually ceased. There was little that NACA engineers could do about this matter except cross their fingers and hope that Moffett Field, already low, would not sink beneath the waves of San Francisco Bay.

INITIAL STAFFING

It was generally understood that the staff of the Committee's new laboratory would be built around a nucleus of experienced men from Langley. There was little surprise therefore when, even before the site for the new laboratory had been officially announced, Dr. Lewis asked John F. Parsons

---

[3] Minutes of the NACA Executive Committee meeting of Feb. 7, 1940, indicate that the Assistant Secretary of War issued, on Dec. 7, 1939, a permit to NACA for the construction of research facilities at Moffett Field (Sunnyvale).

of the Langley staff to take charge of construction. At that time the head of the laboratory had not been named, but Smith J. DeFrance had for nearly a year been carrying out missions associated with the project and appeared a logical choice for the position. It was not until July 25, 1940, however, that DeFrance was formally appointed Engineer-in-Charge.[4]

Smitty DeFrance was an old timer at Langley and his experience in aviation was of still earlier origin. Born in Michigan in 1896, DeFrance was attending the University of Michigan when World War I erupted. He thereupon left the university to serve with the Air Service in Europe as a pursuit pilot and as flight commander of the 139th Aero Squadron. He served with a distinction that won him the Silver Star Medal. At war's end, Smitty resumed his studies at the university and in 1922 was awarded a degree in aeronautical engineering.

DeFrance had joined the staff of NACA's Langley laboratory in 1922 and since then had been responsible for the design and construction of most of that laboratory's major research facilities. Although DeFrance had no official flying responsibilities at Langley, he was involved while there in a flying accident that cost him an eye and nearly his life. At the time of his appointment to the Moffett Field post, DeFrance held the position of Assistant Chief of Aerodynamics and was in charge of Langley's four largest wind tunnels, including the 30- by 60-foot tunnel, the largest of its kind. He also headed a group which was engaged in the design of new research facilities required both for the expansion at Langley and for the new Moffett Field laboratory.

Jack Parsons had come to Langley in 1931 from Stanford University where, after his graduation in 1930, he had served for a year as technical assistant to Dr. William F. Durand in the editing of the major six-volume work *Aerodynamic Theory*, of which Durand was Editor-in-Chief. At Langley, Parsons had worked closely with DeFrance, had been a project engineer in the 30- by 60-foot tunnel for a number of years, and since July 1936 had been engaged in the design, construction, and operation of a new 19-foot pressurized tunnel, one of the most complex and costly wind tunnels that NACA had yet constructed. At the new Moffett Field laboratory, Parsons would be in charge of planning, designing, contracting, and construction.

At this stage, late in 1939, Russell G. (Russ) Robinson entered the picture at Moffett Field. Robinson had come directly to Langley after graduating from Stanford in 1930. He had subsequently been assigned the leading role in the design and operation of Langley's highly advanced, 8-foot, 600+-mph wind tunnel. In 1939 Robinson was chosen as one of the key

---

[4] The appointment was officially documented by a letter (travel authorization TAL–21) dated July 25, 1940, which transferred DeFrance from Langley to Ames. The letter was signed by John F. Victory, Secretary.

Russell Robinson (right) *supervising the first excavation for Ames laboratory Dec. 20, 1939.*

members of the new NACA coordination activity initiated by the actions of the NACA Special Subcommittee on Future Research Facilities. In December 1939, he was sent to California to carry out two missions. One was to establish a California-based coordination activity to handle NACA liaison with the western aircraft industry and universities. His second mission was to serve as the on-site representative of the construction group, which was still at Langley, and to initiate the erection of an inexpensive wooden building which would serve as a construction shack and temporary office building for the new laboratory. Both missions were accomplished very successfully. On December 20, 1939, a photograph was taken of Robinson, witnessing the first minor, but historic, excavation for the first NACA structure at Moffett Field. The site he had chosen for the building, central to the construction area, was squarely in the middle of Colonel Usher's baseball diamond.

DeFrance remained at Langley for a while to carry on with the facility design work; but, to get construction underway, it was necessary for Parsons to get out to Moffett Field as soon as possible. Thus it was that, on January 29, 1940, he and Ferril R. Nickle, also of Langley, arrived on the scene at Moffett Field. They were the first permanent members of the laboratory's staff to arrive on site. Other early arrivals from Langley were: Carlton Bioletti, March 1; Arthur B. Freeman, March 2; Edward R. Sharp, March 11; Manie G. Poole, March 11; H. Julian Allen, April 13; George E. Bulifant, April 17; Howard W. Kirschbaum, April 29; John P. Houston, April 29; Edward W. Betts, May 21; and James A. White, June 3.

Sharp came out from Langley as Administrative Officer but, with the arrival of DeFrance on August 20, he returned to the East to work on the construction of NACA's new engine research laboratory, of which he later became Director. Following Sharp's departure, Arthur Freeman became Acting Administrative Officer under DeFrance.

27

John F. Parsons (left) *and Ferril R. Nickle* (right), *first members of Ames staff, standing in front of construction shack Jan. 29, 1940.*

Ames staff on August 30, 1940, standing in front of new flight research building. From left to right: First row: *M. U. Nettle, M. A. Willey, M. H. Davies, M. W. St. John, S. J. DeFrance, E. R. Sharp, M. G. Poole, V. Burgess, R. A. Pipkin.* Second row: *A. B. Freeman, T. W. O'Briant, L. T. Videll, C. F. Wilson, R. M. Foster, M. C. Massa, M. J. Hood, C. Bioletti, C. W. Frick, W. G. Vincenti, H. W. Kirschbaum, L. A. Rodert, E. C. Braig, C. Gerbo.* Third row: *R. E. Browning, D. H. Wood, R. Hughes, G. Bulifant, J. V. Kelley, H. J. Allen, J. P. Houston, K. S. Burchard, M. A. Greene.* Fourth row: *A. G. Buck, E. W. Betts, R. E. Braig, H. J. Goett, J. F. Parsons, H. S. Dunlap, L. E. Minden, F. J. Clarke,* Fifth row: *W. O. Peterson, W. Walker, C. H. Harvey, J. C. Delaney, T. W. Macomber, A. L. Blocker, N. K. Delany, A. S. Hertzog, F. R. Nickle, P. T. Prizler, R. R. Benn, E. H. A. Schnitker.*

Augmenting the group of early arrivals from Langley were people recruited from other sources, some fresh from school. Among these were John Delaney, Noel Delany, Andre Buck, Alvin Hertzog, Mark Greene, Walter Peterson, Charles Harvey, Walter Vincenti, Charles Frick, Helen Davies, and Marie St. John. By the end of August the laboratory staff had grown to about 50.

The Naming

Within the inner councils of NACA, the question of a name for the Committee's new laboratory at Moffett Field had come up for discussion. In January and February, Dr. Edward Warner had proposed the name of "Ames" to his fellow Committee members.[5] There was a very good response to this suggestion, but the names of Wright and Curtiss were also introduced as alternate possibilities.

The general practice of waiting until a man was dead before so honoring him was noted during the discussion, but there had been exceptions, and most members agreed that it was eminently fitting and just that a man who made such a major contribution both to NACA and to the Moffett Field laboratory as had Dr. Ames deserved to be given the honor while he lived. After further discussion, unanimous agreement was reached on naming the laboratory after Dr. Ames. It was further decided that the announcement of the naming should be made on the occasion of a reunion luncheon of present and former members of NACA to commemorate the 25th anniversary of their first meeting. The event took place in Washington on April 18, 1940.

Dr. Ames was too ill to attend the luncheon, but a special delegation headed by Dr. Warner and including Dr. Lewis and John Victory had earlier been sent to Dr. Ames' residence in Baltimore to apprise him of the Committee's action. The special delegation spoke feelingly to Dr. Ames of their gratitude for his contributions to NACA, and to aviation, and delivered a letter which they had prepared saying that, with the approval of the President of the United States, the NACA had decided to name its new laboratory at Moffett Field the "Ames Aeronautical Laboratory."

The letter went on to say:

The National Advisory Committee for Aeronautics, in recognition of the contributions to progress that have come from its research laboratories at Langley Field, Virginia, is proud thus to honor its distinguished past Chairman, whose great vision, initiative, leadership, and sound professional judgment, over a period of twenty-four years of patriotic and devoted service to his country, have so largely laid the foundations for the science of aeronautics and developed a research organization that has

---

[5] Letter, Edward Warner to Dr. Vannevar Bush, with attachments, Feb. 8, 1940, NACA Executive Committee approved the name at a meeting held on Mar. 12, 1940.

earned the confidence and respect of the people of the United States and the entire aeronautical world.[6]

The honor was most fitting and well deserved. It was announced to the public as planned on April 18, 1940.[7] The Ames Aeronautical Laboratory must now strive to live up to its name. The signature on Dr. Ames' letter of thanks was quavery. It was well that the naming of the Laboratory had not been further delayed.

The layout of the Ames Aeronautical Laboratory provided an opportunity to pay respect to other men who had made important contributions as members of NACA. Thus the street names of the Laboratory have included an Arnold Avenue, a Bush Circle, a King Road, a Durand Road, a Warner Road, and, later, a Wolcott Road.

[6] Letter, Special Committee on Notification (E. P. Warner, Chairman, Charles Abbot, Lyman Briggs, G. W. Lewis, and J. F. Victory) to Dr. Joseph S. Ames, Apr. 17, 1940.
[7] NACA press release, Apr. 18, 1940: "New Sunnyvale Laboratory Named for Former NACA Chairman."

6

Plans and Preparations

L ANGLEY experience was, of course, the dominant influence affecting the selection of facilities for the Ames Aeronautical Laboratory. The principal function of the Laboratory would be research in the field of aerodynamics, and high-speed aerodynamics would be emphasized. Dr. Lewis requested that space along the western boundary fence be reserved for a seaplane towing basin in case it was later decided that Ames should have such a facility.

One of the high-priority items on the Ames facility list was a 16-foot wind tunnel that would develop airspeeds of 500 mph or more. This facility was needed to deal with the design problems of high-speed airplanes then being developed for the Army and the Navy. A couple of workhorse 7- by 10-foot tunnels would be needed, of course, and even these should be fairly fast, perhaps 250 to 300 mph. Then, with Smitty DeFrance doing the planning, it was not surprising that a gigantic 40- by 80-foot so-called "full scale" tunnel appeared on the list. In this facility, full-scale airplanes could be tested with engines running.

The 16-foot and the 7- by 10-foot tunnels were needed first; the 40- by 80-foot tunnel, because of the time required to design and build such a huge facility, must come a little later. Delayed also must be the 12-foot low-turbulence pressure tunnel then under consideration, and a supersonic tunnel of some type yet to be determined. All of these tunnels except the 7-by-10's represented an extrapolation considerably beyond existing experience and thus constituted a very real challenge to designers.

Flight research had from the first been a basic element of NACA's activity. One of the duties of NACA as stated in its founding act was to "supervise and direct the scientific study of the problems of flight with a view to their practical solution . . ." and NACA had always felt an obligation to prove, in actual flight, the practicality of ideas and devices developed in its wind tunnels. Thus, flight research was an important part of the original plans for Ames; indeed, it was given top priority in the facilities-construction program since Ames designers believed it could be started earlier than wind-tunnel research. Construction of the flight research building began late in February 1940; and this unit, the first permanent structure at Ames, was completed early in August.

A technical services building, to house essential machine-shop and model-shop activities, was the second unit to get under way. This building was started in April and completed in October. Construction work on the 16-foot tunnel and the first 7- by 10-foot tunnel began in May; and on the second 7- by 10-foot tunnel, in July. The first test piles for the 40- by 80-foot tunnel were also driven in July. A contract for a utilities building was let in September 1940.

Instrument work required at the Laboratory was first carried out in the flight research building. Later, in July 1941, a contract was let for a science building to house a much-expanded instrument-development activity.

Of the buildings originally planned for the Ames Laboratory, the last to be put under construction was the administration building. It was felt that an administration building would at first be more of a convenience than a necessity and thus priority was given to research facilities. Administrative activities were housed in the construction shack for a while but were transferred to the flight research building when it was completed in August. The administration building itself was not completed until October 1943, and the associated auditorium and cafeteria were not ready for use until January 1944.

INITIAL ORGANIZATION

During the first year of Ames history, the organizational arrangements at the Laboratory were rather informal. Staff was being acquired and almost everyone was busy with some phase of facilities design and construction. There was no research. This troubled DeFrance somewhat as he was afraid his research men, then occupied with mundane construction matters, might lose touch with the current state and subtle arts of aeronautical research. To counter any tendencies of this kind, he organized evening seminars in which research reports from Langley were reviewed.

In 1941, as research work at the Laboratory became imminent, DeFrance began to organize his staff along research functional lines. Following the Langley pattern, he took steps to build a research group around each of the major facilities. One exception to this plan was a Theoretical Aerodynamics Section which dealt mostly with basic theory and thus did not require much experimental equipment. Of course even in the experimental groups, theory would be used in planning experimental programs and in analyzing results, but most of the new knowledge gained by these groups would be in the form of experimental data.

32

PLANS AND PREPARATIONS

The major elements of the organization which DeFrance had established by mid-1941 were as follows:

Engineer-in-Charge _____	Smith J. DeFrance
Construction Division _____	John F. Parsons, Chief
Research Division _____	Donald H. Wood, Chief
16-Foot Tunnel Section _____	Manley J. Hood, Head
7- by 10-Foot Tunnel Section _____	Harry J. Goett, Head
Theoretical Aerodynamics Section ___	H. Julian Allen, Head
Flight Research	
Administrative Division _____	Arthur B. Freeman, Acting Administrative Officer
Clerical and Files Section _____	Manie G. Poole, Head
Personnel Section _____	Walter O. Peterson, Head
Procurement Section _____	Eugene C. Braig, Head
Stockroom Section _____	Frank J. Clarke, Head
Technical Shops Division _____	Edward W. Betts, Chief
Machine Shop _____	Harry Downs, Head
Erection Shop _____	George E. Bulifant, Head
Aircraft Maintenance _____	Raymond E. Braig, Head
Technical Service Groups	
Electrical Section _____	James A. White, Head
Photographic Section _____	Howard W. Kirschbaum, Head
Instrument Section _____	James V. Kelley, Head
Drafting Section _____	Edward H. A. Schnitker, Head

At this stage, the flight research staff consisted mainly of two pilots, W. H. McAvoy and L. A. Clousing; one research engineer, L. A. Rodert; and a very small Aircraft Maintenance Section which, headed by R. E. Braig, was a part of the Technical Shops Division. This group operated effectively as a team but was not formally organized for research until July 1942, when three sections were established as follows:

Flight Operations Section _____	William H. McAvoy, Head
Flight Engineering Section _____	Lewis A. Rodert, Head
Flight Research Section _____	Lawrence A. Clousing, Head

The Aircraft Maintenance Section remained, as before, under Ray Braig.

First Research

Ideas for NACA research projects literally came from anyone who cared to offer them. All ideas were considered but the most fruitful generally came from staff members of the NACA laboratories, from military or other Government agencies, from universities, or from the aeronautical industry. Another important source of ideas was a system of technical committees and

33

subcommittees which reviewed all of NACA's research work and advised NACA management regarding the appropriateness and priority of proposed research projects.[1]

The technical committees and subcommittees, each dealing with a special area of aeronautical research, were appointed by NACA and included representatives from all the aeronautical interests earlier mentioned. These groups advised NACA on research and performed the vital additional function of coordinating the aeronautical research not only of the NACA laboratories but of the Nation. Their coordination came not through coercion—they were only advisory—but through information. If there was any duplication of research effort, it was deliberate and purposeful for, through the NACA technical committee system, the directly interested agencies of the Nation were kept informed of what was being done in Government and university laboratories.

The executive function of NACA's research operation rested in the Headquarters Office of the Director of Aeronautical Research. This office had for years been occupied by Dr. George W. Lewis. It was Dr. Lewis and his staff, acting with the approval of the NACA Executive Committee, who made the final decisions as to which of the carefully considered research projects would be undertaken by NACA and by which laboratory. The individual laboratories were given much freedom in carrying out the research authorizations assigned to them by Headquarters; nevertheless their work was subject to some monitoring and coordination by Headquarters, and they were generally expected to make regular progress reports to the technical committees.

The first research authorization was assigned to the Ames Aeronautical Laboratory in 1941. This authorization, Research Authorization No. A–1,

---

[1] In 1941 the NACA technical committee system consisted of the following:
    Committee on Aerodynamics
        Subcommittee on Seaplanes
        Subcommittee on Propellers for Aircraft
        Subcommittee on Rotating-Wing Aircraft
        Subcommittee on Meteorological Problems
        Special Subcommittee on Lightning Hazards to Aircraft
        Special Subcommittee on Deicing Problems
    Committee on Power Plants for Aircraft
        Subcommittee on Fuels and Lubricants
        Special Subcommittee on Supercharger Compressors
        Special Subcommittee on Exhaust Gas Turbines and Intercoolers
        Special Subcommittee on Induction-System Deicing
    Committee on Aircraft Materials
        Subcommittee on Metals Used in Aircraft
        Subcommittee on Miscellaneous Materials and Accessories
        Special Subcommittee on Metals for Turbo-Supercharger Wheels and Buckets
        Special Subcommittee on Welding Problems
    Committee on Aircraft Structures
    Special Committee on Jet Propulsion

covered a study of means for protecting airplanes from the hazards of icing.[2] The deicing work at Ames was actually a carryover from Langley and was undertaken by the Flight Research group nearly a year before the authorization was formalized. Out of this work came Ames' first research report (ref. A–1) dated April 1941 and entitled "Preliminary Report on Flight Tests of an Airplane Having Exhaust-Heated Wings," by Lewis A. Rodert, William H. McAvoy, and Lawrence A. Clousing. Many more reports on the subject of ice protection were written; the work encompassed by these reports is described in chapter 9.

The first wind tunnel to operate at Ames was the 7-by-10 No. 1. It was near midnight on March 13, 1941, when power was first released through the drive motors of the tunnel and the fan began to turn. Nothing untoward happened. Smitty DeFrance and Andre (Jeff) Buck stood behind the control panel as the test engineer brought the tunnel up to speed. "What is that red button for?" Smitty asked Jeff. "Why, that's the emergency stop button," Jeff replied. "It cuts the power off in one fell swoop when you push it." He had no more than completed his explanation when Smitty reached over and pushed the button. Jeff and the other engineers present stood by with mouths agape as the wheels of their new baby ground to a halt. Smitty's act, though impulsive, was not irresponsible or careless. He felt that emergency equipment of this kind had a very important function and that its performance should be checked out before an emergency occurred. Coming out of their shocked surprise, the engineers began to appreciate Smitty's motives and were pleased that their new tunnel had passed the test so well.

Although the first run was made in March, it was not until August 29 that the first research program, on Consolidated's new XB–32 bomber, got under way. The intervening period was spent in tunnel calibration tests and in overcoming a long-period flow oscillation arising from some minor fault of the original design. The first wind-tunnel test report published by Ames, a report which covered the XB–32 tests in the 7-by-10 No. 1, was authored by Roy P. Jackson and George L. Smith, Jr.[3]

Calibration tests of the 7-by-10 No. 2 got under way in July 1941 and benefited from the experience gained in the No. 1 tunnel. Thus No. 2 was able to begin its first research program on August 20—a few days earlier than No. 1. This program involved tests of a model of the North American XB–28 bomber.

The 16-foot tunnel made its first run, a pitot-head calibration, on Au-

---

[2] Research Authorization No. A–1, "Investigation of Ice Prevention and Elimination on Airplanes," was conveyed in a letter from G. W. Lewis to the Ames Aeronautical Laboratory, Aug. 7, 1941.

[3] Restricted Memorandum Report for Army entitled "Wind-Tunnel Investigation of Sealed-Gap Ailerons on XB-32 Airplane Rectangular Wing Model Equipped with Full-Span Flaps Consisting of an Inboard Fowler Flap and an Outboard Retractable Balanced Split Flap," by Roy P. Jackson and George L. Smith, Jr. Dec. 13, 1941.

gust 22, 1941. That was the earliest of a series of shakedown and calibration tests that lasted until March 1942. The 16-foot tunnel was a very advanced and complex facility; its shakedown period was thus considerably longer than that of the more commonplace 7-by-10's. The period was further prolonged by airflow disturbances arising from interference between the fan blades and the large motor-support struts. Never before had a wind-tunnel fan been required to absorb so much power, and the support struts were unable efficiently to remove the airstream swirl produced by the fan. The struts had to be reshaped.

7

Disruptions of War

WAR COMES

FROM the beginning, work on the new Ames Aeronautical Laboratory had been pushed with an uneasy sense of urgency. On December 7, 1941, the fears that had beset the Nation burst forth in the clear and shocking reality of bloody war. This momentous event confirmed the wisdom of NACA's struggle to secure the new Laboratory and justified the speed with which its construction had been pursued.

The onset of war also changed rather completely the plan of operation. All plans for conducting basic research had now to be laid aside and every effort bent on solving short-range airplane-development problems, for it was in this way Ames could contribute the most toward winning the war. Security at the Laboratory and in all Moffett Field operations was greatly tightened and the Army agreed, at NACA's request, to provide protection for the Ames Laboratory. The danger of direct invasion of the U.S. mainland by the Japanese was considered. A possible enemy plan for such an invasion, it was thought, would be a landing at Monterey Bay with a march up the peninsula to San Francisco. Moffett Field lay adjacent to this route.[1]

DISTRIBUTION OF RESEARCH INFORMATION

In the past most of NACA's work had been unclassified and freely published in the form of Technical Reports, Technical Notes, and Technical Memorandums. Technical Reports were used for major work of lasting value, and Technical Notes for research work of somewhat lesser consequence or for work the value of which might be expected to diminish with time. Technical Memorandums, on the other hand, were generally reserved for translations of foreign technical articles. All of these documents, especially the Reports, were carefully prepared compositions on which editing effort was lavished.

---

[1] According to recollection of DeFrance.

With the beginning of war the NACA introduced several new categories of classified reports which, owing to simplified format and editing shortcuts, were expected to speed the transmission of research data from laboratory to user. These categories were: Preliminary Data Report, Advance Confidential Report, Advance Restricted Report, Confidential Bulletin, Restricted Bulletin, Secret Memorandum Report, Confidential Memorandum Report, and Restricted Memorandum Report. All were commonly designated by their initials together with a number-letter code, for example: ACR 4B30.

The transmission of data from Laboratory to user (aircraft company) was greatly speeded by the use of some of these reporting forms, particularly the Preliminary Data Report. Documents of this kind were hastily produced and consisted largely of raw and unedited data. But the company whose model was being tested at Ames did not have to wait even for the Preliminary Data Report. Generally the company's representative would be in attendance at the Laboratory during the tests and would telephone any critically important results to his home office. Reportedly on one occasion a company's new airplane was sitting on the ramp at the factory with engines warmed up for its first flight awaiting only word from Ames regarding the proper setting for a control surface.

Military Liaison and Industry Relations

Throughout its history, NACA had diligently served the aeronautical research interests of the military services and, in 1939, the Army had indeed found it advantageous to establish a liaison office at Langley. This office proved useful and, in 1941, as the first research got under way at Ames, the Army decided it should have a liaison office at the new Laboratory.[2] Theophile DePort, a civilian aeronautical engineer employed at the Army Air Corps Materiel Division, Wright Field, was sent to Ames in September 1941 to establish the office.[2] This he did and remained until replaced in 1942 by Carl Tusch, also a civilian Army engineer. With the beginning of the war, the Army liaison office at Ames took on new importance, and in October 1942 Captain William A. Bennett, Jr., was placed in charge. Captain Bennett was the first of a series of military officers to hold this post, all supported by the able and amiable Carl Tusch.

Among the wartime functions of the liaison office was the coordination of research programs being conducted by Ames for Army contractors. This function included the difficult task of trying to achieve the most effective balance between the urgent testing needs of the aircraft companies and the limited test facilities existing at Ames and elsewhere. Many a company, im-

---

[2] Letter, NACA (Dr. G. W. Lewis) to AAL (Ames), Sept. 10, 1941, advising of intention of Air Corps to establish a Liaison Office at Ames.

pressed with the importance of its own project, requested more time in NACA tunnels than could be justified by any fair consideration of the Army's total commitment. The Ames management did what it could to limit test programs to the bare essentials, but the Army's liaison office was in a much better position to deal with its own contractors in these matters. Sometimes the competition for time in Ames tunnels was between a Navy contractor and an Army contractor. Adjudication of such conflicts was handled by representatives of an interservice Aeronautical Board. The Navy's representative, Captain Walter S. Diehl, a highly perceptive and agreeable chap, worked so effectively with his Army counterpart that throughout the war no serious interservice conflict over Ames tunnel usage ever arose.

There was always the touchy matter of proprietary interests to deal with, and the Ames staff had to be careful not to reveal the details of, say, a new Lockheed airplane to one of Lockheed's competitors such as Douglas. But the Nation was at war, and sometimes the solution to a design problem revealed in tests of one company's airplane was essential to the success of a military airplane being built by another company. The most urgent of these problems were usually solved, often through the action of the Army liaison office or Captain Diehl.

Although, during the war, there were numerous opportunities for the development of trouble in the relations between NACA and the western aircraft companies, such relations were actually improved during that period. The management of western companies had originally thought of NACA as an "eastern" organization which, though faithfully serving the interests of the Government, and perhaps industry in the East, was not very responsive to the specific needs of western industry. Expressions of antipathy toward NACA by western aircraft people were modestly restrained except in a few cases such as those of Clarence (Kelly) Johnson of Lockheed and Mac Laddon and Harry Sutton of Consolidated.[3] These individuals appeared fairly hostile toward NACA. The atmosphere changed, however, soon after the establishment of Ames. DeFrance visited the aircraft companies, listened to their problems, and assured them that Ames was prepared to cooperate with them in a full and friendly fashion. Such cooperation, he made clear, would be within the scope of the Laboratory's broad responsibilities and would not be servile in character. At Lockheed, Smitty closeted himself with Kelly for a "frank discussion" from which both emerged smiling. As a result of this moment of understanding, the two men developed a mutual respect and a lasting friendship.

The sincerity with which DeFrance promised his cooperation and the fullness with which he honored those promises did much to improve industry's relations with NACA in general and with Ames in particular. NACA-industry relations were further improved by NACA's coordination activity,

---

[3] The author's personal observations made through direct contact with the cited individuals.

begun in 1940 by Russ Robinson, and even more by NACA's decision to include industry representatives on its technical committees. In 1939 the airframe and engine manufacturers had only two representatives on NACA technical committees,[4] but by 1944 the number had risen to 49. A major change of policy was taking place: no longer would NACA listen only to the counsel of sister Government agencies.

MOFFETT FIELD REVERTS TO NAVY

Soon after the war began, the Navy found it desirable to use nonrigid airships (blimps) for patrolling our western shores in search of enemy submarines and mines. Quite a number of blimps were acquired for this purpose and the problem of finding hangar space, and a suitable operating base, for them arose. The answer was pretty simple. The Navy had to have its Moffett Field base back from the Army. The big airship hangar was still there and was only poorly utilized in housing Army airplanes. With Army agreement, the Navy reacquired the base and recommissioned it as an air station on April 15, 1942.[5]

Shortly after the Navy took over, two additional blimp hangars, only a little smaller than the original airship hangar, were built on the other side of the runway and large helium storage, handling, and purifying facilities were also installed. Now the blimps could be handled as well as the spherical balloons used for training blimp crews. But the Moffett Naval Air Station had a long runway and other capabilities beyond those required for the blimp operations. The Navy therefore used the station for both lighter-than-air and heavier-than-air activities; by the end of the war it had become a major overhaul base for Navy airplanes.

The tenor of Ames relations with the Navy was as amicable as it had been with the Army. The Navy granted NACA a use permit for the space occupied by its research facilities and all the other relationships between Ames and the military continued much as before.[6]

ORGANIZING FOR RESEARCH

As the Ames staff expanded and new facilities came into operation, certain changes in the Laboratory research organization became necessary. These changes were made in May 1943. The Ames research activities which heretofore had all come under the Research Division, headed by Don Wood, were now divided, as follows, into two divisions:

---

[4] L. S. Hobbs (Pratt & Whitney Aircraft Co.) and Arthur Nutt (Wright Aeronautical Corp.).

[5] U.S. Navy publication: *Moffett Field 1933–1958 Silver Anniversary.*

[6] Revocable Permit NOy (R)–45929 dated Apr. 11, 1945. Executed by direction of SecNav Apr. 6, 1945, and accepted by NACA Apr. 11, 1945.

From left to right: *James V. Kelley, John P. Houston, and Donald H. Wood.*

Theoretical and Applied Research Division	Donald H. Wood, Chief
16-Foot Tunnel Section	Manley J. Hood, Head
7- by 10-Foot Tunnel Section	Harry J. Goett, Head
Theoretical Aerodynamics Section	H. Julian Allen, Head
12-Foot Tunnel Section	Vacant
Supersonic Wind Tunnel Section	Vacant
Full-Scale and Flight Research Division	John F. Parsons,* Chief
Flight Operations Section	William H. McAvoy, Head
Flight Engineering Section	Lewis A. Rodert, Head
Flight Research Section	Lawrence A. Clousing, Head
40- by 80-Foot Tunnel Section	Vacant

*Also Chief of Construction Division.

At the same time that these changes were being made, Art Freeman, who had been Acting Administrative Officer since E. R. Sharp left in 1940, was appointed Administrative Officer. Early in 1944 the Ames organization was further defined by the addition of a Service Division organized as follows:

Service Division	James A. White, Chief
Electrical Section	Andre G. Buck, Head

Instrument Section _____ James V. Kelley, Head
Instrument Development Section _____ Howard W. Kirschbaum, Head
Photographic Section _____ Fred H. Swartz, Head
Drafting Section _____ Edward H. A. Schnitker, Head

MANPOWER PROBLEMS: THE ARMY-NAVY-NACA PLAN

As the war progressed, a desperate manpower shortage arose not only at Ames but throughout NACA. It arose primarily from the fact that NACA employees and prospective candidates for employment by NACA were being drafted into the military services. These draft actions appeared to be contrary to the wishes of the military and to earlier agreements between NACA and the military.

Shortly before Major General Oscar Westover's accidental death in September 1938, he submitted a report to NACA as Chairman of the Special Committee on the Relation of the NACA to National Defense in Time of War.[7] This Westover report expressed the need for maintaining the efficient functioning of the Committee's organization in time of war and recommended a plan, to go into effect upon declaration of an emergency, whereby the Committee's staff would be stabilized and increased if necessary to meet the needs of the Army and the Navy. The Westover recommendations were approved by NACA and incorporated in the Mobilization Plan of the Aeronautical Board—a top-level military board concerned with aeronautical matters of joint interest to the Army and the Navy.[8]

The Mobilization Plan, which in 1939 was approved by the Secretaries of the War and Navy Departments as well as by the President, specified among other things that, during any emergency declared by the President, the Committee's research laboratories should be placed at the service of the Aeronautical Board and the Committee should execute the projects requested of it by the Aeronautical Board. It did not say, however, that NACA's operations would be managed by the military. This point NACA in its later relations with the military services sometimes felt the need to emphasize. More important, however, the plan established a draft deferment basis for essential members of the NACA staff.[9]

During the early part of the war, draft deferments for essential NACA personnel were achieved without much trouble and the aircraft companies, moreover, allowed NACA to recruit from their engineering staffs such men as they could not themselves withhold from the draft. As the war progressed,

---

[7] Report of Special Committee on Relation of the National Advisory Committee for Aeronautics to National Defense in Time of War, submitted to Chairman NACA Aug. 19, 1938. Report signed by O. Westover (Chairman), A. B. Cook, and W. R. Gregg.

[8] Plan was transmitted to President Roosevelt with letter dated June 22, 1939, from Harry H. Woodring, Secretary of War, and William D. Leahy, Acting Secretary of the Navy. It was approved by the President on June 29, 1939.

[9] *Ibid.*

however, serious objections to NACA deferments began to appear in the local draft boards, in the lower military echelons, and even in the office of General Lewis B. Hershey, Director of Selective Service. Along in 1943 it became evident that no further deferments would be granted NACA personnel.[10]

The military, it may be noted, allowed NACA to recruit technically trained men from the continuous flow of military personnel returning through redistribution and rest centers from service abroad and a considerable number of such men were employed. But most of these recruits were technicians, few were engineers, and scarcely any had any experience in aeronautical research. It was not a good trade for NACA to give the military an experienced aeronautical research scientist and to receive in return a toolmaker or, possibly, a road-building civil engineer. The measure of the Laboratory's desperation in the personnel matter was indicated by Art Freeman's instructions to departing recruiters: "If their body is warm, hire them."

Something more was clearly needed to obtain the highly qualified but draft-eligible college graduates. In 1943 NACA referred the problem to the military at the highest level and asked for a recommendation. Down came the recommendation from the military to put all NACA personnel in uniform—thus presumably putting NACA completely under the dominance of the military.[11] NACA, with John Victory as spokesman, replied that the recommended solution was not acceptable to NACA because it was against the law to force men over a certain age into uniform and because it would destroy the independence of NACA that was needed for efficient operation. Another solution was requested and this, when it was offered, was that irreplaceable draft-eligible men in NACA be inducted into the military or military reserve forces and reassigned to work in NACA laboratories under NACA management. This plan, known as the Joint Army and Navy Plan of 1 February 1944, was approved by all parties concerned and put into effect. At both the Langley Laboratory and the Engine Research Laboratory in Cleveland, draft-eligible men were inducted into the Air Corps Enlisted Reserve. At Ames they were inducted into the Navy and put on active-duty status.[12]

Although the plan was rather late in being developed, it was, nevertheless, very useful to NACA. Within the year following its approval, about 150 of the Ames staff were in the Navy. The plan as applied at Ames was reasonably successful, but Navy regulations did impose certain odd requirements on the individuals involved. The Navy, for example, insisted that all

---

[10] Deduced by Ames from Selective Service Bulletin 169, dated Mar. 25, 1944.

[11] According to the recollection of John F. Victory.

[12] "Plan for the Use of Military Personnel in the Operation of Research Facilities of NACA." Signed by Henry L. Stimson, Secretary of War; Frank Knox, Secretary of the Navy; and Jerome C. Hunsaker, Chairman of NACA. Approved by the President [Roosevelt] on Feb. 10, 1944, and named "Joint Army Navy NACA Plan of 1 February 1944."

members of the Ames contingent undergo the standard 6-week "boot camp" training, and from the standpoint of NACA research this was largely lost time. Also, after working a full day in the Ames laboratories, the men were given regular assignments of Navy duty such as Shore Patrol. The commissioning of officers within the Ames contingent was also rather arbitrary and gave no consideration to the man's duties and status within NACA. Of lesser consequence, and somewhat amusing, was the requirement that the Ames contingent abide by the Navy's precise scheduling of haircutting. Thus an individual might be required to appear at the Navy barbershop on Tuesday at exactly 3:42 p.m., regardless of any important activity he might at the time be carrying out for NACA.

The Joint Army-Navy-NACA Plan did not, of course, solve all of Ames' manpower problems. There were basic shortages in all categories, particularly nonprofessional ones composed of people who could not readily be withheld from the draft. Also many of the people recruited were inexperienced and some were not well qualified for their jobs. Women were recruited to fill certain positions normally held by men and often proved to be very efficient workers. Much in-house training was required, however, and both daytime and evening classes were set up for this purpose.

These, then, were some of the war-induced conditions to which, as best it could, the new Ames Aeronautical Laboratory had to adjust.

8

Facilities Design

WHEN it came to experience and demonstrated ability in building aerodynamic research facilities, NACA had no peer, and some of NACA's most experienced designers and builders came to Moffett Field to build and operate the facilities of the new Ames Aeronautical Laboratory. True, they had a rather limited amount of money to work with, but this was an old and familiar condition which merely whetted their ingenuity. One could scarcely have chosen a better man to build a new laboratory than Smith DeFrance. He and John Parsons worked together as an extremely effective building team. But there were many others at Ames who contributed greatly to the design of the new facilities, men such as Don Wood, Carl Bioletti, H. J. (Harvey) Allen, James White, Walter Vincenti, Manley Hood, and J. S. W. (Sam) Davidsen. Indeed, in the first years of the Ames history, the research men and everyone else turned to and helped with the design of new facilities. Bioletti labored not only on the design of facilities for Ames but also found time to assist in the design of an altitude wind tunnel for the Engine Research Laboratory at Cleveland. Even after research work at Ames had gotten well under way, certain research men were still dealing with the steel and concrete of which the major structures of the Laboratory were composed. Surprisingly perhaps, even the staff of the Theoretical Aerodynamics Section were so involved. Hence, though it was intended as humor, there was plenty of truth in Harvey Allen's greeting when he answered the telephone, "Theoretical Concrete and Reinforced Aerodynamics Section!"

First Tunnels

The builders of the Ames Laboratory faced a real challenge as well as an opportunity to demonstrate imaginative design. The main theme at Ames was to be research in high-speed aerodynamics, yet the military had a need for facilities that could be built in a hurry to perform tests at conventional speeds of around 250 mph.[1] To satisfy the latter need, the two 7- by 10-foot tunnels were built. The pair cost a little under a million dollars. These two facilities involved no important extension of the design art. They were conventional closed-throat tunnels designed to operate at atmospheric pressure and at speeds up to about 280 mph. They were designed to measure forces and moments on relatively simple models that could easily and inexpensively be modified.

Of the wind tunnels originally planned for Ames, the 16-foot tunnel had perhaps the highest priority. It had been assigned this precedence because it was to have a higher speed than any other major wind tunnel in the NACA and would provide aerodynamic data at the speeds at which future military airplanes were expected to fly. There was an 8-foot-diameter, 600 + -mph tunnel at Langley; but the new tunnel at Ames was to operate at speeds up to 680 mph, about 0.9 of the speed of sound, and was to have four times the cross-sectional area of the Langley tunnel. Its cost was nearly $2 million. The huge 27,000-horsepower drive motors of the 16-foot tunnel would generate so much heat that an air-exchange tower had to be provided. The function of the tower was to replace the heated air in the tunnel gradually with cool air from the outdoors. This was a device originated by NACA and first used in the 8-foot high-speed tunnel at Langley.

The motors of the 16-foot tunnel also produced a deep rumble which in the quiet of the night could be heard for miles and sounded like an approaching fleet of bombers. This characteristic caused some trouble when the tunnel was being calibrated during the early months of the war. The military was pretty jumpy at that stage and when the tunnel began to operate in the middle of the night, they were sure the Japanese were coming in as they had at Pearl Harbor. In accord with air-raid plans, all major power-absorbing equipment was ordered shut down and this included the 16-foot tunnel. Happily, the enemy raid appeared to have been a false alarm. The all-clear sounded and the tunnel innocently resumed its tests. But oh those foxy Japs! There they came again and the tunnel was again shut down. "All clear!" and the tunnel start button was pushed. Moments later the sirens shrieked their warning of yet another attack. This was war in its most exasperating form. After a few cycles of on-and-off operation, it began to dawn on someone that there was a connection between the tunnel operation and the suspected air raid. Disillusioned, the military called off their air raid for the night and arrangements were made to avoid such confusion in the future.

Another bit of excitement at Ames came one evening when a hydrogen-filled barrage balloon, used to protect certain installations in the upper Bay region, broke loose from its moorings. Like a homing pigeon, it headed

---

[1] This need was expressed to Dr. Lewis by Maj. A. J. Lyon of the Air Corps and recorded in Lewis memorandums for the Chairman NACA, one dated Dec. 14, 1938.

Above: *16-foot wind tunnel.* Below: *Ames Aeronautical Laboratory on June 10, 1942. Completed buildings include the flight research laboratory, science laboratory (near circle), technical service building, utilities building, and three wind tunnels. Electric substation and outline of 40- by 80-foot tunnel can be seen.*

down the Bay straight for the 110,000-volt substation which Ames had built to provide power for its new wind tunnels. The rendezvous was accomplished with a brilliant flash that could be seen for miles. Confusion again reigned. No one had seen the balloon approach and thus no one knew what had happened. Was it sabotage? Jim White rushed out to find the substation in what, in the twilight, appeared to be shreds. He had trouble in restraining the military guards from crawling over the fence into the danger area. When the scene was illuminated and calm restored, the substation was found to be largely intact. The shreds were the remains of the balloon.

The power requirements of the Laboratory were growing quite rapidly, and the Pacific Gas & Electric Co. was taking steps to meet the demand. The 40- by 80-foot tunnel required 36,000 horsepower to turn six motors driving six fans all mounted in the same plane and all synchronized in their turning. This power, great though it was, moved a lot of air and generated a speed of only 225 mph. Far larger than any previously existing tunnel, the 40-by-80 was 180 feet tall, covered eight acres, and together with the huge airship hangars became the eye-catching trademark of Moffett Field. Its cost was just over $7 million.

The throat of the 40-by-80 was made of steel, of course, but the huge return passages were constructed largely of corrugated asbestos-cement sheet supported on the outside by a steel trusswork. Originally the tunnel plans called for an air-exchange tower to remove the heat and exhaust gases of airplane engines which would be run in the tunnel. But the air exchanger would add a million dollars to the cost and this respectable increment, it was felt, might better be spent on a much-wanted supersonic wind tunnel. Further calculations showed that, because of the huge volume of air enclosed in the tunnel, the air leakage occurring at the purposefully unsealed joints, and the large thermal capacity of the tunnel and its concrete base, the air exchanger was not essential. If, after a considerable period of engine running, the airstream became excessively contaminated and heated, the great doors in the throat could be opened and the hot contaminated air pumped out.

Don Wood and Harvey Allen did much of the design work on the 40-by-80. According to Harvey, they each started at the throat and worked in opposite directions, hoping to meet in some consistent fashion on the opposite side. And this they did. For the joining, Harvey designed a special section which he was pleased to call his "Rumanian joint." To this fancy the others smiled indulgently. Allen's first initial "H" stood for Harry, but the pseudonym "Harvey," applied originally in fun, fell into such popular usage that his real name was soon forgotten. His family, however, called him Julian.

Although construction on the 40-by-80 had begun late in 1941, the task was large and the tunnel was not completed and ready to operate until June

Above: *June 24, 1943, 40- by 80-foot tunnel under construction, Navy Patrol blimp in background.* Below: *40- by 80-foot tunnel completed, technical service building, utilities building, and 16-foot tunnel adjacent.*

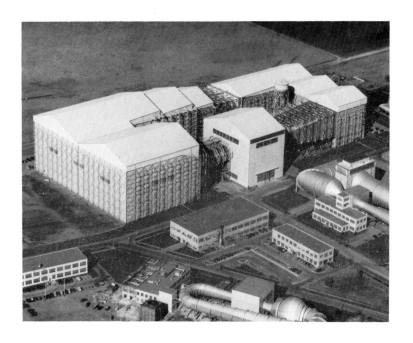

Dr. William F. Durand.

1944. The completion, it was felt, provided an auspicious occasion for holding a formal dedication of the Ames Aeronautical Laboratory. A number of research facilities were in operation and these, together with the 40-by-80, would make quite a show for the invited guests. The administration building also had been completed, thus providing a suitable place for hanging a picture of Dr. Ames. Unfortunately, Dr. Ames would not be present, for he had died a year earlier.

The dedication was held on June 8, 1944. High-level representatives from the aircraft industry, from local universities, and from civil and military branches of the Government were present. The dedicatory address was given by the beloved and respected Dr. William F. Durand of Stanford who, along with Dr. Ames, was one of the original members of NACA. Dr. Durand, though 85 years of age at the time of the dedication, had recently been reappointed to the NACA for the specific purpose of guiding the Committee's work in the new field of jet propulsion.

As a fillip to the dedication ceremony, the group was taken on an inspection tour of the 40-by-80 in which the new XSB2D–1 dive bomber, pride and joy of designers Ed Heinemann and Gene Root of the Douglas El Segundo plant, had been mounted. While the visitors peered through the windows of the test chamber, Dr. J. C. Hunsaker, Chairman of NACA, threw the switch and the six fans, after kicking into synchronism, began to turn. The sight was impressive. The largest wind tunnel in the world was in operation.

Shortly before the Ames Aeronautical Laboratory was founded, Eastman Jacobs, John Stack, Harvey Allen, Ira Abbott, and others at Langley had developed a new class of airfoils having a less arbitrary and more scientific design rationale than earlier airfoils. The new design theory concerned the

50

Douglas XSB2D–1 airplane in 40- by 80-foot tunnel.

boundary layer, the thin layer of air adjacent to the wing the velocity of which has been retarded by skin friction. It had long been known that the air as it passed over a wing would produce much less drag if the flow in the boundary layer was smooth and laminar rather than turbulent; but unfortunately it was generally the case that the airflow over a wing quickly became turbulent, remaining laminar for only a short way along the airfoil chord.

What the Langley men found out was that, if the airflow over the airfoil could be kept in a continually accelerating state by properly shaping the pressure distribution along the chord, the flow would remain laminar. The desired pressure distribution could be achieved by carefully shaping the airfoil—choosing the proper thickness distribution along the chord. The method of calculating the shape (thickness distribution) of an airfoil to achieve the desired pressure distribution was tedious, but the results were rewarding. The viscous drag of a wing might thereby be cut in half. Later the new technique proved useful in designing wings for high-speed airplanes.

John Stack had put some test wings in one of the Langley high-speed air jets and had used a schlieren apparatus to directly observe and photograph any disturbances that might occur. These tests revealed that as the jet airspeed reached a certain value, vicious-looking shock waves would suddenly appear in the flow over the wing. These shock waves, usually one or more on each surface, would occur when the air velocity in the accelerated flow

51

over the wing reached the speed of sound, and this point was reached when the general airflow ahead of the wing was considerably less than the speed of sound.

The airspeed at which these dramatic effects appeared was dubbed the "critical speed" and there was a different critical speed for different configurations. The shock waves sometimes remained fixed in position, but more often danced back and forth causing violent disturbances in the airflow. This phenomenon caused by the compressibility of the air represented a very serious and discouraging problem with which designers of future high-speed airplanes would be faced. But it was found that the onset of the compressibility phenomenon and the violence of its disturbance could be reduced by properly shaping the thickness distribution, and thus the pressure distribution, of the airfoil. The Clark Y and other old types of airfoil having maximum thickness well forward were very bad. New designs that were thinner in front and attained their maximum thickness farther back were much better. There was, indeed, a good deal of similarity between airfoils designed for high speed and those designed to promote laminar flow.

By the time the Ames Laboratory came into being, the subject of airfoil design, which once had seemed fairly well in hand, had opened up into a promising new field of research. Of particular interest to the Ames staff was the design of airfoils having high critical speeds and mild compressibility effects, but a special facility was really needed for the experimental testing involved in such work. Of course the 16-foot tunnel was available, but it was far too large and expensive to be used for that purpose. It would have to be reserved for complete wing or model tests. What was needed was a small inexpensive high-speed tunnel in which whole series of inexpensive airfoil models could be tested. Out of this need came the 1- by 3½-foot tunnel conceived and largely designed by Harvey Allen and manufactured out of material mostly scrounged from various sources around the Laboratory. It was built on a small bit of bare ground within the loop of the 16-foot tunnel. The cost was indeterminate, but the actual outlay was surprisingly little, about $50,000. The two 1000-horsepower motors used to power the tunnel were some the Laboratory had acquired for propeller tests in the 40-by-80.

The power used in the 1-by-3½ was sufficient to drive the tunnel airspeed up to the speed of sound, at which point a tunnel is said to be "choked." The phenomenon of choking had seldom been encountered before, but it was understood in theory and the theory was further elaborated in TR 782 authored by Harvey Allen and Walter Vincenti.

In subsonic tunnels the test model is always located in a constricted portion (throat) of the tunnel where the airspeed is a maximum. But as the wind-tunnel airspeed is increased, the airspeed in the throat remains a maximum only up to the point at which the speed of sound is reached. With further applications of power, the airspeed downstream of the throat becomes supersonic but the speed in the throat remains unchanged—exactly sonic. Thus for subsonic tunnels the term "choking" is descriptive of a point in the speed range where the throat, or test section, of the tunnel is effectively throttled and at which the tunnel loses its ability to simulate free-flight conditions. A much more complicated type of device is necessary for the simulation of supersonic flight conditions.

As the air in a wind tunnel has to accelerate in passing around the test model and its supports, a tunnel will obviously choke earlier (at a lower tunnel airspeed) with a model in place than when empty. Moreover, the larger the model and its supports relative to the tunnel cross section, the sooner the tunnel will choke. Thus while the choking speed of an empty tunnel might approximate the speed of sound, the choking speed of the tunnel with a model in place might be no more than 80 percent of the speed of sound.

In the 1-by-3½, Ames engineers wanted to study compressibility effects on airfoils at the highest possible speed, so the tunnel, and the model-support system, were designed to achieve the highest possible choking speed. Toward this end, the throat was made deep (3½ feet) and narrow (1 foot) and the sidewalls of the tunnel were used to support the model. So designed, the tunnel was able to provide reliable data at airspeeds up to 90 percent of the speed of sound.

Inasmuch as the airfoil model was attached rigidly to the sidewalls of the 1- by 3½-foot tunnel, something special in the way of instrumentation had to be provided if, as desired, the lift, drag, and pitching moment of the model were to be measured. Allen solved this problem ingeniously by designing a unique integrating manometer that quickly determined the desired forces and moments from pressures measured along the top and bottom walls of the tunnel and in the wake of the test model. A brief description of this device is given in some of the test reports later prepared by the tunnel staff.[2]

12-Foot Low-Turbulence Pressure Tunnel

The advantage of operating a wind tunnel under pressure to simulate flight conditions more faithfully had been established at Langley long before the Ames Aeronautical Laboratory was born. To be more precise, what was really needed for faithful simulation of subsonic flight conditions was that the Reynolds numbers of the simulating and simulated conditions be the same. Since Reynolds number is defined as $\rho VL/\mu$ (where ρ is air density, V is air velocity, μ is air viscosity, and L is some characteristic dimension of the model or airplane being tested), aeronautical engineers had a number of factors to juggle to obtain true simulations in wind tunnels.

Any inaccuracies in the test data resulting from an inadequate simulation in wind tunnels were called "scale effect," since they could generally be

---

[2] E.g., NACA TR 832.

related to the scale of the model. Compensation for the size of small-scale models, such as were required in all but the largest and most expensive wind tunnels (e.g., the 40-by-80), could be obtained by increasing either the velocity of the wind-tunnel airstream (costly in terms of power required) or its density. Density could be increased by increasing the operating pressure, but this procedure involved designing the tunnel as a pressure vessel and also introduced a number of operational problems. Nevertheless, NACA had long felt that, to achieve the proper test Reynolds number, the construction and use of pressure tunnels were justified despite all the complications involved.

Aside from pressurization, there were other desirable features a wind tunnel should have. There was a need for high speed, since it had been found that in the near-sonic range of speed certain effects appeared that were significantly different from those produced by Reynolds number. This additional speed effect could be stated in terms of Mach number—the speed of the tunnel airstream, or airplane in flight, expressed as a fraction of the speed of sound. Thus for reliable simulation of high-speed flight, the wind-tunnel conditions should reproduce both the Reynolds number and the Mach number of flight.

There was still another wind-tunnel characteristic that engineers at Langley had recently found to be very important—important at least for tests of the new laminar-flow wings. This characteristic was freedom from turbulence, particularly the fine-grain turbulence that is not found in the atmosphere in which airplanes fly but which unhappily is found in wind tunnels as a result of the churning of the fan and the disturbances of the corner-turning vanes. Unfortunately the prime virtues of the laminar-flow wings and bodies were largely obscured by the turbulence existing in the air streams of ordinary wind tunnels. It had been found that such turbulence could in a large degree be eliminated, but not very easily.

The possibility occurred to NACA engineers that all three of these desirable wind-tunnel features—high Reynolds number (pressure), high Mach number (speed), and very low turbulence—could be incorporated in the design of a single tunnel. Langley engineers thought the idea was worth trying, as did the designers at Ames. Both Langley and Ames wanted this unique tunnel. Langley got started on the design while the fate of Ames was still being debated by the congressmen but, once the establishment of Ames had been confirmed, NACA management, strongly encouraged by Admiral Towers, decided that the tunnel should be designed and built at Ames. The eventual result of this decision was the 12-foot low-turbulence pressure tunnel which became known as the 12-foot tunnel.

The 12-foot tunnel called for design and construction techniques well beyond the state of existing experience or knowledge and represented a tremendous challenge for the Ames designers. Many people contributed to the design, but Carl Bioletti took the brunt of the load. The tunnel was to operate at up to 6 atmospheres of pressure and, to achieve low turbulence, its shell had to be larger in diameter and longer than a conventional 12-foot tunnel. As the welded steel plates of which the tunnel was fabricated had to be very thick (more than 2 inches in some places) to resist the high internal pressure, the total mass of the tunnel shell was tremendous, amounting to over 3000 tons. Moreover, this massive shell had to be supported on the ground in such a way that it was fixed at one point but otherwise free to move in any direction to accommodate the thermal expansions and contractions that were expected. This freedom of motion necessitated the use of a special flexible coupling in the fan drive shaft, as the drive motors themselves were rigidly mounted on the ground.

The stress analysis of a thick-walled vessel of the size and odd shape of the 12-foot tunnel was very difficult, requiring extensions of existing theory. In developing the stress-analysis methods for the tunnel, Walter Vincenti made some major contributions, and in this matter the counsel of Dr. S. Timoshenko, the famous structures scientist at Stanford, was sought on several occasions. An unusual feature (one of many) of the 12-foot design was the absence of corners in the tunnel loop. The almost universal way of designing wind tunnels, until then, had been to incorporate four right-angle corners around each of which the air was guided by a venetian-blind-like array of guide vanes. But in the 12-foot, owing to the high internal pressure, the stresses calculated for right-angle elliptical corner sections were intolerably high. To avoid these high stresses, it was necessary to turn the corner in small angular steps, thus maintaining a more nearly circular cross section throughout the tunnel loop.

There was no way of eliminating the sources of turbulence in the tunnel. It was generated by the fans, by the turning vanes, and by the friction on the sidewalls. The only way to obtain a low-turbulence flow in the test section was to eliminate, or attenuate, the turbulence produced by the disturbing elements. Also it was obvious that the attenuation had to be accomplished just before the air entered the test section. NACA had earlier found that considerable attenuation of turbulence could be obtained if a large contraction in the diameter of the tunnel was incorporated just ahead of the test section. Such a contraction would cause a rapid and large increase in velocity in the throat and thus the small random increments of velocity representing the upstream turbulence became a much smaller part of the increased throat velocity. All wind tunnels had some contraction at the throat, but in most cases this amounted to only 6 or 8 to 1. If the contraction ratio in the 12-foot tunnel were increased to 25:1, the turbulence would be considerably attenuated but its level would still be unacceptably high. Something else was needed—screens.

It was known from British research that, if a turbulent airflow was

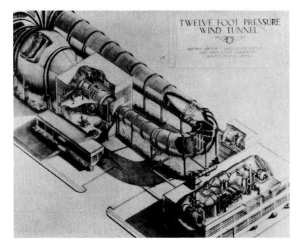

Cutaway drawing of 12-foot tunnel.

Antiturbulence screen and settling chamber in the 12-foot tunnel.

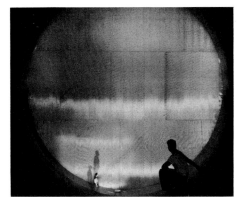

Completed 12-foot tunnel, May 27, 1946.

passed through a fine screen having a drag coefficient of about 2.0, the turbulence downstream of the screen would be largely eliminated. Ames designers calculated that if they could mount not one but eight fine-mesh screens across the 12-foot flow channel, these screens together with the 25:1 contraction ratio would reduce the stream turbulence to the low level required. It was decided to mount the screens in a 63-foot-diameter bulge, or settling chamber, that would be built into the flow passage just ahead of the entrance to the test chamber. In accomplishing this objective, the Ames designers learned the difference between theory and experiment. It was easy to draw a picture of eight screens stretched tightly across a 63-foot settling chamber, but quite a different thing to fabricate such large screens, made of phosphor bronze and each weighing 1600 pounds, and actually mount them snugly in the tunnel. But the feat was accomplished and how it was accomplished would be a long story in itself.

Before the screens and motors were put in the tunnel, however, the integrity of the shell as a pressure vessel had to be confirmed. Filled with air at 6 atmospheres pressure, the 12-foot tunnel was a bomb—a big bomb. Any rupture of the walls while the tunnel was under pressure could cause vast devastation and much loss of life in the local community. It was estimated that the energy of the compressed air in the tunnel was, if properly directed, sufficient to blow the whole tunnel half a mile high. The integrity of the pressure shell was a matter of grave concern, especially considering the uncertainties of the stress analysis and welding techniques. The welding of steel pressure vessels was by no means new, but there had been little if any experience in welding pressure vessels made of plates as thick as those used in the 12-foot, or in welding pressure vessels of complex configuration having many points of stress concentration. To make matters worse, there was no reliable way of inspecting the welds in such thick plates.

To be assured of the soundness of the 12-foot tunnel, the only thing to do, Ames engineers felt, was to run a hydrostatic test—fill the tunnel shell with water and apply hydraulic pressure corresponding to 6 atmospheres. Little energy would be required to compress the water; thus, if the tunnel walls failed during the test, there would be no damage. But it would take a whale of a lot of water, 5 million gallons, it was calculated, and what about the weight of the water? Also, what would happen if an earthquake occurred when the vessel was full? These matters were considered ahead of time and the weight of the water was taken into account in the design of the tunnel shell and the foundations. Indeed, the water weight had dictated the design of some parts of the support system. The earthquake stresses, however, could not be dealt with. The vessel would fail in such an eventuality. In further preparation for the test, 600 wire strain gages were attached to the exterior surfaces of the tunnel at points where, it was believed, stresses might be critical.

When the tunnel shell was ready, 5 million gallons of water were pumped in. A calculated additional 6000 gallons were added to make up for the stretch in the shell. The filling took a week. The water came from an old well on the field. The well must have been approaching exhaustion, for the water was brackish and a certain amount of sediment came in with the water unnoticed. The tunnel, filled with water, had no apparent leaks, and the time had arrived for applying hydraulic pressure. The pressure, it was planned, would be applied on and off in cycles, thus simulating the pressurizing loads to which the tunnel would be subjected in normal service. The applied test pressure, however, would be 120 pounds per square inch which, combined with the weight of the water, would subject the tunnel shell to bursting stresses 50 percent greater than those expected in normal service. This overload was intended to account for the effects of vibration, fatigue, and other unpredictable stress factors present in tunnel operation.

Staff engineer George Edwards was standing near the tunnel as the pressure was being applied. Everything seemed to be going well when, as the pressure reached 107 psi, a terrific report came from a part of the structure just a short distance away. Somewhat jittery, as were all the other people present, George jumped with the sudden noise, whirled about, and saw water pouring out of a rupture in the tunnel wall. The failure had occurred at one end of the tunnel at a point of stress concentration where two shell plates of widely differing thickness had been welded together. As might have been expected, there was no strain gage at that point, so the actual stresses at rupture were undetermined. Before the failure could be repaired, the whole vessel had to be drained. The released water flooded the surrounding field. The nature of the structural problem was not difficult to see and the fault was soon corrected. Five million more gallons of water, this time from the city water supply and costing about $5000, were let into the tunnel. This time it held. The tunnel came through the pressure test with flying colors. The only thing left was to drain out the water—and to clean out the muck. The dirty water from the first test had left the interior of the tunnel a frightful mess, and days were spent in scrubbing and drying it out.

A few more things should be said about the 12-foot-tunnel design. Somehow the heat generated by the 12,000 horsepower transmitted to the coaxial fans had to be removed from the tunnel. In unpressurized tunnels this had been accomplished by an air exchanger, but some other arrangement was obviously required for the 12-foot. The solution adopted was one that had been developed and successfully used at Langley. It was in the form of a water pipe which was mounted on top of the tunnel and which produced a flow of cooling water over the tunnel walls. In addition, a canopy was placed over the top of the tunnel to protect the shell from solar rays and the stresses and strains resulting therefrom.

The requirements for pressurizing a vessel as large as the 12-foot tunnel necessitated the construction of a considerable amount of air-handling equipment. This equipment, which included pumps, air coolers, dehumidifiers, and several electric motors, was installed in an auxiliary building located adjacent to the tunnel. The total cost of the tunnel and auxiliaries was about $3½ million.

An outstanding operational feature of the 12-foot tunnel, as earlier noted, was its low-turbulence airstream. Also, the tunnel could operate at high Reynolds numbers or high, subsonic, Mach numbers but, owing to lack of power, not at both at the same time. Its highest Reynolds number was to be achieved at the highest pressure, 6 atmospheres, but the pressure would have to be lowered to attain high Mach numbers. Indeed, to reach choking speed—the highest speed a subsonic wind tunnel can attain—the tunnel would have to be evacuated to a fairly low pressure. In the original design no evacuation was contemplated, but Harvey Allen had insisted that the lower end of the pressure range be dropped to one-sixth atmosphere. As a result choking speeds were readily attainable. Thus, with much design ingenuity, was produced a unique and extremely versatile wind tunnel, a suitable monument to this great building period at Ames.

Supersonic Tunnels

But now the age of supersonic wind tunnels was beginning. Although the basic principles of supersonic flow had been developed years before, no one really knew very much about designing supersonic wind tunnels. There were a couple of blowdown jets at Langley that reached slightly supersonic speeds, and Arthur Kantrowitz and others at Langley had designed a 9-inch continuous-flow supersonic tunnel which was completed in 1942. Nevertheless, existing knowledge regarding practical means for designing supersonic tunnels was rudimentary.

Supersonic tunnels not only required fabulous amounts of power and high pressures for their operation but also introduced a very difficult problem in the matter of effecting desired variations in their airspeed. In the first place, as earlier mentioned, the maximum airspeed in a supersonic tunnel occurs not at the constricted throat but in the enlarged portion of the tunnel downstream of the constriction. And it is here, in what might be called the supersonic throat, that the test model is located.

But that is not all. In a subsonic tunnel the airspeed through the test section can be varied in a continuous fashion by merely changing the rpm of the tunnel fan, while in a supersonic tunnel speed changes are accomplished only by altering the basic geometry of the throat, or, more specifically, by changing the relative cross-sectional areas of the constricted and the supersonic throats. Moreover, the changes in geometry must be made very precisely if uniform flow in the test section is to be obtained. Thus in the design of the first supersonic tunnel at Ames, the provision of means for varying the speed represented a most challenging problem.

Ames engineers had wanted a supersonic wind tunnel from the start; but Dr. Lewis, while agreeing with the eventual need for such a facility, felt that the other tunnels planned for Ames should have a higher priority and that construction of a supersonic tunnel should be delayed awhile. Nevertheless, in 1943 serious plans were being made for the construction of such a tunnel. Ames engineers had wanted to build a 4- by 4-foot supersonic tunnel,[3] but the 40-by-80 was costing so much that their rather ambitious plans had to be pared down considerably; and Dr. Lewis, still questioning the advisability of embarking in wartime on such a far-out and costly project, was presumably not displeased that the size of the supersonic tunnel was reduced. After all, the dimensions of 1 by 3 feet finally adopted for the new tunnel were a rather large step beyond the 9-inch size of the Langley tunnel and the cost, $1.2 million, was all that could be afforded.

A major decision in the design of the 1- by 3-foot supersonic tunnel was whether or not the tunnel should be pressurized to achieve a wider Reynolds number range. Pressurizing would add complications and cost, but the most convincing argument against it was that Dr. Theodore von Kármán, world-famous aeronautical scientist, then at Caltech, had suggested that the effects of Reynolds number might be expected to disappear at supersonic speeds.[4] Disagreement with von Kármán was, of course, a position to be adopted with caution. Dr. Lewis and certain people at Langley were inclined to agree with the famous scientist, but Harvey Allen was not. He argued the point so effectively that NACA Headquarters, if not fully convinced of the rightness of his contentions, nevertheless yielded to the urgency of his request to pressurize the 1-by-3.

Once the pressurizing decision was made, a group headed by Allen and Vincenti got busy and produced a design for the first supersonic wind tunnel to be built at Ames. The tunnel, having a test section 1 foot wide and 3 feet deep, would be a closed system powered by four compressors each driven by a 2500-horsepower electric motor. The pressure in the system was to be variable from 0.3 to 4.0 atmospheres, giving a Reynolds number range of from 0.5 to 10×10^6 per foot of model length; the speed (Mach number) range of the tunnel would be from 1.4 to 2.2 times the speed (about 760 mph) of sound. To prevent moisture condensation in the low-pressure region of the test section, the air introduced into the system would first be dehumidified. This precaution had also been taken in the design of the 12-foot tunnel.

---

[3] According to recollections of Harvey Allen.

[4] According to Lewis. It is possible that von Kármán in conversations with Lewis put forward this suggestion only tentatively; in any case, there is no question but that Lewis took it seriously or that it had repercussions at Ames as noted.

60

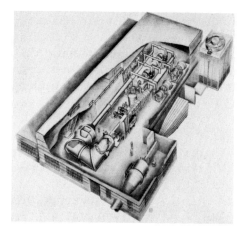

Cutaway drawing of 1- by 3-foot super-sonic tunnel.

The 1- by 3-foot tunnel was to be immediately adjacent to the 12-foot tunnel. This location was chosen as part of a scheme developed by Ames designers for acquiring a second 1- by 3-foot supersonic tunnel for very little more than the million dollars the first one was costing. They reasoned that the compressed-air energy in the 12-foot, which through cruel circumstance could blow the tunnel a half mile high, might with profit be used to operate a supersonic tunnel or jet. If the supersonic jet were conveniently located beside the 12-foot tunnel, the dry air with which the tunnel was filled could be discharged through the jet. The pressure and capacity of the 12-foot tunnel were such as to operate a 1- by 3-foot supersonic jet for several minutes —the higher the speed, oddly, the longer the period. This line of reasoning appealed to Ames and NACA management; accordingly, plans were laid to build both a continuous-flow 1- by 3-foot supersonic tunnel and a 1- by 3-foot blowdown jet, or tunnel, the latter having somewhat higher Mach number capabilities than the continuous-flow tunnel.

The same type of variable-geometry test section was to be used on both the continuous-flow and the blowdown tunnels. The top and bottom walls of the test section would be made of flexible steel plates that could be deflected to the required curvature and configuration for any desired Mach number. Such deflections as were required in the plates would be produced by a number of precisely controlled, motor-driven screw jacks. In the continuous-flow tunnel, it would be possible to change the throat shape, and Mach number, while the tunnel continued in operation; but in the blowdown tunnel the operating periods would be too short to allow any change of throat setting during a test.

The flexible-throat scheme used in the 1- by 3-foot tunnels was fairly simple in theory, but in actuality it was a very complex device with demanding performance requirements. The task of building the throats for the two Ames tunnels was undertaken by the Baldwin Southwark Division of the

Baldwin Locomotive Works.[5] Baldwin had also contracted to build a similar throat for a supersonic wind tunnel which Allen Puckett and his colleagues at Caltech had designed for the Aberdeen Proving Ground.[6] The Aberdeen tunnel, together with the 1- by 3-foot tunnels at Ames, represented perhaps the earliest ventures into the field of large supersonic wind-tunnel design.

Construction work on the Ames 1- by 3-foot tunnels began in 1944 and continued into the next year. Smitty DeFrance, driving his men with his customary explosive vigor, laid down the law asserting that the 1-by-3 would begin operation on August 1, "or else." This dictum was not taken lightly. Ames designers had recognized the difficulties of building the supersonic throats to meet the rather stringent specifications which they had established and were not surprised when Baldwin Southwark began to encounter trouble. Cannily, they had taken the precaution of building two simple fixed-geometry throats either of which could be fitted into the space reserved for the flexible throats. Each of the fixed throats was designed for a different Mach number and thus, if worse came to worst with respect to the flexible throats, the tunnels could still be operated at either of two Mach numbers. In the end it was the use of these fixed throats that enabled Ames engineers to meet DeFrance's operational deadline.

One of the first things discovered in the 1-by-3 tests was that, in supersonic flows, Reynolds number continues to be an important factor, perhaps even more important than in subsonic flows. Thus Harvey Allen's contention, maintained in the face of contrary opinion by the famous Dr. von Kármán, was confirmed.[7] This finding, later substantiated in other supersonic tunnels, supported the later decision of the Langley Laboratory to increase the operating pressure and power of a 4- by 4-foot tunnel it had built.

As the war progressed, the notion of supersonic flight by manned aircraft became increasingly plausible to people engaged in research and military activities. There was a growing feeling that supersonic tunnels were needed immediately to obtain the design information that would be required in the approaching supersonic era. Moreover, it was thought that such tunnels should be large so that the test models could be realistic representations of practical airplane designs rather than the tiny, highly idealized models to which testing in currently planned supersonic facilities would be restricted.

The urgency of building large and expensive supersonic tunnels was not clearly evident, however, to some of the oldtimers in the aeronautical world who had watched our rather slow and labored progress toward that speed

---

[5] Baldwin was a subcontractor. Prime contractor, for the whole tunnel shell, was the Pittsburgh Des Moines Steel Co.

[6] According to Harvey Allen.

[7] Allen surmises that von Kármán's belief was based on the results of sphere tests which proved inapplicable to airfoils.

at which the drag of airplanes leaps upward, seeming like a brick wall to block further advance. And the doubts of these men were further raised by schlieren photographs revealing the alarming patterns of shock waves that form over the wings and tails of airplanes operating at high subsonic speeds. Did not the exigencies of war, and common sense, dictate that NACA devote its limited research energies to solving the problems of current military airplanes rather than expend them recklessly in a premature attempt to breach the sound barrier?

Ames engineers were among those who felt that NACA should proceed immediately to build a large supersonic wind tunnel. It should be, they thought, large enough so that a man could walk into the test section to mount and service a test model. In 1944, they made a rather sketchy design and cost estimate for such a facility and presented them to Dr. Lewis. Normally very progressive with respect to the development of new NACA facilities, Dr. Lewis believed this idea to be a little premature.[8] He may also have felt that the prospect of getting the $4½ million required for the tunnel was not very bright, particularly in view of the watchfulness of economy-minded Albert Thomas, who then was chairman of the House Independent Offices Appropriations Subcommittee. In any case, Dr. Lewis received the Ames proposal with little warmth and, on returning to Washington, was said to have buried it in his lower desk drawer. What happened then is known only from the scattered recollections of a number of NACA people who heard about it later.

According to these recollections, the Ames tunnel design was quickly forgotten by Lewis; but into his office a few weeks later strode Rear Adm. D. C. Ramsey, Chief of the Bureau of Aeronautics. Ramsey spoke of the Navy's need for supersonic aerodynamic data and rather pointedly questioned Lewis on what NACA was doing about building a large supersonic wind tunnel. He gave the impression that he felt NACA had perhaps been a little slow in giving thought to such a project. Somewhat taken aback by this implied criticism, Dr. Lewis hesitated a moment and then, with some relief, remembered the Ames tunnel study buried in his desk. "Well, Admiral," he said, as he searched for and found the Ames study, "we have given this problem a lot of attention. In fact, we have designed a tunnel of the kind you mentioned but don't know where we will get the money to build it." Ramsey examined the design. "How much will it cost?" he asked. "Four and a half million," Lewis sighed, as if he were speaking of a gold mine on the moon. Ramsey pondered a few moments and then declared, "The Navy will give you the money to build the tunnel." [9] Lewis, of course, was both aston-

---

[8] Dr. Lewis was not unprogressive for, according to a memorandum for the files he wrote on Nov. 8, 1938, he listed a 3- by 5-foot, 1400-mph tunnel as one of the facilities that should be built at the proposed new West Coast station.

[9] Recollections: see above.

ished and gratified. Never before had NACA obtained so much money so easily. What a haggling there had been in getting the first $4 million for the Ames Laboratory! What a blessing it was to have wealthy friends!

The transfer of funds from the Navy actually took place on January 27, 1945.[10] By the end of May, the first contracts for the tunnel were let. Clearly the tunnel would not help win the war, but its construction was, nevertheless, very timely and it would certainly fill a very important need.

The new tunnel was to have a test section 6 feet square and would become known as the 6- by 6-foot tunnel. It would be the first of the really large supersonic tunnels built by NACA. The tunnel would be driven by a huge compressor turned by two electric motors delivering a total of 60,000 horsepower—more power by two-thirds than was used in the giant 40-by-80. Despite this great expenditure of power, the tunnel would attain its maximum speed of Mach 1.8 only when the tunnel was partially evacuated. It was designed to operate at stagnation (air at rest) pressures of from 0.3 to 1.0 atmosphere. Higher operating pressures might have been desirable, but the required power would then have been prohibitively high.

The complete air system of the 6-by-6 was to include air pumps, air storage tanks, dehumidifiers, and a circulating-water air cooler built into the tunnel airstream. The tunnel design originally submitted to Lewis had called for the use of centrifugal compressors. An axial-flow fan, it was agreed, might be more compact and efficient, but there were difficult design problems and few if any companies had experience in constructing axial-flow fans of the size required for the tunnel. Once the Ames engineers were able to give the matter serious attention, however, it was found that an axial-flow fan could probably be constructed at a considerably lower cost than the centrifugal compressors. Thus the final design of the 6-by-6 incorporated a huge multistage axial-flow fan.

Before the design of the 6-by-6 had gotten under way, Ames engineers had become aware of problems Baldwin and Southwark was having in the construction of flexible throats for the 1- by 3-foot tunnels. Indeed, Ames designers had from the first been apprehensive about the design of these throats. Harvey Allen felt there must be a simpler, more reliable way of varying throat geometry to accomplish speed changes. At the Engine Research Laboratory, Abe Silverstein and his staff were experimenting with a circular tunnel having a central plug that could be pushed into the throat, thus decreasing the constricted throat area and increasing the speed of the tunnel. Unfortunately the central-plug scheme had some serious faults, one being that the test model would necessarily lie in the disturbed wake of the plug.

Allen reasoned that the wake problem could be solved if the central

[10] As indicated in letter from James E. Webb, Director of the Bureau of the Budget, to the President [Truman], dated Apr. 18, 1947.

The 6- by 6-foot tunnel compressor, one of the early applications of multistage axial-flow compressors to wind-tunnel-air propulsion.

Sliding-block throat of 8- by 8-inch tunnel, prototype of 6- by 6-foot tunnel, which was built to test the sliding-block throat.

plug were replaced by a properly configured sliding block representing the bottom wall of a rectangular supersonic throat. The block could be positioned very precisely by a motor-driven screw. Of course, the flow through the throat would not be symmetrical about the horizontal plane as it had been in all other wind tunnels, but the peculiarities of supersonic flows were such that the flow asymmetry might cause no trouble if the contours of the sliding block and of the fixed top wall of the supersonic throat were carefully designed. Allen first tested his design theory by building and testing a 2- by 2-inch asymmetric, sliding-block throat; this throat was sufficiently successful that he decided to build a larger, 8- by 8-inch model which could be installed in the 12-foot tunnel auxiliaries building and operated with air from the compressors of that tunnel. The experiment proceeded swiftly and the 8- by 8-inch tunnel, as it was called, was put into successful operation late in 1945. In the meantime, design of an asymmetric nozzle for the 6- by 6-foot tunnel was under way.

The asymmetric sliding-block nozzle had numerous advantages but also a few faults. For one thing, it was not quite so efficient, aerodynamically, as a symmetrical flexible-wall throat and required a somewhat higher pressure ahead of it to achieve the same Mach number as a symmetrical throat. Also, since the walls of the throat were rigid, there was no way, such as provided by a flexible throat, to compensate for small discrepancies in the contours of the sliding block and top wall. Moreover, the available methods for calculating the contours were tedious and did not precisely account for factors such as boundary-layer growth. As a result, it might not be possible to completely avoid small flow distortions in the test section. But the simplicity and reliability of the sliding-block throat were very attractive and were expected to overbalance any minor faults. The invention was original with Allen and might well have been called the Allen Throat. Harvey, however, pursuing his fancy of Balkanizing Ames wind tunnels, chose to call it the "Bulgarian throat." In formal literature, the name "asymmetric" or "sliding-block" throat or nozzle was used; but by whatever name, the device represented a notable achievement. Its development was later described by Allen in TN 2919.

Despite the forbidding complications of supersonic tunnels, there was at least one good thing to be said about this type of device. In such a tunnel, with suitable auxiliary equipment, it was possible actually to see important features of the airflow about the test model. And what was seen in the first transonic wing tests at Langley was frightening. It lent encouragement to the notion that the supersonic flight of manned airplanes was a long way off, if not a complete pipe dream. Nevertheless, the technique of making supersonic-flow patterns visible to the naked eye was scientifically interesting and very useful. The use of the technique was certainly a "must" in all supersonic wind tunnels.

The technique for viewing supersonic flows was possible because of the variations in air density found in such flows—variations relating of course to the so-called "compressibility effect." There were actually two important techniques for revealing the density patterns in the wind-tunnel flow, both requiring that a very uniform, collimated beam of light be passed transversely through the tunnel walls and through the airflow in the region of the model. These techniques necessitated the installation of large windows in the sidewalls of the test section. Any distortion of the light beam caused by density variations in either the airstream or other parts of the light path could, by proper focusing, easily be made visible to the naked eye and thus subject to recording by photography. The simplest arrangement of this kind was called a "shadowgraph." It worked best when the density gradients were strong.

A more sensitive device revealing more details was called a "schlieren system." Here the light beam, before it was viewed or projected on a screen, was brought to a sharp focus and then, by cutting the focus halfway in two by a razor-sharp knife edge, the density variations in the visual field would be revealed with great contrast. The schlieren technique was not new. It was the same in principle as the knife-edge test developed by Jean Foucault in the mid-19th century for figuring telescope mirrors. In this application, variations in the curvature of the telescope mirror were observed rather than distortions in the intervening air. And if the light beam was passed through a telescope lens, it would also reveal, with great clarity, all the flaws, striae, and optical distortions of the glass. Therein, as a matter of fact, lay one of the major problems in applying the schlieren system to supersonic wind tunnels. The problem was to avoid having the flow pattern of the airstream confused by flaws and optical distortions in the wind-tunnel windows.

The windows of a supersonic tunnel had to be large, to encompass a suitably large area of the flow field, and they had to be thick, to withstand the pressures in the tunnel. Moreover, their surfaces had to be ground perfectly flat and parallel and their interior had to be free of flaws and optical distortions. Indeed, they had to be made of similar materials and by the same slow painstaking processes as were used in the production of high-quality telescope lenses. But the difficulty of securing high quality in a telescope lens increases very rapidly with the diameter of the lens, and the biggest lens that had ever been built was the 40-inch-diameter lens, made from glass cast in France, of the Yerkes telescope at Lake Geneva, Wis. And the making of this lens was considered an extremely difficult task.[11] It is not surprising, therefore, that many very troublesome technical problems were encountered in applying the schlieren system to large wind tunnels.

The first attempt to use the schlieren system at Ames was in the 1- by

---

[11] See David O. Woodbury. *The Glass Giant of Palomar*, New York: Dodd, Mead & Co., 1941, p. 75.

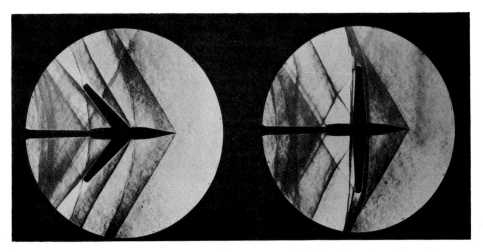

Schlieren photograph of flow around airplane models showing the effect of sweep-back on shock waves (M = *1.2*).

3½-foot tunnel but, owing to the excessively cramped quarters and lack of solid foundation, it was not very successful. The less-sensitive shadowgraph system proved to be more useful in this instance. The first really successful use of the schlieren system at Ames came with its application to the 1- by 3-foot supersonic tunnel. The most difficult and costly application, however, was in the 6- by 6-foot tunnel where windows 50 inches in diameter and more than 4 inches thick—larger than the Yerkes telescope objective—were required.

For Ames, the 6-year period from the Laboratory's beginning in 1940 to the end of the war in 1945 was characterized by construction. During that period, the funds committed to construction at Ames, about $21 million, were five times the amount NACA had spent on construction in the 24-year period from the date of its founding in 1915 to the time in 1939 when the Ames Laboratory was approved by Congress. Indeed, it was 25 percent greater than the total appropriations received by NACA during that period. While the growth of NACA facilities was undoubtedly accelerated by wartime requirements, this growth did, nevertheless, reflect in some quantitative fashion the increasing significance of aviation to the Nation.

9

The Ice Research Story

ANY account of important research conducted at the NACA Ames Aeronautical Laboratory must certainly start with the first research program undertaken at the Laboratory. This program had for its objective the development of means for protecting airplanes from the many hazards of having ice form on their surfaces while flying in moisture-laden clouds. Such hazards were many: for example, ice formation on wings would cause loss of lift; on control surfaces, loss of control; on airspeed heads, loss of airspeed indications; on radio antennas, loss of communications; on windshields, loss of vision; and, in engine intakes and on propellers, loss of power.

By 1940, the airplane had reached a state of development where its users were unwilling to consider it merely a fair-weather device. Flight reliability was becoming increasingly important to commercial users and even more so to the military. As the war got under way, it was imperative that our B–17 and B–24 bombers not be held up by weather; in fact, the safety of clouds might actually be sought by such aircraft. Later in the war, our Curtiss C–46 cargo planes were flying the Himalayan hump with vital materiel that had to get through to its destination despite weather conditions. By 1940 the all-weather flying reliability of airplanes had been much improved by the development of advanced radio aids and blind-flying equipment. But these were to no avail if an aircraft was forced down by ice. It was essential that an ice-protection system be developed. The urgency of developing such a system was endorsed by the military services, the CAA, the airlines, the aircraft companies, and also by NACA. Some ice protection had in the past been obtained by the use of inflatable rubber shoes mounted externally on the leading edges of the wings and tail surfaces, but this device would not work for high-speed airplanes and its drag was very high.

Actually, NACA had been working on the problem of heat deicing at Langley since 1930. TR 403 by Theodorsen and Clay on the subject of ice prevention on aircraft by means of engine exhaust heat appeared in 1931. Following the publication of that report, however, the work had progressed for a while at rather low priority. Clay had left NACA, and the task had

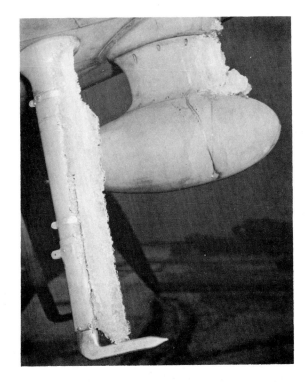

Ice formation on radio antenna and airspeed mast of C–46 airplane.

been taken over by Lewis A. Rodert. Soon Alun R. Jones joined the effort, and the two of them arranged to make some flight tests in which a test wing panel was mounted on a Martin XPM bomber. The airplane was flown by Langley test pilots William A. McAvoy and Lawrence A. Clousing.

The tests on the XPM bomber were fairly rudimentary, but the results convinced NACA of the desirability of buying a small two-engined Lockheed 12 transport airplane for ice-research work. The wings of the Lockheed 12, it was planned, would be rebuilt to incorporate an ice-protection system utilizing the engine exhaust as the means of deicing. The project was supported by the Army Air Corps and by Lockheed. Kelly Johnson and his staff at Lockheed designed, built, and installed the new wings. Earlier NACA had decided that the ice-research project, as it was called, should be transferred to the new Ames Aeronautical Laboratory. Rodert, McAvoy, and Clousing came out to Ames in the fall of 1940 and, while waiting for the Lockheed 12 to be modified, carried out some minor icing flight-research tests with a North American O–47, which was the first airplane assigned to Ames for research purposes. McAvoy made the first flight test with the O–47 on November 16, 1940. But early in 1941 the Lockheed 12 was ready and, with McAvoy and Clousing at the controls, the initial flight was made on

Nov. 16, 1940, test pilot W. H. McAvoy returning from an early flight of first test airplane at Ames, a North American O–47.

Lockheed 12A ice-research airplane.

January 22. From then on, the deicing flight program proceeded at a good pace.

To protect the wings of the Lockheed 12 against icing, the exhaust pipes of the engines had been run out through the leading edges and exhausted at the wingtips. Fresh air taken through openings in the leading edge circulated around the exhaust pipe, then through a double-skin structure ahead of the spar. Passing through openings in the spar webs, the warm air entered the interior of the wings and was finally exhausted to the atmosphere through louvers located far back on the upper surface.

The problem was to provide enough heat for deicing (ice protection) without reducing the wing strength by overheating. The evidence as to how much heat was required was extremely meager but, based on data obtained at Langley, Lew Rodert felt that, if the wing skin forward of the front spar

71

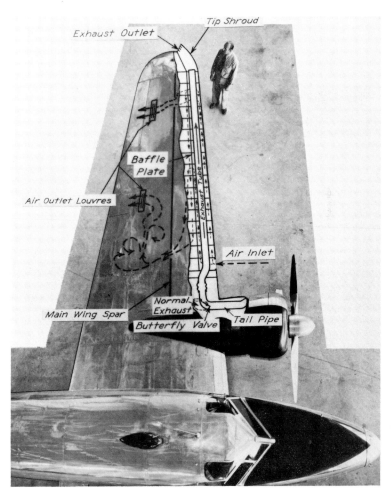

Diagram of the system using exhaust-heated air to prevent icing on the Lockheed 12A wings.

could be maintained at a temperature 100° F above the ambient-air temperature under clear-air conditions, satisfactory ice protection would probably be provided under icing conditions. Although the Lockheed 12 was incompletely protected against icing and despite their limited experience with blind flying, McAvoy and Clousing, together with Lew Rodert and sometimes Ray Braig, flew the little transport plane into some of the worst weather they could find on the West Coast. Ice would sometimes form on the windows so thickly that they could not see whether the wings were ice-free or not, the radio would cut out due to icing, and ice would sometimes form on the tail surfaces which were only partially protected by an inflatable rubber shoe.

Curtiss C-46 ice-research airplane.

In the first report written on this program (mentioned in ch. 6), the authors, Rodert, McAvoy, and Clousing, commented, "The severe icing encountered was accompanied by violent turbulence, snow-and-rain static which stopped radio communication, and occasional dangerous electrical discharges. . . ." Describing one flight, they said:

> The icing rate and violence of the turbulence increased steadily during the flight. About 5 minutes after severe icing conditions were encountered, the tests were terminated because of dangerous flight conditions. The airplane was struck by an electrical charge [lightning] which melted the trailing edge of one propeller blade and the edges of the airplane structure at several points.

Such experiences were all in the day's work for the intrepid crew of the Lockheed 12. Their reward was their finding that the use of exhaust heat for protecting the wings of an airplane such as the Lockheed 12 did, indeed, appear to be feasible. This conclusion did not come just from the fact that they and the airplane had survived the repeated ordeal of flying under severe icing conditions but also from a mass of quantitative data obtained from special instruments with which the airplane was equipped.

Although work on improvements in the Lockheed 12 deicing system continued for several years, the year 1941 had not ended before the Army Air Corps had asked NACA to develop a deicing system for the B-24 and the B-17 bombers. While design information was still pitifully scarce, the Ames Flight Engineering Section launched into the project with a spirit and resolve that were immeasurably bolstered by the catastrophe that had recently occurred at Pearl Harbor. The staff of the Section was considerably increased and was joined by Alun Jones early in 1942.

The same basic deicing principle as developed for the Lockheed 12 would work, it was thought, on the B-24 and the B-17. This process would require a hot-air source and a double-walled leading edge, but the airflow system would have to be adapted to the particular wing structures of the two airplanes. Also, protection would have to be extended to the tail surfaces, windshields, airspeed head, and other points vulnerable to icing. But it would not be feasible to run the exhaust pipe through the leading-edge structure of a military airplane. Suppose the exhaust pipe were ruptured by a bullet? The hot exhaust gas would pour into the wing and probably destroy the airplane. What was needed, it was thought, was a heat exchanger that would transfer the heat of the exhaust pipe to a flow of fresh air that would be ducted into the leading edge. Then the engine exhaust would not enter the wing at all but would be disposed of in pretty much the normal fashion.

Rodert visited the airplane-accessories companies and encouraged a number of them to develop heat exchangers for this purpose. Further, he enlisted the aid of Prof. L. M. K. Boelter and his mechanical engineering staff at the University of California by arranging for UC to be given a NACA contract to study various aspects of the heat-exchange process. A special laboratory facility was set up at Ames to evaluate the performance of heat exchangers, and the heat exchangers were also checked out in flight on the O–47 airplane.

By the end of 1942, the combined efforts of Ames, the industry, and the military had produced prototype installations of heat deicing systems in both the B–24 and the B–17. Reports describing the systems were later written by Rodert and Jones. The Navy had also made an installation on the Consolidated PBY flying boat along the lines of the Lockheed 12 installation. The Navy noted that the deicing installation so decreased the noise and exhaust flame that the airplane could fly over a carrier at night, at part throttle, at an altitude of as low as 200 feet without being detected.

Rodert and the other men involved in the deicing project felt that a special base should be established in the north-central part of the United States for the purpose of evaluating prototype deicing installations such as those incorporated in the B–24 and the B–17. This idea was approved, and such a base was set up and first used in the winter of 1942–1943. It was located at Minneapolis, near the headquarters of Northwest Airlines. At this time the effort to develop deicing systems for aircraft involved many people and agencies. In the first place, NACA had established a technical subcommittee to provide a general surveillance and coordination of the work on deicing. This subcommittee, headed by Karl Larsen of Northwest Airlines, had a membership derived from industry and the airlines, as well as the military, the Civil Aeronautics Administration, and of course NACA. Next, the new Ice Research Base at Minneapolis was staffed by men from NACA and the Air Corps, but it also received much help from Northwest Airlines and United Air Lines.

In addition to the assistance just mentioned, the U.S. Weather Bureau assigned William Lewis to work directly with the Ames group on important meteorological phases of the icing problem. Similarly, the British Royal Aircraft Establishment assigned a very able research man, J. K. Hardy, to work with the Ames group. The RAE apparently felt that it would be foolish for Britain to attempt to duplicate the work done by NACA in the icing matter and that it would make more sense to provide the services of a good man who would not only contribute to the project but also, quite naturally, acquire know-how that would be useful to Britain. The British, of course, received all of NACA's test reports on deicing work. This arrangement proved very profitable to NACA as Hardy's efforts were exceptionally productive.

The prototype deicing systems in the B–24 and the B–17 passed their winter evaluation tests in good fashion and served as models for the design of production systems for these aircraft types. The work on these installations had been carried out at high pressure. The military services had impressed Dr. Lewis with the importance of the work, and Dr. Lewis had passed the word to DeFrance. Smitty in turn followed the program closely and spurred the icing research effort using tactics which were scarcely subtle. In one case, when it appeared that a test airplane might not be ready to fly before the winter icing season was over, Smitty threatened to wipe out the Flight Engineering Section if that eventuality developed. The Section staff thereupon began a 24-hour-a-day operation and the airplane flew on time.

The Ames staff recognized all too well that the design of their airplane deicing systems had so far been on a very empirical basis. Before any really refined systems could be built, a large amount of rather basic design information would have to be acquired by theoretical and experimental means. The acquisition of this information would take time; it was fortunate that sufficient information had been available to serve the immediate needs of the military. Now, however, the problem must be approached from a more scientific basis. Toward this end, a Curtiss C–46 cargo airplane was acquired and modified to incorporate the most complete ice-protection system yet provided for any airplane. Moreover, the airplane was thoroughly instrumented in itself and carried special newly developed instruments for obtaining basic information on the character of the icing cloud. Bill Lewis of the Weather Bureau made major contributions in this phase of the program.

The C–46, which was considered a flying icing-research laboratory, was operated from the Ice Research Base in Minneapolis and flew far and wide searching for icing conditions. Airport habitues were often astonished to see a C–46 airplane come boring in through the murk when all other planes were grounded. The C–46 was flown by a number of pilots but most often, perhaps, by Captain C. M. Christensen, Senior Pilot of United Air Lines. Chris was one of those calm, competent, unexcitable chaps whose appearance and obvious know-how inspire confidence. His contributions to the project were great.

It was the prime objective of Bill Lewis and certain other icing-project people to amass enough statistical data on icing clouds to serve as a reliable basis for future designs of ice-protection systems. Statistics on liquid-water content, temperature, and drop size were of particular interest, as was the interrelationship between these icing factors. Liquid-water content and temperature were perhaps the most important factors, but drop size was also a significant design parameter. It was known that little drops approaching the wing would be deflected by the local airflow around the wing and fly harmlessly by. Larger drops, on the other hand, would be too massive to be deflected by the local airflow and would thus smash into, and freeze on, the leading edge of the wing. And if the drops were prevented from freezing on the forepart of a heated wing, the rainwater might run back and freeze on the cooler afterpart of the wing.

Meteorological data, however, were not the only requirement for the rational design of an airplane deicing system. More information was needed on the aerothermodynamic processes of transferring heat from the wing surface to the surrounding airstream. The problem was complicated by the free-water content of the surrounding air and also by the question of whether the boundary layer on the wing was laminar or turbulent. The boundary layer acted like an insulator the effectiveness of which increased with thickness but, for the same thickness, a laminar boundary layer was a much more effective insulator than a turbulent boundary layer.

A number of theoretical studies of heat transfer from a wing to the surrounding airstream had been made over the preceding 10 years and, in 1942, Harvey Allen and Bonne Look of Ames had made another study which was published in TR 764. All of these studies, as applying to the deicing problem, were somewhat idealized and thus their use for deicing designs was limited. However, in the design of the deicing system for the C–46, the Ames group exerted a great deal of effort to develop rational analytical methods for solving the heat-transfer problem. A major contributor in this effort was Hardy, the RAE representative on the icing project. Hardy's report (ref. A–2) is a good example of his work. Another important contributor in this area was Carr Neel of the Ames staff. His report (ref. A–3), the first of a long series on the C–46 project, covers the analytical phases of the design. Authors of the C–46 report series included Alun Jones, James Selna, Richard Jackson, Carr Neel, and others. At the end, a summary report (ref. A–4) was written by Alun Jones, who at that time had replaced Rodert as head of the Flight Engineering Section.

Lewis Rodert resigned in September 1945. While many people had made contributions to the icing-research project, Rodert had been the driving, coordinating sparkplug. He had lived with the project. It became part of him. Throughout his waking hours, he appeared to be thinking of little else. The methods he used to achieve his ends were frequently blunt, and sometimes irritated his fellow workers. But they were effective, and the results of his early work were vastly appreciated by both the military and the commercial operators of aircraft.

The icing project, first investigation to be undertaken at Ames, was not at all representative of NACA research projects. Seldom before had NACA's research work been carried so far into the hardware stage or so far in achiev-

Carr Neel (left) *and Lewis A. Rodert* (below).

ing a complete and satisfying solution to a major operational problem. The project was unique and NACA management could only be pleased that it had been so successful. Lew Rodert deserved much credit for his important share in this success; his good work was recognized when, at a White House ceremony in 1947, President Truman presented him with the Collier Trophy, regarded as the Nation's highest aeronautical award, "for his pioneering research and guidance in the development of a practical application of a thermal ice prevention system for aircraft."

It should also be mentioned that, in 1943, the Institute of the Aeronautical Sciences had given Ames pilot William H. McAvoy the Octave Chanute Award for "continuous service in the flight testing of experimental planes under hazardous conditions imposed by aeronautical research." Certainly an important part of the motivation for this award came from the hazardous deicing flights of the Lockheed 12 on which McAvoy had served as pilot.

10

Flight Research

THE ice-research project represented a single and very special phase of the flight-research program at Ames. Flight research had always been an essential element of NACA research effort. It was necessary, NACA thought, to prove out in flight the ideas for aircraft improvement that were developed in the laboratory. The scientific techniques of modern flight research had indeed first been established in the United States by NACA, and NACA had remained a leader in advancing these techniques. NACA had never countenanced the old seat-of-the-pants flight testing by undisciplined daredevil pilots whose research results were often measured by survival and whose reports were of a highly subjective and qualitative character.

NACA required a test pilot to have an engineering degree as well as piloting experience and to have the ability and the motivation to perform precise preplanned maneuvers that he and his ground-based engineering colleagues had worked out ahead of time. Highjinks in the sky with valuable test airplanes were not tolerated. The oral report of the pilot was generally only a minor part of the information obtained from a NACA test flight. The major part was in the form of quantitative data obtained with special recording instrumentation carried in the airplane. Henry Reid, longtime head of NACA's Langley Laboratory, had designed and built some of the first recording flight-research instruments at Langley, and since those early days in the 1920's and 1930's such instrumentation had been developed to a high degree of capability and precision. All the techniques and instrumentation that had been developed at Langley were available to Ames as the new Laboratory's flight research got under way, and it was not long before Ames made its own contributions in these fields.

In the early 1940's, faced with the growing threat of war, President Roosevelt had called for the production of 100,000 airplanes—a fantastic number, it seemed. Shortly, the aircraft companies were receiving orders from the military for new types of aircraft as well as production orders for existing types. A new crop of airplanes thus began to appear soon after the United States entered the war. Mostly the new airplanes were equipped with more powerful engines and were capable of higher speeds than earlier types. These new factors generally introduced problems in the areas of handling qualities, stability and control, drag reduction, and structural loads.

Handling, or flying, qualities had always been a factor of great interest to the military but one with which it was hard to come to grips because such qualities were so closely linked to the subjective reactions of the pilot. However, research at Langley led by Robert Gilruth and Hartley Soulé had, by 1941, gone far in establishing quantitative requirements for satisfactory flying qualities. These criteria, which were adopted and adapted by the military, were extremely helpful in evaluating the new crop of wartime airplanes—an evaluation task in which the Flight Research Sections of both Langley and Ames took an active part. The Navy and sometimes the aircraft companies contributed the services of their pilots to further the flight research at Ames. This activity expanded so fast during the war that the hangar in the flight-research building was quickly outgrown. A contract for a new, much larger, hangar with attached offices and shops was let in March 1944.

Handling Qualities from Wind-Tunnel Tests

Ames could, and did, evaluate the handling qualities of many new military airplanes and, when serious faults were found, the military service involved would often ask the aircraft company to make a corrective change in the airplane design. At that stage of the airplane development, however, the necessary design change could be very difficult and expensive to make. If it were possible to correct such faults while the airplane development was in the wind-tunnel-model stage, the whole matter would be vastly simplified. Just how this trick might be accomplished was a problem which the Ames staff attempted to solve, and eventually did solve.

The project just mentioned was jointly undertaken by the 7- by 10-Foot Wind Tunnel and the Flight Research Sections. The key to the solution, however, was found by Harry Goett, who conceived and, together with his 7- by 10-foot tunnel staff, developed methods for predicting flying qualities from data obtained from tests of small-scale powered models in the wind tunnel. The Flight Research group checked the wind-tunnel results by flight tests of the actual airplane. The check was made on numerous airplanes, but the most extensive data confirming the technique were obtained on the Navy's PV–1 twin-engine patrol airplane. The first attempt to interpret the PV–1 model test data in terms of flying qualities was made by Victor Stevens and George McCullough, while Noel Delany and William Kauffman reported confirming results obtained from flight tests of the actual PV–1 airplane. In the end, the staff of the 7-by-10 had devised methods for planning wind-tunnel test programs that would allow the predetermination of those physical features of an airplane which would best satisfy established han-

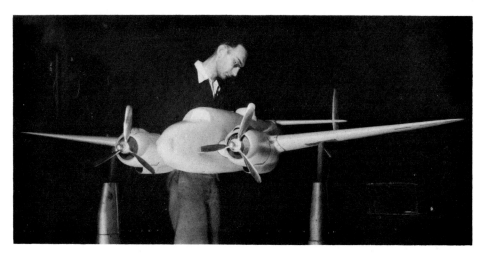

Vega PV–1 airplane model in 7- by 10-foot tunnel.

dling-qualities requirements. One of the most outstanding and useful research accomplishments of the Laboratory during the war, this work was
published as TR 781 (ref. A–5) under the authorship of Harry Goett, Roy
Jackson, and Steven Belsley.

AIRPLANE DRAG IN FLIGHT AND WIND TUNNEL

Although Ames engineers, as just noted, developed procedures for predicting the handling qualities of airplanes from wind-tunnel model tests,
the prediction of performance factors, such as drag and speed, from such
tests was quite a different problem. The test models were usually idealized
with smoother, truer surfaces than the originals and lacked the gaps, excres-
cences, and rivet heads that were found in the actual airplanes. Moreover,
there were other influences peculiar to the wind tunnel that were often difficult to evaluate. Such influences included the interference of the struts on
which the models were mounted, the turbulence in the airstream, and the
subtle effects of the surrounding walls. The rather indeterminate effects of
these many factors placed in some question the accuracy with which the
drag, and thus the speed, of an airplane could be determined from wind-
tunnel model tests.

To obtain information on the subject just mentioned, Ames engineers
undertook to make a comparison of the drag of airplanes as determined first
by model tests in a wind tunnel and then by measurements made on the airplanes in actual flight. The comparison was made for only two airplanes, the
P–51 and the P–80, but the results were expected to have general significance. The first airplane selected for the test was North American's new
P–51 "Mustang" fighter, an airplane on which Ed Schmued, Ed Horkey, and

others of the NAA design group had lavished much attention. The P–51 was a good selection for the test. It was the first of a new class of extra clean fighter airplanes and the first to use the new laminar-flow wing sections developed by NACA. There was still a question of just how much laminar flow one could expect to get in an actual application of these sections considering the effects of propeller slipstream and all the unavoidable surface roughness resulting from conventional, or even refined, manufacturing methods. There was also the question of whether the 16-foot tunnel, in which the model was to be tested, was sufficiently free of turbulence to allow the wings of the P–51 model to develop their full laminar-flow potential. These questions, however, merely added spice to the experiment.

A one-third scale model of the P–51, without propeller, was carefully tested in the wind tunnel through a range of lift coefficients and speeds. This phase of the experiment was not unusually difficult. It was pretty much a conventional wind-tunnel test. The problem came in running the flight test—without a propeller. The propeller had been eliminated because there was no good way of measuring the thrust of either the propeller or the engine exhaust in flight, and these uncertain forces would totally obscure the drag of the airplane, the force which was to be measured. So the propeller was removed, the carburetor inlet blocked off, and the whole airplane polished and waxed to resemble the surface conditions of the model. The usual load of special NACA flight-research instrumentation had been installed in the airplane, and this included a sensitive accelerometer that would measure accelerations in the longitudinal direction with an accuracy of 0.01 g. The drag of the airplane would be measured by the deceleration it produced.

With no propeller, the P–51 would have to be towed to altitude and there released to descend along some prescribed path to a dead-stick landing. The NACA pilot, James M. (Jimmy) Nissen, recognized the hazards involved. True, he did not expect to get any special financial reward for undertaking work involving unusual danger—NACA pilots never did—but if he felt any concern over these dangers, it was buried in his great enthusiasm for the project. In any case, the flights were to be made from the Army base at Rogers—more commonly called Muroc—Dry Lake where the maximum opportunity for a safe landing would be provided.

The airplane chosen to do the tow job was the Northrop P–61 Black Widow. It would be connected to the P–51 by means of two long tow cables having at the P–51 end a special release mechanism which Jimmy could operate if he got into trouble.

The whole operation was a very tricky business. The towed takeoff, the climb to 28,000 feet, the release of the cables, and the descent to a dead-stick landing all added to the thrill of the experiment. But everything went off fine. The first flight was completed successfully and so was the second. On the third flight, however, difficulty arose. For some unexplained reason, the

Northrop P–61A towing propellerless P–51B.

cable released from the Black Widow. It flew back and wrapped around the P–51 like spaghetti around a hot dog. Jimmy was in real trouble. Though trussed up like a Christmas turkey, he found he was still able to control the airplane. Gingerly he brought the P–51 down: in fact, he couldn't stop it from coming down as it had no propeller. He landed in a rather rough area, a quarry. The structure of the P–51 crumpled. When the dust had settled, there was Nissen crawling out of his wrecked plane, shaken but hopefully not seriously harmed. He was taken to the base hospital to be X-rayed for broken bones. Unfortunately, the X-ray machine was not working; Jimmy had clipped the powerline to the hospital on his way in for his ill-fated landing. The instrumentation fortunately survived the crash and provided the evidence that was sought. The flight data confirmed to an acceptable degree the results of the wind-tunnel tests.

A description of the whole project is given in TR 916 (ref. A–6) authored by James Nissen, Burnett Gadeberg, and William Hamilton. A foreword was added to the report by NACA Chairman Jerome Hunsaker in recognition of the special contribution made by Nissen.

The hazards to which NACA test pilots were subjected were considered acceptable only if they could not by any reasonable means be avoided. In this case, the whole project had been rushed and a question remained whether, with a little more deliberation, a little more care and checking, the failure of the cable attachment could have been avoided. The lesson learned was reasonably cheap, but it could have been otherwise.

CRITICAL AIRLOADS

The wartime role of the Ames Flight Research Section was not only to

83

Left to right: *Test pilots James Nissen, William Mc-Avoy, and Lawrence Clousing.*

assist the military in evaluating the flying qualities of military airplanes but also to serve as aeronautical detectives to discover why a particular airplane, or a particular class of airplanes, was killing a lot of military pilots. The discovered cause often indicated no fault of the designer but only that the airplane had advanced into new realms of flight where unknown factors were present.

The flight realms that gave trouble in the midwar years were the high subsonic speed ranges where the uncertain effects of compressibility were being encountered. At low subsonic speeds the air feels the coming of a wing when it is still far off; thus the air has plenty of time to move out of the way and let the wing by. But at speeds approaching the speed of sound, the air receives little warning of the coming of the wing and has little time to get out of the way—so little time, indeed, that it gets squashed or compressed as the wing slams against it. When the sonic speed is reached, the air gets no warning at all because the "feel" of the wing is transmitted forward only with the speed of sound. Hence at sonic and higher speeds the wing, and other parts of the airplane, crash into the air with a terrific impact often heard miles away on the ground. In the early days at Ames peculiar airplane flight characteristics, and also many unexpected airloads, arose from these compressibility effects.

FLIGHT RESEARCH

Along in the midwar years, a rash of tail failures appeared in the operation of some of our new high-speed fighter aircraft. These airplanes had been designed to dive at high speed and perform rolling pullouts and other violent maneuvers, yet failures were occurring under conditions which the designers had considered safe. More than one pilot lost his life as the result of such failures. The Ames Flight Research Section was assigned a Bell P–39 airplane to study the general effect of compressibility on airloads as well as the specific tail-failure problem. The airplane was prepared for test in the usual manner by installing a variety of special NACA instrumentation. Included in this case were instruments to record photographically, as a function of time, quantities from which could be determined such variables as indicated airspeed; pressure altitude; normal acceleration; engine manifold pressure; engine rpm; approximate angle of attack of the thrust line; landing-gear position; aileron, elevator, and rudder positions; aileron and elevator forces; rolling, yawing, and pitching velocities; and the pressure distribution over extensive areas of the wings and tail surfaces.

The instrumented P–39 was used in several rather extensive programs to determine handling qualities and airloads both in steady straight flight and in various maneuvers. Valuable information was obtained which pointed the way to improved methods of design. In most of these programs, the airplane was flown by Lawrence Clousing. His principal, ground-based, engineering colleagues were William Turner and Melvin Sadoff. Typical results of the tests are contained in TN's 1144 and 1202.

In one phase of the P–39 program, measurements were made of the horizontal tail loads during stalled pullouts at high speed. To attain the highest Mach number of which the P–39 was capable, Larry Clousing would put the airplane in a nearly vertical dive at high altitude. From the high speeds thus obtained, he would make sharp pullouts, thus searching the extremities of the conditions for which the airplane was designed. But did the designers really know what the airloads would be under these severe flight conditions and what would happen if they had underestimated the loads? The tests showed that the loads had indeed been underestimated.

In each new dive Larry, with cold courage, would push the airplane to higher and higher speeds and make ever more forceful pullouts. The results

The Bell P–39 test airplane, used for tail-load tests.

are best told by a Memorandum Report that Clousing and Bill Turner wrote on the subject:

> . . . it is seen that the airplane was pulled in until a very violent stall occurred at a lift coefficient of 1.01 and a Mach number of 0.67. The maximum acceleration factor reached was 7.5 at an angle of attack of 19°. The maximum elevator angle was 11.5° up. The buffeting was apparently about the same on both sides of the tail in this run. Rapid fluctuations of pressure of 300 to 400 pounds per square foot occurred at the leading edge of the stabilizer during the buffeting. . . .
>
> During this run structural failure of the horizontal tail occurred. Since the airplane was operating within maneuvering limits which were considered safe by design specifications in use at the time the airplane was designed, it is of interest to examine the nature of the tail failure in relation to the necessity for revision of air load requirements and the manner of specifying safe maneuverability limits to a pilot. The principal failures were on the left side of the tail, although failure had also started on the right side. . . . The left elevator had buckled downward at about the third outboard row of orifices, cracking the elevator spar. The elevator nose balance had been forced downward severely enough to break the elevator nose rib on each side of the tail just inside the outboard hinge fitting. The left stabilizer rear beam was cracked at the inboard hinge bracket, and the two top bolts holding the bracket to the stabilizer rear beam had been sheared completely.

The report calmly went on to say, "Other miscellaneous failures of various degrees of severity occurred to both the elevator and stabilizer structure. . . ."

Other, indeed! That was quite enough. One tiny bit more and Larry would not be here. This was not the first nor the last time that Clousing exhibited the remarkable fearlessness with which he approached all of his flight assignments. Why did he do it? Certainly not for money. All he or the other NACA test pilots received was standard civil service pay. Commercial pilots charged treble the amount for far less dangerous jobs. But it was wartime and perhaps Clousing felt that a little added risk on his part might save the lives of several military pilots. After all, he had been a naval aviator himself. And who knows what Larry really thought, for he was reluctant to talk about it. A historian must get the story from his colleagues or from the cold data of musty reports.

The flight projects so far described are representative, perhaps, of the wartime work that was performed by the Ames flight research people. But it is only a tiny part of the total. To aid military services, the Ames flight research group conducted research programs on many of the new airplanes being produced for war use. Included among these were the Bell P–39 and P–63; Boeing B–17; Brewster F–2A; Consolidated B–24; Curtiss C–46; Douglas SBD, XBT2D, A–20, and A–26; General Motors XP–75; Lockheed P–38, P–80, and PV–1; Martin B–26; North American P–51 and B–25; Northrop P–61; Ryan FR–1; Vought OS2V; and Vultee A–35. Also, late in the war period, a handling-qualities investigation was made on the Navy's K21 non-rigid airship. For this rather unique study, William M. Kauffman was project engineer.

AILERON FLUTTER

Of the airplanes just mentioned, the P–63 and P–80 were used for a number of investigations including a study of aileron flutter, one of the many dynamic phenomena associated with compressibility. Shock waves in the airflow over a wing were bad enough when they stood still, but unhappily they had a demoniacal tendency to oscillate back and forth at high speed and cause pulsating disturbances in the flow. The pulsations would sometimes shake the whole wing and airplane (this was called "buffeting") and sometimes they would cause the ailerons to buzz up and down in an alarming fashion. Shock-induced aileron buzz occurred only at high speed, and this fact added to the danger of any flight investigation of the phenomenon.

Flight studies of aileron buzz on the P–63 were conducted by John Spreiter and George Galster with George Cooper, a new member of the Ames staff, as pilot. No positive cure for the phenomenon was found, but the amplitude of the aileron motion was reduced through the use of an irreversible hydraulic unit in the lateral-control system. Investigation of aileron buzz on the P–80 was undertaken by a research team composed of Harvey Brown, George Rathert, and Lawrence Clousing. The Lockheed P–80 Shooting Star was the Nation's second jet fighter airplane. A remarkable airplane, produced in Kelly Johnson's "skunk works" in a nominal 80 days,[1] the P–80 was sleek and simple—quite the antithesis of earlier Lockheed fighters. It was still subsonic, of course, yet quite the fastest thing on wings. And it was beset with an aileron-buzz problem.

In the tests of the P–80 at Ames, the aileron buzz seemed to grow in intensity as the speed increased; and, in pursuing the matter, there was some worry that at the highest speeds the aileron motions might incite a destructive wing flutter. In a steep dive such a development might be quite a bother. For this reason, most pilots were exceedingly reluctant to dive the plane into these high-speed regimes of flight. But Larry Clousing, as we know, was different. Exhibiting his characteristic fearlessness, he dove the plane to speeds higher than man had ever reached before—to a Mach number of 0.866. The ailerons whipped violently but wing flutter did not occur. When the airplane was later examined, the left aileron was found to have a buckled trailing edge.

The study of the P–80 aileron buzz problem was pursued in the 16-foot tunnel even more intensively, if anything, than in flight. The 16-foot tunnel was ideally suited to this kind of investigation and, with Albert L. (Al) Er-

---

[1] Actually more like 140 days but still an extraordinary achievement.

Lockheed P–80 with vortex generators installed ahead of ailerons to combat aileron buzz.

ickson as project engineer, made important contributions to the understanding of the buzz phenomenon. The urgency of the P–80 problem was such that Al frequently had Kelly Johnson and other Lockheed representatives looking over his shoulder as he sought its solution. Significantly, the P–80 project infused Al with a solid and continuing interest in unsteady aerodynamic phenomena and impressed him with the need for developing special instrumentation for future wind-tunnel investigations in this field.

11

The 7-by-10's in Action

FOLLOWING long-established NACA practice, the research staff at Ames was organized around major facilities and, as earlier noted, there was often collaboration between the various facility-centered groups as they found themselves attacking common problems. With these similarities of makeup and objective, there were also certain important factors which in each group bound the members together, implanted a distinguishing characteristic, and established a certain measure of esprit de corps and effectiveness. Chief among these factors was the leader of the group, but also of great influence was the character of the men in each group.

The group of men who operated the Ames 7- by 10-foot tunnels was quite fortunate. They were lively, original-thinking nonconformists who went on to make major contributions in other branches of the Ames organization In this group were men like Charles Frick, Victor Stevens, Steven Belsley, Charles W. Harper, Robert Crane, Ralph Holtzclaw, and, most notably, Harry Goett who, as leader, guided the spirited team with a firm and sure hand. Harry possessed unique abilities for developing the latent research talents of his men, and his perception of what was really important in aeronautical research was remarkably keen. Through the vigorous exercise of these qualities he was able to mold his individualistic and sometimes recalcitrant staff to the purposes at hand and to direct their efforts into fruitful avenues of research. Some of the more obstreperous members, such as Frick and Belsley, showed a certain resistance to the molding process with the result that the halls of the 7-by-10's often resounded to their protestations and arguments.

Both 7- by 10-foot tunnels began active research operations in the early fall of 1941. They generally had been thought of as "workhorse" tunnels expected to carry out the bulk of the development test work required in the production of new military aircraft. The particular usefulness of the 7-by-10's in development test work lay in the ease and low cost of their operation and the fact that the test models used in them, being made of wood, could

Harry J. Goett. L. A. Clousing (seated).

easily be produced and quickly modified. High-speed tunnels, on the other hand, required models that were partly or wholly made of metal.

With the beginning of the war, Ames received a flood of military requests for tests of a variety of airplanes such as the Consolidated XB–32, the Hughes D–2, the North American XB–28, the Douglas XSB2D–1, and many others. The manifest destiny of the 7- by 10-foot tunnels seemed about to be realized. The tunnels and their staffs went on two-, then three-shift operations, becoming deeply involved in tests aimed at finding and correcting design faults in new military airplanes.

Harry Goett, however, was neither content nor willing to limit the role of the 7-by-10's to development test work. While straining to satisfy head-office requirements for such work, he obstinately maneuvered to reserve one of the tunnels for research of a more basic character. At other times, by strategic planning, program additions, and analyses, he was able to wring basic research results out of otherwise ordinary development test work. Thus, during the war, while the 7- by 10-foot tunnels made important contributions to the development of specific military aircraft, they also, under Goett's imaginative leadership, produced valuable information having much broader application. Of the latter results there are many examples—the most notable, perhaps, being the earlier-mentioned procedure for predicting the handling qualities of airplanes from wind-tunnel tests.

90

Curtiss XF15C–1 model in 7-by 10-foot tunnel used to investigate slipstream effects.

SLIPSTREAM EFFECTS

In early years at Langley, wind-tunnel tests of airplane models generally made no pretense at simulating the effect of operating propellers. It was difficult and costly to provide a powerplant and propellers for the airplane model, and the effects of the propeller slipstream on the model tests were not considered of sufficient importance to justify the added cost and complications. Besides, these effects could probably be calculated. In the late 1930's, however, the Sawyer Electrical Manufacturing Co. of Los Angeles developed a small, high-powered electric motor suitable for installation in airplane models, and these motors were used by Caltech to power models of the DC–4 and other airplanes in its 10-foot wind tunnel.

The value of simulating airplane power in model tests was demonstrated by the pioneering work at Caltech [1] and by the time the Ames 7- by 10-foot tunnels got under way, the technique was becoming common practice. Shortly it became absolutely essential, for the new military airplanes were being equipped with tremendously powerful engines and the slipstream of propellers produced a major effect on the stability and control of an airplane. Indeed, as airplane designers strove to achieve higher speed and greater performance for their products, the effect of the propeller slipstream became the predominant influence on stability and control. In some cases the slipstream problem was so great as to necessitate a major and costly change in the configuration of the airplane or even the abandonment of a design for which a prototype had been built. An example of the new breed of aircraft that were sorely beset by slipstream problems was the Douglas XSB2D–1, but the disease was epidemic.

A great deal of development test work in the 7-by-10's was spent in trying to deal with the destabilizing effects of propeller slipstreams and in

---

[1] See "The Influence of Running Propellers on Airplane Characteristics," by Clark B. Millikan. Third Wright Brothers Lecture, published in *Journal of the Aeronautical Sciences*, vol. 7, no. 3, Jan. 1940.

some cases, as just noted, it seemed almost a hopeless proposition. Ed Burton and his staff at Douglas Santa Monica thought they might have a solution to the slipstream problem when they mounted the propeller of their B–42 at the rear end of the airplane, behind the tail surfaces. This idea never caught on; nevertheless, a model of the B–42 was tested in the 7-by-10.

After struggling with the propeller slipstream for a few years, aeronautical engineers began to wonder if the reciprocating engine and its propeller had not become overdeveloped, overcomplex, and misapplied to modern high-speed aircraft. Like Renaissance scientists viewing the wheels-within-wheels complexity of the pre-Copernican, earth-centered model of the universe, they suspected that they might be on the wrong track. The deceptive simplicity of the first jet engines seemed to lend weight to this belief; but jet engines in the mid-war years were of low thrust and limited reliability and unhappily they became more complex as these deficiencies were corrected.

New Engines: New Problems

October 2, 1942, marked the beginning of a new era in U.S. aviation history. On that day, at Muroc Dry Lake in California, there occurred the first flight of this Nation's first turbojet-powered airplane—the "Airacomet," produced by the Bell Aircraft Corp. The Airacomet was powered by a pair of small turbojet engines, the essential features of which were those of an original jet engine designed by Group Captain Frank Whittle of the British Royal Air Force and flown earlier in England.

Owing to their low thrust and marginal takeoff capabilities, early jet engines were in some instances combined with conventional reciprocating engines. In 1944 there appeared at Ames, for test, a model of the Ryan XFR–1, the first airplane employing such a combination of power plants. The XFR–1 had a conventional reciprocating engine and propeller in front and, inside the fuselage, a small jet engine exhausting through the tail. A model of this airplane was tested in the 7-by-10 with results reported in a paper by Myles Erickson and Leonard Rose.

The jet-powered airplanes which began to appear before the end of the war introduced a brand new set of problems with which the people in the 7- by-10's and other branches of Ames were directly concerned. Two major questions to be solved were: Where should jet engines be located in an airplane? and, How should the huge volumes of air that passed into and out of a jet engine be handled? For single-engine fighter airplanes, it seemed desirable to bury the engine in the fuselage behind the pilot and to duct the exhaust gas out through the fuselage tail. The intake to the engine was more of a problem. There would be some aerodynamic advantage in inducting the air through a single inlet in the nose of the fuselage, but this method gave rise to the problem of passing the air around the cockpit. Also there was a practical need to reserve the fuselage nose for a radar installation.

NACA submerged inlet.

Alternatively, twin inlets leading to the engine could be installed in the leading edges of the wing roots, a scheme used in the XFR–1, or they could be installed on the sides of the fuselage well back from the nose; but in such installations how would the efficiency of the inlets be affected either by the wing or by the thick boundary layer forming on the fuselage ahead of the inlet?

The real problem was that never before had aircraft designers been required to induct any significant amount of air into the fuselages of airplanes and never before had they been forced to concern themselves in such an important way with internal aerodynamics. The new jet engine consumed vastly more air than the largest reciprocating engine ever built; all of this air had in some cases to be passed completely through the fuselage with a minimum of lost momentum at the inlet, at the exit, and throughout the length of the duct. This was a problem, it was quite clear, which would not be completely solved for many years.

One important phase of the jet-engine internal-flow problem was the development of efficient inlets. Any inefficiency of the inlet would not only increase the external drag of the airplane but, possibly even more significantly, would also reduce the thrust of the engine. The obvious way to make a side fuselage inlet was to install a big scoop projecting from the side of the fuselage well beyond the thickness of the boundary layer. A protruding scoop of this kind could, of course, cause a serious flow disturbance and add greatly to the drag of the airplane. At the 7-by-10, Emmet Mossman and others felt that it might be possible to develop a flush, or submerged, inlet that would not protrude from the fuselage—an inlet that would induct air as efficiently as a scoop but with much less external drag. He and his colleagues worked on the idea and found that their hunch was right; they were able to develop a submerged inlet that performed very efficiently at subsonic speeds. The aerodynamics of the boundary-layer flow in the region of the inlet was very complex and no rigorous theory was ever developed to explain how the inlet accomplished its function; nevertheless, the inlet proved very useful and its development represented a significant contribution in the field of aeronautical science. The results of the 7-by-10's first work on submerged inlets was covered in ACR A5I20 (ref. A–7), authored by Charles Frick, Wallace Davis, Emmet Mossman, and Lauros Randall.

While Mossman and his colleagues were working on submerged side inlets, another 7-by-10 group was giving consideration to the design of wing-mounted jet-engine nacelles such as might be required for large multi-jet-engined airplanes. Here there was somewhat less concern with the internal flow through the nacelles than with external drag and the avoidance of intersections between wing and nacelle that would lower the critical speed of the combination. As a result of this work, conducted principally by Robert Dannenberg, Wallace Davis, and George McCullough, designs were evolved for single- and twin-engine nacelles mounted integrally with the lower surface of the wing. These nacelles provided low external and internal drag and did not in any significant degree decrease the critical speed of the low-drag wing on which they were mounted. They provided the basis for the design of the nacelles of the first jet bombers built in this country.

12

16-Foot Tunnel Fills Urgent Need

CONSTRUCTION of the Ames 16-foot tunnel was exceedingly timely. Many of the military airplanes built during the war had pushed up into speed ranges in which compressibility effects were commonly encountered. There were a few, smaller high-speed tunnels, like the 8-foot 600+-mph tunnel at Langley, but none that provided an equal combination of size and speed—not even the new 16-foot tunnel at Langley. The Ames 16-foot tunnel therefore fulfilled a very important wartime need and helped to solve a number of rather crucial problems with which certain new airplanes were afflicted.

Manley Hood was in charge of the 16-foot tunnel during the war years and he was ably assisted by a group of men of whom a number were recent graduates of the University of Washington. Included among the members of the 16-foot staff were Al Erickson, Victor Ganzer, William Hamilton, Edmund Laitone, Henry Jessen, Warren H. Nelson, and Lee Boddy. Hood himself had come from Langley where he had been assisting DeFrance with facility design, a task which he continued during his first 2 years at Ames. At Ames he further demonstrated the technical ability and agreeable disposition which had been appreciated at Langley. Manley was placed in charge of the 7- by 10-foot tunnels when they were first put into operation but shortly was transferred to the 16-foot tunnel when, late in 1941, that facility was completed. It was for reasons of his experience and ability that Hood was chosen to manage and operate the most sophisticated piece of research equipment then completed at Ames. The task was at once a challenge and a heavy responsibility.

Because of the 16-foot tunnel's speed potentialities, it was subjected to intense pressure during the war to carry on both research and development test work. It operated on a three-shift basis, often 6 days a week. DeFrance, whose pervasive influence impressed itself on every phase of the Laboratory's operation, drove his men hard to get the work done. Every section head, every division chief, was keenly aware that at any minute Smitty might burst into his office with a roar that could shatter the glass in the win-

Manley J. Hood.

dows. A rather fearsome apparition he sometimes seemed on such occasions: hat jammed down on head, cigar clenched in teeth, and eye flashing fire—his glass eye relatively benign. Survival always seemed doubtful during the first minute of such encounters, but relief often came quickly if "explanations" were satisfactory. Above all, DeFrance was fair—a square shooter—and he was respected by all of his men. All, too, were aware of his devout loyalty to his staff and had experienced the friendly warmth of his personality more often than his wrath. But the wrath they never forgot. It lent wings to the work of the Laboratory, particularly during the period of construction and wartime urgency.

In December 1943 there were no explanations for the catastrophe that struck in the 16-foot tunnel. The windings of one of the great drive motors burned out in a shower of sparks and a pall of smoke. Smitty and Manley were on top of the problem immediately and a great effort was quickly instituted to repair the motor and return the tunnel to operation. The effort, led by Jim White, Jeff Buck, and Lawrence Montgomery, Sr., of the Electrical Section, was pushed 24 hours a day, Sundays, Christmas, and New Year's. On December 25, in the cold, dark reaches of the tunnel where the work was going on, a Christmas tree was mounted on the motor nacelle and thoughtful individuals brought in a turkey dinner for the crew. Morale was high and everyone turned to with a will to complete the job. The prevailing spirit was revealed by the actions of the General Electric Co., the principal contractor, which even before receiving written authorization, or assurance of pay, began drawing scarce copper into the special wire required to rewind the motor. By early January the challenge had been met, the task completed, and the tunnel returned to service.

CHOKING

With fans driven by motors totaling 27,000 horsepower, the 16-foot tunnel was probably the first large tunnel to encounter the problem of choking. The phenomenon of choking in a wind tunnel, as earlier noted, occurs when the speed has increased to the point where the speed of sound is reached over the full cross section of the constricted throat. Inasmuch as the model and its supporting struts produce an additional constriction, the speed of sound is reached in the plane of the model before it is reached in the region, just ahead, where the tunnel airspeed is measured. Thus, depending on the volume of the model and struts, choking will occur when the tunnel airspeed meter shows some value less than the speed of sound.

The 16-foot-tunnel staff was desirous, of course, of making tests in their tunnel at the highest possible speed but also with large models. Therefore the only means available to them for increasing the test (choking) speed of the tunnel was to reduce the thickness or bulk of the model support struts. In the original design, the tunnel was equipped with three substantial support struts each surrounded by a big, fat windshield. This system was a mistake in design judgment, it was quickly learned, for the choking Mach number was only 0.75. The windshields were removed and the struts made thinner, with the result that the choking Mach number was raised to 0.85. In certain cases, it was found, the choking Mach number could be raised to 0.9 by suspending the model on four very thin tension struts. This then was about the highest test Mach number that could be hoped for in the 16-foot tunnel except perhaps in special cases where the test model was a semispan wing that could be cantilevered, without any support struts, from the sidewall of the tunnel.

The first tests undertaken (in early 1942) in the 16-foot tunnel were of a wing composed of NACA 66,2–420 airfoil sections of 5-foot chord. This test program was NACA's first opportunity to investigate at large scale and high speed one of its new low-drag airfoils. The results were published in May 1942 in a report authored by M. J. Hood and J. L. Anderson.

DIVE CONTROL

The next project undertaken in the 16-foot tunnel was one of great urgency and importance. It was an attempt to find the cause and cure of a very dangerous diving tendency that had been revealed by the Lockheed P–38 airplane. At least one pilot had been killed by this devilish phenomenon and others had gotten into serious trouble. The evidence indicated that in a high-speed descent, or glide, the airplane showed a strong tendency to nose over into a vertical dive from which, once it was well established, the pilot had not the strength, nor the elevator the power, to pull out. If the "tuck under" tendency, as the phenomenon was often called, was not immediately corrected when first felt, the results were likely to be catastrophic. Lockheed management was very much worried. The plane was scarcely suitable for the military purpose intended unless this deadly characteristic was eliminated.

It was suspected that the trouble had to do with compressibility as it seemed to occur only at high speed—at a Mach number above 0.6. The NACA Langley laboratory was asked to investigate the problem and tests were made in the 30- by 60-foot and the 8-foot tunnels. The effect, it was found, was clearly due to the formation of shock waves on the wing and perhaps the fuselage, with a resulting loss of lift. It appeared that Lockheed might have earned the questionable honor of building the first airplane that would fly fast enough to encounter serious compressibility troubles. But what to do about it? Langley made a number of suggestions aimed at increasing the critical speed of the airplane. The recommendations were good in theory but would have required really major modifications in the design. Kelly Johnson would have none of them. What he wanted, and quite understandably, was a quick and easy fix. After all, there was a war on and no unnecessary delays could be brooked.

At this stage, Ames was asked to investigate the problem in the 16-foot tunnel. The job was undertaken with high priority, and Al Erickson was put in charge of the work. Kelly Johnson's men made frequent visits to Ames to discuss ways of dealing with the problem. The first series of tests at Ames confirmed the findings at Langley. The main source of trouble, it now became clear, was the system of shock waves that formed on the upper surface of the inboard wing sections at a Mach number of about 0.65. The shock waves reacted with the boundary layer and caused flow separation and loss of lift over that portion of the wing. The loss of wing lift caused a loss of downwash at the tail; and the tail, suddenly relieved of its downward load, immediately put the airplane into a steep dive. The forces on the stabilizer, which held the plane in the dive, were so powerful that they could not be overcome by the elevator; and there was, of course, no fast-acting means for changing the angle of the stabilizer.

In the first series of tests run at Ames, a number of corrective measures were tried. None of them was very simple though some were beneficial. Other tests were run which were reported by Erickson in April 1943. In Erickson's report, three solutions to the problem were suggested. The first and best one, which had been recommended and actually checked out in flight by Lockheed, was the installation of flaps on the lower surface of the wing at the 33-percent-chord point. The action of the flap was to quickly restore the lift which the wings had otherwise lost. The second suggestion was to install some fixed bumps on the lower surface of the wing. The bumps produced results somewhat similar to those of the flaps but were much less effective. The third suggestion, which doubtless would have been effective, was to install a controllable stabilizer.

The flap solution was adopted by Lockheed and it served the purpose very well. But it was only a fix and it did not obscure the fact that in the race for speed subsonic airplanes, particularly configurationally complex designs like the P–38, had come to the end of the line. Lockheed's next airplane, the P–80, quite different from the company's P–38, P–49, and P–58, was dead simple. It was a beaut.

The tuck-under phenomenon appeared, in a generally milder form, in other airplanes and was the subject of considerable study in the 16-foot tunnel and in flight. An analysis of the problem was prepared by Manley Hood and Harvey Allen and published in TR 767.

P–51 Studies

Not long after the P–38 episode another "fire drill" took place in the 16-foot tunnel. In early flights of North American's sleek new P–51, a strange thumping noise had appeared. Nothing really catastrophic had occurred, but Ed Schmued, Ed Horkey, and others of the design staff at North American were considerably worried. Noises such as had come from the bowels of the airplane might presage an explosion. The noise, it was noted, occurred only in flight.

The P–51 Mustang was one of the cleanest airplanes that had been built up to that time. Reportedly, it had been dived by the British to Mach 0.85, which seems doubtful, but in any case it had certainly traveled faster than any other propeller-driven airplane. The P–51 incorporated, for the first time, NACA's low-drag airfoil sections and great care had been taken to make the wings fair and smooth. Its single, liquid-cooled engine was neatly faired into the nose of the fuselage. The radiator was located in the fuselage behind the cockpit and cooling air was taken in through a large belly scoop under the wing. Despite the advanced features of the P–51's design, the Army Air Corps had shown little interest in the airplane and had ordered only two. It was not until the British ordered 600 of them that the Army pricked up its ears and itself placed an order for 500. The airplane later endeared itself to American bomber crews for whom it provided defensive cover during deep penetration raids into Germany.

It was clearly an urgent matter to find the source of the thumping, or rumble, in the P–51. The assistance of the Ames Laboratory was requested. The project might appropriately have been undertaken by the Flight Research Section, but it was realized that results could be obtained much more quickly in the 16-foot tunnel if it were possible to mount the whole fuselage and wing roots of the airplane in the tunnel. Manley Hood and his staff figured that it was possible—that if the outer wing panels were removed, the fuselage with stub wings would just fit in the 16-foot test section. The installation was quickly made and the tests were begun. Howard Matthews was project engineer.

James A. White.

North American XP–51B with outer wing panels removed in 16-foot tunnel.

The rumble appeared in the wind-tunnel tests and its source was found to be the belly scoop on the undersurface of the wing. More specifically, it was soon learned, the rumble came from disturbances in the inlet airflow when gobs of de-energized air from the boundary layer surged over the inner lip of the scoop and into the air duct. Over the long expanse of wing and fuselage lying ahead of the scoop, a considerable thickness of boundary layer would build up and the thickness was all the greater as a result of the blocking effect of the scoop. North American engineers had considered the boundary layer in the design of the scoop and had lowered the scoop below the surface of the wing a little way to allow the boundary layer to pass harmlessly by. But for reasons of maintaining cleanness of line, they did not want the scoop to project downward any farther than necessary. In fact, they had made it wide and shallow—thus, unfortunately, providing every opportunity for the ingestion of boundary layer.

100

Howard F. Matthews.

A number of minor modifications of the scoop were tried with little effect. The ever-present Smitty DeFrance, who seldom failed to advance his own recommendations, spoke forth on this occasion in no uncertain terms: "Lower the damn thing!!" This measure was pretty obvious, of course, but Manley and his boys were searching for a somewhat more refined method of accomplishing the same end. Nevertheless the lowering idea was tried and it, together with certain other modifications, was found to be a nearly perfect cure. North American people were delighted. An easily applied cure had been found, and that in a matter of only a few weeks. But above the pleasure of finding a solution to the P–51 problem, both NACA and North American had learned a valuable lesson. It concerned the importance of keeping boundary layer out of air scoops. And a thoughtful observer might have taken time to reflect that the boundary layer, so little appreciated by the layman, so infinitely important to the aerodynamicist, had again got in its licks. Certainly this was not the last we would hear from it.

Ames' contribution to the success of the P–51 did not stop with its solution of the duct-rumble problem. Other performance gains for the airplane were achieved in development tests on the airplane that were later run in the 16-foot tunnel under the supervision of Charlie Hall, Henry Jessen, and others. And of course there was the earlier described joint project with Flight Research, the famous "Jimmy Nissen" experiment. All in all, North American had much to thank Ames for, and such thanks were soon forthcoming.[1]

---

[1] Letter, R. H. Rice, Chief Engineer, North American Aviation, Inc., to Dr. G. W. Lewis, Director of Aeronautical Research, NACA, Apr. 21, 1943.

OTHER DEVELOPMENT TESTS

The projects just mentioned are examples of work carried out in the 16-foot tunnel during the war. While they were somewhat more dramatic, they were no more important than many other projects undertaken in that tunnel. Models of at least 16 different airplanes were tested in the 16-foot tunnel and these included the P–80, the first completely jet-powered airplane to be investigated at Ames. Inasmuch as there was a vast lack of information on the effect of compressibility on air loads, many of the models tested were built with orifices distributed over their surfaces to facilitate pressure-distribution measurements. In some instances as many as 800,000 separate pressure measurements were made on a single airplane model.

WINGS for JET BOMBERS

Because of the advanced capabilities of the 16-foot tunnel, all of its available time was given to the development testing of military aircraft. Some time was reserved for obtaining fairly basic information that would be useful in future designs. Along in 1945, the Air Forces were making plans to develop a new class of bombers powered with jet engines. They would be much faster than the B–29, of course, and would require wings that would perform well at high subsonic Mach numbers. Certainly this was an occasion to use NACA's low-drag airfoils which minimized the adverse effects of compressibility and maximized the benefits derived from extended laminar flow. Accordingly a program was undertaken in the 16-foot tunnel concerned with the design and testing of a series of six wings, comprised of NACA 65-series sections covering a range of thickness and aspect ratio that might be used by the new bombers. The tension struts were used and Mach numbers up to 0.9 were obtained. In some tests a dummy, bomber-type fuselage was installed. The results of these tests were described in TR 877 by William Hamilton and Warren Nelson. They were also presented directly to the Air Forces in a conference at Wright Field in September 1945.

The Wright Field conference was called to allow NACA to present all available technical information having application to the new jet bombers then being designed by North American, Consolidated, Boeing, and Martin. By far the most important subject discussed at this conference was wing sweep. Robert Jones of the Langley laboratory had recently shown that compressibility effects could be delayed and perhaps minimized in intensity by sweeping the wings of an airplane backward. And when, at the end of the war, our scientists entered Germany, they found that the Germans had also discovered the benefits of sweep.[2] But how soon the principle of sweep could be applied to American airplanes remained to be seen.

---

[2] One of those who entered Germany at this time was R. G. Robinson of Ames. Inklings of the German work on sweep had reached the United States a year or so earlier, but the significance of this work seems not to have been recognized until the Jones discovery.

13

The 40-by-80 Begins Operations

RESEARCH in the 40- by 80-foot tunnel did not get under way until mid-1944. Harry Goett was put in charge of the facility and in September was replaced as head of the 7-by-10's by Charles Frick. In the years that followed Frick proved to be an aggressive, competent leader, a man continuously on the move, whose furious pipe-smoking practices, incidentally, threatened to burn the place down. Brilliant himself, Frick would exhibit sharp impatience when confronted with obtuseness, or laggardly action, on the part of any member of his staff—a group which therefore remained very alert.

Goett took with him to his new assignment in the 40-by-80 a number of men from his former staff in the 7-by-10's. Victor Stevens, William Harper, and Bradford Wick went with him, and to this group of former comrades were added J. S. W. (Sam) Davidsen, Gerald McCormack, and a number of others including Dean Chapman, a new man who had been doing graduate work at Caltech. Goett thus started out with a very able team and men who worked for him had a way of developing.

The 40- by 80-Foot Wind Tunnel and the Flight Research Sections comprised the Full-Scale and Flight Research Division, which was under the command of Parsons, who also headed up the Construction Division. The 40-by-80 operation and flight research proved to be an extremely compatible and significant combination of activities; indeed, they were complementary as well as compatible. The 40-by-80 had the unique ability to test a full-scale, actual airplane with engines running, even with a "pilot" in the cockpit, and thus the results obtained from it could easily be confirmed by flight tests of the same airplane. And yet while the forces and operation of the airplane could more easily be checked and measured in the wind tunnel, the dynamic handling qualities of the airplane, as appreciated by the pilot, could only be determined in flight.

In wind-tunnel work there were many advantages in testing actual airplanes rather than models. For one thing, it took time to build a model, whereas an airplane with a problem could be installed in the 40-by-80 and

Charles W. Frick.

checked out very quickly. Moreover, no model could be built which in external configuration represented the airplane as perfectly as the airplane represented itself. On the other hand, of course, the speed of a tunnel the size of the 40-by-80 was limited by practical considerations and was much lower than could be achieved in smaller tunnels. The conditions it could best simulate were thus the lower half of the speed range, including landing, takeoff, and climb. Problems in this speed range were becoming increasingly critical as airplane designers attempted to hold takeoff and landing speeds as low as possible while boosting the top speed ever higher. With these strengths and weaknesses the 40-by-80 was a natural and very effective partner of the other facilities at Ames. It was, nevertheless, better adapted to development work than to fundamental research.

The first research project undertaken in the 40-by-80 was a series of tests, begun about August 10, 1944, on an 8- by 48-foot wing having Clark Y sections. It was something of a calibration test.

The first airplane development test program to be undertaken in the 40-by-80 was a series of tests on the Douglas El Segundo XSB2D–1, later designated BTD–1, airplane. Models of this airplane, a rather ambitious design, had earlier been tested in the 7- by 10-foot and the 16-foot tunnels, and the prototype soon was to be tested by Flight Research. The Ames Laboratory probably spent more time on the BTD–1 than on any other single airplane. Soon afterward, the Navy lost interest in the BTD–1 and it was never put into quantity production. It was immediately followed, however, by a series of simple but very successful fighter-bomber naval aircraft which did much credit to Ed Heinemann and his design staff at Douglas El Segundo.

Following the BTD–1 program, which was organized and reported by Sam Davidsen and N. J. Martin, tests were undertaken in the 40-by-80 of a number of airplanes, including the Northrop N9M–2 flying-wing prototype,

104

the Grumman XF7F–1, the Ryan XFR–1, the General Motors P–75A, and the Douglas El Segundo A–26B. Also, under the supervision of Brad Wick and Adrian Anderson, the first 40-by-80 research programs on propellers were run.

The case of the XFR–1 illustrates the value of the wartime development activities in the 40-by-80. The XFR–1 was a promising new type of Navy fighter airplane which, as earlier described, had a composite powerplant consisting of a conventional Wright 1820 reciprocating engine and propeller in front and a General Electric I–16 jet engine enclosed in the fuselage behind the pilot. The jet engine inducted air through leading-edge inlets in the wing roots and its exhaust was ejected through the tail of the fuselage. The Navy's flight tests of the airplane at Patuxent River had shown it to be seriously lacking in certain stability and control characteristics, particularly in the carrier-approach condition. These deficiencies were so serious that the airplane, in its existing form, was unacceptable to the Navy. The assistance of NACA in correcting the faults of the airplane was requested.

First of all, the XFR–1 was flown by the Ames Flight Research Section to confirm and quantitatively evaluate its reported deficiencies. It was then put in the 40-by-80. Within a few weeks a 40-by-80 research team headed by Victor Stevens and Donald Jacoby had discovered a number of fairly simple modifications which largely eliminated the deficiencies and enabled the airplane to satisfy Navy flight requirements. The proposed modifications, though individually fairly simple, were quite extensive and involved a new rudder, new ailerons, revised elevator trim tab, revised wing flaps, revised elevator control system, and revised wing dihedral. Each change was later checked, and its usefulness evaluated, in flight by the Ames Flight Research Section. The Ryan management expressed its gratitude to DeFrance for the major contribution Ames made to the success of the airplane.[1]

The XFR–1 example illustrates not only the extraordinary usefulness of the 40-by-80 but also its rather unique complementarity with Ames Flight Research. Nor was the case of the XFR–1 unusual. There was also, for example, the case of the Douglas A–26B, the mission of which was changed, after the plane was built, to include low-level strafing. But low-level strafing required a lightness of controls which the airplane did not have. A 40-by-80 research team headed by Gerald McCormack investigated the problem and found a solution. Here again there was coordination of effort between the 40-by-80 and Flight Research.

The 40-by-80 had been in use only a year when the war ended, yet by that time the tunnel had demonstrated that NACA had made no mistake in building it.

---

[1] Letter, T. Claude Ryan, President, Ryan Aeronautical Co., to Dr. G. W. Lewis, Director Aeronautical Research, NACA, June 29, 1944.

14

Men and Theory

THROUGHOUT most of the war years, Harvey Allen was in charge of the Theoretical Aerodynamics Section, reporting to Don Wood, who at first was Chief of Research and later Chief of the Theoretical and Applied Research Division. Harvey's staff included Walter Vincenti, Max Heaslet, Gerald Nitzberg, Donald Graham, and, later, Milton Van Dyke. In the early years, as has been noted, the pure theory of this group was rather thoroughly mixed up with the reinforced concrete of design and construction. Allen, in any case, was as much an experimentalist as a theorist; thus it was not long before his brainchild, the 1- by 3½-foot tunnel, became a part of his command. Nor was it surprising when, in July 1945, a new High Speed Research Division was created with Allen as Chief. Within the new Division were established a 1- by 3-Foot Tunnel Section under Vincenti and a 1- by 3½-Foot Tunnel Section under Graham. The Theoretical Aerodynamics Section, now headed by the scholarly Dr. Max Heaslet, remained in Don Wood's Division which itself had been augmented by a 12-Foot Tunnel Section headed by Robert Crane.

Allen, a man of many loves,[1] adapted quite readily to the requirements of his various assignments. While occupied with design and experimentation, he still managed to turn out one of the most outstanding and generally useful theoretical papers produced by the Ames staff during the war years. This was TR 833 (ref. A–8) entitled "General Theory of Airfoil Sections Having Arbitrary Shape or Pressure Distribution." Actually, Harvey had done much of the thinking for this report while still at Langley, but the writing took place at Ames.

Allen's report, and much of the other theoretical research carried on during the early years at Ames, concerned that basic element of all airplanes, the airfoil or wing section. During the late 1930's, as earlier noted, NACA engineers at Langley had developed a new and more scientific method of designing airfoils. This method allowed designers, through ma-

---

[1] Including ancient Isotta Frascini automobiles, symphonic music, and great Saint Bernard dogs—preferably with kegs attached.

From left to right: *Walter G. Vincenti, Dr. Milton D. Van Dyke, and Dr. Max A. Heaslet, theoretical aerodynamicists.*

nipulation of pressure distribution, to achieve airfoil designs having low drag (extensive laminar flow) and high compressibility speeds. All one had to do was first to choose the desired pressure distribution and then to design an airfoil of the right shape to produce that distribution. But ah! there was the rub. How did one proceed from pressure distribution to airfoil shape? The designer was in the classic position of the lost traveler who, on inquiring of a native about the route, was told, after some cogitation, "You can't get there from here!"

Actually, in the case of the airfoil, there was a theoretical method of getting there from here but it was extremely laborious. It was like many other airfoil theories developed by mathematical purists. But Harvey was not a purist. His interests lay not in trying to build a mathematical Taj Mahal. He was much more interested in useful results than in the virgin beauty of his mathematical edifice. He was not above using approximations, reasonable assumptions, unique analogies, and special devices with the result that he often found working solutions to problems that had baffled more polished mathematicians. That is about what he did in the case of the airfoil problem. He developed a simple method for proceeding from an arbitrarily chosen pressure distribution to the physical shape of the airfoil that would produce that distribution. Allen's method was extremely helpful in the attack on the compressibility-effects problem which at that time was troubling Ames research people. The relevance of the method to the compressibility problem lies in the fact that pressures are a measure of the velocity in the local flow over an airfoil, and the velocity of sound in the local flow marks the beginning of the more severe compressibility effects.

The onset and intensity of compressibility effects depended not only on the shape, or thickness distribution, of the airfoil but also on its angle of attack and lift coefficient. The airspeed or Mach number at which these ef-

108

fects began to appear was called the "critical speed" or "critical Mach number" and much effort was spent in devising airfoils having high critical speeds through a wide range of angle of attack. Analytical means for predicting the critical Mach number of airfoils at different lift coefficients, with and without flaps, were developed during this period by Max Heaslet and Otway Pardee. The problem was also attacked in the 1- by 3½-foot tunnel where a systematic investigation was made of the pressure distribution over several NACA low-drag and conventional (old style) airfoils. The latter study, made by Don Graham, Gerald Nitzberg, and Robert Olson, is reported in TR 832 (ref. A–9). Also undertaken in the 1- by 3½-foot tunnel was a program to determine the high-speed characteristics of a promising group of NACA low-drag airfoils. This investigation was carried out and reported by Milton Van Dyke and G. A. Wibbert.

15

Wartime Review

THE end of the war on August 14, 1945, came quietly as far as effects on the operation of the Ames Aeronautical Laboratory were concerned. Through sheer inertia, the work of the Laboratory carried on essentially unchanged into the next year. Although the portents for the future of aviation were impressive, it was a time when the Ames Laboratory people unwound just a bit: a time for reflection. In the furious sweaty environment of war, the Laboratory had passed all tests very well. In this, DeFrance and his staff could take considerable satisfaction. Ames had made useful, sometimes vital, contributions to a great many of the high-performance airplanes the country had developed and had won much praise from the military services and the aircraft companies. Moreover, this contribution had been made while building a new Laboratory—a new Laboratory of facilities and men. There was now in operation or under construction at Ames a rather impressive array of modern aeronautical research facilities valued at about $21 million. There was also a well-organized, functioning staff totaling 800, which included a surprisingly large number of very able research men, a few truly outstanding.

Much of the research effort at Ames during the war had been spent in assisting the military services and the aircraft companies in developing aircraft having a maximum of performance and military usefulness. In reflecting on this work, the Laboratory's only cause for regret was that so few of the new airplanes on which it had worked had made any substantial contribution toward winning the war or, for that matter, now held any great promise for future military usefulness. With a few exceptions such as the B–29, the P–51, and the F6F, the fighting airplanes with which the war was won were designed and first built prior to Pearl Harbor. It was in the improvement of these somewhat older airplanes that Ames had, perhaps, made its greatest contribution to the war effort.

Neither NACA nor the aircraft industry, nor for that matter the military services, was prepared for the avalanche of aircraft development work precipitated by the war. Of course there had been forewarnings since 1935 of what was to come, but these storm signals had either gone unheeded or their significance had not been fully evaluated by those who had authority to take effective action. In retrospect one could see what should have been done. NACA should much earlier and more forcefully have asserted its need for a new powerplants laboratory and a new aerodynamics laboratory. The military services, in the latter half of the 1930's, should have greatly accelerated the development of new aircraft types, thus allowing industry to expand its engineering and design capabilities. Neither of these steps, however, could have been taken without the approval of Congress, which should have been more foresightedly generous with its appropriations for aeronautical research and development.

When war came, the failures of anticipation and action just mentioned were paid for in terms of confusion and inefficiency, and a concomitant waste of effort, talent, materiel, and funds. Conditions would have been worse had it not been for the initial acceleration provided by the substantial orders for aircraft received by American industry from Great Britain during the period 1939–1941. As it was, aircraft procurement during the wartime rush showed evidence of disorderliness, too little thought, and too little planning. In retrospect and in the light of the then-existing shortage of design talent, design information, and test facilities, it appeared that the airplane designs attempted during that period were too many in number and some a bit too exotic and ambitious in character. The rush of aircraft development was so great that by the time model tests were completed in Ames wind tunnels, the development of the airplane was, in some instances, so far advanced that it was not feasible to make the design changes which the wind-tunnel tests indicated were necessary. For this and other reasons of misjudgment, costly prototypes had to be junked.

The war brought into evidence the lack of basic design data available to industry for the proper design of new high-powered, high-speed aircraft types. For certain reasons, the plausibility of which could readily be established, NACA had not provided the required data; moreover, faced with the demands of war, the agency found that it lacked the facilities and staff to carry on both development work and basic research adequately. Nor had the military, long dependent on NACA for research and development support, provided sufficient facilities of its own. Thus there arose, quite legitimately, the question of whether the military had depended too much on NACA.

Aircraft designers utilized such design data as were available and then bravely struck forth to new heights on the basis of engineering intuition. Experienced designers were spread too thinly and exuberant young men, fresh out of college, often gained sharp lessons in design at some cost to the Government. New design groups without inhibitions, and old design groups with inhibitions abandoned, put forward highly imaginative design proposals which found surprisingly ready acceptance by the military. Such cases

112

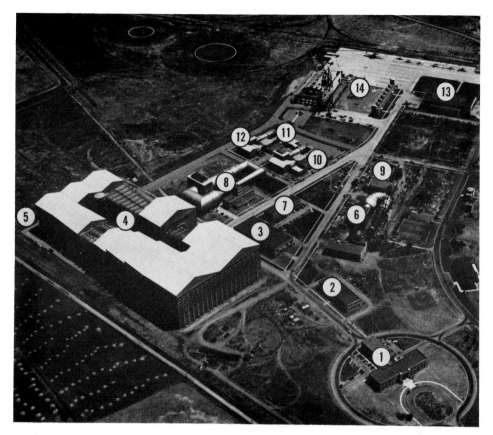

Aerial view of Ames Aeronautical Laboratory on July 3, 1945, at the end of World War II. (1) Administration building, (2) Science laboratory, (3) Technical service building, (4) 40- by 80-foot wind tunnel, (5) Substation, (6) 12-foot pressure wind tunnel, (7) Utilities building, (8) 16-foot high-speed wind tunnel, (9) 1- by 3-foot supersonic wind tunnels, (10) 7- by 10-foot wind tunnel no. 1, (11) Model finishing shop, (12) 7- by 10-foot wind tunnel no. 2, (13) Flight research laboratory, and (14) Airplane hangar and shop.

no doubt represented legitimate wartime gambles and the whole pattern of events described herein perhaps reveals no more than the normal inefficiencies of war.

Some of the aircraft design failures of the war period, it must be noted, arose from the very special circumstance that the war occurred at, indeed precipitated, the end of an era in aeronautical design. Owing to earlier successes, we had found ourselves trying to advance into a new realm of flight using traditional methods, facilities, and data which were not equal to the task. As 1945 ended, this impressive fact was becoming clear and we were ready to take our first faltering steps into the supersonic age.

Part II

A NEW WORLD OF SPEED

1946–1958

1946–1949

1

The Environment

A REVOLUTION in aeronautical science was at hand. The signs, brought into clear focus by a world war, were everywhere. The vistas opening were inspiring and sobering. Indeed, they were humiliating in their revelation of our state of ignorance and unpreparedness. Our experience would do us little good; it related to airplanes of the kind pioneered by the Wright Brothers. We were entering an era of transonic and supersonic aerodynamics, of jet and rocket engines, and of missiles. These developments represented not a normal extrapolation of our aeronautical past but a sudden and magnificent leap into the future.

The technical field we were entering in 1946 was one of undeveloped disciplines, of still rudimentary research facilities; and one in which universities, many of which had been excluded from the classified technical developments of war, were not fully prepared to teach. We had entered an era in which a powerful nation could be brought to its knees without the enemy's setting foot on its soil, an era in which a single bomb could devastate a large city—and such a bomb, it was realized, could be delivered by a flying vehicle capable of great speed and range.

It was clear that jet and rocket engines offered the potential of greatly increased speeds and that the new concept of wing sweep opened the aerodynamic-design door through which this potential might be realized. The United States could not expect to be first in everything; indeed, we had been caught napping in the development of both jet and large rocket engines and had been beaten by the Germans in the use of large missiles and of wing sweep. The Nation was bent not merely on catching up in aeronautical affairs but in developing a commanding lead. This objective would cost real money, in amounts never before provided for aeronautical research. But the development of the atom bomb had so impressed everyone with the importance of science in national defense that the money would probably be forthcoming.

Both the military and the NACA recognized the long-range folly of having NACA devote all of its efforts to development testing while fundamental research went begging. Even before the end of the war—indeed during the black days of the Battle of the Bulge—the military had suggested that NACA revert to fundamental research.[1] But the Bulge quickly faded and the suggestion was not implemented. With the war over, the military services were going to make sure that they would never again depend so heavily on NACA for development test work. They would have their own evaluation and test facilities and their own scientific advisory groups.

The Army Air Forces was particularly positive on these points and its position was aggressively pursued by General Henry H. Arnold and also by Major General Curtis E. LeMay, who had recently been put in command of a new Headquarters office of Deputy Chief of Air Staff for Research and Development. It certainly had occurred to the Air Force that its future and the whole pattern of its operations were in question when one airplane could carry the destructive power of thousands of B–17 or B–29 bombers. No longer would the emphasis lie in the production and operation of vast fleets of airplanes but rather in the development of advanced types of aircraft and the production of relatively small numbers. The logical course for a progressive Air Force thus led directly into aeronautical science and directly into competition with NACA. The intent of the Air Force to carve out new fields of endeavor for itself was bolstered when in July 1947 it was made an independent branch of the defense establishment.

To avoid unnecessary conflict among the several agencies then engaged in aeronautical research and development, NACA in 1946 proposed a National Aeronautical Research Policy which attempted to define the appropriate sphere of activity for each agency.[2] In making this proposal, which was quickly accepted by all the agencies involved, NACA was more concerned about its relations with the military services than with the Civil Aeronautics Authority and the aircraft industry—the other agencies named in the Policy. The Policy indicated the function of NACA as being fundamental research in the aeronautical sciences and that of the military services, evaluation of equipment and exploration of military application of research results. The definitions provided by the Policy were, however, rather vague; the boundary it established between the spheres of NACA and the military services was not sufficiently solid to preclude transgression.

NACA continued to regard the support of the military as its principal role, but it was happy to return to fundamental research. Clearly its research must now be more fundamental and more scientific, and even a bit

---

[1] During the Battle of the Bulge, according to the recollection of John Victory, General Arnold developed a feeling that the war might be prolonged for several years. Accordingly Arnold got the Navy to agree that NACA should restrict its ad hoc testing for the military and launch into basic research. The Bulge offensive, however, was quickly neutralized and the proposed plan was dropped.

[2] See *NACA 33d Annual Report 1947*. A complete statement of policy and background was also given in a NACA Press Release Apr. 1, 1946, entitled, "Government and Aircraft Industry Concur on National Aeronautical Research Policy."

more competitive. Some people in NACA looked upon fundamental research as the establishment of major principles which later could be elaborated and exploited through development. It was a strategic error, they felt—a reversal of proper form—to allow development work to be the guide for fundamental research programs. The same people believed that during the war NACA's stock of fundamental principles had been fully exploited and exhausted and that now, with the war over, it was in desperate need of replenishment.

Unfortunately, fundamental research cannot be legislated, cannot be turned off and on like an electric light. It requires the proper tools, of course, and the right environment; but most of all it requires men with a special inclination and training. Without the latter, one can throw the switch but the light does not come on.

The prerequisites for fundamental research were not wholly present at Ames, nor were they completely absent. Some, but not all, of the tools were available; the environment, owing to the disruptions arising from construction and war, had not yet reached the ideal that was potentially achievable at the Laboratory. The manpower picture at Ames encompassed a surprisingly wide spectrum of talents. The quality of the staff had suffered a little from the wartime necessity of hiring men "because their bodies were warm," but some extremely able men had come to Ames who might well have gone into private industry had it not been for the war.

The most notable features of the Ames staff in 1946 were, first, the nucleus of extremely competent men, and second, the general lack of knowledge about transonic and supersonic aerodynamics. Everyone was aware the Laboratory's work was rapidly becoming more scientific and was impressed with the necessity for training ("retreading," as it was called) the staff in the new disciplines. Arrangements were made with Stanford for the university to give a number of graduate-level credit courses at night in subjects related to transonic and supersonic aerodynamics. Inasmuch as most Stanford professors were not prepared to teach the new subjects—subjects that were developing day by day in the work of aeronautical laboratories—the lecturers were chosen from the few members of the Ames staff who were qualified.

The courses at Stanford were taken by those of the Ames staff who wished to bolster their basic scientific training and improve their abilities to carry on the work at the Laboratory. For men who had served during the war in the Navy contingent at Ames, the GI bill of rights provided the tuition for the courses attended at Stanford and elsewhere. A few such as Dean Chapman, Milton Van Dyke, and Jack Nielsen returned full time to their alma maters or to other universities to seek graduate degrees before reentering on duty at Ames. Thus, in the years following the war, a major effort in self-improvement was made by the Ames technical staff.

121

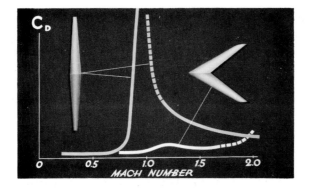

Drag benefit of sweep.

The postwar environment of the Ames Laboratory was affected by a number of technical developments around the world. R. T. Jones had developed his sweep theory at Langley early in 1945 and North American and Boeing were the first American companies having the courage to use it. It required courage, too, for sweep, although offering a tremendous reduction in transonic drag, introduced a multitude of problems for which answers had not yet been found in the laboratory.

In 1945 North American had under design the F–86, the FJ–1, and the B–45—all with straight wings. When the news about sweep came through from NACA and Germany, Ray Rice, Harrison Storms, and others at North American were torn with indecision over whether or not to change any of their designs to incorporate the new feature. It was probably undesirable to change the FJ–1 design because it was to be carrier based and sweep would greatly complicate the landing problem. And the use of sweep on the B–45 was perhaps too much of a gamble—after all, the use of jet power in a bomber was a big step in itself—and in any case the design of the airplane may have been too far advanced for any change of this kind to be feasible. But, now, the F–86: was not the gamble justified in this case? It was, they thought; so off came the straight wings and on went a set of wings that were swept backward a nice round 35°. The modification, of course, was not as simple as indicated; nevertheless the swept-wing F–86 flew in October 1947 and a year later set a world speed record [3] of 671 mph. It was a worthy successor to the P–51.

At Boeing the gamble was even greater. Boeing was in competition with North American, Convair, and Martin for a new jet bomber. George Schairer, Chief of Research at Boeing, had been one of the American group of scientific gleaners who had tailed our armed forces into Germany. He was well aware of the German work on sweep but its application to Boeing's new bomber, the B–47, was a matter not to be lightly undertaken. Sweep would

[3] Welman A. Shrader, *Fifty Years of Flight*. Cleveland, Ohio: Eaton Manufacturing Co.

introduce many problems involving stability, control, aeroelasticity, flutter, strength and performance and no one yet had suggested how jet engines might best be mounted on swept wings. Fortunately, like North American, Boeing had a wind tunnel of its own in which these matters could be studied; but time was short and the work would have to be pressed. The other companies in the competition were well advanced with their designs and, on the surface, Boeing seemed to be getting nowhere. Then late in 1947, after the other airplanes were already flying, Boeing came out with its revolutionary B–47 equipped with swept wings and a unique engine mounting. From that moment on, its competitors' airplanes were as obsolete as Noah's Ark.

With the advent of the F–86 and the B–47, fighter and bomber airplanes would never again be the same. Never again, for that matter, would commercial transport airplanes be the same. The courage of North American and Boeing designers paid off richly for their companies and for their country.

But the dread "sonic barrier" would not be breached, in level flight, by either the F–86 or the B–47. In 1944 the Langley laboratory proposed as a joint project for NACA and the military, the construction and testing of an experimental "research" airplane designed for transonic flight. The idea was approved by the military and thus was begun what was known as the "research airplane program." Late in 1944, the Army Air Force contracted with the Bell Aircraft Co. for the construction of the XS–1 (later X–1) research airplane. About the same time the Navy contracted with Douglas El Segundo for the construction of the D–558–1 research airplane. Both would be instrumented by NACA and would be flown by both NACA and service pilots at the airbase (later named Edwards Air Force Base) at Rogers Dry Lake—a lake commonly identified by the name of the bordering village, Muroc, Calif. NACA in 1946 established a group at Muroc to handle NACA's interests in the research-airplane program. This group was the nucleus of what in 1949 became the NACA High Speed Flight Research Station at Edwards.

The D–558–1 was a more or less conventional, jet-powered airplane, but the XS–1 was strictly a research vehicle. It was powered by a liquid-fuel rocket engine and was carried aloft for launching by a mother airplane. On October 14, 1947, with Air Force Capt. Charles Yeager at the controls, the XS–1 exceeded the speed of sound in level flight. The sonic barrier had at last been breached by a man-carrying airplane, albeit a very specialized research type of vehicle. An operational type supersonic plane was still a way off but, with the XS–1 flight, the longstanding psychological barrier to supersonic flight began to crumble. And before the mystery and magic of Mach 1.0 had completely faded, the pilots who first faced up to this bugbear of aviation were accorded heroic stature by the press.

In the past, conversations regarding aeronautical developments had

North American F–86A.

Boeing B–47.

X–1 in flight.

been concerned largely with man-carrying vehicles and most often with airplanes. Now, with increasing frequency, such conversations included the terms "rocket," "pilotless aircraft," and "missile." The last two terms generally referred to guided unmanned aircraft; and the first, to unguided vehicles carrying explosive charges. Wartime developments in this country had mostly been limited to rocket armament and to a few radio- or TV-guided glide bombs.

At the end of the war there was a tremendous surge of interest in rocket powerplants and guided missiles. This interest sprang in part from the revelation of German developments in these fields. A number of American companies launched into the design of guided missiles and soon demonstrated that the science and technology of missile design in this country were not far advanced.

In their development of large missiles of the V–2 type, the Germans were far ahead of everyone else. It was logical that the V–2 should be used in the United States as a stepping-stone for the development of our own rocket-motor and missile technology. Together with German missile scientists, many V–2 missiles were brought to this country. The missiles were studied by numerous organizations—in the west by the Caltech Jet Propulsion Laboratory (Army sponsored) and by North American's newly formed and rapidly growing Aerophysics Laboratory. The Aerophysics Laboratory built first a copy of the V–2 liquid-fuel rocket motor and then a series of improved versions. It also studied other missile design elements such as aerodynamics, guidance, and structures.

The V–2, fortunately, was a relatively short-range missile; but it opened the door for the development of larger, faster missiles that could span oceans. Indeed, as the war ended, the Germans were already building a missile (A–9) that would reach the United States. It is not surprising therefore that, in 1946, the Air Forces initiated Project MX–774, a design study of an intercontinental ballistic missile to be made by the Consolidated Vultee Aircraft Corp. The specifications for the missile—5000-mile range, Mach 20 speed, 500-mile altitude, and high target accuracy—boggled the imagination.

A revolution in aeronautics certainly was at hand. The prospects facing aeronautical scientists had never been more exciting. But never before had the problems seemed so many or so complex. The work of Ames, of NACA, was certainly cut out. But the task was too great for NACA alone. It would also require the best efforts of other Government laboratories, of university and industry research groups. No longer would NACA be "the" Government aeronautical research agency as it had been in the past. For NACA the work of the other research groups might be thought of as competition but, more realistically, it should be considered as needed support. The total effort would require vast sums of money; and having long been typecast as a small agency, NACA was in a poor position to command large appropriations—immeasurably poorer than, say, the Air Forces.

Although 95 percent of the work of NACA had always been in support of the military, the congressional subcommittee from which NACA was required to seek its appropriations was not the one that also funded the military services. NACA solicited its funds from the Independent Offices Appropriations Subcommittees, which served a group of rather low-priority organizations such as the Battlefield Monuments Commission, the Civil Service Commission, the Public Housing Administration, the Interstate Commerce Commission, and the General Services Administration. Chairmanned by Albert Thomas, a zealous guardian of public funds, the House Independent Offices Appropriations Subcommittee sometimes seemed to people in NACA to lack appreciation for the national defense significance of NACA's basic-research mission. This was a time when all Government agencies found it difficult to convince an immediate-results-minded Congress of the need for basic research. The subcommittee was particularly tightfisted when it came to providing funds for staff increases. Thus Ames (and NACA) at the end of the war, when the urgency of its work and the magnitude of its responsibility were greater than ever before, was required to reduce its staff by about 10 percent.[4]

This was the general environment in which the Ames Laboratory spent the first few years of the New Age of Speed.

---

[4] See app. A.

2

People and Events

IN August 1946, Robert T. Jones, originator of the sweep theory at NACA, transferred to Ames from Langley. Bob Jones, a self-trained aerodynamicist and mathematician, had built up a national, if not international, reputation through his perceptive and original work at Langley. For this work he was given the IAS Sylvanus Albert Reed Award in 1946. The genius of Bob Jones seemed, in part, to lie in his remarkable ability to extract the essence of a problem and express it in understandable and useful terms. His approach to problems was always of a fundamental character and often yielded results of broad significance. Jones would certainly give added strength to the Ames technical staff; and the contributions of his wife Doris, a competent mathematician who also joined the Ames staff, were expected to be substantial.

In 1947 DeFrance's title was changed to "Director" of the Ames Aeronautical Laboratory, and a year later he was awarded the Presidential Medal of Merit for his outstanding leadership in directing research for the advancement of aeronautics. He was further honored in 1948 by being elected vice president of the Institute of the Aeronautical Sciences. Smitty DeFrance had gained the reputation of running a tight and efficient operation at Ames and was highly respected in aeronautical circles.

The Laboratory suffered a blow in April 1947 when John Parsons became seriously ill and it was learned he would not be back to work for some time. Harry Goett assumed the position of Acting Chief of the Full-Scale and Flight Research Division and, in October 1948, was made Chief with Lawrence Clousing as Assistant Chief. In August 1947, Carl Bioletti was appointed Assistant to the Director of the Laboratory, and Manley Hood replaced him as Assistant Chief of the Theoretical and Applied Research Division. Parsons was out for one year and, on his return, was appointed Assistant to the Director, a position parallel to that held by Bioletti. DeFrance had wanted to make Parsons Associate Director at this time, but Headquarters in Washington had objected to the appointment. Nevertheless DeFrance's appreciation of Parsons' great abilities was evident.

Robert T. Jones,
theoretical
aerodynamicist.

Carlton Bioletti.

Dr. Hugh L. Dryden, Director of National Advisory Committee for Aeronautics from 1947 to 1958.

Another event, sad but important, during this period was the death on July 12, 1948, of Dr. George W. Lewis, who for years had been Director of NACA. Everyone in the fields of aeronautics and Government was aware that Dr. Lewis had performed with great vision and ability in guiding the development of the Nation's aeronautical sciences through NACA. Lewis never sought glory for himself but served NACA and his country with the utmost modesty and effectiveness. His death had certainly been hastened by the unselfish way in which he had driven himself in the construction of the new Engine Research Laboratory at Cleveland. Thus, on his death, it was more than fitting that the Cleveland laboratory was renamed the "Lewis Flight Propulsion Laboratory."

Actually Lewis' final illness had required that he give up the NACA Directorship almost a year before he died. Replacing him as Director on August 22, 1947, was Dr. Hugh L. Dryden, a well-known and respected scientist and a member of the National Academy of Sciences, who had come to NACA from the National Bureau of Standards. It was indicative of the times that the leadership of NACA had changed from an engineer to a scientist. In this connection, it may be noted that two additional positions, to be filled by scientists, had been authorized for the National Advisory Committee for Aeronautics.[1]

The end of the war brought a change in the pattern of dissemination of the information produced by NACA. Security conditions eased considerably and a great many classified reports published during the war were declassified and republished as unclassified "Wartime Reports." These reports were thus made available to the information-starved agencies which had not been able to qualify for the classified documents. In the case of new publications, NACA returned to its prewar series of unclassified Technical Reports (TR) and Technical Notes (TN), but added a new series of Research Memorandums (RM) to be made classified only as required. A typical designation for one of the new Research Memorandums was RM A7B05. In this designation, A would stand for Ames, 7 for 1947, B for February, and 05 for the fifth RM issued during that month.

In the postwar period NACA came to the conclusion that it was not sufficient to disseminate technical information only through reports, as the reports often did not appear for a year or more after the research was completed. It was decided that, to supplement the reports, technical conferences should be held, as needed, to dispense late information acquired by NACA in fields of current interest. This plan was put into effect and the resulting conferences were attended by aeronautical engineers from all over the country. They filled a very important need of the industry, the military, and the universities during this period of rapid growth in the aeronautical sciences.

---

[1] As indicated in *NACA 33d Annual Report 1947.*

Conferences were held at each of the NACA laboratories with the other laboratories contributing. At Ames a conference on "Aeronautical Problems of Transonic Airplane Design" was held in November 1947 and a conference on "Supersonic Aerodynamics" in July 1948.

As a further means of transmitting information to the interested public, a custom which had long been followed at Langley but which, during the war, had been discontinued, was restored to general use in NACA This was the custom of holding annual "inspections"—a sort of open house —to which a large number and a broad spectrum of individuals were invited. Special displays and semitechnical presentations were made to give the visitors some appreciation of the problems of aeronautics and the activities of NACA. In the renewal of the custom, it was felt undesirable to attempt to hold an inspection at each laboratory each year. Rather, the task was divided among the laboratories and, at Ames, inspections were held in 1946 and in 1948. The occasion of the 1946 inspection was taken to hold a dedication ceremony for the 12-foot tunnel. The dedication address was delivered by Dr. William F. Durand.

During the early postwar period, NACA became increasingly conscious of its public image. It had more competition and was spending more money, and there was a greater public interest in how that money was being spent. Never before had NACA felt it necessary to employ a public relations agent; in fact, so circumspect was NACA management that the use of a public relations representative was looked on as being almost unethical. Nevertheless, pressure was brought to bear by John Victory and such a representative was appointed for Headquarters and for each of NACA's laboratories. At Ames the man selected for this position, in March 1949, was Don Wiley. NACA, still fearful of the term "public relations," conferred on Don and his colleagues the title of "Aeronautical Information Officer" with all the rights and privileges, few indeed, pertaining thereto.

It is perhaps to be expected that any history of a research laboratory will concern itself largely with the research operations of the establishment and thus will tend to neglect the vital supporting activities that make effective research possible. The heroes of such a history turn out to be research men; whereas all the other contributors, including some in the top echelons, appear to reside *in vacuo*. The present history-writing effort will not deviate greatly from the general rule. Nevertheless an attempt will be made, at various points within these pages, briefly to acknowledge the vitally important contributions to the operations of the Ames Aeronautical Laboratory that were made by the major supporting groups and their representatives.

Throughout the years of initiation, wartime strain, and postwar adjustment, no branch of the Ames organization had a more difficult role to play than did the Administrative Division. Heading this activity, as Administrative Management Officer, was Arthur B. Freeman. His assistant was Miss

Above: *First annual inspection, 1946.* Below: *William V. Shaw* (left) *and Arthur B. Freeman* (right).

Manie Poole. Art had been trained as an engineer; he and Manie were among the charter members of the Ames staff who had come out from Langley.

The task of setting up an Administrative support operation for the new Laboratory was difficult enough, but was even more difficult because De-

Lucille D. Baker.   *Alvin S. Hertzog.*   *Helen M. Davies.*

France had established very high performance standards for his staff and maintained a close scrutiny of every significant detail of the Laboratory's operation. Smitty had a temper, too, and his wrath would suddenly rise in a colorful display that everyone sought diligently, but not always successfully, to avoid. Probably no one at the Laboratory had his hair parted by Smitty's thunderbolts more frequently than Art Freeman, and in some cases Art was not to blame—it was just the devilish circumstances that continuously surrounded his job. Fortunately Smitty's ire would fade very quickly and it was then that he would exhibit one of his outstanding traits: fairness. Quick to pass judgment, he was equally quick to admit error. Nevertheless things were lively in Art Freeman's department and simple survival, which he somehow managed, was evidence of his tremendous success.

Art had a lot of good help, of course, and many of the members of his staff were oldtimers who had either come from Langley or who had been employed soon after the founding of the Laboratory. There were, for example, Bill Shaw, in charge of the Fiscal Branch, and Lucille Baker, the highly dependable head of the Administrative Services Branch which provided typing, filing, reproduction, communication, library, and many other services for the Laboratory. Then also there were John Van Etten, who served as Security Officer, and the team of Alvin Hertzog, Mark Greene, and Charlotte Holmes, who handled the highly specialized and extremely varied procurement needs of the Laboratory.

A very important element of Freeman's organization was the Personnel Branch. Originally headed by Walter Peterson, the Personnel Branch was taken over by Miss Helen Davies when Walter went to war. The selection of a woman for this difficult position may have been a wartime necessity but it turned out very well. By the time that Walter returned and decided to devote his energies to budget rather than to personnel problems, Helen had proven herself the logical person to continue as Chief of the Personnel Branch. She was ably assisted by Vincent Pettine and Lester Briggs. The mission of this triumvirate was of critical importance to the Laboratory and was rendered more difficult by the perennial shortage of qualified manpower and the painful restrictions imposed on the Laboratory's employment activities by congressional and Civil Service regulations.

3

Facilities

WIND TUNNELS AND OTHER CONSTRUCTION

1- by 3-Foot Tunnels.   The Ames 1- by 3-foot supersonic wind tunnels were completed and first operated in August 1945. The manufacturer of the jack-operated flexible throat, however, had trouble perfecting his product and it was another year and a half before the flexible throat was ready for use. In the meantime the tunnels were operated with fixed throats. In the case of the continuous-flow tunnel, one throat was designed for a Mach number of 1.5 and the other for a Mach number of 2.0.

Finally the flexible throats arrived and were installed. They worked very poorly. The motor-driven screw jacks were controlled by cams and microswitches. The control was not sufficiently precise and the curvature of the flexible plates had to be checked by hand. Since it sometimes took as much as 2 or 3 days to make a throat and speed change, such changes were avoided. By 1949, Ames engineers felt that they could not tolerate the nuisance much longer. They submitted a proposal to Headquarters for new nozzles (throats) for the 1- by 3-foot tunnels, which would be improved versions of the sliding-block nozzle earlier designed for the 6-by-6. Included in this proposal was a plan to increase the operating pressure of the 1-by-3 No. 1 and thus also its Reynolds number range. The proposal was not approved, however, and before it was resubmitted, the plan to use sliding-block nozzles in the 1- by 3-foot tunnels had been abandoned.

12-Foot Tunnel.   Robert Crane had been put in charge of the 12-foot tunnel and George Edwards was his assistant. The tunnel made its first run on July 5, 1946, and the next 9 months or so were spent in calibration and shakedown tests. These tests confirmed the low turbulence level of the tunnel. The first test of a research nature, of a low-aspect-ratio triangular wing, was run on May 6, 1947. Research work continued until January 1949 when four blades of the fan were found to be cracked; all blades had then to be replaced. This emergency operation delayed research for more than 6 months.

135

1- by 3-foot blowdown tunnel with variable-geometry-throat mechanism.

Robert Crane.

In a tunnel pressurized to 6 atmospheres, the cracking of fan blades is a serious matter. In this case its discovery before blade failure was only a matter of luck. Ames engineers were aware that blades of essentially the same design had been used in the new Caltech Cooperative Wind Tunnel. The blades in both cases were different from those used in ordinary tunnels as they had to be of variable pitch to accommodate wide variations in wind-tunnel pressure. When a serious blade failure occurred in the Co-op Tunnel, Bob Crane immediately inspected those in the 12-foot fan and it was only then that the cracks in the four blades were discovered. Thus Ames profited by Caltech's misfortune. The blades were redesigned and no more trouble occurred. What would have happened if one of the 12-foot blades had let loose is not known for sure; but, in anticipation of such a contingency, the tunnel wall in the plane of the fan had been heavily reinforced.

Low-Density and Heat-Transfer Tunnels. Two new men appearing on the scene at Ames at this time were Jackson Stalder and Glen Goodwin. They were working under Alun Jones in the Flight Engineering Section. Being original thinkers as well as hardheaded engineers, they wanted to do something different but were not quite sure what. They became intrigued with the problems of the high-speed, high-altitude missiles then being discussed by the aeronautical avant-garde and more specifically with the notion of putting wings on the V–2 missile—a notion that Eugen Sänger, a German scientist, had mentioned. Of interest to Jack and Glen were the aerodynamic forces to which such a missile would be subjected while flying at very high altitudes—way out where the air molecules are so far apart that they act as individuals rather than as members of a close-packed team. "Why are you interested in aerodynamics where there's no air?" Jack was frequently asked. His reply often seemed a little vague but his interest in the subject persisted.

Jack and Glen, supported by Morris Rubesin, a new arrival, got permission to build a small, inexpensive "low-density" tunnel. The tunnel, which had a test section of approximately 2 by 2 inches, was of a nonreturn type through which air was induced to flow by means of an evacuated tank at the exit. Very low pressures were achieved in the tank, and thus in the test section, by a combination of mechanical and oil-diffusion pumps. The tunnel was located under the return passage of the big 40-by-80 where it could draw power for its pumps from the 40-by-80 power supply. As the tunnel approached completion in 1948, it was learned that a similar tunnel was being built at the University of California under the direction of Dr. Sam Schaaf.

Glen Goodwin and Morrie Rubesin had become interested in the heating that occurred in the boundary layers of high-speed aircraft and they sought and secured permission to build a small "heat-transfer" wind tunnel. This tunnel, which was designed largely by Thor Tendeland, was of a closed-circuit, continuous-flow type having a fixed 6- by 6-inch supersonic throat designed for Mach 2.4. It also, for power-supply reasons, was placed under the 40-by-80. The low-density tunnel began operation in 1948, and the heat-transfer tunnel a little later. They were combined in a low-density heat-transfer (LD–HT) section under Jack Stalder who reported to Harry Goett, Chief of the Full Scale and Flight Research Division.

Hypersonic Facilities. In addition to the LD and HT tunnels, two other advanced facilities were proposed in 1946. One was a 10- by 14-inch hypersonic (Mach 6 or 7) tunnel proposed by Al Eggers, and the other was a supersonic free flight (SSFF) tunnel conceived and proposed by Harvey Allen. Funds for each of these facilities, in amounts of about $125,000, were

Glen Goodwin (left), *Morris Rubesin* (above right), *and Jackson Stalder* (below right).

Original low-density tunnel.

authorized by Congress in July 1947. The low cost of each facility was made possible by a plan to use the compressors of the 12-foot tunnel as a source of power.

Justification for the new facilities was based on the need for investigating the aerodynamic characteristics of long-range ballistic missiles, such as the German A–9, which would fly at Mach numbers of 7 or more. Reportedly, certain people in NACA Headquarters, principally Dr. Hunsaker, did not see the need for hypersonic tunnels at that time, but these opposing forces yielded to persuasion and the low cost of the proposed facilities made the persuasion easier.

10- by 14-Inch Tunnel. For convenience in the use of the 12-foot compressor system, it was planned to house the 10- by 14-inch tunnel in a new structure attached to the 12-foot auxiliaries building. The compressors which pressurized the 12-foot tunnel to 6 atmospheres were large enough to operate a tunnel of about 1-square-foot test section at a Mach number of 3.0; and thus, since mass flow decreases with increasing supersonic Mach number, they should theoretically be able to supply more than enough air to operate the tunnel at a Mach number of 6 or 7. The problem was not so

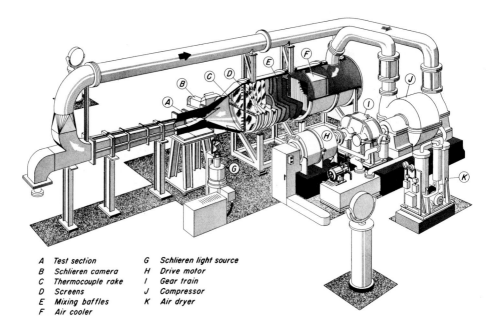

A	Test section	G	Schlieren light source
B	Schlieren camera	H	Drive motor
C	Thermocouple rake	I	Gear train
D	Screens	J	Compressor
E	Mixing baffles	K	Air dryer
F	Air cooler		

6- by 6-inch heat-transfer tunnel.

much with the volume of air available as with the maximum pressure—6 atmospheres. A peculiar characteristic of a supersonic tunnel is that it requires a much higher pressure for starting than for continuous operation. The 6 atmospheres of pressure available from the 12-foot compressor could easily start a Mach 3 tunnel, but starting a Mach 6 tunnel would take 30 atmospheres—a pressure ratio of 30 to 1. If, however, the nozzle were designed with variable geometry, the tunnel could be started at Mach 3 and then quickly increased in speed to Mach 5 or 6. The 12-foot-tunnel air supply could then be utilized with maximum effectiveness. But variable-geometry throat systems were known to be very complicated and expensive and their construction seemed scarcely consistent with the limited funds available for tunnel construction. Al Eggers, however, exercised his ingenuity and came up with the design of a special double-hinged type of double-throated nozzle that was relatively inexpensive and would provide the desired operating characteristics. The system required the use of suction at the nozzle exit to increase the operating pressure ratio and the use of a second throat with boundary-layer removal to increase the efficiency with which the air could be decelerated after passing through the test section.

After the system details for the 10- by 14-inch tunnel had been worked out through model tests, there remained one troublesome problem: air condensation. As air accelerates in the test section of a wind tunnel, not only

140

does its pressure fall but so does its temperature. In tunnels that reach high subsonic or supersonic speeds, the cooling which occurs in the throat causes any moisture in the air to condense as fog. This problem is regularly solved by drying the air before use. But as the speed of a wind tunnel increases to high supersonic levels, the temperature in the test section falls so low that the air itself begins to condense, or liquefy. This situation completely upsets the energy balance in the air, distorts the flow pattern, and limits the speed of a wind tunnel to about Mach 5. In the design of the 10- by 14-inch tunnel, the air-liquefaction problem was thoroughly investigated in a model tunnel. The best solution, it was found, was to heat the air as it entered the tunnel. About 350° F of heating was required to permit tunnel operation at a Mach number of 6.0. This heating, it was determined, could best be achieved in the 10- by 14-inch tunnel by means of a 300-kilowatt electrical heater.

The 10- by 14-inch tunnel was still under construction at the end of 1949; but its operating group, headed by Alfred Eggers, was scheduled to become a Section in Allen's High Speed Research Division.

Supersonic Free-Flight Tunnel. It was pretty clear that wind tunnels had serious limitations for simulating conditions of high-speed missile flight. The heating required to prevent air liquefaction at Mach numbers over 7 or 8 was difficult to achieve and the resulting high inlet temperature would certainly be a troublesome factor in the operation of a wind tunnel. An-

Schematic drawing of 10- by 14-inch hypersonic tunnel.

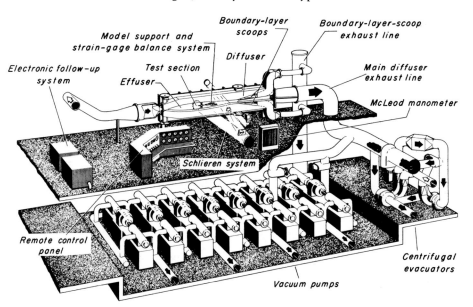

10- by 14-inch tunnel nozzle.

other problem was that the Reynolds number of a tunnel such as the 10-by-14 had the unfortunate characteristic of decreasing with speed. Such considerations led Harvey Allen to believe that some new kind of facility was required to simulate conditions of extremely high-speed flight. The feasibility of attempting such simulations in steady-state, continuously operating wind tunnels was becoming increasingly doubtful. The temperatures, pressures, velocities, costs, and everything else were just too high. It now appeared desirable to build facilities in which the extreme conditions of flight would be simulated only fleetingly. The test measurements would be vastly more difficult to make and the data output of the facility would be very low, but these disadvantages might be tolerable if test speeds could be substantially increased.

Allen was aware of the ballistics range used by armament manufacturers. Presumably one could shoot a model instead of a bullet down the range, assuming that the model could be made strong enough to stand the very high accelerations involved. The fastest guns had muzzle velocities of only 4000 feet per second, but by redesign they might reach speeds of 6000 or 8000 feet per second. Such redesign might also be able to provide a more uniform, sustained impulse that would reduce structural loads on the model. These ideas involved nothing particularly new, but Harvey figured that the scheme might be carried a few steps farther. Inasmuch as the speed of sound is lower at low temperatures, it appeared that the Mach number of a test could be increased 15 percent if the model were fired into an air chamber refrigerated to about $-70°$ F, corresponding to air temperatures a missile might ordinarily encounter in flight. A still better method would be to shoot the model upstream in a supersonic wind tunnel of moderate Mach number. In such a wind tunnel, the air temperature would be just about right and the air velocity would add to the relative Mach number of the model. A Mach number of perhaps 10 or 12 could thus be achieved and the Reynolds number would increase with speed as it does in flight rather than

142

decrease with speed as it usually does in a hypersonic wind tunnel. There would also be no model-support interference to worry about.

These, then, were the principles upon which the design of the supersonic free-flight wind tunnel (SSFF) was based. The idea was a Harvey Allen original; however, the implementation of the idea may have required more genius than the conception. The perfection and full exploitation of the SSFF tunnel test technique was a process that continued for years and required the ingenuity of many people in the High Speed Research and the Research Instrument Divisions.

The new tunnel was located in an addition to the 1- by 3-foot tunnel building immediately adjacent to the blowdown tunnel. Indeed, the supersonic nozzles used were the fixed nozzles of the blowdown 1-by-3 which by now had been replaced with flexible nozzles. One of these nozzles was redesigned for Mach 2.0 and the other for Mach 3.0. A program of gun development also got under way. The guns, procured from the military, ranged in caliber from 0.22 inch to 3 inches. The thrust of the guns was often transmitted to the models through sabots which peeled off cleanly as the model left the gun. A special catcher was installed in the tunnel to recover the model after it had passed through the test section.

The test section of the SSFF tunnel was elongated and in it a series of windows was installed through which shadowgraph pictures were taken. The timing mechanism and other measuring equipment were of unique design and of remarkable precision. The instrumentation not only provided shadowgraph pictures of the flow pattern around the test model as it flew past the windows but also allowed a quantitative determination of the lift, drag, and center of pressure of the air forces to which the model was being subjected.

The supersonic free-flight tunnel was completed late in 1949 but did not become productive until later. Its operating group, first headed by Victor Stevens, became a Section of the High Speed Research Division.

Helium Tunnel. In the development of facilities for investigating the hypersonic aerodynamics of missiles, the 10-by-14 and the SSFF did not exhaust the ideas of Ames engineers. They proposed in 1948 the construction of a 1- by 1-foot blowdown tunnel that would operate with compressed helium gas. Gases other than air, specifically Freon, had been used earlier in a wind tunnel at Langley; the peculiar advantage of helium was that its liquefaction temperature was so low that it could operate in a wind tunnel, without liquefying, at Mach numbers up to 25. Another factor favoring the use of helium at Ames was that storage and transfer facilities for the gas existed at Moffett Field, left over from the days when blimps were operated from the base.

Countering the advantages just noted was the question of whether flight conditions in air could properly be simulated in a wind tunnel using

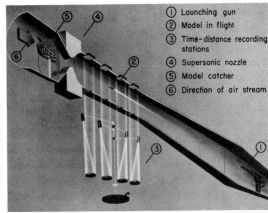
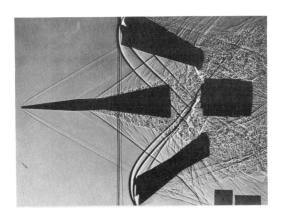
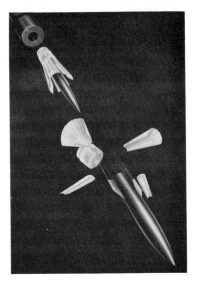

Loading of gun of supersonic free-flight tunnel (top left), *schematic drawing of SSFF tunnel* (top right), *shadowgraph of sabot separation* (bottom left), *and diagram of sabot separation in the SSFF tunnel* (bottom right).

helium. Helium is a monatomic gas and the ratio of its specific heats, γ, is quite different from that of air. These characteristics might affect simulations at high speeds where the thermodynamic properties of the gas are especially important. On the other hand, it might be possible to make an allowance for the thermodynamic differences between helium and air. Besides, how else was one to obtain data, good or bad, at a Mach number of 20? The 10-by-14 apparently was operable only up to Mach 6 or so, and the limits of the SSFF appeared to be about 12. Therefore was not the 1- by 1-foot helium tunnel worth the gamble of an estimated $330,000? Ames engineers thought so. NACA management thought not. The proposal, made in fiscal year 1949, was turned down.

6- by 6-Foot Supersonic Tunnel. The 6- by 6-foot supersonic tunnel was first operated on June 16, 1948. Charles Frick was in charge. In one of the early runs the motor that drove the huge sliding block in the throat suddenly stalled with an awful groan. The block would not move. The side plates were removed from the throat to see what was wrong. The wind-tunnel gang and Carl Bioletti, who had designed that portion of the tunnel structure, stood waiting expectantly. When the walls had been removed, the sides of Harvey's beautifully polished and expensive sliding block, as well as the walls themselves, were found to have been badly scored. Someone had goofed. The sidewalls had not been sufficiently stiff, had deflected inward under internal suction loads, and had seized the block. Was the block ruined? It looked pretty bad. Red Betts, the fixer, was called in. His expression as he viewed the mutilated surfaces was somber indeed. "What do you think, Red?" asked Bioletti. After due consideration, Red shook his head and replied, "Better get a rope." "What can we do with a rope?" Carl queried. "Hang yourself before the boss finds out," said Red, still unsmiling. As it turned out, Carl didn't take Red's advice; and Red, demonstrating once again his mechanical genius, quickly had the gouges filled up with a metal filler of some kind and the block and wall surfaces again as smooth as glass. The sidewalls were stiffened with tremendous I-beams and gave no further trouble. The design fault was an oversight for which Carl took the blame, although he had gone to the trouble of having his design checked by other people, none of whom had observed the weakness.

As had been expected, the fabrication of the 50-inch-diameter schlieren windows for the 6- by 6-foot tunnel turned out to be a difficult task. Corning was the only glass company that would attempt to produce the required flaw-free window blanks. The contract called for Corning to produce four blanks which then would be ground and polished by the Tinsley Laboratories of Berkeley, California. The technique was to pour the blanks and let them cool (anneal) at a precisely controlled rate for 9 months. The first two blanks produced in this manner were at least sound, but the next two, after the annealing period, were found to be cracked. So also, on another try, were the following two blanks. Corning engineers were discouraged but were induced to try two more blanks with the mold temperature a little higher—equal in fact to the temperature of the glass as poured. Happily this attempt was successful. The blanks came out uncracked. Corning was reported to have considered the pouring of the 6- by 6-foot-tunnel window blanks the most difficult task it had undertaken—even more difficult than the pouring of the 200-inch Pyrex blanks for the mirror of the Mount Palomar telescope.[1] But although the window blanks were structurally sound,

---

[1] See David O. Woodbury, *The Glass Giant of Palomar.* New York: Dodd, Mead & Co., 1941.

Throat of 6 × 6-foot supersonic tunnel showing schlieren windows.

they were found, on polishing, to be not completely free of striae and other internal imperfections. The second pair was better than the first in this regard and, in any case, Harvey Allen was able to find a way to minimize the effects of the imperfections on schlieren pictures.

Other Construction. The new hangar was completed in 1946, and early in 1949 construction got under way on a new instrument research building. Also undertaken, late in 1949, was the construction of an administrative building annex intended to augment the capacity of the main administration building which, almost from the first, had proven to be too small.

TRANSONIC TECHNIQUES

The general feeling seemed to be that, once an airplane was well into the supersonic range of flight, the conditions it would encounter should be fairly stable. This belief seemed to be confirmed by the first supersonic flights of the XS–1. There was much concern, however, over the wildly disturbed mixed-flow conditions that prevailed in the transonic range, and this range had to be traversed twice in every supersonic flight. The transonic zone was obviously a regime of flight that required a great deal of study and, if supersonic flight of operational airplanes was to be achieved in the near future, the study was of a most urgent character. Unfortunately, through an ironic twist of nature, the transonic range was one in which wind tunnels would not work properly. According to Dr. Dryden, it was a "blind spot" in the spectrum of tunnel operation. Subsonic tunnels choked by the time they reached Mach 0.8 or 0.9, and supersonic tunnels did not function properly at Mach numbers much below 1.2. In between there was choking and a mishmash of shock waves reflected between model and tunnel walls that precluded any true simulation of actual flight conditions.

Faced with the situation just mentioned, ingenious engineers went to

146

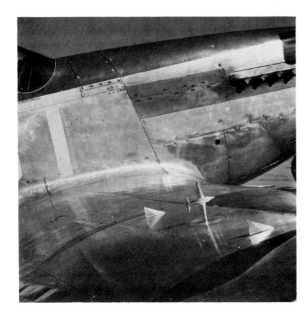

Wing-flow technique of transonic testing. Models mounted on the wing of a North American P–51.

work to devise alternative methods for acquiring design data in the transonic range. At Langley, Bob Gilruth, in 1944, found that transonic data could be obtained by mounting a small test airfoil in the accelerated-flow region over the wing of a high-speed airplane such as the P–51. This technique, called the "wing-flow method," produced some useful data but at very small scale. Langley also, in 1945, established a pilotless-aircraft research station at Wallops Island, Virginia. Here transonic and supersonic data were returned by telemeter from rocket-launched models that later fell into the sea. This technique was made possible by the multichannel telemeter which, incidentally, had been developed in 1941–1942 for aircraft flight testing by Harvey Giffen of Vultee Aircraft, Inc.[2] On the whole, the methods used at Wallops, though effective, were expensive and technically difficult.

The next step in developing transonic test methods came in 1946, when Lockheed and NACA engineers simultaneously observed that the wing-flow-method could be applied to wind-tunnel testing by installing a bump, simulating the wing, on the floor of a high-subsonic-speed wind tunnel. At times the bump technique was applied in the 16-foot tunnel while the wing-flow method was used in flight.

In 1946 the Flight Engineering Section at Ames foresaw the end of the

[2] Telemeter (Radio Data Recorder) described in Memorandum (dated Jan. 24, 1942) from Edwin P. Hartman to NACA Coordinator of Research, covering a visit to Vultee Aircraft, Inc., on Jan. 8, 1942.

deicing work and proposed a continuing program of research in the general field of aircraft operating problems. This proposal was turned down by NACA management. Then along in 1947 Harry Goett, who was in general command of the flight engineering activity, suggested to NACA Headquarters that Ames set up a pilotless-aircraft test operation similar to the one being established by Langley at Wallops. Dr. Dryden was opposed to having Ames duplicate Langley's efforts in developing rocket-launching and telemetry techniques, but he did not object when Harry proposed the dropping of recoverable models from a high-flying airplane. Thus as the icing work began to phase out in 1947, Ames developed the technique for recovering intact, by means of air brake and parachute, instrumented test models dropped at high altitudes from an airplane. In this way aerodynamically clean models, if dropped from a sufficiently high altitude, would traverse the transonic range and, indeed, reach low supersonic speeds before they had to be braked for a landing.

The airplanes chosen by Ames engineers for the drop operation were a group of three Northrop P–61 "Black Widow" night fighters of which one, intended for photoreconnaissance uses, had been equipped with a turbosupercharger. Another one, owing to the relative scarcity of P–61 airplanes, had been borrowed, for cannibalization purposes, from the museum of the Smithsonian Institution. In the drop operation, the supercharged P–61 was flown to altitudes up to 42,000 feet. As it did not have a pressure cabin, the physical stamina of the pilots was sorely taxed. But useful data were obtained and the development of the recovery technique, a notable accomplishment in itself, was helpful to other agencies later in attempts to recover expended missiles. The greatest contributors to the development and use of the drop technique at Ames were Alun Jones, James Selna, Bonne Look,

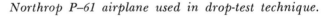

Northrop P–61 airplane used in drop-test technique.

Loren G. Bright.

and Loren Bright. Among the pilots who flew the P–61 for the drop tests were George Cooper, Rudolph Van Dyke, and Robert Whempner of Ames and Joseph Walker of the NACA High Speed Flight Station at Edwards, California.

The methods so far advanced for obtaining transonic data were slow, complex, costly, or otherwise not wholly satisfactory. NACA had no intention of giving up its efforts to make wind tunnels operate in the transonic range, and the matter was being actively pursued by John Stack and his staff at Langley. These efforts bore fruit in January 1947 when Ray Wright and Vernon Ward, who worked under Stack, tested a model of a "slotted-throat" tunnel. By means of this test, and much additional work, Langley found that the installation of a number of suitably shaped slots in the walls of the test section of a wind tunnel would eliminate the choking phenomenon and suppress the shock-wave reflection. With this modification, a wind tunnel could provide a reasonably true simulation of transonic flight conditions. Tunnels capable of transonic operation were nevertheless of a rather special design, and it was not until December 1949 that Langley completed its first transonic wind tunnel. Following Langley's example there was a great rush all over the country to build transonic tunnels, and the wing-flow and bump methods of transonic testing quickly disappeared. The Ames Laboratory converted the 1- by 3½-foot tunnel for transonic operation by drilling holes in the top and bottom walls. Sliding plates were used to open or close the holes to the degree desired. A simple flexible throat was also added. Additionally, Ames proposed that the 16-foot be converted into a transonic tunnel.

Wonderful Unitary Plan

Perhaps nothing more clearly revealed the revolution in aeronautical thinking in the early postwar period than a program of facility planning, then under way, that was known as the "Unitary Plan." Never before had so grandiose a wind-tunnel building program been seriously proposed by responsible people, and never before had the desires of interested groups been so thoroughly canvassed in establishing a facilities program. The tremendous scope of this program, which was at first expected to cost over a billion dollars, gave evidence of the importance which knowledgeable people now attached to aeronautical development. At the doorstep of realization was a vast and wonderful array of transonic and supersonic airplanes, guided missiles, and the portentous hypersonic intercontinental ballistic missile. Such developments would require many facilities so extensive and costly that they must be planned on a national scale.

NACA, of course, would need new facilities for research. The military would need new facilities for test and evaluation. The Air Force, indeed, was firmly resolved to establish itself in the field of aeronautical research and development and had set its sights on a new air engineering development center. It was also considered desirable to provide universities with high-speed wind tunnels to acquaint them better with, and improve their ability to teach, the new disciplines of aeronautical science. Many aircraft companies had by now acquired their own subsonic wind tunnels but would have to rely on the Government to make available the costly transonic, supersonic, and hypersonic wind tunnels required for future aircraft development. Finally, the planners recognized that a number of the facilities proposed would require vast amounts of power for their operation. These, it was felt, could best be accommodated in a new supersonic research center, operated by NACA, and located near the Grand Coulee or the Hoover Dam.

Since the program was of national scope and covered the needs of everyone, it was called the "Unitary Plan"—a name proposed by Dr. Vannevar Bush. The planning began with the Air Force late in 1945, was picked up by NACA in 1946, and was carried on by a galaxy of organizations and people in 1947, 1948, and 1949. Special panels to deal with the problem were formed in NACA and some of NACA's regular technical committees became deeply involved. Various military groups were active in the planning, as were the Joint Research and Development Board, the President's Air Policy Board, and the Congressional Aviation Policy Board. Industry was thoroughly integrated into the planning councils through membership on NACA and military committees and panels. The universities also entered the planning through membership on NACA committees. Finally, and perhaps fortunately, there were the Appropriation Committees of Congress which remained singularly calm about the whole matter.

FACILITIES

The contributors to the Unitary Plan, most of whom were normally sane and sound individuals, fed upon each other's enthusiasm with the result that a truly remarkable state of euphoria developed. The atmosphere of the planning councils was notably inflationary. The plans rapidly mushroomed, the proposed facilities became more numerous, more pretentious and costly, and many were quite beyond the state of design knowledge. Of course the Unitary Plan was intended to be a 10-year program, but it took a brave man in the field of aeronautics to look ahead 10 years.

In any case, everyone's wants were collected into a huge pile which was then consigned, for organizing into a sensible program, to a Special Committee on Supersonic Facilities headed by Dr. Jerome C. Hunsaker, the staid and notably conservative Chairman of NACA. After due consideration, the Hunsaker committee came out with recommendations for a 10-year Unitary Plan Program of facility construction. The Plan was approved by NACA in January 1947.

The building program that had been organized by the Hunsaker committee and approved by NACA involved two new research and development centers—one for NACA and one for the Air Force—and 33 new wind-tunnel facilities, of which 14, costing $5 million, were to go to universities. The total cost was over $1 billion. The plan contemplated, among other things, a 40-foot transonic propulsion tunnel requiring 530,000 horsepower and costing over $171 million; a 15- by 15-foot supersonic propulsion tunnel requiring 657,000 horsepower and costing over $50 million; a 6- by 6-foot or an 8- by 8-foot hypersonic (M up to 10.0) tunnel pressurized to as much as 100 atmospheres, requiring 410,000 horsepower and costing at least $110 million. One of the intended tunnels would cost half again as much as the value of all of the research facilities at all three of the existing NACA laboratories!

The proposed Unitary Plan was now turned over to the Joint Research and Development Board, who reduced it to a 5-year plan costing "only" $600 million. In the course of the next year, it was reviewed by a number of groups and in 1949, in much curtailed form, appeared in an authorization bill jointly submitted by NACA and the military. This bill, which was passed on October 27, 1949, was divided into two parts, Title I and Title II. Title I authorized expenditures of up to $10 million for university facilities and $136 million for new NACA wind tunnels. Title II authorized the construction of a new air engineering development center for the Air Force which was to include among its facilities two Unitary Plan tunnels.

When the authorization bill had gone through, more specific planning got under way. Many meetings of NACA special panels and committees were held to determine characteristics and priorities of facilities that would be built for NACA and the universities. A prototype university facility was actually built at Langley. The money allocated to NACA, it was felt, would be sufficient to build one major wind tunnel at each of the Committee's three laboratories. To deal further with design matters, Dr. Dryden on December 19, 1949, established an NACA Project Office for the Unitary Wind Tunnel Programs and appointed John F. Parsons as chief. In his new capacity, Parsons was to report directly to Dryden.

It was not until spring of the following year that the Unitary Plan legislation came up for consideration before the congressional appropriations committees. It had been expected that Unitary Plan appropriations might be spread over 2 or 3 years; but Albert Thomas, chairman of the House subcommittee, told NACA in effect, "We'll give you $75 million now and don't come back for any more." And this was the way that, on June 29, 1950, the bill became law. NACA got $75 million for Unitary Plan facilities and the universities got nothing. NACA people were a bit let down. After soaring to rare empyrean heights, they were now back at sea level. But $75 million was not to be sneezed at. It was not much less than the combined value of existing research facilities in all three NACA Laboratories. The Air Force had done considerably better than NACA in Unitary Plan acquisitions. The Air Force had obtained a new research center (AEDC) which it shortly was to name for General Hap Arnold, who deserved the honor for he had really started the whole thing

4

Research

Its Nature

IN deciding who should do what in aeronautical research and development after World War II, there was a great deal of interest in the definitions of research. It was commonly and loosely referred to as pure, applied, basic, scientific, fundamental, or something else, but the meanings of these terms remained obscure. Where in the broad spectrum of activity called research did the work of NACA, and Ames, really lie?

Since the object of "pure" research might reasonably be solely the satisfaction of human curiosity, the definition "pure" could not be applied to the activities of NACA. The work of the NACA laboratories would have to be regarded as "applied" research; that is the only kind of research a practical-minded Congress would have funded. It was research applied directly to solving the practical and pressing problems of military and civil aviation. It was also basic and scientific, but only to the extent that it dealt with matters of fundamental significance.

How fundamental was NACA research? If the characteristic being studied applied only to a single specimen, animate or inanimate object, its study would certainly be the least significant activity that could be called research—and even so might better be called "development" or "evaluation." But if the characteristic being studied were the charge on the electron, applying to all the electrons in the universe, or the makeup of the DNA molecule, found in the cells of every animal from cockroaches to humans, then we could truly say that such research had the highest degree of fundamentality. Between these limits lies the vast bulk of research, distributed according to the breadth of application of its results but with no sharply defined divisions. On this scale, most of NACA's work lay well below the midpoint and during the war some of it lay close to the bottom. In general the results of NACA's work applied to a single, narrow class of objects called airplanes; during the war, it sometimes applied to only one or two specific specimens of this class. Fortunately, fundamentality is not necessarily a measure of practical value.

NACA's work generally was an effective mixture of theory and experiment. Theory contributed much to the fundamentality of any research effort. It also was used to limit the extent and establish the direction of required experiment and, metaphorically speaking, to define the major limb structure of the tree of research. In general, fundamental research was a movement downward toward the root source, while applied research was a movement upward and outward toward the leaves. Often the two were profitably combined. The leaf pattern of the tree of research was filled out by experimentation, and sometimes the leaf pattern was used to deduce the position and form of a hidden limb. The limbs were of the utmost importance, of course, but it was among the leaves that the fruits usually lay.

Experimentation might be thought of as a form of observational research such as used in astronomy; but, instead of waiting for Nature to speak in her own good time and place, we ask her questions and deliberately force her to speak at a time and place of our choosing. She withholds nothing from those clever enough to ask the right questions. Our questions are asked by confronting her with a cunningly devised situation or mechanism to which she must react. Devices by means of which such confrontations are achieved are often in the nature of simulators. Members of an important class of simulators used by NACA were called wind tunnels.

In devising simulators for research, the research engineer has no equal, and the NACA laboratories, at least until this time, were laboratories of research engineers, not scientists. They were also laboratories of ingeniously designed simulators the development of which, in some cases, represented true adventures in research.

Basic Configurations and Airflows

Wings. By original work in TR 863 on sweep and in TR 835 on pointed low-aspect-ratio wings, R. T. Jones had provided intriguing evidence of things to come in aircraft configurations. No longer could wings be regarded merely as assemblages of largely independent airfoil sections whose action might be represented in theory by a lifting line. In the past the most significant feature of a wing was the airfoil section and perhaps no other single item had received so much attention in aeronautical research. In the new breed of aircraft, the airfoil sections tended to lose their identity and become aerodynamically and physically blended into a whole lifting surface. Now it was the wing planform, the shape of the wing as viewed from above, that was of greatest importance.

Although less important than in the past, airfoil sections were still regarded at Ames as worthy of some research attention. Before going off for a doctorate at Caltech, Milton Van Dyke, in TN 2670, summarized the work he had earlier done in the 1- by 3½-foot tunnel on NACA 6-series high-speed sections; and during the early postwar period George McCullough and Donald Gault were investigating, in the 7-by-10, a new type of stall that had been revealed by the thin airfoil sections required for high-speed flight. The wings of airplanes had to be thin if shock-wave formation and its bad effects were to be avoided at high subsonic speeds. But wings with thin leading edges performed very poorly in generating the lift required for landing. Even at moderate angles of attack, the air tended to separate from the forward upper surface, the separation appearing first as a bubble and then spreading over the whole surface as a violent stall. McCullough and Gault studied this phenomenon and attempted to cure it by removing air through a suction slot at the point of separation.

Airfoil research was rather old hat, but what was really fun during this period was the investigation of novel wing planforms. In the early part of the period there was little theory and scant knowledge about how to design wings for transonic and supersonic airplanes; thus research people cast inhibitions aside and investigated many different wing shapes, utilizing all available facilities. Ames was in a fortunate position for such studies. It had the 12-foot, the 16-foot, and the 40- by 80-foot tunnels for large-scale subsonic tests, and the 1- by 3-foot and the 6- by 6-foot tunnels for supersonic tests. Moreover, it was prepared to use the bump and wingflow techniques for transonic studies. These facilities would allow testing through wide ranges of size, speed, and Reynolds number and would enable the Ames staff to conduct coordinated test programs in several different tunnels on promising wing configurations.

Wing Theory. In the most favored research technique, theory precedes and guides experiment, but in early 1946 supersonic and transonic wing theory had not advanced very far. Thus initial experiments at Ames were undertaken largely without benefit of theory. Nevertheless, the development of theory proceeded rapidly and there were soon notable contributions from NACA and other sources. At Ames, linearized, lifting-surface, supersonic wing theory was advanced by Max Heaslet, Harvard Lomax, and Arthur Jones, who turned out a number of papers of which TR 889 (ref. B–1) is perhaps representative. The development of transonic theory was shortly initiated by John Spreiter, who had just returned to Ames after completing work for his master's degree at Stanford. Spreiter, extending theories originally developed by Max Munk and Robert Jones, devised methods for predicting the characteristics of slender wing-body combinations at subsonic, transonic, and supersonic speeds. Later, in TR 962 (ref. B–2), he extended this work to include cruciform wing configurations such as might be used in missiles. Max Heaslet, Harvard Lomax, and John Spreiter also collaborated to produce TR 956 (ref. B–3), which was a substantial contribution to linear transonic wing theory. These efforts, though worthwhile, clearly represented only a small part of the work that needed to be done on wing theory, particularly transonic wing theory.

155

Harvard Lomax.   *Dr. John R. Spreiter.*

Wing Experiments.   In wing-study programs, the experimentalists had a rich field to exploit. Of wing variables, they could play with sweep (both forward and backward), aspect ratio, taper ratio, camber, twist, and even airfoil section. Some of the sections investigated were sharp edged, flat sided, and in the form of a very elongated diamond or double wedge. A major objective of such studies was to delay as long as possible the drag rise and other adverse effects arising from the formation of shock waves and then to minimize the severity of these effects where, at the higher speeds, they could not be completely avoided. It appeared that a swept wing of otherwise conventional configuration might serve in the high subsonic and low supersonic speed ranges but for higher supersonic speeds a thin low-aspect-ratio wing would be desirable. Sweep tended to limit aspect ratio and, when it became extreme, there were structural and other practical reasons for filling in the space between the wing and the fuselage. In this way the triangular wing shaped like the Greek letter delta was developed. The delta wing provided sweep, low aspect ratio, structural stiffness, and internal space for carrying fuel. One of its early applications was in the Consolidated XF92A, which incorporated a triangular wing and triangular vertical tail.

At Mach numbers of 1.5 and higher, a simple, thin, low-aspect-ratio straight wing seemed to give good results, and such a wing was incorporated in the Douglas X-3, the design of which was commenced in 1946 or 1947. The X-3, conceived by Francis Clauser, Bailey Oswald, Schuyler Kleinhans,

156

Wing planforms.

Drag of low-aspect-ratio wings.

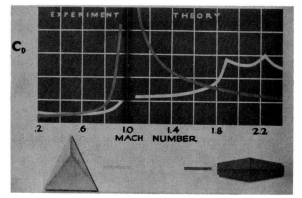

and others at Douglas Santa Monica, represented perhaps the first attempt made in this country to design and build a truly supersonic airplane capable of sustained flight and unassisted takeoffs. Only later, after the development of the airplane had been long delayed by lack of funding, did it become one of the research airplane series. Its daring conception was a landmark in aviation although not adequately recognized as such.

While investigating many wing configurations, Ames devoted more of its attention to triangular wings than to wings of any other planform. Triangular wings incorporating a wide variety of aspect ratios, thicknesses, airfoil sections, and shapes were tested in the Ames facilities. The shapes varied from the delta configuration with tips aft, to the reversed delta with tips forward, and to other configurations having tips at intermediate locations.

Another fairly extensive program of tests was run on a rather special configuration incorporating long tapered wings swept backward 63°. The great interest shown in this particular design stemmed from Bob Jones' report, TN 1350 (ref. B–4), which indicated the possibility of designing an airplane that, at moderately supersonic speeds, would fly with almost subsonic efficiency. This concept was rather intriguing, as supersonic flight had been thought of more in terms of brute force than of efficiency. The achievement of high efficiency (measured in terms of L/D or lift-drag ratio) would, according to Jones, require long, slender, uniformly loaded wings swept sufficiently to fall within the conical shock pattern (Mach cone). Thus the leading edges of the wings would lie in a region of subsonic flow and perhaps could be expected to develop the same leading-edge suction that increased the lifting efficiency of subsonic wings. Accordingly, test models were built of a wing-body combination designed to operate at a Mach number of 1.53 and at L/D, it was hoped, of 10 or more. The wings had an aspect ratio of 3.5, a taper ratio of 0.25, were swept back 63°, and were twisted and cambered to give a uniform loading along the span. These models, and models with slight variations, were tested in several wind tunnels at Ames; but the elusive leading-edge suction upon which high efficiency was dependent was never fully realized. A representative report covering work performed in this program is RM AJ324 by Charles Hall and John Heitmeyer.

As earlier mentioned, most of the Ames wind-tunnel groups contributed to the general study of wing planforms. The 12-foot tunnel was able to test good-sized models at either high subsonic speed or high Reynolds number. George Edwards, Jack Stephenson, and Bruce Tinling investigated and

Twisted and cambered 63° swept wing.

reported on triangular wings. Ben Johnson concerned himself with straight low-aspect-ratio wing, while Bruce Tinling, Robert Reynolds, Donald Smith, Lloyd Jones, and Fred Demele investigated swept wings, including R. T. Jones' 63° wing. In the course of large-scale tests conducted in the 40-by-80, Gerald McCormack, Victor Stevens, and Woodrow Cook investigated wings swept forward and backward, while Lynn Hunton and Joseph Dew studied the effect of camber and twist on the loading and stalling characteristics of a 45° swept wing.

The Flight Research Section at Ames also contributed to the Laboratory's wing-research program. Its contribution was made through the use of a P–51 airplane in an application of the wing-flow technique. This effort, carried out by George Rathert and Carl Hanson, included tests of a straight, low-aspect-ratio wing of the same configuration as a larger model tested in the 12-foot tunnel. It also included tests of a delta-wing model.

When the 1-by-3 got under way late in 1945, there was a feeling, according to Dean Chapman, that operational supersonic aircraft were still a long way off. The transonic range, with its unpleasant compressibility effects, then appeared to be a rather formidable barrier to supersonic speeds. Nevertheless, immediate steps were taken to lay out a program of tests on a number of wing planforms which were thought suitable for supersonic flight. The selection of the planforms to be tested was rather arbitrary since little theory had then been developed. Walter Vincenti, with the help of Elliott Katzen and others, took the lead in carrying out this program. Great pains were taken to coordinate the test results with existing theory and to check theory against experiment. Two important reports resulted from this work: RM A7I10 (ref. B–5) by Walter Vincenti, Jack Nielsen, and Fred Matteson, which presented data on both normal and reversed delta wings, and TR 1033 (ref. B–6) by Vincenti, in which a critical comparison was made of theory with experimental data obtained on a variety of straight-wing and swept-wing models. The tests were all carried out at a Mach number of 1.53 using a fixed-throat nozzle in lieu of the variable nozzle which was still under development.

In the 6- by 6-foot tunnel, Hall and Heitmeyer, as earlier noted, investigated the 63° wing, while Charles Frick and R. S. Chubb made an important analytical study of the longitudinal stability of elastic sweptwings at supersonic speeds. This study, reported in TR 965 (ref. B–7), pointed to the very important role played by structural elasticity in the aerodynamic behavior of large sweptwing airplanes. Wing thinness, required for high-speed flight, and sweep each contributed to wing deflections under load and thus to the static stability and dynamic response of large sweptwing airplanes such as the B–47. Aeroelastic effects on airplane performance were not new, of course, but never before had they assumed such importance as in this new regime of swept wings.

Controls. The 16-foot tunnel during this period undertook quite a lot of work on controls for sweptwing and other high-speed aircraft. Lee Boddy collaborated with Walter Williams of the NACA group at Edwards in preparing a summary and analysis of NACA's work on dive-recovery flaps. This study was published as RM A709. In the same period John Axelson prepared a summary and analysis of wind-tunnel data on the lift and hinge-moment characteristics of control surfaces at Mach numbers up to 0.9, while Walter Krumm and Joseph Cleary produced a series of reports on the lateral control of straight- and swept-wing airplanes. The problem of devising controls for swept wings was particularly difficult owing to the tendency of the boundary layer on such wings to flow spanwise toward the tips, thus causing early stall in the region of the ailerons. To prevent such lateral flow, boundary-layer barriers, called "fences," were often installed at certain points on the upper surface of the wing.

Another very useful bit of control-system work done in the 16-foot tunnel during this period concerned a very serious stability problem that the Douglas Santa Monica people had encountered in early flights of their new C–74 transport. NACA's help was requested and a large segment of the airplane's horizontal tail surface was installed in the 16-foot tunnel. Although it first appeared that the blockage produced by the huge test body might negate NACA's test efforts, the first run in the tunnel revealed the cause of the problem. At high speed, aerodynamic forces caused ballooning of the fabric covering the elevator, thus greatly affecting the hinge moments and controllability of the airplane. To reduce the weight and to facilitate the balancing of movable control surfaces, it had been common practice to cover them with fabric rather than metal. The experience with the C–74 proved that the day was over when this practice could be tolerated; indeed, the day had really been over for some time. The same control problem had earlier been experienced by other airplanes.

Bodies. Although the Laboratory during this period was preoccupied with wing research, there were also several notable investigations relating to bodies (fuselages). Indeed, among the significant early programs run in the 1- by 3-foot tunnel were a number that were concerned with the effects of viscosity on the supersonic flow over bodies of revolution. These studies were made by Dean Chapman, Edward Perkins, and Harvey Allen. The 1-by-3 was particularly useful for investigations of this kind because of the ease with which its operating pressure could be varied. This favorable operating characteristics greatly facilitated the study of Reynolds-number effects.

Perhaps the first report written at Ames on supersonic tests was a paper by Dean Chapman and Ed Perkins on the effects of viscosity on the drag and base pressures of bodies of revolution at a Mach number of 1.5. This paper, which later was published as TR 1036 (ref. B–8), gave considerable atten-

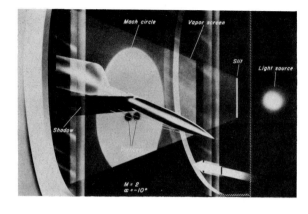

Vapor-screen technique, showing position of vortices.

tion to the flow in the mixing region at the truncated base of a body. The study so aroused Chapman's interest in base-flow phenomena that, when he left shortly thereafter to complete his doctoral work at Caltech, he adopted the base-pressure problem as his thesis subject. Later, on his return from Caltech, his thesis work was included in TR 1051 (ref. B–9), "An Analysis of Base Pressure at Supersonic Velocities and Comparison With Experiment."

While Chapman was at Caltech, Harvey Allen and Ed Perkins made a combined theoretical-experimental study of the flow around an inclined body of revolution. This study, reported in TR 1048 (ref. B–10), provided an approximate method for calculating the force and moment characteristics of inclined bodies and revealed the existence of a pair of vortices shed from the body on its lee side. In tests run in the 1- by 3-foot tunnel, the vortices were made visible by a vapor-screen technique devised by Allen.

In the vapor-screen technique, a small amount of water is introduced into the tunnel; the water vaporizes and condenses into a fog in the test section. A plane of intense light is then passed through the schlieren windows and thence transversely through the test section in the region of the model. The vortices act like a centrifuge on the water vapor and their cores, as they pass through the light screen, leave dark spots in an otherwise glowing sheet of diffused light. Other features of the flow pattern are also revealed. In this and other instances, the study of vortex shedding from bodies and wings was considerably facilitated through the use of the vapor-screen technique.

Meanwhile in the 16-foot tunnel, Lee Boddy and Charles Morrill were investigating the possibility of contouring a fuselage in such a way as to minimize the flow interference at its juncture with a swept wing. This work, which was somewhat prophetic, gave recognition to an incompatibility at the wing-fuselage juncture between the three-dimensional flow pattern over a swept wing and the essentially two-dimensional flow pattern over the fuselage.

INLETS

With the advent of jet engines, the problems of air inlets and internal aerodynamics became of major importance and of great influence in airplane design. The problem of where to locate the engines and the inlets had to be solved; then the detailed design of the inlets and internal flow systems seemed a subject for vital and almost endless research. There appeared in this period to be three promising locations for jet air inlets: in the nose of the fuselage, in the sides of the fuselage, and in the wing roots. Inlets in each of these locations were investigated at Ames in a program thoroughly coordinated with similar work in the Langley and the Lewis Laboratories.

The Ames inlet investigations were conducted in a number of facilities including the 7- by 10-foot tunnel; an 8- by 36-inch flow channel constructed at the 7-by-10 especially for inlet studies; the 16-foot, the 40- by 80-foot, and the 1- by 3-foot tunnels; and the 8- by 8-inch tunnel, which originally was built to check out the sliding-block nozzle but which had since proved very useful for research work. A rather substantial effort was made by the Laboratory in perfecting the submerged inlet developed by Mossman and others in the 7-by-10. This work was carried out at reduced scale in the 7-by-10 flow channel, at full scale in the 40-by-80, and at transonic speeds by bump tests in the 16-foot tunnel. In the 1-by-3, a group headed by Wallace Davis concentrated on side inlets of the scoop variety; and in the 8- by 8-inch tunnel, John Lundell and others investigated supersonic nose inlets, particularly those applying to ramjet-powered missiles.

Among the more significant reports on submerged inlets were RM A7I30 by Emmet Mossman and Lauros Randall and, from the 16-foot tunnel, RM A8B16 by Charles Hall and Dorn Barclay. In the 40-by-80, Norman Martin and Curt Holzhauser investigated twin side scoops which fed a common engine inlet duct, and in TN 2049 they analyzed the instability that was found to occur in such systems at low flow rates.

DYNAMIC STABILITY AND LOADS

Ames engineers were concerned with the dynamic as well as the static stability of new airplane configurations, particularly those required to operate in the transonic and supersonic speed ranges. In the 6- by 6-foot tunnel, triangular wing models were spring mounted, free to pitch, and their damping characteristics measured. This work was reported in RM A50J26 by Murray Tobak, Dave Reese, and Ben Beam.

The flutter of ailerons, excited by oscillating shock waves, had by this time become a fairly common and troublesome phenomenon. Inasmuch as existing knowledge of the subject was rather superficial, Albert Erickson and Robert Robinson of the 16-foot tunnel undertook to learn more about the aerodynamic forces involved. Toward this end they devised special instrumentation and techniques with which they were able to measure instantaneous pressure distributions over a representative section of the aileron while it was in the very act of fluttering. To do this, they enlisted the aid of Jim Kyle, a fellow member of the 16-foot-tunnel staff, who designed a tiny, fast-acting pressure cell that could be mounted flush with the surface of the aileron and wing. This interesting instrumentation and technique was described by Erickson and Robinson in RM A8H03.

As part of a general wing-study program during this period, the 40- by 80-foot tunnel section carried out some very important work having to do with the development of an analytical method for determining the distribution of airloads on swept wings at subsonic speeds. This problem had been solved for straight wings but, in the case of swept wings, it was much more difficult. John DeYoung was the major contributor to this effort and was helped by Charles Harper and Victor Stevens. Key reports issuing from this work include TR 921 (ref. B–11) by DeYoung and Harper and TR 1056 by DeYoung alone. While this work was going on in the 40-by-80, Doris Cohen (Mrs. R. T. Jones) of the 1- by 3-foot tunnel section was engaged in making theoretical determinations of the air loads on swept wings at supersonic speeds. Her work is covered in TR 1050 and other papers.

FLIGHT RESEARCH

Deicing. In the early postwar period the work of the Ames Flight Engineering and Flight Research groups was mostly a continuation of what they had been doing during the war. Icing research continued for a number of years under the able guidance of Alun Jones but became largely concerned with perfecting analytical techniques, obtaining more complete meteorological data on icing conditions, and developing deicing techniques for such airplane components as windshields and propellers. The study of carburetor icing had been taken over by the NACA Lewis Flight Propulsion Laboratory. Major contributors to the icing studies at Ames during this period were Alun Jones, Carr Neel, Norman Bergrun, James Selna, and George Holdaway of the Laboratory staff, and William Lewis of the U.S. Weather Bureau. The fine work done by Lewis throughout the icing research program was recognized in 1949 when he was given the Robert M. Losey Award of the Institute of the Aeronautical Sciences. As the period ended in 1949, the Flight Engineering group was diverting its efforts from deicing to the development of the drop-test method of transonic flight research. This development has earlier been mentioned.

Flying Qualities. Although the wind-tunnel people at Ames were working on some very advanced airplane configurations, none of these configurations had yet appeared in airplanes which the Ames Flight Research group were testing. It was not until 1949 that the F–86, the first sweptwing airplane, came to Ames for flight tests. Until then, the fastest airplane in the Flight Research stable was the straight-wing P–80A which in a dive, as

Clousing found out, could reach a Mach number of about 0.88. Rather extensive flying-quality tests were run on the P–80A, and these were reported by Seth Anderson, Frank Christofferson, and Lawrence Clousing in RM A7G01. Larry Clousing's outstanding work in flight research was recognized in 1947 when the Octave Chanute Award was conferred on him by the Institute of the Aeronautical Sciences.

Other flight research at Ames during this period represented a continuation of earlier efforts to confirm in flight the stability and control of airplanes as predicted by wind-tunnel tests. There was also an application of the wing-flow technique to transonic studies both of straight wings, such as used on the X–3, and delta wings.

Loads. Also carried over from the war years was the program on wing and tail loads in which Larry Clousing, Melvin Sadoff, William Turner, and others were playing such an active part. More recently the Ames Flight Research Section had begun an investigation of buffeting—an unpleasant, if not dangerous, phenomenon encountered by high-speed airplanes in dive pullouts. The buffeting, occurring at high subsonic speeds, appeared to arise from oscillating shock waves which caused cyclic separation of the flow on the upper surface of the wing. The conditions under which the buffeting occurred were investigated on a number of different airplanes and it was while testing one of these airplanes, the P–51, that George Cooper, the pilot, thought he could actually see the shock wave on the wing. Further investigation showed that what he had seen was indeed the shock wave or, more precisely, a refraction pattern caused by the sun's rays shining through the shock wave. The shock wave was then seen on the wings of two other airplanes and the conditions under which it would appear—the angle of the airplane with respect to the sun, etc.—were determined. Photographs were taken of the shock waves and it was noted that the shock wave would move backward, toward the trailing edge, as Mach number increased and forward as lift coefficient increased. It was also noticed that, at some value of Mach number and lift coefficient, the shock would dance back and forth through an amplitude of 2 inches or more. Moreover, buffeting appeared just when the dancing began. As the technique of visually observing shock waves was thought to be useful, George Cooper and George Rathert wrote a report on the project which was published as RM A8C25.

Variable-Stability Airplane. By far the most important contribution of the Ames Flight Research group during this period was the development of the variable-stability airplane. In this project, William Kauffman played the leading part while G. Allan Smith and others played important supporting roles. Apparently the idea of a variable-stability airplane was not new (it had been mentioned in German literature), but it was one of those things the practical accomplishment of which requires greater genius than the original conception.

Visible shock waves in flight
(left) *and William M. Kauff-*
man (above).

Aside from its application to the wing-flow method, the airplane had generally not been used in the past as a simulator. In flight it represented only itself; it was indeed the ultimate yardstick against which wind-tunnel model tests were measured. And the airplane, of course, could provide information on flight dynamics, on the interrelationships between pilot and airplane, that were quite beyond the powers of any wind tunnel, or any other simulator, to produce. But was this statement precisely true and could not the airplane itself be made a simulator, to simulate the dynamic behavior and pilot-machine relations of other airplane configurations? The concept was most interesting. Such a simulator would be a wonderful tool for studying the flying qualities of the radically different airplane configurations that shortly would be in use. But was the development of such a simulator a practical possibility? It certainly was, said Kauffman, and let's get at it. Immediately enlisted in the project was Dr. G. Allan Smith, expert on servomechanisms, from the Instrument Research Section. The conservative propeller-driven Grumman F6F would be used in this first attempt to produce a variable-stability flying simulator.

Of greatest interest at the moment were the lateral-directional dynamics of airplanes; thus the study of this area of airplane performance was selected as the first application of the variable-stability airplane. But to simplify the variable-stability airplane development problem, only one aspect of lateral-directional performance would be investigated—the effect of changing the wing dihedral. The physical alteration of the dihedral in any airplane represents a major structural modification, but the effect of changing

165

dihedral could be obtained by installing a powered servomechanism in the test airplane that would deflect the ailerons in proportion to the angle of yaw. However, it would be necessary for the device to accomplish this objective without moving the control stick or changing the stick force required for the pilot to operate the ailerons. In others words, the pilot would not sense that the device was operating except for the fact that the dihedral of the airplane would appear to have been changed. The design of the device to accomplish this objective was very tricky and had to be worked out with great care if the plane and pilot were not to be endangered. But the job was done and done well. By the adjustment of the mechanism in flight, any effective dihedral from $-18°$ to $+28°$ could be obtained.

The variable-stability airplane was flown by five different pilots under conditions simulating landing approach, cruising, and high speed. Under each of these conditions, the effective dihedral was changed through a wide range and the opinion of each pilot as to the quality of the airplane performance at each dihedral setting was noted. In this way, the optimum dihedral and the tolerable range of dihedral were ascertained for each condition of flight. Special flight instrumentation provided useful quantitative data, of course, but in the end it was the pilot's opinion of the flying qualities of the airplane that counted most. Clearly, pilot opinion would become increasingly important as the new class of airplane, having radically different inertia and control characteristics, came into use. For such airplanes, past experience and existing data were largely inapplicable. In any case, the very significant story of the conversion of the F6F and the results of the first tests were reported in TR 948 (ref. B–12) by Kauffman, Liddell, Smith, and Van Dyke. Rudolph Van Dyke was one of the Ames pilots who flew the airplane.

The results of this first use of a variable-stability airplane by NACA at Ames were very promising and extensions of the idea quickly came to mind. To obtain a better simulation of the whole lateral-directional stability syndrome, it would be necessary to drive the rudder, as well as the ailerons, in accordance with yaw angle and also, perhaps, to introduce roll rate and yaw rate as inputs in addition to yaw angle. Steps to accomplish these changes were soon taken.

Sonic Boom. The F–86 was the first operational airplane capable, in a dive, of reaching supersonic speeds. The XS–1 (now called the X–1), carried aloft by a mother airplane, had of course achieved supersonic speed in level flight at high altitudes over the desert. Ames received one of the first F–86's for flight tests in 1949 and shortly was running tests involving prolonged dives at very high speed. Rudolph Van Dyke and George Cooper were the pilots. Soon after the program got under way, the local newspapers began reporting mysterious explosions the source of which could never be located. One day such an explosion shook the plates off the plate rail in the Interna-

*Forced landing of a Douglas XSB2D–1 airplane in a prune
orchard by George Cooper and Welko Gasich.*

tional Kitchen near Niles, Calif. A sheriff's posse was sent out to investigate
the cause but had no luck. Another explosion occurring in the region of the
Calaveras Reservoir seemed to be focused by a box canyon and reportedly
caused some slight damage to a house at the head of the canyon.

Newspaper headlines reporting explosions became bigger and blacker.
McAvoy, walking into the pilots' office with a newspaper in his hand one
morning, jokingly asked Van Dyke and Cooper, "What are you fellows
doing to cause so much noise?" Mac's remark was a bit of purely innocent
humor but it caused something to click in Van Dyke's mind. Good Lord!
Could the explosions have something to do with their dives in the F–86?
Smitty DeFrance had similar suspicions and, as he sat in his office one day,
he heard a boom or explosion such as had been reported in the papers. He
noted the time and called the Flight Research Section to see if the F–86 was
up. Yes, it was, and yes, it had made a scheduled dive at the same minute
that the boom had occurred. The suspicions of Smitty and Rudy Van Dyke
were confirmed. The explosions had been caused by the F–86 diving beyond
the speed of sound. Ames, as a matter of policy, did not publicize the matter, but it was not many months before the sonic boom was observed elsewhere and associated with the supersonic flight of airplanes. Soon the boom
became commonplace; but Ames, it is believed, was first to encounter and
recognize the phenomenon.

Hazards. In dive testing the F–86, Ames pilots Cooper and Van Dyke
were probably flying through the transonic range more frequently than anyone else in the country. Other hazards were encountered with slower air-

Test pilot George Cooper.

planes—for example, the incident that occurred one day while George Cooper and Welko Gasich were up in a Douglas SB2D carrying out some mission over the Los Gatos countryside. The engine, demonstrating a habit of this particular model, backfired and started a fire in the induction system. George could not get back to the field, so he set the plane down between rows of trees in a prune orchard. The plane's wings clipped the treetops off neatly in a descending path; but, as the wings got down to the trunks, the going got rough. The airplane was a wreck by the time it came to rest; George and Welko walked away from it badly shaken but not seriously harmed.

Another time George was up in a P–47 investigating the effect of reversing the propeller pitch on the stability and control of the airplane in a dive. His engineering pals on the ground assured him that "all you have to do if you get in trouble is to push this button here and the prop will snap back to normal pitch." Well, in one dive, though he was not in any trouble, he wanted to discontinue the test, so he pushed the button. Nothing happened. The prop did not move a degree and continued its devilish braking effect. George was then faced with the miserable task of making a forced landing with the propeller reversed. He carefully made his approach and, when he was only a couple of hundred feet from the runway, the propeller suddenly snapped into normal pitch. He slammed the throttle open and with a roar took off over the treetops to make another, normal, and successful landing.

Incidents of the kind mentioned were all in the day's work for Ames pilots. Unhappily they did not all turn out so well. Luck ran out for Ryland D. Carter, Ames test pilot, as he was flying a P–51H airplane on May 17, 1948. The wing of the airplane, incidentally, was equipped with a glove and otherwise adapted for wing-flow tests. For reasons unknown, the plane came apart in the air, its fragments scattering widely over farmland near Newark,

Calif. Although Carter was thrown clear, he was unable to activate his parachute and was killed.

AERODYNAMIC HEATING

Boundary-layer heating resulting from skin friction and air compression had been of rather small concern to aerodynamicists, but now became a matter of some importance when supersonic flight speeds were being considered. Aerodynamicists at Ames, and elsewhere, were interested in the effects of aerodynamic heating on the structure and contents of flight vehicles as well as in such related problems as the heat transfer to the body from laminar and turbulent boundary layers, the effect of heat transfer to, or from, the body on boundary-layer transition, and the effect of boundary-layer heating on skin friction.

At Ames there had been some early work on heating; this was reported by Allen and Nitzberg in TN 1255 and by Tendeland and Schlaff in TN 1675. In 1947, Richard Scherrer made a theoretical study, reported in TR 917, of the effects of aerodynamic heating on bodies of revolution at supersonic speeds and, in 1949, Dean Chapman and Morris Rubesin presented a paper to the IAS (ref. B–13) on temperature and velocity profiles in the compressible laminar boundary layer with arbitrary distributions of surface temperature. At about the same time, Richard Scherrer and William Wimbrow ran some tests in the 1- by 3-foot tunnel on heated and unheated cones. This work, which compared experimental results with theory, was summarized by Scherrer in TR 1055 (ref. B–14). In general it appeared that experiment confirmed the earlier theories, including one which predicted that a laminar boundary layer would be stabilized if the body were cooler than the surrounding airflow and destabilized if the reverse were true. This factor would have to be considered in future wind-tunnel model tests.

Jack Stalder and Glen Goodwin, as earlier noted, had built a very special, if low-cost, tunnel to operate at very low air densities, such as those to be found at altitudes of perhaps 50 to 70 miles, where future missiles might conceivably fly. This realm of flight, called the "free molecule" range, is a region wherein the air molecules are far apart and the average distance they travel before bumping into another molecule is considerably greater than the length of the missile or the model in the wind tunnel. Jack admitted that simulation of a somewhat lower altitude range might have been a little more practical; but the free-molecule range had the distinct advantage of being more amenable to theoretical analysis than the lower ranges. Before the low-density tunnel was completed, Jack and David Jukoff had made an analysis of heat transfer to bodies traveling at high speed in the upper atmosphere. This study, published as TR 944 (ref. B–15), dealt with air molecular energy transport to a body and developed a general method for calculating surface temperatures in steady high-speed flight in a rarefied atmosphere.

When the low-density tunnel was completed, and the difficult problems of devising low-pressure instrumentation were solved, tunnel calibration tests began. It was found that the boundary layer on the walls expanded under the influence of the low pressure and nearly filled the throat. Only a $1/2$-inch-diameter core of untrammeled air at the center remained. This condition considerably limited the test possibilities of the tunnel. Jack and Glen decided that their first test, a test with which theory could be checked, would be of the aerodynamic heat transferred to a cylinder mounted transversely across the flow. The cylinder was actually a wire; indeed, it was an iron-constantan thermocouple with the butt-welded junction located in the core of the tunnel airstream.

The results of the tests in the new tunnel were classic. They confirmed the scarcely believable indications of theory, that the temperature of the wire in the low-density airstream should be higher than the at-rest temperature of the air in the tunnel. At pressures and densities found in any ordinary tunnel, the maximum temperature the wire could be expected to reach would be the at-rest, or stagnation, temperature of the tunnel air; but, at low densities, the wire temperature was as much as 65° F higher than the stagnation temperature of the tunnel when nitrogen, a diatomic gas, was used in the tunnel and as much as 147° F higher when helium, a monatomic gas, was used. The drag on the wire, though exceedingly small, was also measured and found to confirm theory.

The results of these first tests alone justified the money and time spent on the tunnel. They are contained in TR 1032 (ref. B–16) by Jack Stalder, Glen Goodwin, and Marcus Creager. The report not only develops the theory of the wire heating but also gives the confirming experimental results. In addition, it provides a good description of the tunnel and its auxiliary equipment.

The new 6-inch heat-transfer tunnel also was put into operation in 1949. The first test report to come from it was TN 2077 by Jack Stalder, Morrie Rubesin, and Thor Tendeland. The subject of this report, which included a description of the tunnel, was the temperature-recovery factors on a flat plate in a supersonic airflow.

1950–1953

5

....

The Environment

A SUBSTANTIAL relaxation of world tensions occurred at the end of the war, but unhappily this favorable situation did not long prevail. Our relations with the Soviet Union and China soon became strained, and the cold war was on in earnest, and the dire necessity of maintaining our technical and military lead over the Soviets was very evident. The Korean war began in 1950 and the aircraft companies, all of which had suffered a business letdown at the end of World War II, were soon again busy designing and building new and advanced types of airplanes and missiles. The Korean armistice was signed in July 1953, but Russia shortly exploded its first H-bomb and tensions continued to mount.

Many technical advances in the field of aviation were made during this period. Service airplanes were regularly diving to supersonic speeds in the early fifties and, in October 1953, the 50th anniversary of powered flight, first Douglas El Segundo's new bat-wing XF4D and then North American's new F–100 reached approximately sonic speeds (754 mph) in level flight. At the same time research airplanes were going even faster. The first airplane to travel at a rate of twice the speed of sound was Douglas El Segundo's D–558 II which, dropped from a mother airplane and flown by NACA test pilot Scott Crossfield, reached Mach 2.01 in level flight on November 20, 1953. Less than a month later this record was exceeded by the Bell X–1A, which went to Mach 2.5 (1612 mph).

Missile development was also proceeding apace. The first target intercept by a homing Lark missile was made in January 1950; in September 1953 the first target intercept was made with a heat-seeking Sidewinder missile. The first full-guidance flight of the radar-guided Sparrow missile was also made early in 1953. Even more significant was the establishment in December 1953 of a Nike-Ajax battalion in the Washington area. This was the first operational surface-to-air missile system in the United States. Missiles were also being used to explore the upper atmosphere. The Army was achieving record altitudes (up to 244 miles) with its two-stage, V–2+ Wac Corporal vehicle; while the Navy's Viking and Aerobee missiles, the latter

At left: *The North American F-100*. Below: *the Douglas F4D-1, two of the first Mach 1 fighters.*

often carrying animals, were reaching many miles into the sky. Most important of all missile development was the reactivation in 1951 of the intercontinental ballistic-missile project which had been stopped in 1947 with the cancellation of Air Force Project MX 774. As Air Force Project Atlas MX 1593, the renewed ICBM program moved ahead with considerable vigor.

During this period there was discussion in military and technical circles regarding the possibility and desirability of launching a small earth satellite. The matter was brought up by Dr. Fred Singer in August 1953 at the Fourth International Congress of Astronautics and was seriously considered by a special international committee (CSAGI) established in May 1952 to coordinate plans for an International Geophysical Year. NACA itself had become interested in problems of flight beyond the earth's sensible atmosphere and in July 1952 instructed its laboratories to initiate studies of means for attacking these problems. Later, as a result of such studies, NACA proposed the development of a hypersonic, high-flying research airplane (the X–15) as a joint project between itself and the military services.

174

THE ENVIRONMENT

The period 1950–1953 was one of considerable frustration for NACA. The Committee felt that a crisis existed with respect to maintaining the Nation's supremacy in the air; yet congressional appropriations committees seemed unwilling to grant NACA the facilities,[1] and more particularly the manpower quotas, to meet this crisis. At a time when the backlog of vital research work had never been so large, NACA's manpower quota was held constant or if anything decreased. At Ames the staff in 1953 stood at 1120—lower than it had been since 1949.[2] To make matters worse, the manpower quota, low though it was, could not be filled.

There had been no increase in Civil Service salaries for some time; and NACA, in acquiring scientific talent, was at a serious disadvantage with respect to the industry and the military services, the latter being able to get research work done by contracting. In the competition for technical manpower, the only factor favorable to NACA was the Government ruling in April 1950 allowing NACA, alone among Federal agencies, the privilege of granting selected employees time off with pay to pursue university studies that could be expected to contribute to their work for the agency. This privilege, while very valuable to a few, altered but little NACA's unfavorable manpower position.

The national requirements for scientific manpower were expanding rapidly and could not, it seemed, be fully met. Every aircraft company was enlarging its technical staff to cope with advanced design work and with research-and-development contracts given to it by the military—particularly the Air Force. The Air Force had established a new Air Research and Development Command which was launching into all manner of research either in its own facilities or in industry and universities via contract. With military support or sponsorship, a number of universities were setting up rather large research organizations whose function had little to do with education. Thus, with Federal funds, which the military seemed able to command, many agencies and people were being drawn to the field of aeronautical research. With some justification, therefore, NACA's Chairman Hunsaker could complain to Congress, as he did in his Annual Report of 1951, that "the military research and development program has been increased threefold but to date the funds and manpower authorized for NACA have not expanded to support adequately the military need."

In the production of aeronautical research information, NACA still occupied a preeminent position but its preeminence now came more from product quality than from dominance of output. Many in NACA felt that

---

[1] Years later members of Ames management were to acknowledge that almost all of the facility items they had requested over the years had been approved by NACA Headquarters and Congress, though sometimes only after a delay of a year or two. The delays they then also admitted were often beneficial, as some of their initial proposals were overblown and technologically premature.

[2] See app. A.

research quality would certainly suffer if, as in the military, research was second in importance to operations or, as in the industry, second to production and profitmaking. Nor were they sure that a university, departing from its traditional role of teaching and associated small-scale fundamental research, had any special qualifications for managing large research and development operations. But the field of aeronautical research had expanded tremendously and there was a need for the services of every competent agency and person. NACA had repeatedly tried to expand its own university contract operations and had repeatedly been turned down by Congress. At this stage, NACA could still take some satisfaction from the fact that, in the field of aeronautical research, no other agency in the country had the magnificent research facilities or the breadth and depth of experience that it possessed.

6

People and Events

BETWEEN 1950 and 1953 there were a number of important developments at Ames relating to personnel, organization, and events. On January 1, 1950, Russell G. Robinson joined the staff of the Laboratory as Assistant Director. He had had a part in the very first construction efforts at Ames but had then been called back to NACA Headquarters to assist S. Paul Johnston, Coordinator of Research, and Dr. Lewis. Robinson's work was particularly valued in Washington because of his technical experience, progressive viewpoint, and savoir faire. These important qualifications he brought to Ames together with a good understanding of just how the Headquarters office operated.

The rapport with Headquarters which Robinson provided was particularly valuable to a new laboratory located far from Washington. Ames people sometimes felt that Headquarters did not fully understand their special problems and occasionally showed favoritism to Langley. Ames was, of course, the junior partner of NACA's two aerodynamics laboratories, but

Russell G. Robinson.

Gerald E. Nitzberg (left) *and Ralph F. Huntsberger* (right).

did not particularly like to have the distinction emphasized. When Headquarters would turn down an Ames research proposal because "we think Langley is shortly going to propose the same thing," it was not surprising that Ames people felt chagrin and some annoyance. In any case it appeared that Russ Robinson could provide a real service to Ames. At the time of Robinson's arrival, Carl Bioletti, who since 1947 had held the position of Assistant to the Director, was also made an Assistant Director. The two then shared the responsibility of managing the Laboratory's research programs.

William Kauffman, the expert on variable-stability airplanes, was detailed to Washington in April for a year; and in June 1950, Ralph Huntsberger was appointed head of the Unitary Plan design group at Ames. Reporting to John Parsons, Ralph would be responsible for the design and construction of the Ames Unitary Plan facility. At the end of July 1952, Dr. Dryden, Director of NACA, appointed Parsons Associate Director of the Ames Laboratory, a position which he was to hold while continuing to serve as Chief of the NACA Unitary Plan programs. Parsons discharged these heavy responsibilities with the quiet efficiency for which he was noted; he was ably supported by Gerald Nitzberg, who had been appointed his technical assistant. One of Nitzberg's assignments was the technical editing of all publications produced by Ames people to assure their accuracy and quality. Inasmuch as technical publications were the principal products of the Laboratory, the commodity on which Ames performance was judged, their proper editing was regarded as a matter of great importance.

Early in 1953 Don Wiley resigned from his position as Aeronautical Information Officer and was replaced by Daniel Wentz II. Dan's job was made a little easier by some softening of NACA's attitude toward public relations. But NACA still had a way to go. Also in 1953, Ames made certain changes in its organization to satisfy a desire of the Congress to establish a uniform organization for all Government agencies. One result was that the organizational units known as "Sections" became "Branches." Other elements of the change can be observed in the organization chart for 1953.

There were Inspections at Ames in 1950 and 1952, and three important technical conferences: the first was on Supersonic Aerodynamics in February 1950; the second, on Aerodynamic Design Problems of Supersonic Guided Missiles, in October 1951; and the third, on the Aerodynamics of High-Speed Aircraft, in July 1953. The trend of the Laboratory's work was evident from the conference titles. There were also one or more conferences at Langley to which the Ames staff contributed.

An essential element in the establishment of a successful research laboratory is the creation of a favorable climate for research; this is one of the prime functions of the management group. In such an environment the research men are shielded as much as possible from administrative and political distractions, are provided the stimulating fellowship of other first-rate research men, are encouraged to exercise their ingenuity in attacking new problems, and are given the facilities and assistance which their work requires.

The very favorable research climate that prevailed at Ames was no accident. It was the product of a management group each member of which, from his own experience, was keenly aware of the needs of research. It resulted in a high productivity of useful information and it enabled the Laboratory to hire and hold good men who might otherwise have been attracted by the higher wages offered by industry.

In the top echelon of Ames management were Smith DeFrance, John Parsons, Russell Robinson, Carlton Bioletti, and Donald Wood. DeFrance's personal staff included Marie St. John, who for years had been his Administrative Assistant, and through whom some of his nontechnical orders were issued. Also reporting directly to DeFrance were the Budget Officer, Ferril Nickle, and his assistants, Edward Schnitker and Walter Peterson.

DeFrance's operation of the Ames Laboratory was efficient, businesslike, and remarkably free of waste. In particular he encouraged and conserved research talent by shielding it from political pressures and unproductive routine and red tape. He never relinquished the reins of management but, as the Laboratory's activities grew in size and complexity, he leaned more heavily on the judgment of his senior staff. The explosive pressures which DeFrance had applied so freely during the period of construction and war were now applied less frequently and seldom to the more fundamental

DIRECTOR — S. J. DeFrance
ASSOCIATE DIRECTOR — J. F. Parsons

ADM. ASST. TO DIR. — M. W. St. John
T/ASST. TO ASSOC. DIR. — G. E. Nitzberg
INFO. SPECIALIST — D. S. Wentz

BUDGET OFFICE — F. R. Nickle, B. Off. / W. O. Peterson, Asst. / E. Schnitker, Asst.

AMES UNITARY PLAN DESIGN GROUP — R. E. Huntsberger
UNITARY WIND TUNNEL PROGRAM PROJECT OFFICE — J. F. Parsons

ASSISTANT DIRECTORS — C. Bioletti / R. G. Robinson

AIR FORCE LIAISON — D. R. Latham, Maj. / C. W. Tusch / F. Crabhow

THEORETICAL AND APPLIED RESEARCH DIVISION
D. H. Wood, Ch / M. J. Hood, ACh
- ELECTRONIC MACHINE COMPUTING BRANCH — W. A. Mersman
- THEORETICAL AERODYNAMICS BRANCH — M. A. Heaslet
- LOW DENSITY AND HEAT TRANSFER WIND TUNNELS BRANCH — J. R. Stalder

FULL SCALE AND FLIGHT RESEARCH DIVISION
H. J. Goett, Ch / L. A. Clousing, ACh
- 16-FOOT HIGH SPEED WIND TUNNEL BRANCH — A. L. Erickson, Ch
- 12-FOOT PRESSURE WIND TUNNEL BRANCH — R. M. Crane
- 7- BY 10-FOOT WIND TUNNELS BRANCH — M. D. Erickson
- FLIGHT RESEARCH BRANCH — S. E. Belsley
- FLIGHT OPERATIONS BRANCH — W. H. McAvoy
- FLIGHT ENGINEERING BRANCH — A. R. Jones
- 40- BY 80-FOOT WIND TUNNEL BRANCH — C. W. Harper

HIGH SPEED RESEARCH DIVISION
H. J. Allen, Ch / V. I. Stevens, ACh
- SUPERSONIC FREE FLIGHT WIND TUNNEL BRANCH — A. Seiff
- 10- BY 14-INCH SUPERSONIC WIND TUNNEL BRANCH — A. J. Eggers
- 6- BY 6-FOOT SUPERSONIC WIND TUNNEL BRANCH — C. W. Frick
- 1- BY 3½-FOOT HIGH-SPEED WIND TUNNEL BRANCH — D. J. Graham
- 1- BY 3-FOOT SUPERSONIC WIND TUNNELS BRANCH — W. F. Davis

ADMINISTRATIVE DIVISION
A. B. Freeman, Ch / M. G. Poole, ACh
- SECURITY OFFICER — J. B. Von Etten
- PROCUREMENT AND SUPPLY BRANCH — A. S. Hertzog
- PERSONNEL BRANCH — M. H. Davies
- FISCAL BRANCH — W. V. Shaw
- ADMINISTRATIVE SERVICES BRANCH — L. D. Baker

RESEARCH INSTRUMENTATION AND ENGINEERING SERVICES DIVISION
J. A. White, Ch / A. G. Buck, ACh
- PHOTOGRAPHIC BRANCH — F. H. Swartz
- INSTRUMENT BRANCH — J. V. Kelley
- INSTRUMENT DEVELOPMENT BRANCH — H. W. Kirschbaum
- ENGINEERING DESIGN BRANCH — J. S. W. Davidsen
- ELECTRICAL BRANCH — M. S. Nourse

CONSTRUCTION DIVISION
C. H. Harvey, Ch
- CONSTRUCTION INSPECTION BRANCH — A. E. Wilson
- CONSTRUCTION ENGINEERING SERVICES BRANCH — C. H. Harvey

TECHNICAL SERVICES DIVISION
E. W. Betts, Ch / R. E. Broig, ACh / G. E. Bulifant, ACh
- MODEL CONSTRUCTION BRANCH — W. Ward
- MACHINE BRANCH — H. D. Citti
- AIRCRAFT INSPECTION BRANCH — J. C. Smith
- AIRCRAFT SERVICES BRANCH — J. D. Morris
- AIRCRAFT MODIFICATION BRANCH — W. Quigg
- TRANSPORTATION BRANCH — R. S. Loucks
- MAINTENANCE BRANCH — R. A. Barcelona
- STRUCTURAL FABRICATION BRANCH — S. A. Oliver
- AVIATION SHEET METAL BRANCH — J. P. Houston
- MODEL FINISHING BRANCH — A. W. Moore

Organization chart of Ames Aeronautical Laboratory, July 1953.

Left: *Edward H. A. Schnitker and Ferril R. Nickle.* Right: *Marie W. St. John.*

DeFrance (left) *and Parsons* (right) *confer.*

research efforts in which the Laboratory was increasingly engaged. Research men could look to him for a sympathetic consideration of their far-out schemes, for freedom to pursue their work unhindered, and for solid logistical support for their projects. Moreover, Smitty was particularly diligent in looking after the interests of the wage-board employees and that segment of the Laboratory staff which provided vital supporting services.

The excellence of DeFrance's work was recognized well beyond the bounds of the Laboratory. In 1952 he received an honorary doctor of laws degree from the University of California at Los Angeles; this honor was followed in 1953 by a doctor of engineering degree from his alma mater, the University of Michigan.

Of all the members of DeFrance's staff, Jack Parsons was the one upon whom he placed the greatest dependence. Jack, a quiet operator and no salesman, was widely liked and respected. He had demonstrated his solid abilities in research, in facility design, and in executive management. Jack was "The Builder" at Ames and perhaps knew more than anyone else of what the Laboratory consisted. His loyalty and level-headed dependability were traits which DeFrance much appreciated.

The others in the top management—Russ Robinson, Carl Bioletti, and Don Wood—contributed greatly to the prosecution of the Laboratory's mission by bringing to their posts good judgment, long experience, and, particularly in the case of Robinson, a fine sense of diplomacy—a characteristic frequently lacking in research types. Don Wood, originally Chief of Research at Ames, was a solid, experienced, and conservative engineer who was swayed but little by radical technical proposals and showed a magnificent resistance to being rushed into new things. Except for occasional flashes, his keen sense of humor was hidden behind a facial expression that was at least somber if not misanthropic.

Leadership at the division-head level was, for the most part, very effective though oddly diverse. The qualities just mentioned are well illustrated by a comparison of the leadership techniques employed by Harry Goett and Harvey Allen, two outstandingly successful division chiefs.

Harry Goett's name did not appear on any of the reports coming from his division and, except for providing advice and solid support, he did not himself become directly involved in carrying out a project: he was not in competition with his men. Nevertheless, Harry had a remarkable ability for guiding his men into new and useful lines of endeavor, for keeping them alert and moving ahead. One means that he used was his famous, or infamous, biweekly meetings for each branch in his division. These sessions were in the nature of inquisitions in which project heads were put on trial by Harry and their peers to ensure that nothing was lacking in the manner and method with which their projects were being conducted. The questions asked were very pointed and it was always with considerable apprehension

182

Victor I. Stevens.   *Steven E. Belsley.*

that each project leader contemplated his "day on the block." But despite the rigorous environment to which the members of Goett's division were subjected, the esprit de corps and the effectiveness of the division remained continuously at peak level.

Harvey Allen's leadership was entirely different from Harry's but equally effective. Harvey, unlike Harry, became emotionally involved with his work and his compulsive urge to carry on research personally would brook no interference. No matter to how high an administrative post his good work condemned him, he always found time for research; paper shuffling was never more than a troublesome sideline. Harvey's originality and research brilliance, combined with an agreeable outgoing personality, made him a natural leader—an example which the younger men of his staff strove to emulate. In research his team lunged forward like a pack of beagles with Harvey baying in the lead. It was a marvelous sight. Of course Harvey looked nothing like a beagle. In respect to appearance, he resembled a king-sized cherub charging about among the wind tunnels.

At the branch-head level, there were many at Ames who contributed mightily to the research output of their groups but, in most cases, modestly refrained from including their names on the reports. This extremely deserving group included men like Bill Harper, Bob Crane, Vic Stevens, and Charlie Frick, all of whom had demonstrated leadership potentialities well beyond the requirements of their positions. Indeed Vic Stevens, who was the first head of the SSFF Tunnel Branch, was in September 1953 made Assistant Chief of the High Speed Research Division under Harvey Allen. Similarly, there were men like Jack Stalder, Myles Erickson, Al Erickson, Steve Belsley, and, of course, many others whose names seldom appeared on reports but whose contributions were the life's blood of the Laboratory.

Steve Belsley, though not typical of Ames employees, was in many respects the classic example of a research engineer. His mind was keen, analytical, and intensely practical. He was also rough-edged, undiplomatic, and quite intolerant of technical fraud, political expedients, or devious approaches. When such appeared in technical conferences, his derisive laughter and snide, sotto voce comments jarred the decorum of the meeting. Despite his bad-boy tactics, Steve was well liked and was respected by his men to whom he gave his confidence and firm support—along with a few verbal arrows. An effective branch head, Belsley was a typical product of Harry Goett's school of research leadership.

Of such individuals as those described was the technical management at Ames composed. They, together with the others at the Laboratory, created a lively, open-minded environment in which research flourished.

7

....

Facilities

SUPERSONIC WIND TUNNELS

THE new 10- by 14-inch hypersonic wind tunnel was put into operation in 1950. It was described by Al Eggers and George Nothwang in TN 3095, and some of the related work on air condensation was reported in TN 2690 by Fred Hansen and George Nothwang.

The unique supersonic free-flight wind tunnel was also put into useful operation in 1950. This tunnel was described by Al Seiff in TR 1222 (ref. B–17) and a description of its unusual instrumentation is presented in RM A52A18 by Messrs. Briggs, Kerwin, and Schmidt of the Research Instrumentation Division.

During the period 1949–1952, the Ames 1- by 3-Foot Tunnel Section put forward numerous proposals for improving the performance—increasing the ranges of Mach and Reynolds numbers—of its No. 1, continuous-flow tunnel. For one reason or another, these proposals were rejected and it was not until 1953 that the latest version was presented to Congress as a part of the NACA fiscal year 1954 appropriations request. The principal change specified in the proposal was a doubling of the power used to drive the tunnel. The power increase was to be obtained by applying forced-draft cooling to the 2500-horsepower motors driving each of the four original compressors and by adding a fifth compressor driven by a 9000-horsepower motor. A further improvement, in the form of downstream injection, was also contemplated. Diverting some of the compressor output to the supersonic diffuser exit would make it possible to reduce the inlet pressure required for starting and thus, also, the starting shock loads on the model. With these modifications, it was expected that the Mach number of the tunnel could be increased to 4.0 and the Reynolds number to about 1.5 million per foot—well over the RN at which an undesirable phenomenon known as "laminar separation" occurs.

Plans also were made during this period to replace the unsatisfactory electrically operated flexible throats with which the 1- by 3-foot tunnels were then equipped. Designed for this purpose, by Paul Radach, was a new type of throat having walls flexed and positioned by a set of positive, fast-acting hydraulic jacks. The new throat, with which each of the tunnels was later to be equipped, would allow Mach-number settings to be made in seconds where the old throats had required hours for the same changes.

Ames' work in the fields of low-density aerodynamics and heat transfer had begun on a modest scale. The first facilities were small and, although they were performing usefully, their deficiencies were all too apparent. The low-density tunnel when in operation became nearly filled with boundary layer; moreover, it was designed for a density that was somewhat below the practical range of interest. The 6- by 6-inch heat-transfer tunnel was also too small and too slow, and it lacked any means for adding heat to the airstream. Yet while these deficiencies were being noted, the research fields in which such facilities could potentially contribute were becoming increasingly important. In particular, the problems of the ballistic missile were looming larger; and it was realized that aeronautical scientists, having recently conquered the mighty sonic barrier, were now confronted with an equally formidable obstacle—the heat barrier. New facilities to investigate problems of heat transfer and low-density aerodynamics were thus felt to be necessary.

Proposals for new low-density and heat-transfer wind tunnels were included in the fiscal year budgets for 1950 and 1951 and were approved in 1951. Construction began in 1952. The estimated cost of the two facilities was about $1.3 million. Covered in this estimate were an 8-inch-diameter low-density tunnel, a 10- by 10-inch heat-transfer tunnel, and a new building to house the two facilities. The building would be adjacent to the 12-foot-tunnel auxiliaries building where supplementary air power could conveniently be drawn from the 12-foot compressors. It was amazing how many parasites the 12-foot tunnel had attracted.

The 8-inch low-density tunnel would be of the nonreturn type, powered and evacuated by steam ejection pumps. It would be designed to operate at a density corresponding to an altitude range of from 20 to 40 miles. By removal of boundary layer through porous nozzle walls, a 6-inch-diameter usable jet was believed obtainable at a Mach number of 3.0 and a somewhat smaller diameter jet at the top Mach number of 5.0. The Reynolds number, of course, would be very low—under 10,000. The tunnel was described in TN 4142 authored by Marc Creager.

The 10- by 10-inch heat-transfer tunnel, as planned, would be a continuous-flow tunnel of the return type and would be equipped with a special link-type variable nozzle allowing operation at Mach numbers from 2 to 5. The tunnel would be operated on air from its own compressor augmented by air from the compressors of the 12-foot tunnel. With this power source, stagnation pressures up to 10 atmospheres would be attainable as would also

High-temperature test section of 10- by 10-inch heat-transfer tunnel.

Reynolds numbers of 24 million or more. To extend the possible range of heat-transfer measurements in the tunnel, an electric heater capable of heating the inlet air to 1000° F was provided. Never before at Ames had a wind tunnel been designed to operate at so high an air temperature.

The new low-density and heat-transfer tunnels were still under construction as 1953 ended; but, throughout the 1950–1953 period, research was proceeding in the old facilities, particularly in the old heat-transfer tunnel.

Transonic Wind Tunnels

Since the end of the war, aerodynamicists and aircraft designers had been most apprehensive about the problems to be encountered in the transonic range of flight. The dancing shock waves, separated flows, and violent disturbances which seemed inherent in this flow regime were alarming. Fear of the unknown was a psychological aspect of the problem; transonic aerodynamics was not well understood because, for one reason, the transonic range represented a blind spot in the test spectrum of existing wind tunnels. Another reason was that the confused pattern of transonic flow did not lend itself to theoretical treatment. However, in 1947–1948, the work of John Stack and his colleagues at Langley opened the way to the design of transonic tunnels, and soon thereafter light was shed on the little-known phenomena of the transonic range. Theory came a little later in this case, following, rather than leading, experiment.

Transonic tunnels suddenly became *de rigueur* for all aeronautical research agencies and the effort and expense of acquiring them may perhaps have exceeded the point of diminishing returns. The transonic range was clearly not a place for an airplane to linger, and it later became common practice to remain just below this range or to push through it so fast that the disturbing effects were of minor consequence. But these practices could not always be followed, and in any case there were many useful things to be done with transonic tunnels. Indeed, the payoff for the construction of the first transonic tunnel at Langley was immediate and huge. In 1951 the unique capabilities of this tunnel allowed Richard Whitcomb to confirm, and thus bring into early use, an important design principle. This principle, dubbed "Area Rule," made possible large reductions in the "brick wall" of transonic drag that heretofore had prevented most airplanes from reaching supersonic speeds. The Area Rule principle had existed in theory prior to Whitcomb's work but, as is frequently the case, the significance of the theory remained largely unrecognized until revealed by experiment.[1]

At Ames the first tunnel modified for transonic operation was the 1-by-3½, but the modification of the 1-by-3½ was only a small part of the transonic-wind-tunnel program undertaken at the Laboratory. Proposals to convert the 16-foot tunnel to a 14- by 14-foot transonic tunnel were put forward by the Laboratory in 1947, 1948, and 1949. Also, in 1950, plans were laid to build an 11- by 11-foot transonic tunnel as a part of the Ames Unitary Plan facility. As a pilot model for the 11- by 11-foot tunnel, a 2- by 2-foot tunnel was built in 1951. Finally, in 1953, plans were made to modify the 6- by 6-foot supersonic tunnel in a way that would allow it to cover the transonic range. The total amount of time and money involved in these plans was rather large.

There was quite a little resistance both in Washington and at Ames to the proposal for converting the 16-foot tunnel. The $2 million originally invested in the tunnel had been amply repaid by its contributions, but the conversion was to cost a whopping $9 million. An important justification offered for the conversion was that a large transonic tunnel was needed to fill the gap between the test ranges of the 16-foot and the 6- by 6-foot tunnels. The justification seemed valid at the time, but was later weakened when the 6-by-6 itself was converted for transonic operation. And since power was already available in a supersonic tunnel, there was a practical question as to whether it was not more feasible to convert a supersonic, rather than a subsonic, tunnel to transonic operation.

Some people at Ames felt the conversion of the 16 foot represented a very poor investment. "A damned waste of money," said Carl Bioletti, who argued strongly against the undertaking. The transonic problem, he felt, would be solved by simpler means long before such grandiose facilities as

---

[1] The concept of Area Rule is further discussed in the next chapter.

the 14- by 14-foot tunnel were completed. The arguments pro and con seemed to hinge on whether transonic problems were of a transient or a long-range nature. And there was the further consideration that it was always easier to get money from Congress for a modification than for a new tunnel. In congressional eyes, a new facility meant additional staff, a larger activity, and a permanent increase in annual operating costs. The modification of the 16-foot tunnel could perhaps thus be regarded as a relatively easy, if not a wholly efficient, method of augmenting the Ames test facilities.

Those who favored the 16-foot conversion prevailed. Congress approved the expenditure and design work got under way. The modifications to the 16 foot would be extensive—essentially a new tunnel. It would still operate at one atmosphere stagnation pressure but would have both a transonic throat and a flexible nozzle and would be powered by a new axial-flow compressor driven by motors totaling 110,000 horsepower. Construction began in 1951–1952 and was still under way at the end of 1953.

Actually Ames did not launch into the modification of the 16 foot or the construction of the 11- by 11-foot transonic leg of the Unitary Plan facility without a great deal of preparatory work at small scale. This work led to a variation of the transonic throat design originally developed and first used at Langley. Both laboratories recognized the purposes of a transonic throat: (1) to eliminate choking; (2) to allow speed changes to progress smoothly from subsonic to supersonic while maintaining a uniform velocity distribution in the test section; and (3) to absorb shock waves by the tunnel walls, thus preventing reflection of the waves back onto the test model.

Langley felt that these objectives could be accomplished reasonably well, and most simply and quickly, by a fixed-geometry ventilated throat. Harvey Allen and others at Ames felt that a useful improvement could be made to the Langley version by adding a simple flexible nozzle just ahead of the fixed ventilated throat. The flexible nozzle would relieve the ventilated throat of the task of providing flow uniformity, thus allowing more freedom in the design of the throat as a wave trap to prevent reflected shock waves. This improvement would add complexity and cost but it was thought would be worthwhile. Moreover, the simple single-jack nozzle which Allen designed for the purpose was not required to be very precise in its operation, for any wave disturbance that it produced in the flow would be removed by the wave-trap action of the ventilated walls. Allen's theories of transonic throat design were first tried out in an experimental 5- by 5-inch nozzle which the Laboratory built and also in the 1- by 3½-foot tunnel. They were then incorporated in a new 2- by 2-foot transonic tunnel which, during 1951, was built inside the loop of the 40-by-80. Although the 2-by-2 was considered a pilot model for the 11-by-11, it also served as a very useful research facility and was the first wind tunnel at Ames that was built from the start with transonic capabilities.

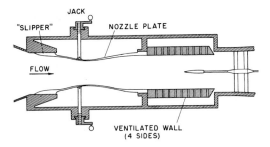

Schematic drawing of single-jack ventilated throat.

Model installed in 2- by 2-foot transonic tunnel. Air passes through the corrugations. Segmented schlieren windows are mounted between corrugations.

The 2- by 2-foot transonic tunnel was designed to operate through ranges of Mach number from 0.60 to 1.4, of Reynolds number from 1 to 8.7 million per foot of model length, and of static pressures from 0.16 to 2.33 atmospheres. It was quite a versatile facility and was the first Ames tunnel to use the new color schlieren technique. Color added definition to schlieren pictures and compensated for errors arising from flexibilities or other inaccuracies in the mountings of the optical components of the schlieren system. It was thus particularly valuable in transonic wind tunnels where windows were broken into segments by the ventilating slots. Joseph Spiegel and

Frank Lawrence, who contributed much to the design and use of the 2-by-2, described the tunnel in RM A55I21.

During this period of transonic-tunnel excitement, Ames put forward a proposal to boost the power of the 12-foot tunnel by 50,000 horsepower to a total of 60,000. The idea was not, at least not immediately, to make the tunnel transonic but rather to increase the operating pressures, thus Reynolds numbers, at high subsonic speeds. As the proposed power augmentation involved many costly modifications to the tunnel, the proposal was rejected by higher authorities. Thus the operating characteristics of the 12-foot tunnel remained unchanged except that, near the end of the period, the maximum operating pressure was, for reasons of safety, reduced to 5 atmospheres from its original value of 6.

Unitary Plan Facility

The amount ($75 million) finally appropriated for NACA Unitary Plan facilities was considerably less than had been authorized and expected. The building program thus had to be greatly curtailed and every effort made to economize. The funds appropriated would provide one major facility at each laboratory. Of the Unitary Plan facilities, an 8-foot, Mach 0.7 to 3.5 tunnel planned for Ames had been assigned highest priority and its construction was now scheduled to proceed, although at a reduced budget of a little over $27 million. A slightly lower priority had been given to a 4- by 4-foot Mach 1.5 to 5.0 missile-development tunnel at Langley, and to a large supersonic propulsion tunnel at Lewis.[2] The construction of all, however, was to proceed with minimum delay.

Design work on the Ames Unitary Plan wind tunnel began late in 1949 and it was soon discovered that the 8-foot dimension originally adopted for the tunnel was impractical. Instead, by clever design, it was found possible within the limited budget to have three tunnels. To achieve this worthy objective, the three tunnels were to be in the form of a Siamese triplet, if the term will be allowed, in that they were to have certain important and expensive elements in common. This arrangement provided for an 11- by 11-foot transonic tunnel (Mach 0.7 to 1.4), a 9- by 7-foot supersonic tunnel (Mach 1.55 to 2.5), and an 8- by 7-foot supersonic tunnel (Mach 2.45 to 3.45), all capable of operating at stagnation pressures ranging from 0.1 to 2.0 atmospheres.

The major common element of the tunnel complex was an enormous electric powerplant consisting of four intercoupled motors capable of generating a total of 240,000 horsepower continuously. With but one powerplant, only one tunnel, or leg, could operate at a time; however, this limita-

---

[2] Priority was established by representatives of NACA, military, industry, and universities. Stated in minutes of meeting of NACA Panel on Research Facilities in Washington, D.C., Dec. 16, 1949.

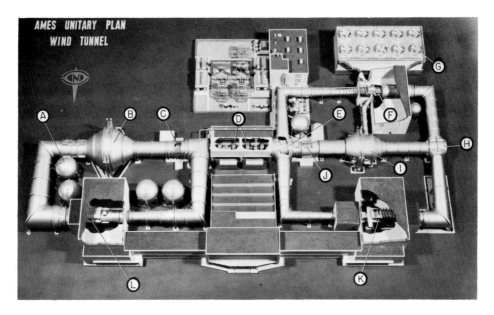

Model of Unitary Plan wind tunnel. (A) Dry air storage spheres, (B) Aftercooler, (C) 3-stage axial flow fan, (D) Drive motors, (E) Flow diversion valve, (F) 8- by 7-foot supersonic test section, (G) Cooling tower, (H) Flow diversion valve, (I) Aftercooler, (J) 11-stage axial flow compressor, (K) 9- by 7-foot supersonic test section, and (L) 11- by 11-foot transonic test section.

tion was felt to offer no serious handicap, as supersonic tunnels seldom operated more than a third of the time. Other common elements of the two supersonic legs were a portion of tunnel tube and an 11-stage axial-flow compressor. The compressor, made of steel the better to resist heat, was a massive machine. Its 22-foot-diameter rotor contained 1,122 solid-chrome-steel blades and weighed 445 tons. The momentum of the rotor was, indeed, so great that the rotor, while operating at low air density, would have taken up to 2 hours to come to rest after power was shut off had not electrodynamic braking been provided. The difficult problem of matching the output of the compressor to the widely varying air volume and pressure requirements of the two tunnels was solved by providing a variable-speed drive for the motors as well as means for bypassing air around the 8- by 7-foot nozzle.

The use of a common portion of tunnel tube, for the two supersonic legs, was necessitated by the fact that the common compressor was contained in this portion of the tube. So that the common portion of the tube might be used in either of the supersonic tunnels, it was necessary to install a flow diversion valve at each end of that portion of the tube. These valves were of unique design, 20 feet or more in diameter, and weighed over 250 tons—the largest airtight valves of this type ever built. Designed by Paul Radach

192

of the Ames staff, the valves were but another unusual feature of a most unusual wind-tunnel facility.

The 11- by 11-foot transonic tunnel had its own, separate, air circuit and its own compressor—a huge three-stage unit with aluminum blades. But it used the same powerplant as the other tunnels. The powerplant was equipped with clutches by means of which its four motors could be connected to either the 11-stage or the 3-stage compressor.

The transonic throat of the 11- by 11-foot tunnel incorporated a single-jack flexible nozzle and a slotted section—the same system that had been developed for the 2- by 2-foot tunnel. The 8- by 7-foot tunnel was equipped with a symmetrical, flexible-wall throat, the sidewalls of which were positioned by a system of jacks operated by hydraulic motors. The 9- by 7-foot tunnel, on the other hand, had an asymmetric sliding-block-type nozzle. It also had a flexible upper plate by means of which any minor flow corrections that later seemed necessary could be made.

The shell of the Ames Unitary Plan facility was constructed of welded steel plates from 1 to 2½ inches thick. Its supporting structure was designed with unusual care to allow for thermal expansion and to resist 0.2-g seismic side loads. The shell was designed as a pressure vessel to operate at static pressures ranging from 0.1 to 2.0 atmospheres; the critical loads were found

11-stage compressor of the Unitary Plan wind tunnel.

to occur in the low-pressure range of operation. Hydraulic tests to confirm the integrity of the shell were considered unnecessary.

Construction of the Ames Unitary Plan facility began in 1950–1951 and was still under way at the end of 1953. The facility was certainly a landmark in the development of more or less conventional supersonic wind tunnels. In it, such wind tunnels had probably reached the ultimate in size, complexity, and refinement. The facility was the largest, most complex, supersonic wind-tunnel system ever built by NACA and certainly the most costly ever erected at the Ames laboratory. Moreover, it appeared that, in view of trends developing in aeronautical research, the Ames facility represented perhaps the end of the line in large, continuous-flow wind-tunnel construction. The extreme conditions of flight now becoming of interest to aeronautical engineers would doubtlessly require smaller, specialized facilities having short operating periods.

The Ames Unitary Plan facility spoke well of the design skill of NACA engineers. Among those of the Ames staff who were most responsible for its design and construction were Jack Parsons, Ralph Huntsberger, Gerald McCormack, Lloyd Jones, Adrien Anderson, Paul Radach, Edward Wasson, Joseph Spiegel, and Norman Martin. Others, such as Loren Bright, Ed Perkins, and Alun Jones, made important contributions in getting the new facility into operation. A paper describing the Ames Unitary Plan wind tunnel was prepared by Lloyd Jones and Ralph Huntsberger, and the Ames philosophy of large wind-tunnel design is given in a paper (ref. B–18) entitled "The Design of Large High-Speed Wind Tunnels," by Ralph F. Huntsberger and John F. Parsons.

GUNS and GUN TUNNELS

It now appeared that for simulating the flight of ballistic missiles, which travel at very high speeds in the upper atmosphere, the usefulness of continuous-flow tunnels was rapidly diminishing. The thermal conditions encountered by such missiles were so extreme that neither the model nor the wind tunnel, nor for that matter the missile itself, could withstand them for any length of time.

In view of the limitations of continuous-flow tunnels, Ames engineers turned their attention to the design and development of special research devices in which the extreme conditions of missile flight could be produced for brief periods of time. Such facilities would, of course, greatly increase the importance and cost of individual data points; and the development of instrumentation to recover data on so fleeting a basis would certainly tax the ingenuity of the Laboratory's designers. Moreover, the transient flow conditions would greatly complicate the analysis of such data as were obtained. The disadvantages of transient-flow test facilities were all too apparent, but how else were the extreme conditions of flight to be investigated in an earth-bound laboratory?

At Ames the supersonic free-flight tunnel represented the first important step taken by the Laboratory in the development of transient-flow test devices. The next step was taken with the arrival, in January 1952, of Dr. Alex Charters. Alex came from the Aberdeen Proving Ground where he had acquired considerable experience with ballistic ranges, in which bullets fired down the range are observed in flight by means of special optical instrumentation. Alex was assigned to the SSFF tunnel, reporting to Alvin Seiff, who was then in charge of that facility. As his first assignment, Alex was encouraged by Seiff to undertake the design and development of a special model-launching gun similar to, but hopefully better than, one that had been developed for range work by the New Mexico School of Mines. When developed, the Ames gun, it was expected, would be used to shoot simple models down an instrumented test range. Such a test arrangement had, indeed, already been demonstrated in the SSFF tunnel by launchings made with zero tunnel airspeed.

The fastest ordinary rifles had muzzle velocities of about 4000 feet per second, and those that had been modified for use in the SSFF achieved velocities of perhaps 6000 feet per second. What Charters was attempting to do, however, was to develop a gun that would shoot simple bulletlike models at speeds of 10,000 feet per second or more. The gun would derive energy from exploding powder and use rifle barrels for accelerating tubes, but would otherwise bear little resemblance to a conventional rifle. In the new gun, exploding powder would drive a metal piston down a barrel (driving tube) compressing, just ahead of it, a charge of helium gas. The hot compressed gas would finally burst through a sealing diaphragm into a second barrel (launching tube) in which the test model would be located. The compressed helium gas would then propel the model out of the second barrel at terrific speed. The reaction would be taken by ejecting a second piston out of the driving tube in the opposite direction. The reaction piston was to be caught in a special "catcher." Since the gun in effect shot bullets in two, opposite, directions, it was named Janus and the range in which it was first used was called the Janus range. Inasmuch as the driving gas in the gun was helium, used because its small mass absorbed little accelerating energy, the gun was known by the generic name of "light-gas gun." It was on the development of such a device that Charters and his colleagues were working as 1953 ended.

Meanwhile Al Eggers had conceived the idea that a gun something like the one being developed by Alex Charters could be used to power a supersonic wind tunnel. In this case, the gas compressed by the piston—it did not have to be helium—would exit through a supersonic nozzle in which a test model could be rigidly mounted. Such a device, he felt, would generate a

195

high-temperature, high-Mach number gas flow for a sufficient length of time to allow data to be taken. A rather small-scale version of the gun tunnel, made with a barrel of 20-mm bore, was built in 1952 and actually used for certain heat-transfer measurements, which were reported by Eggers and Charters at the Conference on the Aerodynamics of High Speed Aircraft held at Ames in 1953. The gun tunnel produced flows at speeds up to 8200 feet per second for periods of about 1 second; but, as a result of flow unsteadiness arising from oscillations of the piston, it was not a very satisfactory research instrument. Although the gun tunnel, as built, was little used, it nevertheless represented a pioneering effort in the design of transient-flow wind tunnels and led to more useful developments.

The gun tunnel, it now appeared, might possibly be improved if the shock front of the exploding gas, rather than a metal body, were used as the driving means. This principle had, of course, been employed in shock tubes used elsewhere. Jack Stalder, and later Warren Ahtye, experimented with small shock tubes at the Laboratory, but Ames management considered it impracticable to compete with certain other groups, such as AVCO, which were further advanced in the design and use of such equipment. On the other hand, a shock-driven tunnel, producing a flow of relatively long duration, was regarded by Ames engineers as being a feasible development project as was also a shock-driven light-gas gun, for the launching of test models. In one case, the device would shoot air, or any chosen gas, past a fixed model; and, in the other, it would shoot a model into a stationary body of gas, as in a range. By applying the SSFF tunnel counterflow principle, two such devices could be put in opposition, one firing a model into an oncoming gas stream produced by the second. The relative velocities thus developed would be tremendous. These certainly were good ideas to work on, but associated development problems were of shocking complexity.

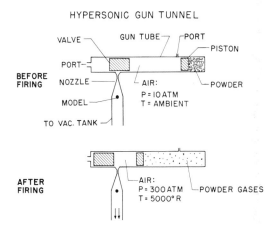

Schematic drawing showing principles of operation of original gun tunnel.

FACILITIES

Use of Gases Other Than Air

In wind-tunnel simulations, air had commonly, indeed almost universally, been used as the working fluid. Air seemed a logical choice for the simulation of flight in the earth's atmosphere but for the simulation of flight at very high speeds, where compressibility became an important factor, a case could be made for the use of some other gas mixture or gaseous element. For example, the troublesome liquefaction problem could be solved through the use of helium; and other benefits, such as the reduction of tunnel size, power, and cost, could conceivably be achieved through the use of various gas mixtures. During the period 1950–1953, the subject of the use of gas mixtures in wind tunnels was rather thoroughly and competently explored by Dean Chapman. The results of Chapman's work in this field appeared in TR 1259.

Helium was first used at Ames by Jack Stalder in the low-density tunnel and, for several years in succession, Ames had proposed the construction of a 1- by 1-foot helium tunnel for the simulation of very high Mach number flow. Each year and again in 1950, the proposal was turned down by Headquarters. Even at Ames there was some question about the use of helium for, although it did overcome the liquefaction problem, it nevertheless could not take the place of air in simulations of certain important conditions of flight.

Computing Facilities

The first electronic computing machine used at Ames was a Reeves Analog Computer (REAC) acquired in 1949. It was used by the Flight Research Section for control simulation work and, as this kind of work expanded, so also did the Laboratory's supply of analog-computer elements.

Ames in 1950 gave its first serious consideration to the use of electronic digital computers and the next year leased a Card Program Calculator (CPC) from IBM for wind-tunnel data reduction. Shortly, a second CPC was procured and a portion of the time of this machine was given over to the theoretical studies. However, in the 1951–1952 period, some of the more

Dr. William A. Mersman.

extensive theoretical calculations at the Laboratory were performed under contract by the U.S. Bureau of Standards Computing Center in Los Angeles.

In 1952 the computing-machine work at Ames had reached a level such as to justify the formation of an Electronic Computing Machine Section in the Theoretical and Applied Research Division. This Section, which was to deal only with digital computers, was established in May of that year with Dr. William Mersman as its head. Harold Harrison and Marcelline Chartz joined the computing section at that time. Harrison, who shortly became Assistant Section Head, concerned himself with the application of computers to the working up of wind-tunnel data. Mersman, on the other hand, devoted much of his time to the use of computers in theoretical research.

8

···

Research

PATTERN

AMES research during the 1950–1953 period was marked by a strong trend toward the more fundamental. A massive effort was made to develop the theory required for deeper understanding of transonic, supersonic, and hypersonic flows. The term "hypersonic," it should be noted, referred to a speed regime generally of Mach 5 and above, where linear theories, dependent on small disturbances, two-dimensionality, and constant gas properties, broke down. The trend toward fundamentality was also, and surprisingly, apparent in the field of flight research. The view being taken of the flight dynamics of an airplane and its relation to automatic electronic-guidance equipment was becoming increasingly scientific and sophisticated.

Of particular interest during this period was the dawning appreciation of the oneness of an airplane or a missile. In prewar days the wings of an airplane were regarded as assemblages of airfoil sections which required independent study. In the early postwar period it became clear that airfoil sections had lost much of their individual significance and that the wing had to be considered as a whole. Now, during this period, it was realized that the wings, body, and tail surfaces of an airplane or a missile were so powerfully interrelated that they could properly be dealt with only as a whole. Two factors were principally responsible for this situation. First, the fuselages of aircraft, and particularly of missiles, had become large relative to their wings; thus their mutual interference or interaction was great. Second, at transonic and supersonic speeds, the interferences between wings, bodies, and other components of an aircraft tended to be much more adverse than they were at subsonic speeds. In the higher ranges of speed, each component of the airplane produced a pressure wave which, depending on the arrangement of the components, would tend either to fortify or to cancel others; and when they fortified each other, the drag was usually much higher. The Area Rule developed by Whitcomb of Langley in 1951–1952 showed that, by properly

199

shaping and distributing the components of an airplane, the transonic drag could be greatly reduced. It was now clear that the airplane must be designed as a whole and that much greater care must be exercised in the placement of its various parts. Inasmuch as transonic drag was a major barrier to supersonic flight, the Area Rule discovery was regarded as an important breakthrough and was kept secret for several years.

Over the country, and the world, many people and agencies were now engaged in the ever-broadening field of aeronautical research. Thus it was often difficult to assign credit for the many overlapping accomplishments of the workers in this field. Research was in effect the game of trying to fill in the immensely complicated and endless jigsaw puzzle of nature with many players participating. The game would seem at one time to be approaching a standstill and then someone would lay down a key piece. This move would immediately inspire a great flurry of action. Players from all over the world would suddenly see how they could add to the pattern. A whole block would quickly be filled in and then the game would again slow down awaiting inspiration from the placing of some new key piece. Key pieces were obviously important but even they depended on the many pieces that had been laid before. Similarly the achievements of the Ames research men rested on contributions from many sources—sources too numerous and widespread to be properly credited in this volume.

Basic Configurations and Airflows

Wings. In the early postwar period the general lack of transonic and supersonic theory made it necessary for experiment to proceed without the guidance that theory normally provided. But the development of theory was pressed with considerable vigor and during this period the output of theoretical papers reached rather impressive proportions, much of this work relating to wings. At Ames, wing theory was advanced by several different groups and individuals. A team composed of Harvard Lomax, Max Heaslet, Franklyn Fuller, and Loma Sluder produced TR 1077 (ref. B–19), an important work on two- and three-dimensional unsteady lift problems in high-speed flight. Max Heaslet and John Spreiter, in TR 1119, made interesting and useful additions to the reciprocity theorem, which states that the drag of a nonlifting wing at supersonic speed is the same whether the wing moves forward or backward. The reciprocity theorem had earlier been confirmed by Walter Vincenti through tests of a delta wing in the 1- by 3-foot wind tunnel.

In TR 1183 Milton Van Dyke added to the general theory of unsteady wing lift by including nonlinear thickness effects; and, in TR 1217, John Spreiter and Alberta Alksne provided an interesting method of predicting pressure distributions on nonlifting airfoils at high subsonic speeds. In the same period, Alfred Eggers, Clarence Syvertson, and others of the 10- by 14-

inch-tunnel staff derived a shock-expansion method by means of which some hypersonic flows could be calculated with an accuracy comparable to that obtainable with the generally more precise but far more tedious method of characteristics. An example of the use of the shock-expansion method in calculating hypersonic airflows around airfoils is to be found in TR 1123 authored by Eggers, Syvertson, and Kraus.

It was not uncommon in the field of theoretical aerodynamics that flow patterns were expressed in terms of generalized mathematical formulas which could not readily be solved for any desired case. This situation prevailed in the field of transonic aerodynamics. Walter Vincenti and Cleo Wagoner found, however, that it was possible to use the equations of transonic small-disturbance theory to determine the aerodynamic characteristics of a double-wedge (elongated diamond) wing profile for the short range of supersonic speed that occurs just before the shock wave becomes attached to the leading edge.

As the flow around a wing (or fuselage) reaches the sonic speed, a shock wave forms across the flow just ahead of the wing. This normal shock wave moves closer as the speed increases and, if the wing has a sharp leading edge, it soon makes contact with the wing. With further speed increase, the shock inclines backward into the classical oblique wave, the angle of which is a function of Mach number. The flow condition which Vincenti and Wagoner chose to investigate, the one in which the normal wave had not quite made contact with the wing, was clearly of limited scope. But it was only because this condition offered the simplification of subsonic leading-edge flow that a solution was at all achievable.

The analysis produced by Vincenti and Wagoner is covered in TR 1095 (ref. B–20), dealing with nonlifting wings, and in TR 1180 (ref. B–21), which treats the case of a lifting wing operating at a small angle of attack. These reports, which delineated the useful scope of existing theory, are generally regarded as being of the high precision and quality that typified all of Vincenti's efforts. Vincenti's work was technically impeccable and his writings so lucid and unambiguous that editing could generally do only harm.

Solutions to transonic-flow equations had proved so difficult that alternative approaches of a simpler character were sought. Although exact solutions could not always be achieved, certain mathematical relationships were discovered which were common to all known exact solutions and presumably were basic to all solutions. These "similarity parameters," or "similarity rules," were particularly useful in correlating and giving meaning to the diverse experimental data that had been obtained in wind tunnels and in flight. The transonic similarity rules had been defined originally by von Kármán and others, but during this period their application was usefully expanded by John Spreiter in work published in TR 1153 (ref. B–22). This work not only contributed to similarity-rule knowledge but also provided a better interpretation of the few exact solutions that had been obtained by Vincenti and others.

An excellent example of the application of the transonic similarity rules was provided by John McDevitt in TR 1253 (ref. B–23). In this report, McDevitt was able to correlate a rather large amount of experimental transonic wing data which, as reported in TN 3501 and TN 3502, he together with Warren Nelson and Walter Krumm had obtained on the 16-foot-tunnel bump. The value of the transonic similarity rules for correlation purposes was clearly demonstrated in McDevitt's report.

In the meantime Dean Chapman's work on separated flows had led him into considerations of the optimum shape of airfoils for supersonic and hypersonic aircraft. There had been earlier indications that at high supersonic speeds the trailing edge of a minimum-drag airfoil should be blunt rather than sharp. This situation resulted from the fact that the suction losses behind a blunt trailing edge were more than offset by the lower pressure forces on the fore part of the airfoil made possible by the blunting. At hypersonic speeds the pressure forces on the fore part were predominant and, to minimize these forces, it was necessary to divert the oncoming air as little as possible. If it was assumed that some thickness of the airfoil was required for strength, minimum flow diversion would be accomplished if the airfoil was in the form of a thin wedge with an absolutely blunt, or bluff, trailing edge. At lower supersonic speeds, where the fore drag was somewhat less important, the trailing edge was rounded down (boat-tailed) a certain amount to reduce base suction drag. But how much should the airfoil be boat-tailed for any particular speed? This was the nature of the problem which Chapman attacked. His approach, of classic form, began with theory and ended with experiment. The theory is contained in TR 1063 (ref. B–24). The confirming experimentation, in which he was aided by William Wimbrow and Robert Kester, is reported in TR 1109 (ref. B–25).

Chapman's work had from the first been marked by breadth, originality, thoroughness, and genuinely scientific character. For his work on skin friction, base pressure, and heat transfer, he was in 1952 chosen to receive the Lawrence Sperry Award, one of the outstanding honors in aeronautics given annually by the Institute of the Aeronautical Sciences.

As noted, the theoretical research on wings during this period was extensive; the experimental work likewise was considerable. In the 7- by 10-foot tunnel, George McCullough and Don Gault continued their earlier work on the stalling mechanics of thin wings. This work was reported in TN 2502. Thin wings had an unfortunate habit of stalling suddenly as a result of separation of the flow at the leading edge. A possible solution to this problem was the application of suction through a porous surface installed over a portion of the leading edge. A study of porous materials suitable for

Dr. Dean R. Chapman.   *L. Frank Lawrence.*

such applications was made by the 7-by-10 team of Dannenberg, Weiberg, and Gambucci and reported in TN 3093 and TN 3094. At the same time, a rather extensive series of tests on tail surfaces was carried out in the 7- by-10 and the 12-foot wind tunnels; the results of these tests were summarized by Jules Dods and Bruce Tinling in TN 3497.

Airfoil studies in the 1- by $3\frac{1}{2}$-foot tunnel were continuing and this work was aided by the development of some special instrumentation which made oscillating shock waves and vortical wake flows appear to stand still. This useful device, worked out by Frank Lawrence, Jeff Buck, Stanley Schmidt, and Floyd Looschen, is described in TN 2509 entitled "A Self-Synchronizing Stroboscopic Schlieren System for the Study of Unsteady Air Flows."

The study of wing planforms begun so enthusiastically in the early post-war years carried over into the current period; and the results of a large part of this work, performed in several wind tunnels at Ames, are summarized in RM A53A30 entitled "Lift, Drag and Pitching Moment of Low Aspect Ratio Wings," by Charles F. Hall. This report gives particular attention to airplane configurations having delta, or triangular, wing planforms and likewise considers the matter of twisting and cambering delta wings to reduce the increment of wing drag caused by lift.

As the angle of attack of a wing is increased to produce lift, the resultant force vector tilts backward, thus increasing its component in the drag

203

direction. This additional increment of drag, due to lift, is reduced by any leading-edge suction that may be generated by the wing. Although theory indicates that a plane wing with leading edges swept within the Mach cone will develop leading-edge suction, in actuality the predicted suction does not appear. It was realized that the higher drag-due-to-lift resulting from this unfortunate circumstance could significantly reduce the performance of supersonic airplanes in climb and cruising and could curtail their range. In his investigation of this matter, Charlie Hall found that a substantial reduction of drag-due-to-lift could be achieved with a delta-wing airplane if the wing was twisted and suitably cambered throughout its span. For practical reasons it was desirable, he found, to incorporate the camber only in the forward portion of the wing. In the selected arrangement the cambered part of the wing appears as a segment of a cone varying linearly in extent from zero at the root to a maximum at the tip. Ames engineers felt that conical camber had the potential for significantly improving the performance of future delta-wing airplanes.

Bodies. Al Eggers and his staff in the 10- by 14-inch tunnel were in charge of one of the first hypersonic test facilities at Ames and thus eagerly sought, by both theoretical and experimental means, to advance the science of hypersonic aerodynamics. As Al was a very able and energetic leader with a very good staff, progress was quite rapid. The theoretical attack was headed by Eggers himself, with effective support provided by Clarence Syvertson, Raymond Savin, Frank Hamaker, Stanford Neice, Thomas Wong, and others. In their theoretical work these individuals made use of the existing method of characteristics to develop the more amenable shock-expansion method for computing hypersonic airflow patterns. The shock-expansion method accounted for the entropy rise in oblique shocks and also, to some extent, allowed for changes in gas properties arising from the high temperatures produced by shock waves.

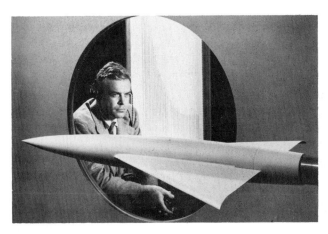

Charles Hall and conical-camber wing.

RESEARCH

In TR 1249 (ref. B–26), Eggers and Savin applied shock-expansion methods to the flow around bodies of revolution. In this work they made use of an earlier determined hypersonic similarity parameter represented by the ratio of the free-stream Mach number to the fineness ratio of the body. Hypersonic similarity rules had themselves been studied (TR 1147 by Hamaker, Neice, and Wong, as well as TN 2250 by Ehret, Rossow, and Stevens) with a resulting extension of their range of application.

In the meantime, Milton Van Dyke had become interested in second-order supersonic-flow theory. He made a number of contributions in this field, beginning in 1949 with his doctoral thesis at Caltech (later published as TR 1081) which dealt in particular with flow over cones. Van Dyke's work continued in TR 1194 entitled "A Study of Hypersonic Small-Disturbance Theory" (ref. B–27).

Whenever possible, theory was checked by experiment and, for the experimental study of hypersonic flows over bodies, the supersonic free-flight tunnel was very useful. One of the early reports from that facility was RM A52A14b entitled "Experimental Investigation of the Drag of 30°, 60°, and 90° Cone Cylinders at Mach Numbers between 1.5 and 8.2", by Alvin Seiff and Simon C. Sommer. There was at this time considerable interest in the problem of determining the optimum shape of a body for supersonic and hypersonic flight. Because the pressure forces on the forebody represented such an important part of hypersonic body drag, the determination of the shape of the forebody was considered a most important phase of the overall problem. The noses of many of the bodies tested were in the form of sharp pointed cones. This choice of nose was convenient since, in most theories, sharp-nosed bodies had been assumed, but there was considerable interest also in the effect of rounding the nose. A coordinated program of body tests was conducted in the 1- by 3-foot and the supersonic free-flight tunnels. This program, concerned mainly with nose shapes and covering a Mach-number range of 1.24 to 7.4, is reported in TR 1386 (ref. B–28) by Edward Perkins, Leland Jorgensen, and Simon Sommer. Jorgensen had earlier derived optimum nose shapes for flight at various Mach numbers and had noted that, as far as pressure drag was concerned, the optimum shapes for supersonic and hypersonic flight were much the same.

Wing-Body Interference. For a number of years the trend in the design of supersonic airplanes and missiles had been toward vehicles with larger, longer bodies and smaller, shorter wings. This trend was accentuated in missile design where it was common practice to use small wings in cruciform configuration and where considerable dependence was placed on the lift of the body itself. A separate set of control surfaces was often mounted on the forebody. The aerodynamic interference and interaction between the various surfaces and the body became a matter of great importance to designers. The lifting body produced a pair of vortices, as Allen and Perkins had shown; and these, combined with the vortices, shock waves, and down-wash fields generated by the lifting surfaces, contributed to an extremely complex, mixed-up flow pattern. It would be supposed that no one would have the courage to attempt a theoretical study of such complicated interference phenomena but that is exactly what Jack Nielsen of the 1- by 3-foot-tunnel staff undertook to do. He spent several years studying various phases of the wing-body interference problem and in confirming his theories through wind-tunnel tests. Representative of the work that Jack did during this period was the theoretical-experimental study reported in TR 1252 (ref. B–29). Another example of his work is TR 1307 (ref. B–30), a study in which he collaborated with William Pitts and George Kaattari. Confirmation of Nielsen's theories was provided by Tom Canning and Pat Denardo in RM A52C24, which covered a program of tests in the supersonic free-flight tunnel on the lift and the center of pressure of low-aspect-ratio cruciform and rectangular wings in combination with a slender fuselage at Mach numbers up to 6.2.

Area Rule. One of the most significant developments of this period was the discovery, by Richard Whitcomb of Langley, of a method, called the Transonic Area Rule, for reducing the transonic drag of aircraft.[1] Actually the theoretical basis for the Area Rule had been established a little earlier, but it was not until Whitcomb, using the new transonic tunnel at Langley, made his independent discovery that the significance of the method was fully appreciated. The Transonic Area Rule expresses the concept that the transonic drag of an airplane is strongly dependent on the distribution of the cross-sectional area of the airplane, including the wing and all other components, and that as far as pressure drag is concerned the airplane could be represented by a body of revolution having the same longitudinal distribution of cross-sectional area as the airplane.

The optimum distribution of area was not precisely determined by Whitcomb, but it was concluded that the area distribution curve should be nicely rounded and free of sharp peaks or humps. The fuselage of a transonic airplane usually had an area distribution of this kind, but the addition of a wing, an engine nacelle, or a wing-tip fuel tank produced a hump in the area curve which caused the pressure drag of the airplane in the transonic range to rise to a high peak. Airplanes that designers hoped would be supersonic were thus sometimes limited to sonic speed as a result of unexpectedly high transonic drag. Whitcomb showed that the hump in the area curve, and thus the high transonic drag, could be eliminated if the added area contributed by the wing was balanced by a deliberate reduction in the cross-sectional area of the fuselage at the wing juncture. The resulting fuselage shape had a constriction like a Coca-Cola bottle, and the terms "Coke bottle" or "Marilyn Monroe" fuselage were often heard.

---

[1] See preceding chapter.

B–58 model in tunnel, which incorporates conical camber and Coke-bottle fuselage.

As it turned out, necking the fuselage was only one of several measures that could be taken to improve the area distribution. Although it was generally desirable to reduce the cross-sectional area as much as possible, a nicely rounded area curve could sometimes only be achieved by adding area to the fuselage at strategic points. Also it became clear that, on airplanes carrying externally mounted bodies such as engine nacelles, rocket pods, and fuel tanks, an opportunity was provided the designer to arrange these various items in such a way as to obtain a desirable area curve and a low transonic drag.

The Area Rule discovery precipitated a surge of research-and-development activity throughout the country that clearly would last for several years. At Ames the Area Rule was confirmed by tests in available transonic facilities and also by means of the drop-test technique which the Ames Flight Engineering Branch had developed. Representative of the Area Rule drop-test work was a study reported in RM A54F22 entitled "An Experimental Investigation of Reduction in Transonic Drag Rise at Zero Lift by the Addition of Volume to the Fuselage of a Wing-Body-Tail Configuration and a Comparison with Theory," by George H. Holdaway.

The Transonic Area Rule at the time of its discovery had a very limited theoretical basis, a condition which certain members of the Ames staff took immediate steps to correct. One of the early contributors to Area Rule theory at Ames was R. T. Jones, who reviewed the whole subject in TR

1284 (ref. B–31) and introduced the concept of the Supersonic Area Rule. Through measurement of the area along Mach cones rather than along transverse cross sections, the Supersonic Area Rule made it possible to minimize the drag of an airplane for any chosen supersonic Mach number. TR 1284 was a substantial contribution to the theory and application of the general Area Rule.

Another group at Ames, comprising Barrett Baldwin and Robert Dickey, approached the Area Rule problem with a slightly different viewpoint. They observed that the Transonic Area Rule minimized the drag at sonic speed and the Supersonic Area Rule minimized it at some specific supersonic speed; but what was needed, they felt, was a method of minimizing the drag over a range of transonic and low supersonic speeds. In RM A54J19, Baldwin and Dickey developed a theory, known as the Moment of Area Rule, which, as confirmed by tests in the 2- by 2-foot tunnel, accomplished the desired objective to a useful degree.

PROPELLERS AND INLETS

Although at this time the use of jet propulsion was well established, there was still considerable interest in propellers. The turboprop engine was felt to be applicable where takeoff thrust and cruising efficiency were important; such applications included cargo, transport, and reconnaissance types of aircraft, some having high-speed capabilities. Propeller requirements were now substantially different from what they had been when reciprocating engines were in vogue. The power to be absorbed was much greater than for a reciprocating engine and airplane speeds were generally higher. On some of the faster airplanes, propellers would have to operate efficiently at supercritical, if not supersonic, tip speeds.

To satisfy these requirements, a new class of propellers was being developed, the performance of which remained to be evaluated. To perform this service, and to learn more about the subject in general, the 12-foot tunnel in 1951 began an extensive series of propeller investigations. Some of the first work in this program was reported by Robert Reynolds, Robert Sammonds, and John Walker in TR 1336 (ref. B–32). In this phase of the program, advanced types of blades were tested at both forward and reverse thrust in configurations representing four-blade, single-rotation and eight-blade, dual-rotation propellers. The propellers were tested at wind-tunnel speeds up to Mach 0.84, but at tip Mach numbers up to 1.4.

Meanwhile in the 40-by-80, a research team led by Vernon Rogallo and Paul Yaggy was investigating the unsteady airloads to which propellers are subjected while operating in nonuniform flow fields such as might be encountered in front of straight or swept wings that are producing lift. Of principal concern to the investigators was the structural integrity of propellers as affected by the stresses arising from such unsteady airloads. Examples of work performed in this program are contained in TN 2308 and TN 2957.

Inlet work continued during this period but at a fairly moderate pace. Studies in this field were carried out in the 7- by 10-foot and the 1- by 3-foot tunnels as well as by Flight Engineering through the use of drop-test models. One of the more significant contributions during this period was TR 1141, entitled "Method and Graphs for the Evaluation of Air Induction Systems," by George B. Brajnikoff.

DYNAMIC STABILITY AND LOADS

Problems concerned with dynamic stability and loads received a limited amount of attention from Ames research groups from 1950 to 1953. As indicated in TR 1088, the theory of missile dynamics was advanced through the efforts of Gaynor Adams and Duane Dugan of the 6- by 6-foot tunnel. Contributions were also made in this field by Robert Chubb and Dave Reese of the same Branch.

The Laboratory's experimental efforts in the study of aircraft dynamics included some interesting drop tests by Norman Bergrun of the Flight Engineering Branch. These tests, reported in TN 2985, confirmed the existence of a peculiar type of inertia-coupling instability that William Phillips of Langley had predicted. The instability was characteristic of aircraft of advanced type having long fuselages and short wings.

While Bergrun was making his drop tests, Ben Beam, in the 12-foot tunnel, was giving further attention to the pitch damping of triangular wings; and Alfred Boissevain, in the SSFF tunnel, was measuring the damping in roll of triangular wing-body arrangements at Mach numbers up to 6.0. The SSFF tunnel was particularly good for this sort of work as the test model was completely free.

In addition to the tests just mentioned, a number of transonic wing buffeting and flutter studies were made in the 16-foot tunnel using the transonic bump for some and, for others, a demountable, two-dimensional throat installed in the test section. Of the buffeting studies, one was made by Charles Coe and Jack Mellenthin, and another by Andrew Martin and James Reed. Data from the latter study were confirmed by flight tests of the F8F–1 and the X–1 airplanes. The flutter studies were performed by Robert Barnes, Raymond Herrera, John Wyss, and James Monfort and are reported in RM A51I25, RM A54A29, and RM A54C24.

The theoretical studies of static airloads on wings of arbitrary planform, studies far advanced in the early postwar years, were continued during this period. In TR 1071, John DeYoung extended his span-load analysis to include the effects of flap deflection. Lynn Hunton and Harry James, in TN 3040, used the DeYoung method to predict loads on swept wings with both leading-edge slats and flaps.

FLIGHT RESEARCH

Guidance and Control. A large part of the work of the Flight Research Branch falls naturally into the field of guidance and control. Under the leadership of Harry Goett, Larry Clousing, and Steve Belsley, the work of this Branch was advancing along new and productive lines. With the advent of automatic control for airplanes and missiles, the dynamic behavior of aircraft was being looked at in a much more sophisticated and scientific light than ever before. The pilot with his enormous ability to compromise and adapt had been able to compensate for the imprecision of existing design knowledge regarding airplane dynamics; but the electronic and mechanical servo systems that would now guide our aircraft did not have these rare abilities. If we were to let electromechanical systems fly our aircraft, we must be able to describe with great precision, and in a language meaningful to such systems, exactly how the aircraft might be expected to respond to a deflection of its control surfaces. Thus any successful attack on the problem would require the marrying of two rather diverse disciplines—one being flight aerodynamics and the other electronics and servomechanisms.

Also to be considered were the cases in which a combination of human and electronic guidance would be required. These cases would include fighters with computing gunsights and interceptors with automatic or semiautomatic missile fire-control systems. Here a compatibility between human and electronic elements would have to be achieved. The resulting system would be expected to satisfy essential requirements of both pilot and electromechanical system. The whole picture clearly indicated that flight research had taken a quantum jump in complexity and sophistication.

Swept wing Problems. By no means was all of the flight research during this period concerned with exotic new trends. Investigations were made, for example, of the special stability and control problems of sweptwing airplanes. For this work the F–86 proved useful. In sweptwing airplanes, the boundary layer forming along the span tends to run out toward the tips and cause early stalling of the outboard sections of the wings. Such stalling often causes one wing to drop abruptly, a phenomenon called "wing dropping," and if both wing tips stall at the same time, the center of lift suddenly moves forward, causing a disconcerting and possibly dangerous "pitchup." To overcome this fault, a number of cures were attempted. As earlier noted, chordwise barriers called "fences" were installed at various points on the upper surface of the wing. Leading-edge extensions on the outboard part of the wing were also tried as were vortex generators installed on the outboard upper surface of the wing. The vortex generators were simply a row of small, airfoil-like projections which, by promoting turbulent mixing, reenergized the sluggish boundary layer, thus rendering it less susceptible to separation. All of these devices were helpful in some degree.

A number of studies of sweptwing control problems of the kind just mentioned were made during this period. One of these is described in TN 3523 by Norman McFadden, George Rathert, and Richard Bray. A second study, published in RM A54F21, was made by Norman McFadden and Donovan Heinle. Heinle was an Ames test pilot as well, of course, as an engineer.

Pilot Opinion. The basic stability and control characteristics of the new types of fighter aircraft being developed were much different from those of the older propeller-driven types. The differences resulted for the most part from the elimination of the propeller, the change in configuration and mass distribution, and the higher operational speeds and altitudes. Much was yet to be learned about the stability and control of these new aircraft, and also about their handling qualities as appreciated by the pilot. Quantitative evaluation of both the mechanical-aerodynamic and the human aspects of the control problem for such aircraft was required. For studies of this kind, the variable-stability airplane, earlier described, proved to be particularly useful.

When the F6F variable-stability airplane was first used, its ailerons were driven to allow simulation of various degrees of dihedral. Arrangements had subsequently been made to drive the rudder as well as the ailerons so that a wider range of lateral-directional stability variables might be investigated. A study in which the modified variable-stability airplane was used is reported in RM A51E16 by Charles Liddell, Brent Creer, and Rudolph Van Dyke. In this investigation lateral-directional handling qualities were evaluated by 12 different pilots including two from the Air Force, four from the Navy, five from NACA, and one from the Cornell Aeronautical Laboratory, which had begun work with variable-stability airplanes at about the same time as Ames. The pilots were asked to assign numerical ratings to each of the configurations simulated by the airplane and were given specific questions to answer with the aim of obtaining the reasons for their ratings. This was an interesting attempt to obtain pilot opinion in quantitative form and to correlate it with airplane design parameters.

Tracking. A critical measure of the controllability of a fighter airplane was the accuracy with which its pilot could follow a moving and maneuvering target such as another airplane. Such tracking studies were accomplished through the use of gunsights and gun cameras using a second airplane as a target. Through the statistical analysis of the tracking errors revealed by the gun camera, much could be, and was, learned about the dynamic response and control characteristics of airplanes. Particularly instructive was the comparison of the performance characteristics of the older types of airplanes, about which much was known, with the characteristics of the new high-speed and high-altitude fighters about which little was known.

A program of tracking tests was undertaken at Ames in 1952. In an early phase of this program, a comparison was made of the tracking performance of the F–51H, the F8F–1, the F–86A, and the F–86E airplanes representing two straight-wing and two swept wing types. The tests, reported in RM A53H12 by George Rathert, Burnett Gadeberg, and Howard Ziff, were made with a fixed gunsight; in other words, there were no electronic elements in the guidance circuits. The next step in fighter development was to install electronically controlled and computer-equipped gunsights that would "lead" the target by an appropriate amount.

Automatic Control. Owing to uncertainties in existing knowledge of aerodynamic loads at high speeds, the proof testing of new airplanes to design limits subjected the pilots of such airplanes to great hazard. To avoid such hazards, the Naval Air Experiment Station developed a radio-operated control system by means of which the flight of a test airplane could be remotely controlled from another aircraft or, for takeoff, from a ground-control station. Such a system was installed in a Curtiss SB2C–5 dive bomber while a Grumman F6F–5 was equipped to serve as the base of control. The airplanes were turned over to Ames for investigation and they became the Laboratory's entry into the new and important field of automatic control.

The first investigation undertaken with these aircraft, reported in TN 3496 by Howard Turner, John White, and Rudolph Van Dyke, was essentially an evaluation of the system, the measuring of responses, and the establishment of control settings. In these determinations use was made of the opinion of "check" pilots who rode as passengers in the drone airplane or who sometimes operated the "remote" control equipment from within the airplane.

The Navy apparently lost interest in the remote-control system, at least for the use originally intended, and thus the SB2C–5 drone became available to Ames for research on automatic control systems. One of the notable studies made with the airplane is reported by Howard Turner, William Triplett, and John White in RM A54J14 (ref. B–33). For this study, additional equipment was installed in the airplane to allow it to simulate a radar-controlled interceptor. The radar was represented by an optical system—a manually controlled periscope. The periscope was pointed at a maneuvering target (another airplane) and the SB2C–5 was then flown directly toward the target. Photographs of the target taken simultaneously through the periscope and through a gun camera rigidly mounted on the airplane were later compared to determine tracking accuracy. To obtain the most desirable control settings, a detailed investigation of the responses of the airplane was made both in flight and on the ground. The ground studies were simulations using the Reeves Analog Computer. Much knowledge and know-how useful in later work on automatic control systems was obtained during these tests.

An essential ingredient in the design of an automatic control system for a high-performance airplane is a set of quantitative expressions representing the dynamic response of the airplane to movement of its controls. These response characteristics can be predicted from wind-tunnel test data but can be determined more reliably, perhaps, by flight-test methods. The latter methods of obtaining the dynamic response characteristics of an airplane, specifically of the F–86A airplane, are illustrated in TR 1250 (ref. B–34) by the flight research team of William Triplett, Stuart Brown, and G. Allan Smith. Smith was a member of the Research Instrumentation Division which, under the quiet but effective direction of Jim White, gave valuable support to much of the work at the Laboratory.

In the method illustrated in TR 1250, the transient response (motion) of the airplane arising from a pulsed input to the controls is recorded as a function of time. By means of a Fourier transformation, these time histories are converted to a basic frequency-response form which is not only more amenable than the time history to detailed analysis but also more compatible with servomechanism analysis methods. The frequency-response data thus obtained are in the form of phase angle and amplitude ratio plotted against frequency. From these graphical data, simple analytical expressions for airplane response, called "transfer functions," are obtained by a semiempirical method using templates and, as a final refinement, an analog computer.

Hazards. Flight research, though now more sophisticated, was nonetheless hazardous. On June 1, 1953, while putting an F8F through some step-control maneuvers, Rudolph Van Dyke crashed into San Francisco Bay and was killed. The cause of the crash was never determined, but it was conjectured that, since the crash had been preceded by a long steep glide in which no evidence of recovery attempt was apparent, Van Dyke had perhaps failed to connect his oxygen mask and had lost consciousness from a lack of oxygen. Rudy had served as a research pilot at Ames since 1947 and had made important contributions to many of the Laboratory's flight-research projects. His passing was a serious loss to the Laboratory and caused much sorrow.

Boundary Layer, Skin Friction, and Aerodynamic Heating

Aerodynamic heating was becoming of prime importance in the 1950's to the designers of high-speed aircraft. The heating to be experienced by hypersonic aircraft would not only affect the skin friction and thus the overall drag of such craft but ultimately would melt the leading edges of the vehicle unless some form of thermal protection was provided. The optimum form of such protective means was still unknown.

Aerodynamic heating of aircraft is directly related to the compression and viscous shear (skin friction) that occurs in the boundary layer as well as to the heat-transfer efficiency of the boundary layer—its ability to transfer its heat to the body. As the skin friction and the heat-transfer efficiency were known to be much higher for turbulent than for laminar boundary layers, a turbulent boundary layer was to be avoided if at all possible. The boundary layer at the nose of a body was always laminar but, as it flowed backward along the body, it would at some point become turbulent. The position of this transition point was affected by a number of factors such as surface roughness, pressure gradient, and Reynolds number and it also seemed to be affected by the temperature of the body relative to that of the boundary layer. It appeared that transition was delayed, that it occurred farther downstream, if the body was cool and heat from the boundary layer was flowing into it. This fortunately was the normal condition encountered both in flight and in hypersonic test facilities, but in the test facilities the temperature difference was usually much less than in flight.

Analysis of the heat-transfer problem was considerably simplified as a result of a direct relationship, called the Reynolds analogy, that existed between skin friction and heat transfer. The analogy was known to apply at moderate speeds where aerodynamic heating was caused largely by viscous shear, but there was a question as to whether it would also apply at higher speeds where the heat of compression became important. In the investigation of these matters, there was clearly much to be done both theoretically and experimentally. Facilities for experimental studies were still, however, somewhat limited.

One of the early reports from the small heat-transfer wind tunnel at Ames was TN 2740 by Randall Maydew and Constantine Pappas. The work covered by this TN was an investigation of the skin friction in the laminar boundary layer of a flat plate at Mach 2.4 and a comparison with existing theory. On the theoretical side, Morris Rubesin, in TN 2917, provided a modified Reynolds analogy which allowed for compressibility effects in the boundary layer. In the supersonic free-flight tunnel, James Jedlicka, Max Wilkins, and Alvin Seiff made an experimental determination of boundary-layer transition on bodies of revolution, with both rough and smooth surfaces over the nose portion. This study, reported in TN 3342, revealed that under some conditions the boundary-layer transition, instead of occurring all at once, developed as a series of bursts of turbulent flow separated by short periods of laminar flow. This phenomenon was revealed very clearly in shadowgraph photographs of the test body in flight.

In TN 3284, Al Seiff added to the growing store of knowledge on heat transfer by analyzing a collection of test data from several wind tunnels and from flight to confirm the validity of the Reynolds analogy and, more particularly, the modified analogy proposed by Rubesin. Although the analyzed data represented a diversity of sources and test conditions, the results of the analysis supported the modified analogy to a remarkable degree.

A growing concern over the difficulties experienced in cooling pointed bodies led to a number of studies of the feasibility and benefit of using bodies with bluff or blunt noses. Pursuing this matter, Howard Stine and Kent Wanlass analyzed the effect on boundary-layer heat transfer of a strong negative pressure gradient (rapidly accelerating flow), such as would occur on a hemispherically shaped body, and followed up their analysis with tests in the 1- by 3-foot tunnel of round-nosed bodies at a Mach number of 1.97. The results of their work are presented in TN 3344.

Aerodynamic heating of the exterior surfaces of high-speed aircraft had become a major problem. Without thermal protection, these surfaces, particularly the leading edges, could reach structurally intolerable temperatures at Mach numbers as low as 2 or 3. Among the more promising methods for protecting wing leading edges that had appeared was one called transpiration or "sweat" cooling. In this method a cooling fluid is introduced between the hot boundary layer and the wing surface by forcing the fluid through a porous wing skin. One of the early studies of transpiration cooling at Ames was made by Morris Rubesin and published in TN 3341. In this report Rubesin provided an analytical method for estimating the effect of transpiration cooling, assuming air as the cooling fluid, on the heat-transfer and skin-friction characteristics of a compressible turbulent boundary layer. Most of the earlier analyses had been restricted to considerations of a laminar boundary layer; thus Rubesin's report covered new and interesting ground.

BALLISTIC MISSILE PROBLEM

The development of the intercontinental ballistic missile was a tremendously complicated task and an undertaking of the utmost importance to the Nation. It required the solution of many difficult technical problems, most of which were beyond current experience and some beyond current knowledge. The missile would have to be flown at speeds of 15,000 miles per hour or more and to altitudes of perhaps 500 miles; it would then have to be accurately guided to a target 5000 miles away by a guidance system that could not be jammed by enemy action; and finally, and most importantly, it would have to deliver its nuclear warhead, in operating condition, to the target.

The necessity of minimizing the structural weight of the missile was a problem in itself. Any unnecessary weight in the structure would either greatly increase the weight and cost of the whole missile or, more likely, reduce the weight and power of the warhead. Thus the slightest unnecessary weight in any part of the missile was intolerable. The explosive charge itself had a structural container the weight of which had to be minimized. Sitting atop the missile, this warhead structure had been of pointed configuration in early designs. The use of a pointed nose for rifle shells and high-speed missiles was traditional. The concept was firmly implanted in the thinking

215

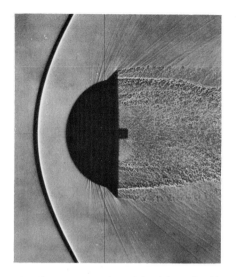

Shock waves produced by blunt bodies
(above) *and pointed bodies* (right).

of the aerodynamicists and aeronautical engineers who were designing the missile.

It was clear that the objective of missile launching would be completely frustrated if the warhead burned up owing to aerodynamic heating before it reached its target. This danger was very real for, as it reentered the atmosphere, the warhead would generate a temperature rise in the surrounding air of many thousands of degrees. Some means of protecting the warhead against reentry heating was required, but every scheme proposed for this purpose involved painful weight penalties. It was at this stage that Harvey Allen bent his mind to the problem.

Harvey knew that the kinetic energy lost by a missile, or a warhead, as it enters the earth's atmosphere is totally converted into heat. The heat comes from two sources and, significantly, is generated in two places: i.e., inside and outside the boundary layer. The heat appearing outside the boundary layer is generated by shock-wave compression. Of the heat generated in the boundary layer, some results from compression but much more arises from viscous shear or skin friction. The heat generated by the shock wave outside the boundary layer is for the most part well removed from the body and cannot reach it by convection through the insulating blanket of boundary layer. On the other hand, the heat generated in the boundary layer has ready access to the body and even readier access if the boundary layer is turbulent than if it is laminar. It thus appeared to Harvey that for any overall rate of heat generation—which would be determined by the de-

216

gree of deceleration—the body would be heated less if a larger fraction of the heat were generated by the shock wave (by pressure drag, as Harvey put it) and a smaller fraction by the viscous skin friction. How could this juggling of heat inputs be accomplished? The answer seemed quite obvious to Harvey: by making the nose blunt in order to strengthen the bow shock wave and increase the pressure drag.

The bow wave standing out in front of a bluff body is much more powerful, and generates much more heat, than the oblique waves leaning back from a pointed nose. Very significantly also, the bow wave, unlike the oblique wave, does not touch the body at any point. The oblique waves, though cooler than the bow wave, touch the pointed body at a spot where the insulating boundary layer is very thin or nonexistent. They are thus able to transmit their heat to the tip of a missile with great ease and so fast that it cannot be carried away by conduction. A hot spot develops and the point generally melts off.

It appeared then that much less heat would be transmitted to a blunt-nosed warhead than to a pointed one and that the heat reaching the blunt warhead would be more evenly distributed and less likely to produce hot spots. The desirability of reducing skin friction by maintaining laminar flow over the heated area was also evident. But there was more to the problem

H. Julian Allen explaining blunt-nose principle.

than appeared in this analysis, which assumed that the maximum rate of heat generation would be the same for a blunt body as for a pointed one. Inasmuch as heat generation depends on rate of deceleration, this assumption seemed rather broad. The dynamics and trajectory of the warhead would have to be examined, and this Harvey Allen and Al Eggers undertook to do. In due time the two men were able to demonstrate mathematically that the maximum deceleration of a body entering the atmosphere—and thus the maximum rate at which it generates heat—is determined by its entrance angle and velocity and is independent of its physical characteristics: i.e., mass, size, shape, or drag coefficient. This astonishing conclusion was based on the assumption, appearing reasonable for warheads, that the body in all cases will reach the point of maximum deceleration before hitting the ground. It was also regarded as a reasonable assumption in the analysis that, regardless of their shape, bodies with the usual densities of warheads would convert most of their kinetic energy into heat before hitting the ground. The trajectory analysis thus supported Harvey's blunt-body heating theory by showing that the maximum rate of heat generation by a warhead, and the total amount of heat generated, would be the same regardless of whether it had a blunt or a sharp nose. The important difference between the two body shapes was in the amount of the generated heat that actually entered the body.

Allen's blunt-body theory was conceived in late 1951. It was published as a classified document and later as TN 4047. Finally, it was published as TR 1381 (ref. B–35). Al Eggers was a contributor to the analysis and a co-author of the report. Pointed-body tradition was still strong in 1952. Harvey's idea was not quickly picked up by industry; it just lay there and steamed for a while.

218

1954–1957

9

The Environment

I N all technical fields and particularly in aeronautics, the years between 1954 and 1957 were characterized by rapid growth and even more rapidly expanding horizons. The stimulus for such developments arose not only from the exciting prospects of things to come but also from a worried concern over the impressive technical developments in Soviet Russia. National leaders recognized that we were in a technical race that could have the gravest consequences. Indeed, NACA Chairman James H. Doolittle pointed this out to Congress in January 1957 and implied that the leveling off of NACA's appropriations over the past few years was scarcely a rational response to the challenge from Russia.

Mach 2 fighters and bombers were now a reality. A research airplane, the North American X–15, was being designed to fly at Mach 5 or more. But the military services were devoting an ever-increasing fraction of their budgets to guided missiles and, in 1955, President Eisenhower assigned the highest priority to the ICBM project. Before the period was over, two ICBM's (Atlas and Titan) had been authorized as well as three IRBM intermediate-range ballistic missiles (Thor, Jupiter, and Polaris).

The eyes of aeronautical scientists, however, were turning toward space. The Bell X–2 research airplane had reached an altitude of over 126,000 feet in 1956 and the X–15, when completed, was expected to go more than twice as high. During the 1955–1957 period, the Air Force pushed its Aerobee-Hi sounding rocket to 193 miles. Russia, still earlier, announced that its rockets had reached 240 miles. Moreover it was clear that the huge rocket motors being developed for ballistic missiles would be capable of putting a small test body into orbit around the earth. The possibility of launching a series of earth satellites as part of the International Geophysical Year operations had been discussed in scientific circles and on July 29, 1955, President Eisenhower announced plans for the launching of an earth satellite. The following day the U.S.S.R. announced similar plans. The race between the United States and the Soviets to launch the world's first satellite was clearly on, but not until late in 1957 was it revealed that the winner was Russia. Russian *Sputnik I* was successfully launched on October 4, 1957; and *Sputnik II*, carrying a live dog, was launched on November 3 of the same year.

The immediate environment of NACA during this period had one very bleak aspect. It concerned the severe disadvantage at which NACA found itself in the keen competition for technical manpower. The national demand for engineers and scientists had mushroomed beyond all expectations and the supply, particularly of those with above-average qualifications, was exceedingly short. The demand stemmed partly from the fact that the country was in the midst of a scientific explosion and partly also from the widespread use by the military services of research and development contracts. The aircraft companies and other research and development organizations were busily expanding their technical staffs, and new research and development groups were trying to get established. All were in the manpower market, bidding up salaries well beyond those which the Civil Service Commission would allow NACA to pay.

NACA's activities had recently been restricted by manpower quotas imposed by Congress but now, because of the low salary scale, the quotas, low as they were, could not be filled. Not only that, but NACA was losing senior staff members, key men, owing to the attraction of the much higher salaries offered by industry. Men like Charlie Frick and Bill Kauffman were lost by Ames during this period. Had the loss not been so painful, Ames might have felt flattered that NACA-trained men were so much desired by industry. NACA fought hard to improve its salary position but, while making some gains, it never achieved equality with industry. Thus the organization continued to operate under a severe manpower handicap.

10

People and Events

F OR various reasons, some of which have been mentioned, the services of a number of key personnel were lost to Ames between 1954 and 1957. Charles Frick and William Kauffman resigned in 1956; and William McAvoy, NACA's senior test pilot, having survived exciting incidents and close calls during his 35 years of test piloting at Langley and at Ames, retired on July 31, 1957. He was replaced as Chief of the Flight Operations Branch by George Cooper. In 1954, by virtue of excellent work on second-order flow theory, Milton Van Dyke won, simultaneously, a Fulbright Award for Research and a grant from the John Simon Guggenheim Memorial Fund. These awards offered the privilege of carrying on a year's advanced study abroad, which Milt proceeded to take at Trinity College, Cambridge. In 1955, Walter Vincenti won the Rockefeller Public Service Award, which also carried with it a year at Cambridge; and in December 1956, a few months after his return, he resigned to assume a professorship at Stanford. Vincenti's leaving was a distinct loss to the Laboratory.

In May 1954, Carl Bioletti took leave from his job as Assistant Director of the Laboratory to spend the better part of a year sailing among the tropical islands of the Pacific. Carl was an unusually intelligent person with a healthy skepticism for the motives and objectives of mankind. Inasmuch as man in any case was probably on the wrong track, there would be little harm and perhaps some gain, he felt, in his sailing off to the South Seas. Besides, he wanted to pursue his travels before old age either foreclosed the activity or dimmed its pleasures. Carl returned in fine fettle in May 1955 but, after a few months, was again claimed by the temptations of the sea. In September 1955, he resigned. Carl always undervalued his services to the Laboratory. He was missed during his excursions at sea and people at Ames were pleased when he returned to the Laboratory in March 1956, apparently none the worse for his experience.

The total responsibility of the Assistant Directorship rested exclusively with Russ Robinson after Carl's first departure and it was not until Carl resigned that Merrill Mead, of the 6- by 6-foot-tunnel staff, and Manley

Merrill H. Mead   *Andre G. (Jeff) Buck.*   *Angelo Giovannetti.*

Hood were assigned to Robinson as Technical Assistants. The position of Assistant Chief of the Theoretical and Applied Research Division which Manley vacated was assumed by Robert Crane.

The Unitary Plan wind tunnels, which were completed during this period, became an operating division of the Laboratory and the Unitary Plan Project Office was dissolved in March 1956. This change, and all of the others mentioned, are reflected in the Ames organization chart of September 1957.

Special events at Ames during this period included an inspection in 1955 and a conference on the Automatic Stability and Control of Aircraft, also in 1955.

The Engineering Services and Technical Services Divisions were vital adjuncts of the Ames research organization and were made up of people who as much as any others at the Laboratory lived by their wits. Heading the Engineering Services Division was Andre G. (Jeff) Buck, who had joined the Laboratory staff in the early days and ever since had managed to get his fingers into most of the design and construction work that took place. Jeff, a man of mellow voice and pleasant disposition, served the many needs of the research divisions with great effectiveness and unvarying good humor. Often the ingenuity which he and his staff brought to their assignments produced results which in themselves represented research contributions.

The Engineering Services Division held responsibility for most of the facility design and construction at the Laboratory. Assisting Jeff were Charles Harvey, Assistant Division Chief; Angelo Giovannetti, Chief of the Construction Engineering Branch; Alfred Wilson, Chief of the Construction Inspection Branch; Merrill Nourse, Chief of the Electrical Branch; and J. S. W. (Sam) Davidsen, Chief of the Mechanical Engineering Branch.

As head of the Electrical Branch, Nourse occupied a position which Buck, himself, formerly held. It was concerned not only with the selection,

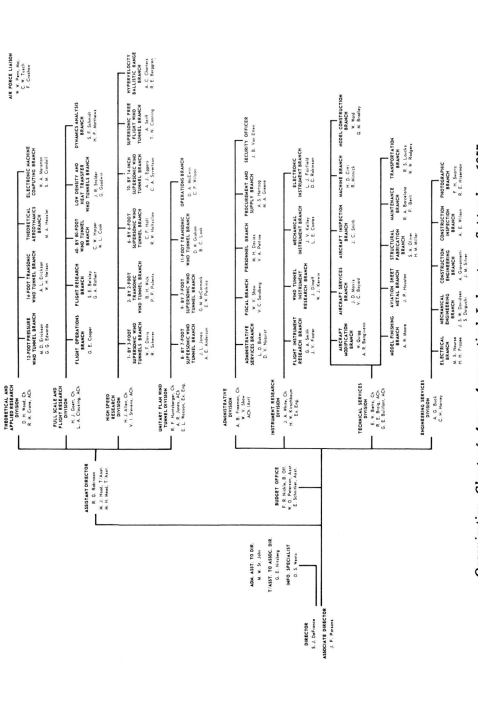

Organization Chart of Ames Aeronautical Laboratory, September 1957.

installation, and operation of the huge motors and control units required to drive the Laboratory's wind tunnels but also with the solution of the even more sophisticated electrical problems associated with the design of the new and specialized forms of research equipment. Sam Davidsen also had many opportunities to demonstrate his skill in the design of specialized research equipment. It was he who often was expected to build complex new equipment at little, or no, cost—who, at the behest of some scheming research engineer, at times attempted to build a new facility item out of available materials before the project had either been approved or budgeted by Headquarters. Sam's design ingenuity was matched only by his knowledge of where to scrounge parts for his new productions.

Attached to the Engineering Services Division was an important but somewhat anomalous element known as the Photographic Branch. This Branch of the Ames organization was headed by Fred Swartz who, late in 1953, had taken over the job from Howard Kirschbaum. Fred was responsible for the extensive photography required for records and reports, and he was also involved in photography as used in the research process. The use of photography at Ames increased rapidly over the years and was accelerated by the development of gun tunnels, ranges, and other short-period test facilities.

The Technical Services Division performed vital and heroic services in furthering the purposes of the Laboratory. The Division was headed by E. W. (Red) Betts with Ray Braig and George Bulifant as assistants. All three were experienced and competent men who had come from Langley to help found the Ames Laboratory. Other men in the Division, in particular John Houston and Walter Quigg, had also come from Langley for the same purpose. Their experience had from the first proved a great asset to the Laboratory and their contributions had been substantial.

The Technical Services Division had charge of all the shops—machine, model, and structural fabrication—as well as of the maintenance, modification, and inspection of all aircraft operated by the Laboratory. The Machine Shop Branch was headed by Henry Citti; the Model Shop Branch, by William Ward; and the Aircraft Modification Branch, by Walter Quigg. And there were several other branches in the Division. The work of the various branches was by no means routine. Nearly every item the shops were asked to construct was of a highly specialized character that only a wild-eyed research engineer could dream up. The work of the model shop—the construction of test models of airplanes and missiles—became ever more complex as wind-tunnel speeds increased and as new materials and fabrication techniques were developed and exploited.

The contribution of the Technical Services Division, and more particularly of Red Betts, its chief, was well illustrated by the Laboratory's experience in building the blades for the compressor powering the supersonic legs

From left to right: *Clindon G. Glass, Raymond E. Braig, and Edward W. (Red) Betts.*

George E. Bulifant.

of the Unitary Plan facility. This compressor, which was 22 feet in diameter and designed to absorb over 200,000 horsepower, was to contain nearly 1200 solid-chrome-steel blades. Heretofore aluminum alloy had most commonly been used for compressor blades; but in this case, to avoid trouble from high operating temperatures and fatigue, it was considered necessary to make them of alloy steel. But trouble was encountered in finding a manufacturer who could build the blades or one who would even think of attempting the task. One manufacturer thought it might be done with a tracer-controlled planer and made a bid for $2000 per blade—a total of $2,400,000 for the job. Ames, desperately short of money for the Unitary Plan facility, could not pay this huge amount for compressor blades and, in

Red Betts' airfoil milling machine.

any case, seriously doubted that the manufacturer would be able to deliver the blades on time or at all.

Milling a twisted, cambered, steel blade with precision was an extremely difficult task because, for one thing, the blade would deflect while the thin tip sections were being milled. Red Betts figured that, if all the carving could be done immediately adjacent to the blade support, the deflection problem could be eliminated. This would take a new type of machine in which the blank from which the blade was to be carved would gradually be extruded upward through a tight-fitting hole in a massive mounting block. The milling cutters, controlled by a template—an enlarged wooden model of the blade—would do their cutting immediately above the mounting block. Thus, as the blank moved up through the block, the blade would be carved out from tip to base. Devising machining operations was something at which Red was good. Like Harvey Allen, he was not satisfied with administering an activity but had to get personally involved in it. In fact, the routines of administration were not greatly to his liking.

Anyway, Red sold DeFrance on the idea of building a machine such as he had conceived and using it to carve out the blades for the Unitary compressor. Red and Sam Davidsen set out to visit the big machine-tool companies to see if they would build a machine according to Red's specifications.

The big companies, Pratt & Whitney and Cincinnati, agreed that the machine was feasible but were too busy to undertake its construction. The Danly Machine Specialties Co., however, agreed to build it at a price not to exceed $600,000.

Red Betts' machine was built and installed at Ames in June 1953. It was a huge success. Shortly Ames operators were carving out four blades in a 24-hour day. When the additional butt milling, sanding, and inspection were included, the cost per blade came to about $650. Thus, on this job alone, Red's machine not only paid for itself but in addition saved NACA $1 million according to one estimate.[1] Also it assuredly saved a great deal of time in getting the Unitary tunnels into operation.

But the saving on the Unitary tunnel compressor was only a beginning of the contributions of Red's machine. In October 1956, about a year after the Unitary tunnels went into operation, the blades of the 11- by 11-foot tunnel compressor were wiped out by a blade failure and had to be replaced. This calamity provided additional work for the machine, and there was yet more to come. Red's machine has been in operation almost continuously since it was built and has saved Ames and NACA several millions of dollars and much valuable time. Its development was all in the day's work for Red, who received no monetary reward nor any special acclaim for his outstanding contribution.

---

[1] H. D. Citti and J. S. W. Davidsen, associates of Betts, gave this estimate of the savings in an Ames internal memorandum dated July 1, 1968.

11

Facilities

CONTINUOUS-FLOW WIND TUNNELS

OLD wind tunnels never seem to die of themselves; they have to be killed, deliberately. There is a tendency to keep them going well beyond the point of diminishing returns. At Ames, the growing shortage of manpower made the abandonment of marginally producing wind tunnels an urgent necessity. The 1- by 3½-foot tunnel was deactivated in 1954 and later completely dismantled. The old low-density and heat-transfer tunnels were abandoned, too, in 1954 when the new facilities were put into operation. The old heat-transfer tunnel was later consigned on indefinite loan (given) to the University of California at Berkeley.[1] In September 1956 the 7- by 10-Foot Tunnel Section was disbanded and the tunnels turned over to the 40-by 80-Foot Tunnel Section to operate as needed.

Several tunnel modifications were also completed during this period. Beginning about September 1954, the 6- by 6-foot tunnel was shut down for major modifications that required nearly 1½ years to complete. The modifications included measures to convert the tunnel for transonic operation. Toward this end, a slotted throat and a new model-support system were provided. Also, arrangements were made to inject air removed from the slotted throat into the supersonic diffuser, thus increasing diffuser efficiency and tunnel performance.

The 6- by 6-foot tunnel, as a result of the changes made at this time, could operate at Mach numbers ranging from 0.6 to 2.3. Moreover, the operation of the tunnel was made so simple that the task could easily be handled by one man. Indeed, one lonely night it was operated by a cat that somehow became entrapped in the switchgear. The regular operator was on hand finishing up his paperwork for the night when, to his surprise, he

---

[1] Transfer was later formalized in a letter from Arthur B. Freeman, Assistant Director for Administration, to Dr. E. W. Strong, Chancellor, University of California, Berkeley, dated Feb. 16, 1962.

heard the wheels begin to turn. Investigation revealed the cat—in what condition was never disclosed.

A number of relatively minor alterations were made in the 6-by-6 both before and after the major modifications just mentioned. The model-support system had earlier been rotated to accommodate an unplanned nonlinearity in the airflow, and the speed control of the tunnel had been altered to allow subsonic operation. Also, the aluminum compressor blades had given trouble and had been replaced by hollow welded steel blades. Cracking, which occurred in the steel blades as a result of vibration, had in turn been cured by filling the interior of the blades with a plastic foam. Following the major modification a fire, starting from an oil leak, ignited the magnesium compressor (J–33) blades of the auxiliary air system. The resulting soot, together with the water used to quench the fire, thoroughly fouled the whole tunnel interior.

A number of other tunnels at Ames underwent modifications during this period. The 14-foot transonic conversion of the 16-foot tunnel was completed in 1955; and general improvements, including the installation of more sighting stations and a Mach 3 nozzle, were made in the supersonic free-flight (SSFF) tunnel. Through the skillful efforts of Al Seiff and his staff, the great potential of the SSFF tunnel was being realized. Guns, instrumentation, and flow characteristics had continuously been improved and many ingenious research techniques exploiting the possibilities of the counterflow test principle had been developed.

The capabilities of the 1- by 3-foot tunnel had also, to a surprising degree, proved amenable to expansion. During the 1954–1955 period, in accordance with earlier plans, the power of the continuous-flow 1- by 3-foot tunnel was doubled and a new flexible throat, operated by hydraulic jacks, was installed. A year or two later a similar throat was installed in the blowdown tunnel. The new flexible throats reduced the Mach-number change time to a matter of seconds and with the further addition to each tunnel of a second throat—a constriction at the exit to the test section—the operating efficiency of the tunnels was greatly improved. The second throat increased the efficiency with which the supersonic stream of air could be slowed down, as it had to be, after passing through the test section. As a result of this benefit, the top Mach number of the power-augmented, continuous-flow tunnel was raised to 6.0. That of the blowdown tunnel was a little less than 6.0.

Among the major new wind tunnels completed during this period were the three Unitary Plan tunnels which went into operation in 1955. However, as earlier noted, the compressor of the 11- by 11-foot transonic leg suffered a blade failure in October 1956 with the result that the tunnel was out of commission until late 1957.

The power involved in running the equipment at Ames had reached large proportions by 1957. The total connected load amounted to nearly

232

Below: A model of the 14-foot transonic tunnel. At right: A model in the test section of the 14-foot tunnel.

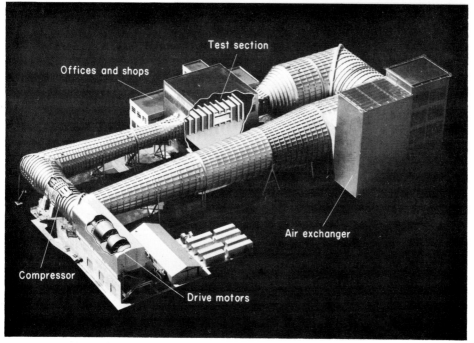

Offices and shops

Test section

Air exchanger

Compressor

Drive motors

half a million horsepower and the yearly power bill for electricity was approaching $2 million.

GUNS AND BALLISTIC RANGES

The interests of aeronautical research scientists had now advanced from the field of aerodynamics to the much more complex field of aerothermodynamics. The heating to which high-speed aircraft would soon be subjected had become a matter of paramount importance to design engineers. A missile traveling at 7000 miles per hour, for example, could theoretically generate air temperatures behind its bow shock wave of as much as 8000° F— nearly as hot as the surface of the sun. The kinetic energy of the missile would be in effect converted to kinetic energy in the molecules of the surrounding air. The motion of the molecules thus heated would become so violent that they would break apart—"dissociate," as it was called. Thus a molecule of oxygen O_2 would break down into two individual oxygen atoms. The process of dissociation would absorb heat, which would considerably alter the thermodynamic balance of the airflow around the missiles. The aerothermodynamic processes were complex and not readily amenable to theoretical treatment. Thus in this period a massive effort was begun to devise experimental test facilities in which the aerothermodynamic properties of hypervelocity flows could be simulated.

The idea of a ballistic range in which a test model could be launched into a body of still air by a gun was not new; in 1947 Ames engineers had proposed such a range to NACA management but the proposal had been rejected. However, the supersonic free-flight tunnel devised by Harvey Allen was in effect a rather sophisticated version of the ballistic range in which the air was in motion. In either case the gun was the critical item in determining performance. One of the fastest rifles built, the 220 Swift, developed muzzle velocities of about 4000 feet per second, and the ultimate velocity that seemed likely to be achievable with a rifle powered only by gunpowder appeared to be under 10,000 feet per second. It was clear that the flight of ballistic missiles which reentered the atmosphere at speeds of 20,000 feet per second or more could not be simulated by models launched with an ordinary gun.

As earlier mentioned,[2] Alex Charters in 1952–1953 set about designing a high-performance "light-gas" gun in which the test model was to be propelled through a "launch tube" by a charge of highly compressed helium gas. The gas was compressed in a gun barrel or driver tube by a heavy metal piston driven down the tube by an exploding charge of gunpowder. The reaction to the explosion would be neutralized by driving a second piston out of the open rear end of the driver tube. In this manner, Charters and his two teammates, Pat Denardo and Vernon Rossow, hoped to achieve model launch speeds of well over 10,000 feet per second—perhaps as much as 20,000 feet per second. The maximum velocity actually achieved was about 13,000 feet per second. Charters and his colleagues did a thorough design job on the gun. They first developed the theory and then built several prototype versions. These piston-compressor guns are believed to be the first

---

[2] See ch. 7.

light-gas guns built for model launching in this country and perhaps in the world. The gun and its development were described by Charters, Denardo, and Rossow in TN 4143 (ref. B–36).

An early small-scale version of the Charters gun was first incorporated in the Janus range in which the gun fired its tiny bulletlike model into a small, gas-filled cylindrical chamber 21 feet long. By 1955, however, plans had been laid for building a large range in which test models would be fired into a cylindrical test chamber 8 feet in diameter and 500 feet long. The test chamber, it was planned, could be filled with air or any other gas and could be pressurized or evacuated through a range of from 0.001 to 5.0 atmospheres. The construction of this range, called the main range, was approved by NACA management. Before going too far with its construction, however, the designers felt it desirable to build a prototype, much smaller than the main range but considerably larger than the Janus range. Construction of this facility, called the pilot range, got under way in 1956 as did also, a little later in the year, the construction of the main range. Robert Berggren and Paul Radach carried much of the responsibility for this work. Both ranges were completed in 1957. All three of the ranges used the piston-compressor light-gas guns and all were housed in a new building constructed along the western border of Ames territory on ground that had been reserved, but never used, for a seaplane towing basin.

Dr. Alex C. Charters.

Main range of hypervelocity ballistic range.

Also proposed during 1955, and approved, was the construction of a pressure range in which the aerodynamic, the thermodynamic, and particularly the dynamic-stability characteristics of fairly good-sized models could be investigated at high Reynolds numbers and at Mach numbers of about 10. The pressure range, designed by Al Seiff and his staff, was put under construction in 1956 but was not completed until 1958. This range was located beside the 12-foot tunnel, and its test chamber, 10 feet in diameter and 200 feet long, was pressurized or evacuated by the facilities of the 12-foot tunnel. The range of pressures available in the new facility was from 0.01 to 10 atmospheres and, at the highest pressure, Reynolds numbers up to 300 million per foot of model length were obtainable. In all of the ranges, the test chamber was equipped with a row of sighting stations through which photographs, or shadowgraphs, of the test model could be obtained by electronically controlled spark or flash photography. The model was timed as it passed the sighting stations and drag coefficients were calculated from the rate of deceleration. In the pressure range, the observed pitching and plunging motions of the model were expected to provide data from which dynamic stability derivatives could be calculated if suitable analysis methods were developed.

Despite the tremendous effort put into the development of the piston-compressor light-gas gun, the performance of the device proved rather unsatisfactory. It had a number of basic faults which in retrospect seemed rather obvious. Trouble arose from the heavy pistons. The idea of having the reaction piston fly out the rear end of the driver tube was really not practical; and the action of the other piston slamming against the end of the smaller-diameter launch tube was notably destructive. The idea, of course, was to have a residual of gas stop the piston just before it hit the launch tube, but this was hard to arrange and introduced an element of thermodynamic inefficiency which reduced the performance of the gun.

Al Eggers and a number of other people at the Laboratory felt that it

236

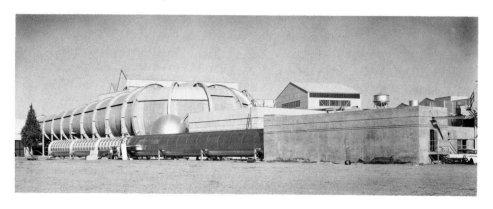

Pressurized ballistic range.

should be possible to compress the driving gas in a light-gas gun with shock waves instead of with the heavy steel pistons used by Charters. The task of investigating this possibility was undertaken in 1956 by Carl Bioletti and Bernard Cunningham. They first built a gun, much lighter than Charters', consisting of a closed-breech driver tube and a smaller-diameter launch tube separated by a diaphragm intended to rupture at a prescribed pressure level. The driver tube held an explosive charge in its rear end but otherwise was filled with compressed helium. The exploding charge would generate a shock wave that would travel down the tube like a piston, heating the helium and compressing it beyond the rupture strength of the diaphragm barrier. As the diaphragm burst, the test model, mounted just ahead, would be hurled down and out of the launch tube. Carl and Bernie found that, while the shock wave did indeed serve as a piston, improved performance could be obtained if a very lightweight floating diaphragm was used to separate the helium from the gas generated by the exploding powder. In this way, more energy could be imparted to the test body, and muzzle velocities of 11,000 or 12,000 feet per second could be obtained with a gun much lighter and simpler than the one developed by the Charters team.

The next step in the development of what was now variously called the shock-driven, shock-heated, or shock-compression gun, was to install an intermediate shock tube, filled with helium, between the driver and the launching tube. In the operation of this two-stage shock-compression gun, the gas in the shock tube was compressed by a lightweight piston which was driven by the compressed gases of the driver tube. Proportioning of tube length and diameter as well as piston weight and powder charge were critical matters which Bioletti and Cunningham worked out with some care. The resulting gun, which was relatively simple and particularly adapted for launching lightweight models, was capable of achieving muzzle velocities of 20,000 feet per second. The two-stage gun and its development were later

237

described in TN D–307,[3] entitled "A High-Velocity Gun Employing a Shock-Compressed Light Gas," by Carlton Bioletti and Bernard E. Cunningham.

ATMOSPHERE-ENTRY SIMULATOR

Although a single-stage shock-compression gun was installed in the supersonic free-flight tunnel, the gun had been specifically designed for use in an interesting new simulator, called the atmosphere-entry simulator, or AES, which had been devised by Al Eggers. Al had become extremely interested in the heating problem encountered by missile warheads and other reentry bodies as they plunged back into the atmosphere. He had worked with Harvey Allen on the famous blunt-body concept and was all too aware of the limitations of theory in predicting the aerothermodynamic environment which reentry bodies encountered. Would it be possible, he wondered, to gun-launch a model into a test range in which the air density varied in the same pattern as that encountered by a body entering the atmosphere? It should be possible, he believed, to design a supersonic tunnel in which, by shaping the tunnel walls, the air density and pressure along its length could be made to vary in a prescribed fashion. Atmosphere entry might thus be simulated by launching a model into such a wind tunnel after the fashion of the SSFF tunnel. While it thus appeared that an atmosphere-entry simulator could be built, it would first be necessary to determine analytically whether a true simulation of reentry phenomena could actually be achieved in such a device. Eggers' analysis of this matter, together with a description of AES design features, is contained in TR 1378 (ref. B–37). Inasmuch as the analysis was favorable, immediate steps were taken to build the simulator. Al's analysis had been made early in 1955; a successful prototype was built in 1956; and the construction of a larger version, located in the range building, was begun in 1957. In the design and development of these unique facilities, Stanford Neice, of Eggers' staff, played a major role.

Al Eggers' work on reentry aerothermodynamics won much acclaim from the scientific community. For this work, he received, in 1956, the Arthur S. Flemming Award conferred by the Washington Junior Chamber of Commerce. This award is given each year to the 10 most outstanding young men in the Federal Government. Al, like a number of others at Ames, had earned his Ph. D. at Stanford while working at the Laboratory. He had a keen and very original mind, was a slashingly aggressive leader, and his ability to sell his ideas to others was of singular character.

SHOCK-TUNNEL APPLICATIONS

The idea of using an explosive charge to operate a wind tunnel had

---

[3] NASA report series to be described later.

238

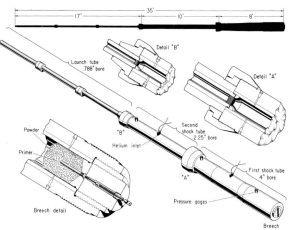

At left: *The shock-compression light-gas gun.* Above: *The atmosphere-entry simulator.*

Labels in diagram: Launch tube .788" bore; Detail "B"; Detail "A"; Powder; Primer; Breech detail; "B"; Helium inlet; Second shock tube 2.25" bore; "A"; Pressure gages; First shock tube 4" bore; Breech

first been applied at Ames in the gun tunnel developed by Al Eggers. The gun tunnel, like Charters' gun, involved a heavy metal piston and did not work very well. It led, however, to the development of the shock tunnel which used shock compression to generate a hot, hypersonic airflow of short but adequate duration. The shock-tunnel development proceeded in parallel with the gun development; in fact, one might be thought of as a hot-air gun and the other as a model-launching gun. In the shock tunnel, however,

Dr. Alfred J. Eggers.

it was found desirable to use a mixture of oxygen, hydrogen, and helium as the explosive element. A gas mixture of this kind, suitably proportioned, provided a burning rate and an impulse that were more compatible with the requirements of a shock tunnel than were those of a solid explosive.

Development of the shock tunnel in 1956–1957 was proceeding on two fronts, one carried forward by the team of Bernie Cunningham and Fred Hansen under the supervision of Al Eggers, and the other by Tom Canning who, under Al Seiff, was Assistant Head of the Supersonic Free Flight Tunnel Branch. Tom, following a suggestion earlier presented by Jack Stalder, proposed that the shock tunnel be used in a counterflow (à la SSFF tunnel) arrangement with a light-gas gun to achieve a relative velocity between model and airstream which would be much higher than ever obtained before. He sold Al Seiff on the idea and together they undertook to present it to Harvey Allen, their division chief. Harvey thought the idea was not very practicable. The expectation of being able to obtain useful data in the fleeting instant during which the pulse of air from the shock tunnel and the speeding model from the gun came together appeared overly optimistic and was almost too much for Harvey to swallow. Nevertheless, Tom and Al kept up the pressure and finally won Harvey's somewhat reluctant consent to try out the scheme. The trial was made with makeshift equipment, but was sufficiently promising to justify the construction of a pilot model of the arrangement.

The problem of naming the many hypersonic test devices that had been invented was by now becoming troublesome. The name chosen for the arrangement proposed by Canning and Seiff was "hypervelocity free-flight facility," or HFFF for short. Thus what was under construction in 1957 was a relatively small and inexpensive pilot HFFF made up mainly

240

of parts scrounged from other places in the Laboratory and built, no doubt, without Headquarters' knowledge or sanction. At the same time, Bernie Cunningham and his colleagues had designed and were beginning the construction of a 1-foot shock tunnel in which stationary models could be tested at very high airspeeds.

SIMULATION PROBLEMS

Although the ballistic range, the supersonic free-flight tunnel, and the hypervelocity free-flight facility all had outstanding capabilities for simulating the aerothermodynamic conditions of high-speed flight, they nevertheless possessed, in common, a couple of rather obvious faults. The conditions of model freedom and the short operating time rendered all measurements difficult and some impossible. Another problem was the severe restrictions on the size and complexity of test models. The models had to be small enough to be inserted into a rifle barrel and rugged enough to withstand accelerations of about 1 million times that of gravity.

In view of these circumstances, there remained a great need for facilities in which prolonged tests could be made at high Mach number and temperatures on fixed models of reasonable size. Hypersonic wind tunnels partially satisfied these requirements, but their speed capabilities were too low and the air-heating requirements troublesome. In such facilities it was necessary to heat the inlet air to fairly high temperatures to avoid liquefaction in the supersonic test section and to still higher temperatures if reasonably faithful simulation of aerodynamic heating effects was to be achieved. Indeed it could be calculated that the preheating requirements for simulating conditions encountered by a reentry body would lead to air temperatures of many thousands of degrees—well beyond levels that could be tolerated in a continuous-flow wind tunnel.

Though troublesome, the heating of wind-tunnel air seemed essential if aerodynamic-heating effects were to be properly simulated. The only question remaining was how such heating might best be accomplished. Shock heating had proved an effective means of increasing the temperature of the air in shock tunnels, while in continuous-flow tunnels, such as the 10- by 14-inch and the new 10- by 10-inch heat-transfer tunnel, preheating of the air had been accomplished by electrical-resistance heaters. In another preheating scheme being investigated at this time, the inlet air was passed through a thick bed of refractory pellets which previously had been heated to high temperature by a gas or an electric heater of some kind. It appeared that this device, called a "pebble-bed" heater, would serve for a short period of operation, perhaps a few minutes, but would not do for a continuous-flow tunnel. Late in 1957 Jack Stalder made an experimental installation of a pebble-bed heater in his 8-inch low-density tunnel. At the same time Al Eggers and his staff were engaged in the design of a 3.5-foot-diameter hypersonic blowdown tunnel that would make use of a large pebble-bed heater.

3.5-FOOT TUNNEL

The 3.5-foot tunnel represented a very ambitious project with an estimated cost of about $11 million. Its approval, first by Ames management and then, late in 1957, by NACA Headquarters and Congress, gave effective attestation to the salesmanship of Al Eggers. The intended purpose of the 3.5-foot tunnel was to investigate the aerodynamic and thermodynamic conditions encountered by hypersonic airplanes and boost-glide aircraft flying in the Mach-number range from 5 to 10. The tunnel would be a closed system. During its operation, vessels of highly compressed air would be released by suitable valving to pass through a pebble-bed heater, thence through the test section, and into four large evacuated spherical recovery tanks.

The 3.5-foot tunnel was to be equipped with a set of interchangeable fixed nozzles allowing operation at discrete Mach numbers of 5, 7, 10, and 14. Operating periods would last from 1 to 4 minutes. It was expected that the pebble-bed heater, a huge insulated steel pressure vessel filled with 125 tons of aluminum and zirconium oxide pebbles, would raise the inlet-air temperature to 4000° F. The new facility was to permit simulation of flight Reynolds numbers for Mach numbers up to 10 and of corresponding flight temperatures for Mach numbers up to about 7.0.

The tunnel walls, according to plan, would be cooled by a boundary layer of helium gas introduced through slots in the constricted, sonic throat and recovered downstream of the test section. The recovered helium gas would be contaminated with air, of course, and a purification plant would be required to process it for re-use. Indeed, the plans called for a separate, rather large building to house the impressive array of auxiliary equipment associated with the tunnel. Cooling of the tunnel was quite a problem. Aside from the helium cooling of the tunnel walls, the great steel shell of the pebble-bed heater, 8 inches thick and weighing over half a million pounds,[4] would be insulated on the inside with refractory brick and be further protected by water cooling coils installed between the brick and the inner steel surface. Internal water cooling would be used to protect the model-support struts as well as the internal strain-gage balances with which the models would be equipped. The output of the balances was to be fed directly into an electronic computer for data workup. The 3.5-foot tunnel, it was realized, would be the most expensive piece of test equipment built at Ames since the construction of the Unitary Plan facility.

[4] Designed to withstand an internal pressure of 2000 psi, this massive vessel was reported to be the heaviest single item the Southern Pacific Railroad had ever transported.

242

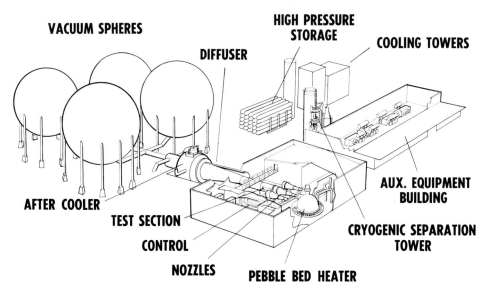

VACUUM SPHERES

DIFFUSER

HIGH PRESSURE
STORAGE

COOLING TOWERS

AFTER COOLER

TEST SECTION

CONTROL

NOZZLES

PEBBLE BED HEATER

AUX. EQUIPMENT
BUILDING

CRYOGENIC SEPARATION
TOWER

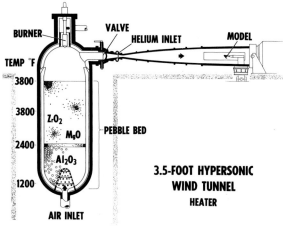

BURNER

VALVE

HELIUM INLET

MODEL

TEMP °F

3800

3800

2400

1200

Z_rO_2

M_gO

Al_2O_3

PEBBLE BED

AIR INLET

3.5-FOOT HYPERSONIC
WIND TUNNEL
HEATER

Schematic drawings of the 3.5-foot hypersonic wind tunnel (above) and (at left) the 3.5-foot tunnel pebble-bed heater.

ARC-JET

The pebble-bed heater, though serving perhaps for Mach numbers from 5 to 10, could not, it was clear, provide the heat required for representing the conditions encountered by reentry bodies. There was yet, however, a possibility of accomplishing this objective in a tunnel capable of operating for reasonably long periods of time. This possibility lay in the use of an electric arc to heat the air as it passed through the tunnel. The initial investigation of arc-heated jets was made in 1956 by Jeff Buck, R. W. Eglington, A. Kamiya, Merrill Nourse, and others. Later the work was continued by William Carlson and Carl Sorenson. First investigated were some arc-jet ideas which had originated in Germany. This study, however, was just the beginning of work that was still in progress and accelerating at the end of 1957. Aside from keeping the tunnel walls and electrodes from melting, one of the problems in the design of an arc-jet facility arose from the contamination of the air by vaporized material from the electrodes. The problems in the development of a practical arc-jet tunnel were obviously great, but the need for such a facility was also great and the project was pushed with ever increasing vigor.

COMPUTING FACILITIES

The use of electronic computing facilities expanded rapidly during this period. An Electrodata Datatron digital computer was purchased in 1954 and was soon being used for "on-line" data reduction for the 6-by-6 and the three Unitary Plan wind tunnels. In the on-line procedure, the electrical strain-gage balances with which wind-tunnel models were generally equipped transmitted their electrical outputs directly to the computer for the application of calibration factors and the immediate computation of aerodynamic coefficients. An earlier "off-line" procedure was to have the strain-gage readings appear on punched cards which at some convenient later date were fed into the computing machine for the computation of coefficients. With on-line computations, the results of a test were immediately available for inspection and also, if desired, an automatic plotter could be used to plot the coefficients as they came from the computer.

In 1955 an IBM 650 digital computer was leased for the specific purpose of serving the computational needs of the theoreticians in the various sections. At this time the first effort was made to train people in the various research sections to do their own computer programing.

In 1956 or thereabouts, a second Datatron computer was purchased. This computer, like the first Datatron, was used for wind-tunnel data reduction, both on-line and off-line.

Additional analog-computer elements, used in flight-simulation work, were also procured during this period. These, however, were separately located and under the control of Stanley Schmidt and Howard Matthews of the Dynamics Analysis Branch, Full Scale and Flight Research Division. The digital computers, on the other hand, remained in the Electronic Machine Computing Branch of the Theoretical and Applied Research Division. This Branch, as earlier mentioned, was headed by Dr. Mersman. The original Assistant Branch Chief, Harold Harrison, resigned in 1955 and his position was then assumed by Stewart Crandall.

12

Research

PATTERN

THE trend of Ames research toward the more scientific and the more
fundamental continued during the period from 1954 to 1957. Many
of the Laboratory's scientist-engineers were gaining worldwide reputations,
and with increasing frequency they were invited to deliver papers before
scientific societies at home and abroad. Among those who traveled abroad
for this purpose were Max Heaslet (London, 1948), Jack Stalder (London,
1951), Ralph Huntsberger (The Hague, 1954), John Parsons (Stockholm,
1954), Harvey Allen (Paris, 1954), Walter Vincenti (Brussels, 1956), and
Al Seiff (The Hague, 1957). As 1957 ended, John Spreiter was preparing
a paper for delivery in Tokyo the following year.

Ames research was advancing along a broad front, but increasing emphasis was being given to the theoretical approach. Aerodynamicists were
devoting much effort to the task of determining optimum configurations for
supersonic and hypersonic aircraft. In flight research there was a continuing
interest in automatic control and at the same time an accelerating trend in
the use of flight simulators of both the airborne and the ground-based types.
The later trend focused considerable attention on the interpretation of pilot
opinion. Dynamic stability was receiving attention in all branches of the
Laboratory during this period; also, efforts were being made to reduce the
landing speed of airplanes by means of boundary-layer-control systems
which utilized the surplus air-pumping capacity of the jet engines.

Perhaps the most notable feature of Ames research during this period,
however, was the tremendous effort applied to related studies of boundary
layer, skin friction, and aerodynamic heating. Although of a basic character,
this research was aimed at a number of specific applications in which the
Laboratory was particularly interested. These applications included hypersonic airplanes, man-carrying rocket-launched gliders called "boost-glide vehicles," and ballistic vehicles. A variety of thermal-protection schemes for
such craft was under consideration.

This period was also noted for the initiation of research in the new Unitary Plan facility. The intended function of the new facility was to serve the development needs of the industry and the military and to free other facilities at Ames for research of a more fundamental character. Although at the end of World War II there had been a feeling that NACA should be relieved of some of its development-test burden, NACA's services to the military had proved much too valuable to be abandoned or even greatly diminished. Ames' contribution to the development-test effort since the end of the war was substantial and of great value; but, since it was often concerned with classified or proprietary matters, it is largely omitted from this history.

BASIC CONFIGURATIONS AND AIRFLOWS

Wings. Important contributions to wing theory were made during this period by Max Heaslet, Harvard Lomax, R. T. Jones, Doris Cohen, John Spreiter, Alberta Alksne, and Milton Van Dyke. Work of the first four of these people appeared in volumes VI and VII of the monumental Princeton Series of books covering the general field of aeronautical science. The Princeton Series, organized under an editorial board headed by Dr. Theodore von Kármán, presented material written by recognized American authorities. NACA and the Ames Laboratory were well represented in the group of authors. In volume VI, published in 1955, Heaslet and Lomax contributed a section dealing with supersonic and transonic small perturbation theory; and in volume VII, published in 1957, Jones and Cohen presented a very comprehensive review of the aerodynamics of wings at supersonic speeds. There were, it should be mentioned, many other Ames contributors to the Princeton Series. Among them were Harvey Allen, Joseph Spiegel, John Dimeff, Ben Beam, Jack Stalder, Al Seiff, and Alex Charters.

During these years, John Spreiter continued his work in the general field of transonic aerodynamic theory and, together with Alberta Alksne, turned out TR 1359 (ref. B–38), entitled "Thin Airfoil Theory Based on Approximate Solution of the Transonic Flow Equations." Also during this period, John and Alberta, together with Al Sacks, were studying the vortex patterns shed by cruciform wing arrangements and the rollup of the vortex sheet behind such wings. This important work, having direct application to missiles with short wings, was published in TR 1296 and TR 1311.

Meanwhile, Milton Van Dyke, pursuing his studies of second-order flow theory, turned out a number of papers of which TR 1274, "Second-Order Subsonic Airfoil Theory Including Edge Effects," might be considered representative.

Experimental research on wings continued during these years but less of it was concerned with wings for what were at this time thought of as conventional transonic or supersonic airplanes. In the 1- by 3-foot tunnel, Walter Vincenti ran tests to confirm his earlier mentioned theory regarding the

246

flow over double-wedge airfoils operating just below the speed of shock attachment. This work was reported in TN 3225 and TN 3522. It was as a result of his excellent work in developing and applying wing theory that Walter received the Rockefeller Public Service Award granting the privilege of a year of study at Cambridge.

One of the most outstanding results of experimental wing research at Ames was the development of conical camber as a means of reducing the drag-due-to-lift and thus of increasing the range of supersonic airplanes, particularly those equipped with delta wings. Conical camber was a form of camber which, for practical reasons, was restricted to the forward part of the wing. The portion of the wing involved in the camber increased linearly from root to tip and thus appeared as a segment of a cone. Conical camber originated with Charles Hall in the 6- by 6-foot tunnel, but its study was taken up in other facilities such as the 12-foot tunnel and covered a period of 6 years and tests of more than 25 models.

Among the numerous reports dealing with the conical-camber investigation were RM A55G19 by John Boyd, Eugene Migotsky, and Benton Wetzel, and RM A58C21 by Robert Sammonds and Robert Reynolds. To the great satisfaction of Ames engineers, conical camber found immediate and very profitable application to three delta-wing airplanes produced by the Consolidated-Vultee Aircraft Corp. The airplanes thus benefited were the supersonic F–102 and F–106 fighters and the new double-sonic B–58 bomber. The added range and flight endurance which conical camber gave to these airplanes were especially valuable.

Bodies. Although research at Ames was becoming increasingly concerned with the airplane as a whole, a considerable amount of effort was still being spent on important components such as wings and bodies. Bodies had become major lift-producing elements in the configurations of hypersonic aircraft and thus were assuming an increasing importance. The desirability of flattening the fuselage to increase its lifting ability was considered by Leland Jorgensen in TR 1376. Through such a measure, it was felt, the wings might be reduced to stubs or completely eliminated.

Much of the research on bodies that took place at Ames during this period was of a theoretical nature. Contributors included Milton Van Dyke who produced TR 1374, "The Similarity Rules for Second-Order Subsonic and Supersonic Flow," and TN 4281, "Second-Order Slender-Body Theory —Axisymmetric Flow." Another contribution to the theory of flow around bodies was TR 1328, "A Second-Order Shock-Expansion Method Applicable to Bodies of Revolution near Zero Lift," by Clarence Syvertson and David Dennis. This report, dealing with hypersonic flows, represented an extension of the generalized shock-expansion method which Eggers, Savin, and Syvertson had presented to the Institute of the Aeronautical Sciences in 1955 and which had appeared in volume 22, No. 4 of the IAS Journal.

In the study of aircraft bodies, interest continued in the problem of defining the body shape that would offer the minimum drag. In order that the body so defined should have some utility, it was necessary to impose certain conditions having to do, for example, with the length, volume, maximum diameter, or base area of the body. Minimum-drag shapes for subsonic and supersonic flight had been fairly well established by 1955, but some uncertainty remained concerning the optimum shape for hypersonic flight. An attempt to solve the hypersonic problem is described in TR 1306 (ref. B–39) by Al Eggers, Meyer Resnikoff, and Dave Dennis. The approach used by the authors of this report was a combination of theory and experiment. The experimental phase of the program was carried out in the 10- by 14-inch tunnel at Mach numbers ranging up to 6.28.

Area Rule. The flurry of research activity that took place after the discovery of the Area Rule lasted for a number of years and changed in character with time. There was an effort first to confirm the rule experimentally and then to establish a more solid theoretical basis for it. Additionally, there were moves to extend the rule beyond the original transonic speed range and also to determine the limits of its application, particularly as to airplane configuration. These developments led aerodynamicists to a fuller appreciation of the possibilities of manipulating the wave patterns of the various components of an airplane to achieve beneficial results such as drag reduction, lift improvement, or improved inlet efficiency. Instead of enclosing engines, rocket pods, and other components within the structure of an airplane, it now seemed desirable to mount them externally as individual units strategically positioned to produce shock-wave cancellation or lift augmentation. Consolidated's double-sonic B–58 bomber was built on this principle. The optimization of airplane designs using Area Rule methods thus became a fascinating game which, like chess, was a matter of knowing where to place one's pieces.

As mentioned in an earlier section of this volume, R. T. Jones had developed what was known as the Supersonic Area Rule. At the same time the theoretical basis of the rule and the limits and manner of its application were being studied by Max Heaslet, Harvard Lomax, John Spreiter, and Frank Fuller. In TR 1318, Heaslet and Spreiter reviewed three-dimensional transonic-flow theory as related to the Area Rule concept; and, in TR 1282, Lomax and Heaslet provided a special method for applying the Area Rule at supersonic speeds.

Among the experimentalists working on the Area Rule problem were George Holdaway, William Page, John McDevitt, Fred Sutton, and Robert Dickey. The extremes to which the experimentalists went in their studies are revealed in RM A58C03 (ref. B–40), an interesting report authored by George Holdaway and Elaine Hatfield.

Optimization Studies. Area Rule developments aroused the interest of a few aerodynamicists at Ames in the somewhat fanciful question of what would be the minimum possible value of wave drag obtainable by any distribution of the elements of an airplane within a prescribed region. Optimization studies of this kind were reported by Bob Jones in TR 1335, and by Max Heaslet and Frank Fuller in TR 1385 (ref. B–41). Jones' study went so far as to consider drag-due-to-lift in addition to wave drag.

Optimization studies of a somewhat more immediate value were also underway. One line of effort was aimed at the development of an airplane configuration to operate at the highest possible efficiency (highest L/D), at a Mach number of about 3.0. This particular Mach number was one good design step beyond the operational capabilities of current military airplanes and close to the aiming point of a new bomber (B–70) which, late in 1957, was being considered by the Air Force.

The work of Bob Jones and others drew the attention of the Laboratory to arrowhead-wing configurations characterized by long, slender, highly swept spans tapering uniformly to pointed tips. Such wings, properly twisted and cambered and swept behind the Mach cone, appeared to give rather high values of L/D at supersonic speeds. A number of analytical and experimental studies of arrowhead-wing configurations were undertaken during this period. One of these was reported in TN 4361 by Elliott Katzen of the 1- by 3-Foot Tunnel Branch. Elliott found that, with a twisted and cambered arrowhead wing, it was possible to achieve a trimmed (wing in longitudinal balance) lift-drag ratio of as much as 9.0 at a Mach number of 3.0. The addition of fuselage, tail fins, engine pods, etc., of course, could be expected to reduce this value of L/D by several points; nevertheless, at Mach 3.0, such an efficiency was regarded as being very high.

While arrowhead wings had some possible use for airplanes designed to fly at Mach numbers up to 3.0, they were, unfortunately, structurally weak and unsuitable for aircraft such as boost-glide vehicles, which were expected to fly at hypersonic speeds. For hypersonic aircraft, new configurations were needed and also new principles for achieving maximum flight efficiency. The thoughts of Ames engineers on this subject led to the development of the interference method for designing hypersonic aircraft. The method was based on ideas proposed by Vernon Rossow (RM A55L08) and others outside of NACA. However, as reported in RM A55L05 (ref. B–42), it was first seriously applied to airplane design by Al Eggers and Clarence Syvertson.

The interference method as applied at Ames took cognizance of the intense and sharply defined pressure fields cast by the various parts of hypersonic aircraft and was an attempt to so arrange these parts that the interference between the pressure fields they cast would produce certain specific benefits. For example, any portion of the fuselage lying below the wing would generate a pressure field that would favorably augment wing lift, whereas any part of the fuselage lying above the wing would have the opposite, unfavorable, effect.

Application of the interference method at Ames resulted in a characteristically flat-topped configuration having no portion of the fuselage above

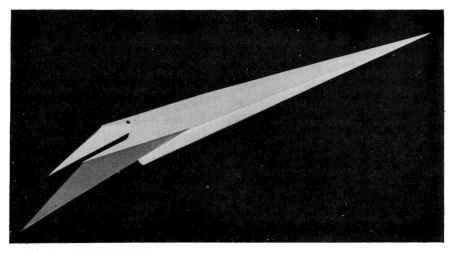

Flat-topped hypersonic airplane configuration. Points at left are deflected wing tips.

Clarence A. Syvertson.

the wing. The fuselage was typically a semicone, uniformly tapered and extending from the nose to the trailing edge of the wing. The wings were swept just within the shock cone of the fuselage and the tips were bent sharply downward to provide some stability and to take greater advantage of the pressure field of the fuselage.

Clarence Syvertson, it should be noted, had been an important contributor to hypersonic-flow research and it was in recognition of his outstanding achievements in this field that in 1957 the Institute of the Aeronautical Sciences presented him with its Lawrence Sperry Award.

Complete Configurations. A number of interesting investigations were made during the mid-1950's of complete configurations representing flyable aircraft. One such investigation, run in the 12-foot tunnel by a team headed by George Edwards, was concerned with the aerodynamic problems involved in the design of a large turboprop-powered, swept wing airplane of the bomber or transport type. Although turbojet engines dominated the aeronautical scene at this stage, there was still a great deal of interest in the use of turbopropeller engines for long-range high-speed transports. But the well-known peculiarities of swept wings combined with the disturbing effects produced by the slipstreams of powerful turboprop tractor engines were expected to generate many unpredictable stability and control problems. Hence it was considered desirable to run tests on a powered model of what Ames engineers considered a practical, perhaps an optimum, configuration for such an airplane. A rather large amount of effort went into this study, which was reported in TN 3789 and TN 3790. Ames engineers were later reassured concerning the validity of their work when the Russians came out with a turboprop transport, or bomber, which closely resembled the configuration that had been found in the 12-foot tunnel to be optimum[1].

The movement of the wing toward the rear end of the fuselage appeared to be a trend in the design of supersonic aircraft. This trend arose partly from an increase in the length and fineness ratio of the fuselage and partly from a rearward movement of the center of gravity as the engines were brought closer to the base of the fuselage. In a number of designs the fuselage projected far in front of the wing but only a short distance behind. The question then arose as to whether it would not be better to mount the horizontal tail at the front end of the fuselage rather than, according to tradition, at the rear. At Ames, tail-first arrangements, known as "canard" configurations, were investigated extensively in the 6- by 6-foot tunnel and other facilities. Such studies were said to have led to early conceptions of a supersonic transport airplane. Major contributors in the canard investigations were Victor Peterson, John Boyd, Gene Menees, and Charlie Hall. A summary and analysis of the results of these studies are contained in RM A58D24 (ref. B–43), "Effects of Canards on Airplane Performance and Stability," by Charles F. Hall and John W. Boyd.

One of the important research and development programs undertaken by the Ames Laboratory between 1954 and 1957 concerned boundary-layer control (BLC) as actually applied to an F–86 airplane. The program, jointly conducted by the 40- by 80-Foot Tunnel and the Flight Research Sections, covered an investigation of three different kinds of boundary-layer control: (1) boundary-layer removal by suction at the leading edge of the wing, (2) boundary-layer removal by suction at the leading edge of the flap, and (3) the use of a jet just ahead of the flap to energize the boundary layer. All forms of BLC were intended to improve the landing characteris-

---

[1] Tupolev *TU-20*, otherwise known as "Bear."

John W. Boyd.

tics of the airplane and all were intended to exploit the air-pumping capacity of the jet engines which in landing is otherwise largely unused.

In the 40-by-80, where the BLC program was strongly led by Bill Harper, details of the flow system were worked out through the use of a model incorporating a jet engine and the actual wings of the F–86 airplane. The design features thus developed were then applied to an actual F–86 airplane and their performance was checked by flight tests. In the flight tests the landing approach with and without BLC was evaluated by a number of Air Force, Navy, contractor (North American), and NACA pilots.

The BLC program was of rather large magnitude. Its results are summarized in three technical reports. The work on leading-edge suction is reported in TN 1276 by Curt Holzhauser and Richard Bray; and the work on flap suction in TR 1370 by Woodrow Cook, Seth Anderson, and George Cooper. The work on the jet flap, perhaps the most practical arrangement, is reported in TR 1369 (ref. B–44) by Mark Kelly, Seth Anderson, and Robert Innis. Aside from the authors of these reports, there were many contributors to the program, including Jules Dods and Earl Watson who, as reported in RM A56C01, investigated the jet flap in the 7- by 10-foot wind tunnel.

During this period, interest began to develop in airplanes having vertical takeoff and landing (VTOL) and short takeoff and landing (STOL) capabilities. A number of investigations of VTOL or STOL devices were made in the 40- by 80-foot tunnel. These devices included a full-scale helicopter rotor, a wing having a propeller mounted in a circular hole cut through the chord plane, and the McDonnell Model XV–1 Convertiplane which was a combination of helicopter and airplane.

252

Propeller studies of limited scope continued during this period. In the 40-by-80, Vernon Rogallo and Paul Yaggy completed their study of once-per-revolution stresses that occur in tractor propeller blades operating in the nonuniform flow field of a wing. This study is reported in TR 1295 authored by Rogallo, Yaggy, and John McCloud. Meanwhile work on the performance of supersonic propellers was continuing in the 12-foot tunnels under the supervision of Fred Demele, William Otey, and Carl Kolbe. Representative work conducted by this team, a study of the effect of blunting the trailing edge of a supersonic propeller, is contained in RM A55J12, authored by Demele and Kolbe.

By this time inlet design had developed into a rather sophisticated science. Many people, all over the country, had contributed to it. The problems of inlet design had increased with the speed of airplanes. The main inlet problem arose because the air received by the inlet had to be slowed down[2] to subsonic speeds before it was delivered to the engine. The aim was to accomplish the slowdown with a minimum of external disturbance and a maximum of pressure recovery at the engine face. But it was in the slowing-down process that much of the inefficiency of supersonic inlets arose. A supersonic airstream, unlike a subsonic airstream, does not slow down gradually. It does so in one or more discrete steps in the form of compression shock waves and the final step, often the only step, from supersonic to subsonic speed is always in the form of a shock, called a normal shock, that lies directly across the flow. The remaining shock waves, if any, are of the oblique variety.

The pressure rise through a compression shock is diminished by thermodynamic losses which are a function of shock intensity—itself varying in accordance with some moderately high power of the velocity drop across the shock. The pressure diminution, or pressure loss, that results from a given shock-induced slowdown in an airstream is thus less if the slowdown is accomplished through a series of mild shocks rather than through a single intense normal shock. The ordinary scoop inlet, which operates on the basis of a single normal shock, was known to incur pressure losses of several percent at a Mach number of 1.6 and quite intolerable losses at higher Mach numbers. It was clear that, for airplanes of higher speed than M 1.6, some way had to be found to introduce additional, oblique shocks into the inlet airstream.

The oblique shock represents the means by which a supersonic stream changes direction, and it may be produced by enforcing a direction change

---

[2]Aeronautical engineers, through an odd mental quirk and perhaps through the conditioning of wind-tunnel experience, always think of the airplane as standing still with the air flowing past it.

Schlieren photograph of air inlets showing wedge production of oblique shock waves ahead of inlet at Mach number 1.95.

in the stream. Enforced turning, it was found, could be accomplished externally (ahead of the inlet) by a system of cones or wedges, or internally, as in the diffuser of a supersonic wind tunnel, by a contraction of the internal flow passage of the inlet. The pressure loss of either system was low compared with that of a normal shock inlet, but the internal compression (shock) system had two distinct advantages over the external compression system—and these were of a kind which increased in value with Mach number.

One advantage of the internal compression inlet was that it offered the possibility of eliminating the external drag that unavoidably accompanies an external compression inlet. The second advantage was that, since the direction change it produced was convergent rather than divergent, its overall volume could possibly be made smaller. Unfortunately, the internal compression inlet, like a supersonic wind tunnel, required a variable geometry. This feature, Emmet Mossman found, could be provided by incorporating a translating centerbody. The resulting inlet operated on the basis of a combination of external and internal compression (a combination of divergent and convergent direction changes) and thus was no longer a pure internal compression type. Nevertheless, it constituted an arrangement that was both practical and efficient.

It was in the investigation of ideas such as those mentioned that a number of men at Ames were engaged for many years. Representative work performed by this group during the current period is reported in RM A56F06 by Emmet Mossman and Frank Pfyl and in RM A55F16 (ref. B–45) by Wallace Davis and Richard Scherrer. The latter report is a comprehensive summary of inlet research conducted at Ames and elsewhere.

Since wind-tunnel models required quite a firm mounting to withstand air forces, the conventional wind tunnel had long been regarded as a rather difficult means by which to study dynamic stability. Nevertheless, in such facilities it had proved feasible to allow control surfaces, such as ailerons, a degree of motion so their dynamic performance could be studied. Also, in 1949, the pitch damping characteristics of certain delta-wing configurations had been investigated in the 6- by 6-foot tunnel through the use of spring-mounted models.

The scope of this work was narrow, however, and, with the development of new airplanes having widely different configurations and operating ranges, the need for the adaptation of wind tunnels for dynamic testing greatly increased. While theory was useful in predicting dynamic stability, a method for obtaining confirming data in wind tunnels was needed. Two groups of men at Ames undertook to solve this problem. Neither group attempted to change the basic wind tunnel—only the model-mounting system.

One group consisting of Henry Lessing, Tom Fryer, and Merrill Mead developed a rather ingenious mounting system in which the model was given two degrees of freedom (roll and yaw) and was forced to oscillate in roll. This device, described in TN 3348, worked fairly well and was able to provide reasonably reliable information on rolling derivatives as well as on certain directional stability and damping in yaw parameters.

The second group working on the dynamic stability problems consisted principally of one man, Benjamin Beam, who was ably supported by the Wind Tunnel Instrument Research Branch. Beam's device, somewhat more sophisticated and elaborate than that of the first group, allowed the model freedom to roll, pitch, or yaw (any two in any one test) as excited by forced oscillations about one of the three axes. The exciting oscillations were controlled by velocity feedback that permitted testing through ranges of variables which, for practical reasons, could not be covered by the more conventional types of oscillatory testing. The processing of data from the device was greatly simplified by the use of analog-computer elements in the strain-gage circuitry. The system was designed primarily for the measurement of damping derivatives, in pitch, roll, and yaw, as well as of cross-derivatives, such as rolling moment due to yawing.

Beam's device, which he described in TR 1258 (ref. B-46), was first used in the 12-foot tunnel and later in other tunnels. It provided advance information on the dynamic stability of many new aircraft—even warheads —and thus was extremely valuable. Some of the applications of the device are reported in RM A55A28, RM A56I04, and RM A58F09.

The analog computer was now also being used for dynamic stability studies. In such use the computer actually simulated, or pictorially reproduced through graphs, the motions of the airplane as affected by control mo-

Benjamin H. Beam and dynamic-stability spring-mounted model of Convair F–102 airplane.

tions, changes in control, stability or inertia parameters, or changes in flight conditions (altitude, etc.). To do this, the computer had first to be programed with certain inputs including (1) the equations of motion; (2) the basic stability derivatives or transfer functions of the airplane, separately obtained; and (3) the calculated or measured changes in the transfer function as produced by those changes in control and stability parameters which were to be investigated. Once the computer was set up, stability and control problems could be studied easily, cheaply, and with no risk of life or property. An example of the use of the analog computer for dynamic stability studies is given in RM A56H30 by Brent Creer. The nature of the study is indicated by the title, "An Analog Computer Study of Several Stability Augmentation Schemes Designed to Alleviate Roll-Induced Instability." The characteristics of the North American F–100 fighter were used in this investigation.

During this period, as always, a number of studies were undertaken at Ames on the subject of airloads. In RM A55C02, Perry Polentz, William Page, and Lionel Levy of the 2- by 2-foot tunnel reported on a wind-tunnel investigation at Mach numbers up to 0.9 of the unsteady normal-force characteristics of a series of 27 representative airfoil sections. Also, as reported in TN 3346 and TN 3500, John DeYoung, aided by Walter Barling, continued the span-load studies which he had begun years before. In the 6- by 6-foot tunnel, Dave Reese undertook an investigation, reported in RM A55F01, of the unsteady lift induced on a wing in the downwash field of an oscillating canard control surface. This was another instance of the kind just mentioned in which problems of dynamic stability or airloads were studied by forced, or free, oscillations of a control surface.

Murray Tobak had by this time become quite well known for his theoretical studies on the dynamics of airplanes and missiles. One of his contributions during this period was a study, reported in TN 3290, on the minimization of airplane response to random gusts. In addition to giving mathematical descriptions of the responses of airplanes to gusts, Murray in this paper considered the problem of minimizing the response and derived the theoretical requirements of a compensating force system.

FLIGHT RESEARCH

Simulators. A new trend had begun in flight research. This movement was toward the use of simulators for studying aircraft guidance and control problems. The simulators were of two kinds: airborne and ground based. Work on airborne simulators had actually begun several years earlier with the development of the variable-stability airplane. The first variable-stability airplane was the propeller-driven F6F. The converted F6F had proved very useful and a more modern airplane, the F–86 swept-wing jet fighter, had then been converted for variable-stability work. It, also, proved very useful. Ames' work with variable-stability airplanes was indeed responsible for the use of negative dihedral in Lockheed's sleek new double-sonic F–104 fighter. Negative dihedral had perhaps never before been used in an airplane, and the concept of its use was quite foreign to the thinking of airplane designers. It was therefore with considerable astonishment that Kelly Johnson, Lockheed's chief designer, heard that an F–104 simulation at Ames had shown negative dihedral to be distinctly advantageous. He immediately dispatched Tony Lee Vier, Lockheed's crack test pilot, to the Laboratory. Tony flew the variable-stability airplane and confirmed the Ames finding. The upshot was that negative dihedral became one of the distinctive features of Lockheed's outstanding F–104 airplane.

Other uses of the variable-stability airplane at Ames during this period are reported by Walter McNeill and Brent Creer in RM A56C08, "A Summary of Results Obtained During Flight Simulation of Several Aircraft Prototypes With Variable Stability Airplanes." Creer had been project engineer in the conversion of the F–86 airplane with which much of the reported test work was done.

Another flight simulator developed and used at Ames consisted of an F–86 airplane in which a variable-control system had been installed. This device allowed the test pilot to vary the dynamic characteristics of the airplane's longitudinal control system over a wide range and thus to study such factors as control feel, sensitivity, breakout force, and time constant. Research applications of the variable-control-system airplane are reported in RM A57L10 by Norman McFadden, Frank Pauli, and Don Heinle.

The research story for the previous period (1950–1953) described the tracking investigation made by Ames flight engineers with several airplanes equipped with cameras and fixed gunsights. The next phase of this program was to perform tracking tests with an F–86 airplane equipped with a gyro-mounted, electronically controlled, computing gunsight that would automatically provide the proper "lead" on the target as dictated by its course, speed, and distance. The accuracy with which a pilot could track a maneuvering target airplane with this additional automatic element in the control system was thus determined and reported by Burnett Gadeberg and George Rathert in RM A54K16.

A target airplane had always been used in the tracking tests at Ames, but this practice created added trouble and expense and there was also some danger of collision between the two airplanes. Ames engineers had become so adept in their automatic-control-systems work that they felt it would be possible to simulate the maneuvering target airplane with a special arrangement of equipment that could be carried in the tracking airplane. This system was duly developed and described by Brian Doolin, Allan Smith, and Fred Drinkwater (pilot) in RM A55F20, "An Air-Borne Target Simulator for Use in Optical-Sight Tracking Studies." The target airplane in this simulation appeared as a moving spot of light on a glass screen in front of the pilot's windshield. The system was very complex but it worked well except that the spot of light which simulated the target airplane did not give the forewarning of a turn that was provided by the banked wings of an actual target airplane.

The target simulator developed by Ames engineers was shortly adapted for simulations of the guidance of the radio-controlled Bull Pup missile that the Navy had developed. This missile was designed to be air-launched and, through a radio-control link, visually guided by the pilot to a ground target. Since the Bull Pup guidance was a tracking job of sorts, it could be simulated quite readily through a modification of the Ames tracking simulator. The results were highly successful and the resulting simulator proved very useful in training Navy pilots in Bull Pup missile operations. The Bull Pup simulator and its use were described by Joe Douvillier, John Foster, and Fred Drinkwater in RM A56G24 (ref. B–47), "An Airborne Simulator Investigation of the Accuracy of an Optical Track Command Missile Guidance System." Along the same line, Bill Kauffman, who had contributed much to the simulator work at Ames, prepared a paper on "Flight Applications of Target Simulator Principles" which was published in the November 1955 issue of the IAS Aeronautical Engineering Review. For his flight simulator work, Kauffman, in 1955, received from the Washington, D.C., Junior Chamber of Commerce the Chamber's Arthur S. Flemming Award.

The ground-based simulator studies at Ames began with a short investigation of the longitudinal stability and control characteristics to be expected of the X–15 airplane as it traveled through the upper reaches of—essentially out of—the sensible atmosphere. In this study, which was carried out by Howard Matthews and Robert Merrick and reported in RM A56F07, a pilot was incorporated in a closed-loop simulator which also included a simple control panel, a control stick, and an analog computer programed to represent the dynamics of the airplane. The control panel and control stick were mounted on a table in front of which the pilot sat. Thus the cockpit representation was rather crude. Nevertheless, some useful information, including pilot's opinions, was obtained regarding the pilot's ability to control the airplane as it departed from and returned to the earth's atmosphere.

Perhaps the next use of a ground-based simulator at Ames was in a study, reported by Maurice White and Fred Drinkwater in RM A57D30, of the approach speeds of carrier-based aircraft. The objective of the study was to find out exactly what it was in the stability and control characteristics of an airplane that caused a pilot to select a certain approach speed in a carrier landing. Here again pilot opinion was a dominant element of the study and the opinions of numerous pilots were elicited. The simulator was again of the simplest kind, similar to the one used in the X–15 study, with a patchwork of gadgetry and the pilot sitting on a stool "flying" an airplane onto a carrier deck. The airplane and carrier deck were represented in simulated form on an oscilloscope screen. The simulations covered four of the Navy's new jet fighters and the results obtained seemed to confirm the value of ground-based flight simulators as a research tool. The validity of the simulator results was in this case confirmed by a flight program in which the carrier-approach handling characteristics of 41 different types of fighter airplanes were obtained together with extensive pilot opinion data. The flight program was reported by Maurice White and Bernard Schlaff in RM A57L11.

At this stage, ground-based flight simulators failed by a wide margin to completely simulate the flight of an airplane and it seemed too much to expect that complete simulations would be possible. It was clearly desirable to simulate the important elements for each study—if one only knew what they were. One obviously incorrect feature of the simulations was that the pilot was sitting still and thus his voluntary and involuntary responses to the motions and attitudes of the airplane in flight were not excited. This omission perhaps had little effect in the carrier-approach studies where the simulated airplane was presumably in a long steady glide. But what if the problem under study was that of pitchup, in which the motions of the airplane not only provide the pilot with a cue for corrective action but throw him around a bit? For such studies the pitching motion should certainly be represented—but how? This was a problem of interest to Melvin Sadoff, who had done so much work on the pitchup problem.

Mel found that unfortunately there was no simple inexpensive way to incorporate even one degree of motion into a ground-based flight simulator. He discovered, nevertheless, that it was possible to use a Link trainer to obtain certain empirical data on pilot response to pitching motion which could later be used in analog studies of the pitchup phenomenon. This procedure was followed in a study reported in RM A55D06, "A Method for Evaluating the Loads and Controllability Aspects of the Pitch-Up Problem," by Melvin Sadoff, Frederick H. Matteson, and C. Dewey Havill. Shortly after this investigation was completed, there was undertaken at

Ames a design study of a pitch-roll chair—a motion generator that could be used in future simulator studies. This then was the beginning of the Laboratory's work on ground-based, piloted flight simulators.

Pilot Opinion. The interpretation of pilot opinion was clearly becoming increasingly important in flight research conducted either with airplanes or with ground-based flight simulators. For a number of years George Cooper had given considerable attention to this matter. To him, the problem of obtaining consistent and useful data from a group of pilots had four important elements. First was the formulation of the question—the choice of the particular factor upon which pilot-opinion data were to be accumulated and the elimination of all ambiguity with regard to the question. Second was answering the question in words the meaning of which had been agreed upon. A standardized rating system was required. Third was weighing the answers of the pilot, taking into consideration his experience, adaptability, and current duties. Fourth was the use of ground-based piloted flight simulators for comparison with flight so that the pilot could conveniently study his own reactions in safety and could also evaluate the importance of what had been left out of the simulation. A much more complete description of George's thoughts in these matters is contained in his paper "Understanding and Interpreting Pilot Opinion" (ref. B–48) which in March 1957 was published in the *IAS Engineering Review*. A notable contribution contained in this paper was Cooper's Pilot Opinion Rating Scale, which became widely accepted as a standard in flight-research circles.

George Cooper, a quiet competent individual and an excellent engineering test pilot, was much liked and highly respected by his colleagues. They felt that Cooper, because of his unassuming character, had never received the credit he deserved and pointed out that back in 1948–1949, while the heroic, much lionized pilots of the X–1 were occasionally breaking the sound barrier at Muroc, he and Rudy Van Dyke at Ames were doing it twice a day in an F–86 without any publicity whatsoever. George's fine work received official recognition in 1954, when he won both the Octave Chanute and the Arthur S. Flemming Awards.

Automatic Systems. Work on automatic control systems for aircraft continued at a good pace during this period. A fairly large part of this effort had to do with the optimization of systems used for guidance of missiles and automatically controlled interceptors. The missile-system studies can perhaps be represented by two investigations: one was covered in a paper by Marvin Shinbrot entitled "Optimization of Time-Varying Linear Systems with Non Stationary Inputs," published in the *ASME Journal*, volume 80, No. 2; and the other was presented in RM A55E11, "Application of Statistical Theory to Beam-Rider Guidance in the Presence of Noise. I—Wiener Filter Theory," by Elwood Stewart. This paper was an important first application of Wiener's filter theory to the elimination of certain spurious radar signals, called "noise" or "glint," which often caused serious, if not completely defeating, errors in missile guidance systems.

Ames research on automatic interceptor systems during this period is well represented by two studies. One of these was carried out by Stanley Schmidt and William Triplett and reported in TN 3387, "Use of Non-Linearities to Compensate the Effects of a Rate-Limited Servo on the Response of an Automatically Controlled Aircraft." The other study was reported by Bill Triplett and Francis Hom in RM A57D09, "Flight Tests of an Automatic Interceptor System with a Tracking Radar Modified To Minimize the Interaction between Antenna and Interceptor Motions." It can be said that Bill Triplett's contributions in this area of research at Ames had become very large and extremely important.

Dynamic Response. Investigations of the dynamic response of airplanes were also carried on during this period. Of particular note was a study undertaken jointly by Ames and the High Speed Flight Station at Edwards. This study, carried out by Henry Cole, Stuart Brown, and Euclid Holleman (of HSFS), was reported in TR 1330 (ref. B–49), "Experimental and Predicted Longitudinal and Lateral-Directional Response Characteristics of a Large Flexible 35° Swept-Wing Airplane at an Altitude of 35,000 Feet." The airplane in this case was a B–47 which had been very thoroughly instrumented to measure the dynamic response of various parts of the airplane structure to excitation in the form of pulsed control motions. The measured response motions of the aircraft were converted to frequency response and transfer functions, which were compared with analytically predicted values. The study was of particular interest because it gave an insight into the dynamic problems of the highly flexible bomber and transport airplanes then being built.

Boundary Layer, Skin Friction, and Aerodynamic Heating

The boundary layer, that thin reaction zone between an airplane and its external environment, had always been of interest to aerodynamicists and airplane designers. At first the interest lay mainly in its potentialities for causing flow separation with accompanying loss of lift and high-pressure drag. Soon it had assumed additional importance as a result of its effect on skin friction. More recently, the boundary layer had acquired an extremely important new meaning relating to its effect on aerodynamic heating; and now great significance was being attached to its chemistry and thermochemical reactions with the aircraft. Inasmuch as the significance of none of the earlier interests had lessened in any large degree, the overall importance of the boundary layer had now reached impressive proportions. It is not surprising therefore that, during this period, the boundary layer and its related influences were important items for study at the Ames Laboratory.

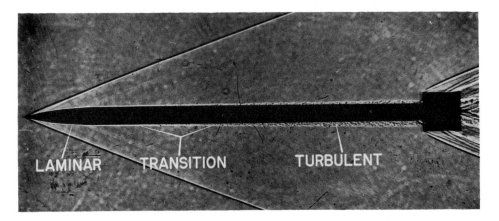

Shadowgraph of boundary-layer transition at Mach 3.

In an interesting investigation made in the supersonic free-flight tunnel, Carlton James, as reported in TN 4235, demonstrated again that the boundary layer did not change suddenly from laminar to turbulent, but rather did so through an intermediate series of bursts of turbulent flow. The same boundary-layer transition characteristic was found in the 12-foot tunnel where, as mentioned in RM A56G17, Fred Boltz and his partners were able to detect transition by means of a microphone. Another significant study of boundary-layer transition, on a body of revolution, was made in the supersonic free-flight tunnel by James Jedlicka, Max Wilkins, and Al Seiff (TN 3342).

Meanwhile, Dean Chapman was continuing studies, begun years earlier, of separated flows. In TR 1356 (ref. B–50), Dean, together with Donald Kuehn and Howard Larson, presented the results of an investigation of the effect of the location of the transition point on the character of separated flows. Chapman also, as described in TN 3792, made a theoretical analysis of heat transfer in regions of separated flow.

As much of the heating of an airplane's surface was known to be caused by the viscous frictional forces of the boundary layer, considerable effort was spent at Ames on the difficult technique of actually measuring the skin-friction force on an isolated surface element by means of a cleverly designed, extremely delicate balance. This notable work was performed by Donald Smith and John Walker of the 12-foot tunnel and reported in TN 4231 (ref. B–51).

The problem of predicting the rate of heat transfer from the boundary layer to a body as affected by Mach number and body-wall temperature was made much easier by an extremely useful report, TN 4236 (ref. B–52), turned out by Thorval Tendeland late in this period. Earlier, a team comprising Glen Goodwin, Marc Creager, and Ernest Winkler had, in the old

262

6-inch heat-transfer tunnel, investigated the local heat-transfer and pressure-drag characteristics of a yawed circular cylinder, representing the blunt leading edge of a swept wing. It was well known then that the heat transfer to sharp leading edges was so intense that the edges would quickly melt off —better, it was felt, to make them blunt to start with. Sweep could then be used to reduce the drag penalty caused by blunting as well as to further reduce aerodynamic heating. This investigation, by Goodwin, Creager, and Winkler, was reported in RM A55H31 and is said by Ames engineers to have significantly influenced the design of the X–15 hypersonic research airplane. In an extension of the study, reported in TN 4142, Marc Creager investigated the heat-transfer and pressure distributions over flat plates (representing wings) with blunt, swept-back leading edges. This TN, one of a series of reports by Creager on similar configurations, was the first to issue from the new 8-inch low-density tunnel and contains a description of that facility.

Although the heating of the wings of airplanes represented a very difficult problem, it was less critical than the heating of the blunt noses of ballistic missiles or of spacecraft returning from extra-atmospheric flight. The problem of the ballistic missile was all the more difficult because the flow pattern about the blunt nose of such a vehicle was extremely complex and did not lend itself to theoretical treatment. Indeed, the "blunt-body problem" was one over which theoretical aerodynamicists throughout the country lost considerable sleep. They could thank Harvey Allen for that. Much credit, then, is due to a team composed of Al Eggers, Fred Hansen, and Bernard Cunningham, who were able to develop an approximate theory for predicting the rate of heat transfer to the stagnation region of blunt bodies. This analysis was reported in TN 4229.

The supersonic free-flight tunnel had proved to be a very fine instrument for investigating the boundary layer, skin friction, heating, and stability of missiles, but achievable Mach numbers were still too low to simulate ballistic-missile conditions fully. Nevertheless, a large number of studies relating to ballistic missiles were made in the facility. Among these investigations was a study of the boundary-layer-transition characteristics of high-drag bodies of revolution, which was reported in RM A56I05 by Alvin Seiff, Simon Sommer, and Thomas Canning. There was also a very important study by Si Sommer and Barbara Short of turbulent skin friction in the presence of severe aerodynamic heating at Mach numbers up to 7.0. This study was described in TN 3391 (ref. B–53).

Another very significant study in the SSFF tunnel, reported in RM A57C25 (ref. B–54) by Tom Canning and Si Sommer, was an investigation of boundary-layer transition on flat-faced bodies of revolution at Mach numbers up to 9.0. The results related directly to the design of blunt-nosed ballistic missiles and spacecraft. Allen and Eggers had shown that the heating of ballistic-missile warheads could be reduced by making them blunt, thus increasing their pressure drag and bow-shock-wave strength. It was also clear that the heating could be reduced by lowering the skin friction, and one important way of doing this was to induce the boundary layer to remain laminar. The nose of the warhead obviously had to be blunt, but was it possible that the maintenance of a laminar boundary layer would be favored by one form of bluntness over some other? The tests reported by Seiff et al. in RM A56I05 had not been very encouraging with regard to the expectation of obtaining much laminar flow over some forms (round-nosed cones) of blunt body. But perhaps, if the blunt nose was absolutely flat, like the top of a fencepost, or nearly flat, laminar flow might be achieved, and heating reduced, over the whole flat face. This was what Sommer and Canning actually found and reported in RM A57C25.

The prototype version of the atmosphere-entry simulator was put into operation early in 1957; the first research investigation made in it involved tests of copper-clad flat-faced cylindrical test models that were launched by means of the single-stage shock-compression gun at speeds of 14,000 feet per second. The tests were of limited scope; however, spectroscopic measurements of the glowing wake were made, and the models were recovered and examined for erosion or loss of material from the front face. The results, though not overly significant, did nevertheless have some bearing on the design of IRBM nose cones. They also confirmed the feasibility of the AES test method. The study was carried out by Stanford Neice, James Carson, and Bernard Cunningham and was reported in RM A57I26.

Earlier findings had suggested that the first step to be taken in minimizing the aerodynamic heating of a hypervelocity vehicle was to choose the right nose shape. The use of the best temperature-resistant high-strength materials was likewise obvious. Some heat could also be dissipated from the body by radiation to outer space but, since radiation varies as the fourth power of the temperature, it appeared that the body would not become a very effective radiator until surface temperatures rose beyond the endurance of most structural materials. Thus as speeds and heating increased, resort had to be taken to artificial cooling methods. It was recognized that a cooling fluid could be circulated within the body or extruded into the boundary layer through pores or small openings in the surface of the body. The latter method was called transpiration, or sweat, cooling and, since it dissipated material that had to be carried in the vehicle, it was also known as "mass transfer" cooling.

Transpiration cooling, it was realized, could be very effective. First of all, the cool transpired fluid carried off some of the body heat. Second, it tended to insulate the body from the hot boundary layer; and third, it reduced skin friction. There were, moreover, other beneficial effects of a more subtle nature. The magnitude of these benefits depended greatly on the nature of the transpiration fluid. It could be air, of course, and also water. Water was effective because it absorbed heat in changing to a gas. Aside from these two choices, the transpiration fluid could be one of the lighter gases, such as helium or hydrogen, which had certain properties that were suitable for the purpose.

At Ames, transpiration cooling became the subject of considerable attention. A typical report resulting from this work is RM A56D05 by Thorval Tendeland and Arthur Okuno. This report provides experimental evidence of the effect of cool-air injection on the skin friction of a turbulent boundary layer. Another example is TN 4149 by Morris Rubesin and Constantine Pappas, which contains a theoretical analysis of the effect on skin friction and heat transfer of injecting either helium or hydrogen into a turbulent boundary layer. The latter report shows that the injection of helium and hydrogen, particularly of hydrogen, is several times as effective in reducing both skin friction and heat transfer as the injection of air. It thus indicated the advantage of using a cooling fluid of low molecular weight. Of course the use of hydrogen is perhaps only a theoretical concept as it would burn if used to cool the external surfaces of an air vehicle.

As the air in the boundary layer and behind the bow wave of a hypervelocity body becomes heated, its thermodynamic and chemical properties change. Properties such as thermal conductivity, heat capacity, and viscosity vary with temperature and, as the temperature continues to rise, the two atoms that make up a molecule of oxygen or nitrogen become so agitated that they fly apart in a heat-absorbing chemical process called "dissociation." Later, when the air begins to cool, they recombine, a process that generates heat. If the temperature of the air rises much above the dissociation level, the atoms themselves attain such violent motions that some of their electrons are torn loose and float freely within the body of gas; in this state, the gas is called a "plasma." Inasmuch as the negatively charged electrons and the positively charged nucleus of an atom are normally in electrical balance, the removal of an electron leaves the remainder of the atom with a positive charge. Thus a plasma, containing many separate positively and negatively charged particles, is electrically conducting and subject to the influence of magnetic fields.

It is understandable that the aerodynamicists and physicists at Ames were now becoming very much interested in the properties of air at high temperature and that they should seek to expand the knowledge on this subject which was of limited extent, inaccurate, or nonexistent. One of the major contributions in this field was made by Fred Hansen and reported in TN 4150 (ref. B–55). In this report, Fred computed and tabulated eight or more useful properties of air for temperatures ranging up to 15,000° Kelvin. A somewhat more modest study on "Effects of Oxygen Recombination on One-Dimensional Flow at High Mach Numbers" was made by Steve P. Heims.

Another very interesting study, in a somewhat related field, was made by Vernon Rossow (ref. B–56). Rossow examined theoretically the possi-

C. Frederick Hansen.

bility of reducing skin friction and heat transfer in a flow of plasma over a flat plate by applying a transverse magnetic field. He concluded that the skin-friction and heat-transfer rate could be reduced by this method; whether or not the attempt to do so would be practicable was another matter.

BALLISTIC AND BOOST-GLIDE VEHICLES

A fairly serious question had arisen at Ames regarding the aerodynamic stability of the blunt-nosed configurations which Allen and Eggers had recommended for the warheads of ballistic missiles. It was necessary for the blunt and otherwise heat-protected face of the warhead to remain pointed forward. Any wild oscillations or tumbling of the reentry body would affect the aerodynamic heating and possibly also its trajectory and its internal workings. Then too, the idea of a man-carrying ballistic missile had appeared and human physical endurance placed another limit on the oscillations and tumbling of a reentry body.

The subject of warhead stability was investigated both experimentally and analytically. In the SSFF tunnel, as reported in RM SA57K18, the use of a single-stage shock-compression gun made it possible to run dynamic-stability tests at Mach numbers up to 15. The study covered by this report was made by Simon Sommer and demonstrated the static stability of one specific warhead design.

One of the early analytical approaches to the reentry stability problem was reported by Harvey Allen in TN 4048, "Motions of a Ballistic Missile Angularly Misaligned With the Flight Path Upon Entering the Atmosphere and Its Effect on Aerodynamic Heating, Aerodynamic Loads and Miss Dis-

266

tance." A somewhat more thorough analysis, jointly undertaken by Murray Tobak and Harvey Allen, was reported in TN 4275, "Dynamic Stability of Vehicles Traversing Ascending or Descending Paths Through the Atmosphere." These reports took into consideration the peculiar pseudo-stability that a reentry vehicle acquires by virtue of the fact that the air density along its path is continuously increasing. For an ascending vehicle, a pseudo-instability was evident.

At this time much interest had risen at Ames and elsewhere concerning the usefulness of rocket-launched man-carrying gliders for long-range hypersonic flight in the outer reaches of the atmosphere. NACA had undertaken discussions with the Air Force on the desirability of building an experimental boost-glide vehicle as the next step beyond the X–15 in the research-airplane program. The Air Force was much interested because of the military potentialities of such an aircraft; and, as 1957 ended, it was about to initiate Project Dynasoar which called for the development of a world-girdling, man-carrying boost-guide vehicle.

Ames was already engaged in configuration studies for aircraft of the boost-glide type. Notable examples of these studies are to be found in RM A55E26, "Some Aspects of the Design of Hypersonic Boost-Glide Aircraft," by Alvin Seiff and H. Julian Allen, and the earlier mentioned RM A55L05, "Aircraft Configurations Developing High Lift-Drag Ratios at High Supersonic Speeds," by A. J. Eggers and Clarence A. Syvertson. Eggers and Syvertson proposed some highly swept configurations the design of which was based on elemental considerations of pressure-field interference and aerodynamic heating.

For transporting weapons and people over long distances at high speeds, there now appeared to be several possibilities: a ballistic missile with nonlifting reentry body, a boost-glide vehicle, and, of course, the vastly slower, but possibly more efficient, supersonic airplane. What was really needed was a comparative systems study to evaluate the feasible range of application as well as the principal design and operating problems for each type of vehicle. Such a study, at least as far as the basic elements of the subject were concerned, was undertaken by Alfred Eggers, Harvey Allen, and Stanford Neice and reported in TR 1382 (ref. B–57).

The study made by Eggers, Allen, and Neice, carried out during 1955 and 1956, was very timely and created much interest in aeronautical circles throughout the country. It revealed a number of interesting facts. On an efficiency basis, the study showed, the ballistic and boost-glide vehicles could compete quite favorably with supersonic airplanes at ranges equal to or greater than half the circumference of the earth. The study also showed that while a ballistic vehicle, sufficiently blunt, could protect precious cargo from the rigors of aerodynamic heating, such a vehicle would, nevertheless, have some limitations as a human carrier owing to excessive reentry deceleration. These limitations, however, which were shown to depend on reentry angle,

267

would not apply at ranges equal to or greater than half the circumference of the earth. Nor would they apply at very short ranges.

The boost-glide vehicle, it appeared, would have a number of advantages over the ballistic vehicle. Its lifting ability and high lift-drag ratio (L/D) would allow it to achieve a greater range than the ballistic vehicle for a given initial boost velocity. Also the boost-glide vehicle could control its flight-path angle and thus its heating rate; its maneuverability in landing was regarded as an obvious additional advantage. It was found, however, that the benefit of lift in increasing the range of the boost-glide vehicle would tend to disappear at ranges approximating the circumference of the earth. At such ranges, owing to the near-satellite speeds involved, lift would lose significance as its role was taken over by centrifugal force. Clearly, with just a little more speed, the vehicle would be in orbit and its range would then no longer be dependent on lift or, for that matter, on drag.

The boost-glide vehicle, it was pointed out, could remain in the atmosphere or be boosted beyond the atmosphere later to return. For flight within the atmosphere, low drag, high L/D, and minimal aerodynamic heating were obviously desirable conditions. These conditions, it was felt, could best be achieved with a wing having blunt, highly swept leading edges. Of course, even with a blunt and swept leading edge, the wing would get very hot; but the heating could be minimized by controlling the rate of descent, and the same method could be used to provide time for a large part of the vehicle's heat burden to be dissipated by radiation into the surrounding sky.

Seiff and Allen, in RM A55E26, looked into the radiation matter and calculated the wing equilibrium temperatures that would obtain when the convective heat input and the radiative heat output were in balance. They found that, for a blunt-nosed, highly swept wing, at a Mach number of 7 and an altitude of 120,000 feet, the equilibrium temperature of the leading edge would be about 2000° F. The remainder of the wing would be cooler. The upper surface would have an average temperature of about 700° F. and the lower surface 1400° F if the flow were laminar and 1900° F if it were turbulent. The higher temperatures found on the lower surface resulted largely, of course, from increased friction arising from the higher air pressure applied to that surface as part of the lifting process.

The importance of Allen's blunt-nose principle was now being recognized and his other major contributions to the development of hypervelocity vehicles were also widely appreciated. In 1955 he received the Sylvanus Albert Reed Award of the Institute of the Aeronautical Sciences and in 1957 he was awarded NACA's Distinguished Service Medal. Allen was also honored by being invited to present the prestigious Wright Brothers Lecture in Washington, D.C., on December 17, 1957, the 54th anniversary of the Wright Brothers' first flight. The subject of the paper (ref. B–58) that he presented on that occasion was "Hypersonic Flight and the Re-Entry Problem."

Takeoff of an early model Atlas.

It was clear that the work of the Laboratory, in terms of speed and altitude, was reaching out to the very edge of space. Indeed, by the end of 1957, rather serious consideration was being given to the problems of space flight. One of the first studies of this kind to be carried out at Ames was made by Fred Hansen in 1956 and reported in TN 3962 (ref. B–59). Fred was concerned with the heating and resulting erosion of the surfaces of space vehicles as they reentered the earth's atmosphere at speeds up to the escape velocity of 37,000 feet per second. Facilities in which tests at such speeds could be made were unavailable, but Fred recognized that in nature such tests were, in effect, being made continuously. He felt that, through the study of meteor flight and meteor trails, much could be learned that would apply to the problem of returning spacecraft. Fred's study was of limited scope, but it represented an interesting concept and produced some useful results.

Some time later, another subject relating to meteors and spacecraft became of interest. A question had arisen as to the extent and nature of the damage to the skin and structure of spacecraft when struck by the small meteoroids which in great numbers whiz through space. Although usually tiny, these meteoroids, because of their tremendous speed (from 7 to 50 miles per second), might well do a lot of damage. There was in fact very little information available on the character of the crater that would be formed from the impact of an object traveling at such speeds. However, the light-gas guns and ballistic ranges developed at Ames offered a means for an introductory investigation of this interesting physical phenomenon. Bullets of any desired shape or composition could be fired into targets of any selected material at speeds up to about 20,000 feet per second. Such test speeds were far from meteor speeds but were the best that could be achieved at the moment. Such a study was undertaken by Alex Charters and G. S. Locke and reported in RM A58B26. In this investigation, which was of limited scope, small spheres made of a variety of metals were fired into targets composed of either copper or lead. Some effort was made to correlate the observed cratering with impact theory. Obviously the whole subject had only been scratched.

Although many—perhaps half—of the Laboratory's recent projects had in some degree been related to space flight, the two just mentioned were among the few that dealt exclusively with the subject. The pace of space research was quickening, however, and it acquired additional impetus from the launchings of *Sputniks I* and *II*.

*   *   *

One might at this time reflect with some amazement on the rapid increase in man's speed of travel. In the 42 years of aeronautical history prior to the end of World War II, man had achieved a speed of travel of about 650 miles per hour. In the 12 years following World War II, his pace had tripled and at this increasing rate could be expected to grow fivefold or more in the next five years. Truly we were living in a new world of speed.

1958

13

The Environment

ALTHOUGH both the United States and the Soviet Union had in 1955 announced plans for launching satellites, the appearance of *Sputnik I* on October 4 and of *Sputnik II* on November 3, 1957, came as a tremendous shock to much of the civilized world. A door now opened on new vistas for man's exploration, a new and inviting frontier lay open to world scientists and engineers, and the human spirit was quickened by the realization that man had suddenly acquired the power to escape from his planet.

Cutting briskly through dreams of grandeur came sobering thoughts of where the Sputnik launchings placed us vis-a-vis the Russians. *Sputniks I* and *II* revealed that the capacity of Russian rockets was far beyond anything we had or were likely to have for years to come. And their techniques for the launching and control of large rockets were clearly also far advanced. In meeting this challenge there was no time to lose.

Confronted with this combination of spiritually inspiring and competitively stimulating prospects, the American people required no further convincing that a major space-research effort, costly though it would assuredly be, should promptly be undertaken. The only questions were: of what should the effort be composed and by whom should it be administered?

The space-research operation was a tempting plum for any organization: scientific, military, or political. It offered much of sound scientific interest but also glamour, glory, and not least of all, power. It is not surprising therefore that many organizations reached out to share in, if not to dominate, the operation. The like had not often been seen of the scrambling, infighting, behind-the-scenes campaigning, and political scheming by which Government agencies and their various supporters sought to influence the trend of events.

Each agency claiming a share in the space program marshaled its arguments as best it could. One of the major contenders for the privilege of running the space show was the Department of Defense; indeed, each of the three services appeared willing to take on the job individually and each was competing with the other two services as well as with the civilian interests.

The Navy, of course, was already heavily involved in the Vanguard satellite project. The Army had perhaps given earlier and more thought to the design of satellites than had either of the other two services. The Air Force was building the rocket motors most likely to be used in a space program, was in command of the Atlantic Missile Range, and was perhaps the most aggressive and powerful and certainly not the least ambitious of the three services.

On the civilian side, the National Academy of Sciences under whose IGY Committee the Vanguard project had been organized had a serious interest in any national space program and, together with the American Rocket Society, gave evidence that it favored the establishment of a new civilian-oriented national space research agency. President Eisenhower, in founding the American IGY satellite project, had indicated a desire to avoid the militarization of space and had shown some concern over the possible adverse reaction of other countries to an American satellite launched by the military with a ballistic-missile rocket.

Other civilian agencies interested in sharing in or controlling the Nation's space effort were the Atomic Energy Commission and NACA. AEC's chief qualification for the job seemed to lie in its experience in managing big projects and in its control of promising sources of power for future spacecraft. It also enjoyed the strong backing of Senator Clinton Anderson and the Joint Committee on Atomic Energy. Many of the NACA staff believed that their organization was best qualified and equipped to take the lead in space research. Moreover, they felt that since space research was a logical extension of NACA's current work, the organization's future would be dim indeed if it was not allowed an important share in the new enterprise. But NACA management appreciated that the challenge of space was large and to meet it would require a diversity of talents. Accordingly, in January 1958 Dr. Dryden, speaking for NACA, proposed that the Nation's space program be jointly undertaken by DOD, NACA, the National Academy of Sciences, and the National Science Foundation together with the universities, research institutions, and industry of the Nation.

Despite the powerful sales efforts of the military, the predominating feeling seemed to be that, aside from such few military applications of space vehicles as seemed likely to develop, the majority of the Nation's space programs would be scientifically oriented and thus might best be controlled by a civilian agency. President Eisenhower's recently reconstituted Scientific Advisory Committee seemed to share this belief.

The military, however, had by no means given up. Early in 1958 DOD formed the Advanced Research Projects Agency (ARPA) to manage the military, and hopefully the Nation's, space research program. It was noted that while the head and many of the staff of ARPA were civilians, the agencies that would carry out ARPA's programs were our old friends, the Army, the Navy, and the Air Force. ARPA appeared to be a possible means for curbing the rampant space rivalry of the individual military services. In any case, ARPA received the endorsement of President Eisenhower and moved ahead with great alacrity.

Space organizational matters had reached something of a climax and a feeling of uneasiness was prevalent in civilian circles. DOD was off and running with the ball while other fronts appeared disappointingly quiet. But the multitudinous forces involved, though exceedingly diverse, did have a prevailing direction and decision-making action began to take place. This action became definitive when, on March 5, 1958, President Eisenhower approved the recommendation of his Advisory Committee on Government Organization that the "leadership of the civil space effort be lodged in a strengthened and redesigned National Advisory Committee for Aeronautics." It became still more definitive when, on April 2, draft legislation establishing a new National Aeronautics and Space Administration, using NACA as a nucleus, was sent to Congress. The act establishing NASA, known as the National Aeronautics and Space Act of 1958, was passed by the Congress and signed by President Eisenhower on July 29, 1958. The conversion of NACA to NASA was to take place in 90 days or sooner if appropriately proclaimed by NASA's appointed Administrator.

Throughout all of these proceedings, the members of the NACA research staff were very enthusiastic about the prospects of undertaking space research and very keen to have their organization take the lead in the space effort. Thus they were generally elated with the final outcome yet, at the same time, somewhat apprehensive over their own future and that of NACA. They were all dimly aware that mighty changes were at hand. NACA had begun action to assume its expected space role well before the Space Act was passed. It had in November 1957 authorized the establishment of a new space technology committee to plan a space research program. At about the same time it initiated plans for a revision of its Headquarters organization to accommodate space-research requirements. By the time the Space Act was passed, action on both of these matters was well advanced.

The dawning of 1958 at the laboratories found their members operating in a bittersweet atmosphere of sadness and elation. The end of a comfortable, if somewhat impoverished, old NACA appeared to be in sight; yet future prospects, though uncertain, were most exciting. Clearly the pattern of operation of the Laboratory was in for a major change: things would never be the same again. But change is a basic ingredient of research and the year's work was undertaken with zest. The general excitement of the times was heightened with the launching of the U.S. *Explorer I* satellite on January 31, 1958, and *Explorer III* on March 26, 1958. However, *Sputnik III* was put into orbit on May 15, 1958, and the space race, though not officially acknowledged, became nevertheless a matter of pressing reality.

14

People and Events

SINCE major changes in NACA were expected shortly, the Ames organization during this period was left largely as it had been. For the most part, changes were limited to those necessitated by staff resignations. The ferment of the times was such, in 1958, as to encourage research people to feel that rich opportunities might exist elsewhere. A group composed of Jack Stalder, Morris Rubesin, Jack Nielsen, and Wallace Davis left the Laboratory in June to form a private research and consulting firm. This departure represented a severe blow to Ames because all these men had demonstrated a high degree of competence and originality in aeronautical research.

Jack Stalder, though a solid hardheaded engineer, had exhibited farsightedness in research planning that put him at the disadvantage of appearing ahead of his time. Actually he was not ahead of it—only in the lead—and his judgments, though advanced, were sound. Morris Rubesin had demonstrated rare originality in his theoretical heat-transfer research, and Jack Nielsen had shown solid competence in dealing with the theory of aerodynamic wing-body interference. Wallace Davis was respected not only for his important contributions in the field of supersonic inlets but also for his managerial abilities, demonstrated as head of the group of sophisticated scientist-engineers who individually had, by uncertain circumstance, gravitated to the 1- by 3-Foot Tunnel Section.

After the departure of Stalder and his coconspirators, the 1- by 3-foot tunnel group was put under Richard Scherrer and the 2- by 2-foot tunnel group under Perry Polentz. Both groups were classified as sections and were incorporated into a new Fluid Mechanics Branch of which Bradford Wick was appointed Chief. In a somewhat similar fashion the sections operating the low-density and the heat-transfer tunnels were completely integrated to form a new Low-Density and Heat-Transfer Wind Tunnels Branch which was placed under the command of Glen Goodwin.

Another serious loss to Ames during 1958 was the resignation in October of Milton Van Dyke, an original and highly talented mathematician. He left Ames to join the faculty of Stanford University, after completing some outstanding work on the blunt-nose problem. Also in October, Donald Wood, in ill health, relinquished his position as Chief of the Theoretical and Applied Research Division (TARD) and was made Technical Assistant to the Associate Director. Robert Crane, who had been Assistant Chief of TARD under Wood, moved up to fill the gap that Wood left.

In March 1958 there was a noteworthy technical conference on "High Speed Aerodynamics," and in July what appeared might be the final Ames Inspection was held. Both events emphasized the space-related research that had been underway in NACA and together gave convincing evidence of NACA's qualifications for leading the Nation's space research effort. The Science Trophy of the Air Force Association in 1958 was presented to Harvey Allen for his conception of the blunt-nose principle and its application to the design of reentry bodies.

None of the supporting activities at Ames bore a more intimate relationship to the principal function of the Laboratory than did the work of the Instrument Research Division. The intimacy, indeed, was all the more apparent as instrument development at Ames often partook of the nature of research. The instruments developed were generally the product of a close collaboration between representatives of instrument and aeronautical research groups. The general purpose of the developed instruments was to facilitate the quantitative determination of physical phenomena of interest in the experimental research carried on by the Laboratory. As the aeronautical research of the Laboratory became more complex, so also did the task of the instrument research man. Never-ending pressure was placed on him to produce smaller and more reliable instruments which more rapidly and accurately would measure a wider variety of physical phenomena under more adverse conditions. The challenge was tremendous.

Instrument work at Ames was initiated in 1940 by James Kelley who for many years had done similar work at Langley. Kelley's efforts were soon augmented by those of Howard Kirschbaum. In 1943, Kirschbaum was put in charge of an Instrument Development Section which was shortly incorporated into a new Service Division headed by James White—another Langley emigré. White's group in 1953 became the Research Instrumentation and Engineering Services Division, of which Jeff Buck was appointed Assistant Chief. In 1955 the Engineering Services Division was split off under Jeff Buck, leaving Jim White in charge of a newly constituted Instrument Research Division. Of this Division, Howard Kirschbaum was made Executive Engineer.

By the time the new Instrument Research Division had been created, the scope of instrument development had so expanded that considerable specialization was necessary. Inasmuch as there had always been a dissimilarity between the instruments required for flight research and those required for wind-tunnel research, it was natural that there should, within the

Instrument Research Division, be formed a Flight Instrument Research Branch and a Wind Tunnel Instrument Research Branch. There were also created a Mechanical Instrument Branch under Jim Kelley and an Electronic Instrument Branch under Leonard Fairfield to deal with the construction, calibration, maintenance, and installation of the instruments conceived by the two instrument research branches.

Dr. G. Allan Smith was made Chief of the Flight Instrument Research Branch, with Taft Wrathall, an oldtimer in instrument work at Ames, as his assistant. Taft resigned soon after his appointment and his position was filled by John Foster. The task confronting Smith and Foster became increasingly difficult as flight research moved into areas of greater sophistication. The two men, in meeting this challenge, made major contributions to the development of variable-stability airplanes and also to the development of the specialized equipment required for studies of tracking, target simulation, and automatic control.

The development of wind-tunnel instrumentation was an activity which grew in complexity and volume, and before the end of 1958 represented a rather large part of the total instrument development effort. Wind-tunnel-instrument development work was originally carried out by Howard Kirschbaum, who later was aided by Taft Wrathall and John Dimeff. When the new Instrument Research Division was formed, John Dimeff was made Chief, and William Kerwin, Assistant Chief, of the Wind Tunnel Instrument Research Branch that was created within the Division.

In the early days of the Ames Laboratory, wind-tunnel instrumentation was fairly simple. Wind-tunnel models and their heavy supporting systems were mounted on several large scales, the individual readings of which could be taken by eye or printed on a paper tape. Pressure distributions were measured by huge banks of liquid manometer tubes which were photographed at appropriate intervals. The task of working up the data from such instrumentation required much human labor and was very tedious.

Around 1942 the electrical resistance wire strain gage reached a useful stage of development. This small device proved to have great utility in the measurement of the hinge moments of control surfaces or the bending stresses occurring in the wings or tails of airplanes or airplane models. The response of the wire strain gage was very fast but could readily be followed by the galvanometer elements of the multichannel oscillograph which had recently come into use. It was not long before wire strain gages were being used in a new type of "strain-gage balance" capable of measuring, simultaneously, all six of the force and moment components applied by the airstream to a wind-tunnel model. The strain-gage balance was so small that it could be mounted entirely within the test model. Its development permitted the elimination of the conventional bulky support struts which, as wind-tunnel speeds increased, had become an intolerable nuisance. The support system that now came into vogue was composed of a single shaft, or sting, which

From left to right: *John V. Foster, Howard W. Kirschbaum, and John Dimeff.*

entered the model from the rear and was attached firmly to the strain-gage balance. Liquid multiple manometers continued to be used for a while but later were largely replaced by tiny pressure cells which generated an electric current pattern that could be recorded with an oscillograph or displayed on the face of a cathode-ray oscilloscope.

Most wind-tunnel measurements now appeared as electric currents or voltages, and this circumstance led to the mechanization of data handling and workup. It was shortly found that the output of the wind-tunnel bal-

Internal strain-gage balance.

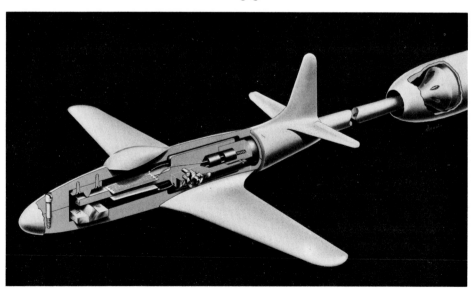

ances could be transferred directly to punched cards or punched paper tape which later could be fed, for data workup, into one of the new electronic computers then coming into use. Still later, as mentioned in an earlier section, the wind-tunnel signals were transmitted through wires directly to the computer with no intermediate card system. The wind-tunnel data, having been converted to coefficient form by the computer, were retransmitted to the wind tunnel and automatically plotted. With this so-called "on-line" system it was possible for the wind-tunnel operator to watch the data being plotted as the test proceeded and to alter his test plan as necessary.

The problems facing John Dimeff and his staff became an order of magnitude more difficult with the development at Ames of low-density and high-temperature wind tunnels and intermittent-flow facilities such as the SSFF tunnel and the gun ranges. X-ray and other techniques were devised for investigating low-pressure flows, while schlieren and interferometric methods were developed for qualitative and quantitative airflow studies at higher pressures. Also, a requirement had recently developed for radiometric equipment with which to analyze the glowing wakes of high-velocity test models. The Wind Tunnel Instrument Research Branch had, moreover, been involved in the development of the highly specialized and extremely precise instrumentation required for the facilities in which models were launched by means of guns. It also had collaborated with Ben Beam of the 12-foot tunnel in the development of his famous dynamic-stability balance and with Don Smith of the same tunnel in the development of a supersensitive balance for the direct measurement of skin friction.

15

....

Facilities

RANGES AND SHOCK TUNNELS

DURING 1958 the atmosphere-entry simulator and the pressure range were completed and put into operation. The simulator was one of the principal displays at the inspection in July. The main range, which had been completed late in 1957, was also put into service in 1958 but for a time was used principally for gun-improvement studies. Meanwhile the development work on shock tunnels was continuing. In the 10- by 14-Inch Tunnel Branch, a team comprising Bernie Cunningham, Fred Hansen, Sam Kraus, and Charles Hermach was giving attention to a tunnel in which fixed models could be tested in a high-energy airflow for reasonably long (100-millisecond) periods of time. At the same time Tom Canning and his colleagues in the SSFF tunnel were developing a shock tunnel, capable of producing flows of modest speed (6000 fps) but relatively high density, for use in counterflow arrangement with a shock-driven light-gas gun. One such arrangement, called the pilot hypervelocity free-flight facility, was completed in 1958 and used for investigating the radiation from the glowing wakes of aerodynamically heated test bodies. Radiation studies of this kind were, indeed, the intended function of the facility.

The pilot hypersonic free-flight facility was a modest pioneering sort of device built "on a shoestring" at a cost of less than $30,000. It used a two-stage shock-driven light-gas gun, capable of launching small models at speeds of about 20,000 feet per second, and a shock tunnel that produced air (any gas) speeds of about 5500 feet per second. The relative speed was approximately 25,000 feet per second, which equaled the reentry speed of an earth satellite. The available Reynolds numbers also covered the satellite reentry conditions fairly well except in the low-altitude portion of the flight trajectory. Heating conditions as determined by stagnation temperatures at the nose of the reentry vehicle, and density or Reynolds number, were also fairly well represented in the new facility.

The nose-stagnation temperature of a model in a test facility is largely determined by initial air temperature (preheating) and relative velocity. It may also be thought of in terms of the thermal-energy content of the air under nose-stagnation conditions. The thermal content of the air, in Btu's per pound, has been given the name "enthalpy." Thus for proper simulation of aerodynamic heating, the stagnation enthalpy and the air density or Reynolds number obtaining in flight must be reproduced in the test facility. What then were the flight-stagnation enthalpies and Reynolds numbers to be matched in the new test facilities at Ames? Approximate flight enthalpies for cases of particular interest are:

		Btu/lb
(1)	Reentering ballistic missile warhead	8,000
(2)	Returning earth satellite	14,000
(3)	Returning lunar spacecraft	25,000
(4)	Returning planetary spacecraft	50,000

Reynolds numbers for the same cases range up to nearly 100 million per foot for the returning planetary spacecraft and perhaps only a million or two for the returning earth satellite and lunar spacecraft.

The new pilot hypersonic free-flight facility provided the highest enthalpy yet attained in an Ames facility—about 13,000. The Reynolds numbers attainable under these conditions were 1 million or less. This performance was not bad, but clearly, for space research, facilities having higher ranges of both variables would be needed. In a comparison of test devices, it was apparent that a desired value of enthalpy could be achieved with less preheating of the air in a device in which the model itself was in motion than in a device in which the model was fixed. And, since preheating was always troublesome, it also was clear that the hypervelocity free-flight facility had a certain advantage over other test devices such as the arc-jet, the shock tunnel, and, quite definitely, the heat-transfer tunnel.

Heat or Helium

The new heat-transfer and low-density tunnels were now in operation but were not entirely satisfactory. The low-density tunnel, while useful, did not provide adequate simulation of aerodynamic heating, and the heat-transfer tunnel was beset by a multitude of operational problems arising in large part from the use of high preheating temperatures in a continuous-flow tunnel having a variable-geometry throat. The latter facility provided Glen Goodwin and his staff with some valuable, if painful, experience in wind-tunnel design. The low-density tunnel, on the other hand, had a fixed throat and was of the nonreturn, blowdown type; in it preheating of the air was quite feasible. To achieve such heating, Jack Stalder was in 1957–1958 experimenting with a pebble-bed heater. This was the pioneer application of pebble-bed heaters at Ames and, as earlier noted, led to the use of such heating means in the new 3.5-foot hypersonic tunnel.

FACILITIES

The troubles that Goodwin had with his hot tunnel caused him to take an increased interest in helium tunnels such as had been proposed to, and turned down by, NACA management. Glen's interest in helium tunnels was shared by Al Eggers, and during 1958 each of them set about designing such a facility. As a result of this work, the construction of a 12- by 12-inch helium tunnel was proposed to NACA management and included in the appropriations request for fiscal year 1959. Congressional approval was obtained in the fall of 1958 and the detail design of the facility was begun. The tunnel was to be located just north of the Unitary Plan facility. It would be of the unheated blowdown type designed to operate with fixed nozzles at Mach numbers of 10, 15, 20, and 25. The helium, stored under pressure in steel cylinders, would be released through the test section whence it would flow into evacuated, spherical recovery tanks.

Despite the intriguing qualities of helium tunnels, such facilities, as earlier noted, lacked the capability for realistically simulating reentry heating conditions. As this limitation was generally recognized, Ames research engineers maintained a keen interest in arc-jet developments. Arc-jet development work at Ames had begun in 1956 and since then had been carried on at an increasing tempo but still at a fairly low level of effort. This work now, in view of space research needs, acquired a new urgency. The idea of the arc-heated wind tunnel (arc-jet) was not new by any means, but the theory behind such devices and also the design techniques were in a rudimentary and very incomplete state. The development of an arc-jet in which the extreme aerothermodynamic conditions of space-flight reentry might successfully be simulated would clearly require years of theoretical and experimental investigation.

Although begun in 1956, the arc-jet project in 1958 seemed not to have progressed very far. The work in 1958 was being carried on by William Carlson, Carl Sorensen, James Jedlicka, Warren Winovich, Nick Vojvodich, and others. Initial specifications were established for an arc-jet facility of the type which was felt to be needed at Ames. The specifications were: 100-atmosphere pressure, 1-megawatt power input, 14,000-Btu-per-pound-energy (enthalpy) addition to the air. No arc-jets then available would come anywhere near meeting these specifications. It was up to Ames to develop its own unit. The work undertaken at this time led to the development of the Ames concentric-ring arc heater. In the operation of this heater, the position of the arc between the water-cooled ring electrodes was to be continuously moved by means of a rotating magnetic field to avoid excessive evaporation of the electrode material.

AEROPHYSICS FACILITY

It had been clear for some time that much basic research on the physics of gases and particles was needed to support the studies of hypervelocity

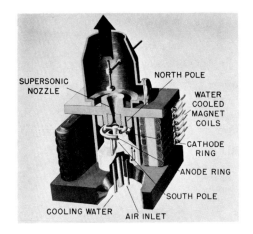

SUPERSONIC NOZZLE

NORTH POLE

WATER COOLED MAGNET COILS

CATHODE RING

ANODE RING

SOUTH POLE

COOLING WATER   AIR INLET

Concentric-ring arc-jet.

aerothermodynamics to which the Ames Laboratory was heavily committed. The required studies were now of such magnitude and complexity as to preclude their accomplishment with makeshift equipment located in some odd corner of an existing building. A separate new laboratory facility would be required; and such a facility, it was felt, should be equipped with a variety of research instrumentation such as shock tubes, particle accelerators, a Van de Graaff generator, an ionized-gas tunnel, magnetohydrodynamics facilities, and a host of smaller items. In the fiscal 1959 construction budget, which was prepared in 1958, such a facility was proposed. This budget item, called the hypervelocity research laboratory, was approved by the Congress and put under design in the fall of 1958. It was to be located immediately north of the Unitary Plan facility and adjacent to the new helium tunnel.

Computing Facilities

Computing facilities at Ames were further augmented during 1958 and their uses expanded. A powerful 704 computer was leased from IBM to serve the needs of theoretical research. It was planned that any time remaining to the machine after performing its principal function would be devoted to off-line wind-tunnel-data reduction. A beginning was made during this period in the application of computer techniques to administrative accounting. The EAM (Electronic Accounting Machines) system used for this application involved a combination or a mechanical card sorter and an electronic computer.

16

Research

Pattern

WHILE the thinking of the Ames staff was markedly altered by the foreknowledge of NACA's new responsibilities in space research, the inertia of the Laboratory's ongoing research program was such that the program continued largely unchanged during 1958. The inertia was somewhat less in the theoretical than in the experimental field with the result that a few analytical studies of spacecraft trajectories were completed during this period. On the whole, however, 1958 was not a period of high research productivity at Ames. There appeared to be several reasons for this. One was that the research leaders at the Laboratory were devoting time to the planning of future space-age operations. Another was that the staff gave more than the usual attention to the inspection and the Technical Conference that were held during 1958. A third factor was the hovering shadow of impending changes in NACA. Not only did this cause a general psychological disturbance at the Laboratory but it may also have been an important influence in the tendering of resignations by a number of the Laboratory's high-ranking research men.

Basic Configurations and Airflows

Investigation of arrowhead-wing configurations continued during 1958. An experimental study made by Leland Jorgenson was reported in Memo 4–27–59A,[1] and another, carried out in the 8- by 7-foot leg of the Unitary Plan facility, was described in TM X–22 [1] by Edward Hopkins, Don Jillie, and Alan Levin. Further studies were also made of hypersonic configurations designed by the interference method. One of these was reported in RM A58G17, "Aerodynamic Performance and Static Stability of Flat-Top Hypersonic Gliders," by Clarence A. Syvertson, Hermilo R. Gloria, and Mi-

---

[1] New NASA report designations to be described later.

chael F. Sarabia. Another program, in which two optimized configurations designed for $M = 5$ were investigated, was described by David Dennis and Richard Petersen in Memo 1–8–59A. And inasmuch as even hypersonic airplanes must land, it was considered necessary to investigate the slow-speed characteristics of some of the more promising hypersonic configurations. This work, reported in RM A58F03 by Mark Kelly, was carried out in the 40- by 80-foot tunnel.

The canard program, which had earlier received so much attention in the 6- by 6-foot tunnel, was extended during 1958 through the work of John Boyd and Gene Menees, reported in Memo 4–21–59A. Also extended, but in a small way, was the work on boundary-layer control (BLC) which had reached a peak during the previous period in the 40- by 80-foot tunnel. This activity was carried on by Roy Griffin, Curt Holzhauser, and Jim Weiberg. Ames engineers drew considerable satisfaction from the fact that the BLC ideas which they had researched were now being applied to several new fighter aircraft.

The Area Rule was still under investigation in 1958, but as a research subject had about been exhausted. Lionel Levy and Kenneth Yoshikawa produced a simplified numerical method for calculating wave drag using Area Rule principles, and George Holdaway together with Jack Mellenthin and Elaine Hatfield made an experimental investigation, in the 14-foot tunnel, of an interesting blended diamond configuration. The latter work is reported in TM X–105.

During 1958, John Spreiter's extensive work in the field of transonic aerodynamic theory reached a culmination, and end, in a paper (ref. B–60) entitled "Aerodynamics of Wings and Bodies at Transonic Speeds." John presented the paper at the Eighth Japanese National Congress for Theoretical and Applied Mechanics held in Tokyo in September 1958.

INLETS

Work on air inlets, particularly internal compression inlets, continued at Ames during this period. One such study, concerned with the ever-present and ever-troublesome problem of dealing with the boundary layer, was described in Memo 2–19–59A by Frank Pfyl and Earl Watson. This report covered tests made in the 6- by 6-foot, the 8- by 7-foot, and the 8- by 8-inch tunnels. Additional inlet studies, most of them carried out in Unitary Plan facilities, were made by a number of Ames engineers including Norman Martin, John Gawienowski, Norman Sorenson, Edward Perkins, and Warren Anderson.

STABILITY

The X–15 research airplane was of fairly unusual configuration and was designed to operate in the outer fringes of the atmosphere where aerodynamic forces were low. The stability and controllability characteristics of the airplane under these conditions of flight were of very great interest to the designers and prospective operators of the craft. Numerous research programs were undertaken at Ames to establish the operational characteristics of the airplane, and a number of these had to do with measurements of its static and dynamic stability. In the dynamic-stability phase of this work, the test technique developed by Ben Beam (TR 1258) was particularly useful. One study of the static and dynamic rotary stability characteristics of the X–15 was made in the 12-foot tunnel and reported in RM A58F09 by Armando Lopez and Bruce Tinling. Similar studies, but at supersonic speeds, were made in the Unitary Plan facility by two teams comprising, in one case, Ben Beam and Kenneth Endicott and, in the other case, Jack Tunnell and Eldon Latham.

In addition to the studies just mentioned, a couple of quite comprehensive analyses were made of the numerous factors affecting the static stability of airplanes representing advanced types. Covered in the analysis was the rather extreme range of conditions which such airplanes are expected to encounter. These studies were made by George Kaattari and Fred Goodwin and were reported in Memo 12–1–58A and Memo 12–2–58A.

FLIGHT RESEARCH

Simulators. Increasing interest was now being taken at Ames in ground-based flight simulators. It was beginning to appear that many of the stability and control characteristics of manned aircraft and perhaps of spacecraft could be evaluated more quickly and cheaply, as well as more safely, with ground-based flight simulators. Before such a program was gone into too deeply, however, it was neccessary to determine the adequacy of flight simulators by comparing their results with those obtained in flight. And inasmuch as all of the flight conditions could not feasibly be represented in a simulator, it was essential to determine which conditions could safely be disregarded. Many of the flight simulator studies so far undertaken at Ames dealt with these problems.

Typically, the elements of a flight simulator consisted of (1) a cockpit with control stick and flight instruments and/or special visual display; (2) an analog computer to compute both the response of the airplane to control motions and other input factors, and to transmit the information to the instrument display; and (3) a pilot to operate the controls in response to cues offered by the instrument display or in accordance with some other prearranged plan. The cues used by a pilot in the guidance of an actual airplane come from three principal sources: the instruments on the control panel, the motion and attitude of the airplane, and the view of the sky horizon and terrain as seen through the windows of the airplane. In a simulator the instrument display could be provided rather easily, but the simulation of airplane motion and external view could be achieved only at great cost and with much difficulty.

The question of the necessity for simulating airplane motion was of the greatest interest to Ames engineers. There were to be considered six degrees of motion: angular motion about the three (pitch, roll, and yaw) axes, and translational motion along each axis. Of these, angular motions could most readily be simulated; the simulation of translational motions would, however, be difficult. A peculiarly representative combination of angular and translational motions could, it was realized, be obtained by mounting the simulated cockpit on a centrifuge; and Langley, using the Navy's large centrifuge at Johnsville, Pa., had exploited this technique in studies of the X–15.

Langley's work with the Johnsville centrifuge generated a determination in Harry Goett to build moving flight simulators at Ames. In the first such simulator built at Ames, the simulated cockpit was mounted on two motor-driven axes providing a certain amount of angular motion in pitch and roll. This device, called the "pitch-roll chair," was relatively crude; but as 1958 ended, Harry Goett and his staff were laying plans for more sophisticated moving flight simulators.

Of the Ames reports that defined the need and requirements of flight simulators and established their usefulness, three could be taken as representative of this period. First was Memo 10–1–58A by Mel Sadoff, which showed that, except in certain operational ranges, the control system characteristics of airplanes could quite successfully be pilot-evaluated in a fixed flight simulator. Second, there was Memo 1–29–59A, "A Pilot Opinion Study of Lateral Control Requirements for Fighter-Type Aircraft," by Brent Y. Creer, John D. Stewart, Robert B. Merrick, and Fred J. Drinkwater III. This report described one of the early uses of the pitch-roll chair and provided a comparative evaluation of the lateral-control requirements of fighter aircraft as determined in actual flight and through the use of flight simulators of both the fixed and the moving types. It showed among other things that, although a fixed flight simulator provided satisfactory results in most cases, there were certain ranges of control variables which could be studied in a simulator only if motion effects were included. The third report was Memo 3–6–59A, "The Use of Flight Simulators for Pilot-Control Problems," by George A. Rathert, Brent Y. Creer, and Joseph G. Douvillier, Jr. This report provided, for that time, a useful survey of the application and requirements of ground-based flight simulators.

Automatic Control. Lines of guidance and control research begun earlier were continued during this period. William Triplett and Stanley Schmidt were occupied with studies of control-system dynamics and Elwood Stewart and Gerald Smith were busy with the optimization of missile guidance systems. The latter work is covered in Memo 2–13–59A, "The Synthesis of Optimum Homing Guidance Systems."

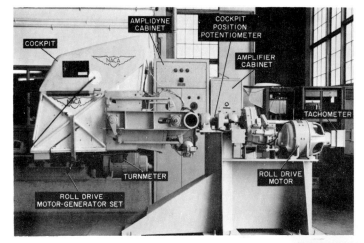

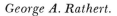

Pitch-roll chair.

George A. Rathert.

Landing Approach. The landing-approach studies commenced during an earlier period were also continued during 1958. One important result of this later work was Memo 10–6–58A, "A Flight Evaluation of the Factors Which Influence the Selection of Landing Approach Speeds." This report, written by Ames test pilots Fred Drinkwater and George Cooper, discussed, from a pilot's point of view, the factors which influence the selection of landing approach speeds. In the end they recommended a certain "power approach" technique designed to take some of the guesswork and variability out of the landing maneuver.

The rather extensive landing-approach studies made by the Ames Flight Research Section had indicated that the landing-approach maneuver could more easily be accomplished if a simple, reliable method were available for quickly controlling the thrust of jet engines. The thrust response of jet engines was notably sluggish and when the pilot wanted a little more, or

291

From left to right: *Allan E. Faye, Donovan R. Heinle, and Glen W. Stinnett.*

a little less, thrust to change his approach-path angle, the desired thrust increment was not quickly obtainable. If, however, it were possible to leave the engine running at a good output and then to modulate the engine thrust by means of a fast-acting thrust reverser, the problem would be solved. The use of a thrust reverser after an airplane had touched down was generally accepted as feasible and desirable, but most aeronautical engineers shuddered at the thought of reversing the thrust of the engine while the airplane was still in the air. But this was exactly what Ames engineers proposed to do and did do. They built a thrust reverser, mounted it on a Lockheed F–94C fighter airplane and, after checking it out in the 40- by 80-foot tunnel, demonstrated its usefulness and safety in flight. This work attracted much attention in flight circles as it represented the first in-flight use of a jet thrust reverser. It was reported in Memo 4–26–59A (ref. B–61) by Seth Anderson, George Cooper, and Alan Faye.

BOUNDARY LAYER, SKIN FRICTION, AND AERODYNAMIC HEATING

For several years, Al Seiff had been exploiting to the fullest the unique capabilities of the supersonic free-flight (SSFF) tunnel. His conceptions were marked by originality and his technical and administrative leadership was of a very high quality. His staff, too, had been demonstrating great ability. On the covers of SSFF reports there were appearing with increasing frequency the names of such people as Tom Canning, Simon Sommer, Barbara Short, and Carlton James. In the background supporting this research were of course numerous individuals whose contributions in such fields as instrument design, model building, facilities construction, and mathematical analysis were vital to the whole operation.

During 1958 the work of the SSFF group in the field of boundary layer, skin friction, and aerodynamic heating was represented by two reports, one of which was TN 4364 (ref. B–62) by Alvin Seiff and Barbara Short demonstrating the use of a Mach-Zehnder interferometer for boundary-layer work. The Mach-Zehnder interferometer was an extremely sensitive and somewhat fickle optical instrument, and its successful application to the precise measurement of boundary layers on models flying past at thousands of feet per second represented in itself a beautiful demonstration of experimental technique. Having mastered the technique, Al and Barbara were able to study the distribution of density gradients within the turbulent boundary layer and thereby to learn much about the heat-transfer characteristics of the boundary layer and the physical flow processes that take place within it.

The second SSFF project to be mentioned is one reported in Memo 10–9–58A, "An Investigation of Some Effects of Mach Number and Air Temperature on the Hypersonic Flow Over a Blunt Body," by Alvin Seiff and Simon C. Sommer. In this project, which was actually carried out in 1957 but was not reported until late in 1958, an attempt was made to separate the effects of Mach number and enthalpy on the pressures and temperatures in the flow around blunt bodies as well as on the forces and moments to which the bodies were subjected. In these tests a shock-compression light-gas gun was used to obtain overall test Mach numbers of up to 15 and enthalpies of up to 2200 Btu/lb.

One of the more interesting boundary-layer studies made during 1957–1958 was conducted by Fred Matting, Dean Chapman, and Jack Nyholm and reported in TR R–82 (ref. B–63). These tests were particularly interesting because they represented the Laboratory's first major use of helium as a substitute for air in wind tunnels. Jackson Stalder had earlier used very small amounts of helium in his first low-density wind tunnel but, for this later application, quantities of helium were brought over in trailers from the Navy's helium storage facility at Moffett Field. This helium was used alternately with air in a special 1- by 10-inch blowdown tunnel, or channel, constructed within the building that housed the 1- by 3-foot tunnels. In this facility, direct measurements were made of the local skin friction in a turbulent boundary layer through a Mach-number range from 0.2 to 9.9 and a Reynolds-number range from 2 to 100 million.

Air was used as the working fluid at Mach numbers up to 4.2 and helium for the higher Mach numbers. The change to helium facilitated the attainment of high air-equivalent Mach numbers and at the higher test speeds enabled the attainment of much higher Reynolds numbers. The physical measurements made during the tests were correlated with theory and it was demonstrated that boundary-layer measurements obtained with helium could be interpreted in terms of measurements made in air. This correlation, however, would not be expected to hold if the boundary layer were intersected by strong shock waves.

The 10- by 14-Inch Tunnel Branch during 1958 remained active in the general field of aerothermodynamics. Fred Hansen and Steve Heims continued their useful studies of the properties of gases at high temperature, while Bernie Cunningham and Sam Kraus made the first practical use of a prototype shock tunnel which they, with the help of others, had recently completed. The work of Cunningham and Kraus was in the form of heat-transfer measurements made on a yawed cylinder representing the leading edge of a swept wing. This work, which seemed to demonstrate the potential value of shock tunnels, was reported in RM A58E19.

BALLISTIC MISSILES AND SPACECRAFT

By early 1958, NACA had become engaged in the planning of a space-research program. Its interests in this regard were reflected in the subject matter of the papers presented at the NACA Conference on High Speed Aerodynamics held at Ames in March. A major item in NACA's space research plans was the launching into orbit of a manned vehicle and the question arose as to what kind of a vehicle it should be. A number of possibilities existed. The vehicle could be a simple blunt-nose capsule like an ICBM warhead, having no lifting capability. It could also be a relatively simple capsule which by virtue of a nonsymmetrical shape and elementary control flaps would be capable of producing small amounts of lift (L/D from 0.5 to 1.0) for achieving a degree of reentry flight-path control. Or it could be a winged glider providing considerable control over its reentry path and landing site.

Each of these possibilities was explored in papers presented at the Ames Conference. In general, it appeared that Langley research men favored a nonlifting vehicle, and Ames research men, a lifting vehicle of some kind. Each had certain advantages. The lifting vehicle held out possibilities for controlling deceleration and heating, which were critical factors in a man-carrying device, and its ability to maneuver in landing was an obvious advantage. A prime advantage of the nonlifting body was the simplicity of its construction and operation. Also its weight, which would be less than that of a lifting vehicle, was more in line with the limited thrusting capacity of existing booster rockets. As long as the aerodynamic heating and decelerations were not beyond human endurance, the nonlifting vehicle, it appeared, should be very satisfactory. In this connection, Allen and Eggers had demonstrated how aerodynamic heating could be controlled through blunting, while Eggers, Allen, and Neice in TR 1382 had shown that, for long ranges as well as for very short ranges, the decelerations to which a nonlifting vehicle would be subjected could be made humanly tolerable.

For the time being, at least, the virtues of the nonlifting vehicle seemed to outweigh those of the lifting vehicle. The dominating influence was perhaps competition. The Russians had convincingly demonstrated their satellite-launching capabilities as well as the impressive power of their booster rockets. They would not be long in putting a man into space. Also, the Air Force had initiated a man-in-space project and was moving ahead with it with all possible speed. It was clear that for NACA, as well as for the Nation, the watchword was speed. The vehicle that would allow the man-in-space task to be accomplished most quickly was the one to be chosen at this time. Later, other types of vehicles could be tried. The answer now seemed to be the simple, nonlifting vehicle.

The Ames Laboratory at this time became interested in orbits and trajectories. Material evidence of this interest appeared in the form of Memo 12–4–58A, "Three-Dimensional Orbits of Earth Satellites, Including Effects of Earth Oblateness and Atmospheric Rotation," by Jack N. Nielsen, Frederick K. Goodwin, and William A. Mersman. This was one of Nielsen's last projects before leaving NACA.

Another trajectory analysis, certainly one of Ames' most outstanding productions for the year, was made by Dean Chapman and published as TR R–11 (ref. B–64), "An Approximate Analytical Method for Studying Entry into Planetary Atmospheres." This study, which again demonstrated Chapman's impressive research capabilities, shed a large amount of light on reentry problems and provided valuable analytical procedures for dealing with those problems. The blunt-body analysis made by Allen and Eggers and the performance study of long-range hypervelocity vehicles made by Eggers, Allen, and Neice had years earlier dealt in a somewhat limited way with certain vital aspects of the aerodynamic heating and reentry [2] problems. Chapman's analysis, however, was much broader; it encompassed the two earlier theories and provided more exact and versatile mathematical tools for dealing with reentry problems. It considered the special problems of entry into the atmospheres of other planets (Venus, Mars, Jupiter) as well as into that of Earth. It also considered a variety of lifting and nonlifting entry bodies or vehicles and several entry techniques.

---

[2] There was some argument as to whether the term should be "reentry" or just plain "entry." Purists held that a vehicle could not be said to have reentered the atmosphere if it had not made a prior entry or had not at least departed from the astronomical body in question. Both terms referred to the inward traversing of planetary atmospheres but in the most common case—that of a spacecraft returning to a planet (Earth) from which it had earlier departed— "reentry" seemed the more descriptive term and was more widely applied. Both, however, are used in this work.

Chapman's study indicated that, during entry, the total heat absorbed by a spacecraft is less, and the deceleration it experiences is greater, as the entry angle relative to the local horizon increases. In the case of nonlifting vehicles, entry angles much above 3° produce decelerations beyond the limit of human endurance. Confirming earlier predictions by Eggers and Allen, Chapman found that a lifting vehicle entering the atmosphere at a moderate entry angle would tend to skip like a flat stone thrown at a millpond. While the total heat energy gained by the vehicle in this case would be less than for a nonskipping entry, the intensity of heating and deceleration at the bottom of the skips would, on the other hand, be particularly high and hard to cope with. It was thus becoming clear that returning spacecraft, particularly those of the nonlifting variety, would have to be guided into the Earth's atmosphere with considerable precision if safe and sure landings were to be accomplished.

One of the useful findings of Chapman's study was that only a small amount of lift was required in a satellite reentry vehicle to achieve a rather large amount of good. From a decaying circular orbit a vehicle developing a lift-drag ratio of only 0.5 would experience a much lower maximum deceleration and be subject to a much lower (about half) maximum heating rate than a nonlifting vehicle. It would, however, owing to longer flight times and lower average Reynolds numbers, absorb more heat. On balance, the advantage appeared to lie heavily with the lifting vehicle.

A spacecraft capable of producing an L/D of from 0.5 to 1.0 did not require wings. A body having the shape of a blunt cone, with the upper half removed, might do the trick, though some simple control flaps would probably be required to keep it flat side up and stable. Such a configuration had, indeed, been proposed by Al Eggers and investigations of the Eggers flat-topped lifting bodies were now being undertaken in a number of Ames facilities.

One of the important reports resulting from these investigations was Memo 10–2–58A (ref. B–65), "Re-entry and Recovery of Near-Earth Satellites With Particular Attention to a Manned Vehicle," by Alfred J. Eggers and Thomas J. Wong. Since the lifting vehicles were expected to be controllable in landing as well as in reentry, their slow-speed characteristics were of much interest. Representative of the slow-speed tests run on such vehicles were those conducted in the 12-foot tunnel and reported in Memo 12–24–58A, "Subsonic Aerodynamic Characteristics of Several Blunt, Lifting, Atmospheric-Entry Shapes," by Howard F. Savage and Bruce E. Tinling.

Interest in the dynamic stability of ballistic-missile warheads, an interest which had originated in an earlier period, now extended to man-carrying reentry bodies having even more stringent stability requirements. Allen had earlier pointed out that a reentry body acquires a degree of apparent or pseudo-dynamic stability by virtue of the fact that the density of the air it encounters in its descent is rapidly increasing. This benefit, which is a function of the rate of change of density with time, would tend to die out as the speed decreased and would then be overcome by any basic instability that the body might have. The degree of apparent stability, depending as it does on rate of descent, and thus on path angle, would obviously be less for a lifting manned vehicle.

Considerations of the kind just noted added to the interest in reentry dynamics that prevailed at this time and provided the instigation for a number of research projects. One of these, reported in TM X–20 by Barbara Short and Simon Sommer, was an investigation in the SSFF tunnel of the static and dynamic stability of two blunt-nose bodies through a range of angles of attack. Another project, of analytical character, was reported in Memo 3–2–59A, "Study of the Oscillatory Motions of Manned Vehicles Entering the Earth's Atmosphere," by Simon C. Sommer and Murray Tobak.

Late in 1958 the Ames Laboratory became actively interested in an airloads problem of unusual character. It concerned the airloads produced by the action of wind on large missiles of the ICBM type standing vertically on the launching pad. The wind produces a pulsating pattern of loads that must be considered not only in the structural design of the missile but also in the design of its guidance system. The pulsating aspects of the wind load arise from the unsteady processes represented by the formation and shedding of vortices in the wake. The phenomena involved were the same as had much earlier been encountered in wind flow around smokestacks, but the structure of a missile was necessarily much more fragile, and certainly more costly, than that of smokestacks. To investigate this problem, a dynamically scaled model of the Titan ballistic missile was installed in the 12-foot tunnel. The air loads, both static and dynamic, were measured, as were the effects of a model umbilical tower mounted adjacent to the missile model. The results of this study were reported by Don Buell and George Kenyon in TM X–109.

Before leaving NACA, Milton Van Dyke attacked one of the more difficult remaining problems in the field of aerodynamic theory. This was the problem of developing a convenient analytical procedure for determining the aerodynamic-flow conditions that exist in the restricted zone between a blunt body and the bow shock wave it produces. This problem, known as the "blunt-body problem," had proved extremely resistant to theoretical treatment even when simplifying assumptions were made—assumptions that the properties of the air behind the shock wave remained constant and that the viscosity of the air was zero.

The blunt-body problem was the more difficult because of the existence of a mixed-flow region behind the shock wave. At the nose of the body is an occluded pocket of subsonic flow which becomes transonic and then supersonic as the air accelerates around the curve of the body. The problem also involved the questions: What was the shape of the shock wave produced by a blunt nose of a given configuration? And what was the standoff distance between the shock wave and the nose?

Van Dyke's study of the problem resulted in the development of a rapid numerical method, suitable for machine computation, for analyzing the flow around certain important classes of blunt body. The usual simplifying assumptions were made in Van Dyke's analysis, but these were by no means invalidating. The analysis dealt mainly with the subsonic region of flow, began with an assumed shape for the shock wave, and proceeded downstream to determine the nose shape that would produce such a shock wave. If the nose shape did not correspond to the one of interest, the process would be repeated until the desired nose shape was achieved. Repetitive numerical procedures of this kind had become feasible and attractive as a result of the fantastic operational speeds of electronic computers. Van Dyke's method was original in character, was timely and useful, and was amenable to improvement. First described in the *Journal of the Aeronautical Sciences* (ref. B–66), the method was demonstrated through a number of applications in the report TR R–1, "Supersonic Flow Past a Family of Blunt Axisymmetric Bodies," by Milton D. Van Dyke and Helen D. Gordon.

17

The Legacy From NACA

O N October 1, 1958, the National Advisory Committee for Aeronautics, an agency which had served its country for 43 years, came to an end. But its body and spirit were not dead. They were transformed by official fiat into the living heart of a new and more powerful organization, the National Aeronautics and Space Administration. Becoming part of NASA on that day were the approximately 8000 employees of the former agency together with $300 million worth of research facilities located at the late agency's three major laboratories and two field stations. At the Ames Aeronautical Laboratory, the transfer included approximately 1450 people and a plant worth about $79 million.

But NACA transferred more than bodies and hardware on October 1, 1958. It transferred a scientific know-how that had won it a highly respected place in aeronautical circles and it transferred an integrity and an efficiency that had made it outstanding among Government agencies. It also transferred a frugality that had been impressed on it from its beginning as a small struggling agency by an economy-minded Congress. The efficiency and frugality acquired by NACA during the difficult years of growth had, indeed, become something of a handicap. The step-by-proven-step procedures used by NACA brought results at the lowest cost and greatest efficiency but not necessarily in the shortest time.

Certain other agencies to which Government funds were available had demonstrated that a rather high effectiveness could be achieved by a method employing multiple-path approaches, tons of money, and rather low efficiency. This method could perhaps be likened to shooting squirrels with a double-barreled shotgun; whereas NACA, with the pride of a professional hunter, had chosen to stalk the game and shoot it between the eyes with a .22 rifle. Certainly the shotgun method was effective and, if time was of the essence or the goal sufficiently important, its use might well be justified. And perhaps the space age with its keen competitive challenges was such an occasion. Certainly the Congress now appeared in the mood to spend real money for space research. But the shotgun method was so foreign

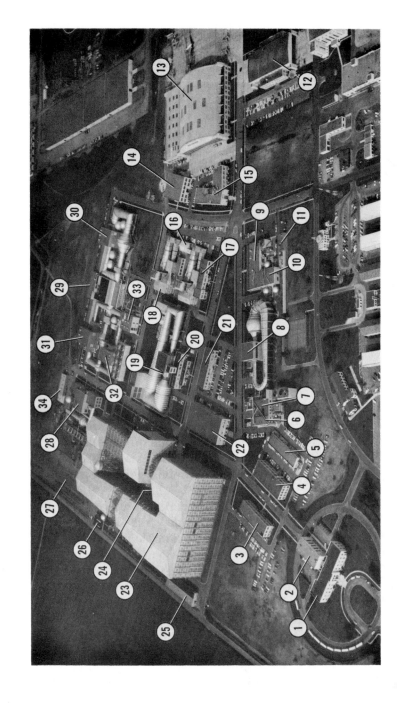

to NACA that a serious question remained as to whether the agency's conservative management could bring itself to use it.

NACA was indeed conservative—not in its daring scientific conceptions, nor in the brilliance of its research techniques, but rather in the economically practical approach it used in the solution of problems. These qualities of strength, or weakness, represented an important part of the legacy that NACA bestowed on NASA in 1958. But however defined, the qualities conveyed would not be allowed to dominate NASA's operations. An Administrator from outside of NACA had been chosen to head the new agency.

←

Mar. 19, 1958, aerial view of NACA Ames Aeronautical Laboratory shortly before it became the NASA Ames Research Center. (1) Administration building, (2) Auditorium and cafeteria building, (3) Administration building annex, (4) Engineering and services building, (5) Low-density and heat-transfer wind tunnels, (6) 10- by 14-inch supersonic wind tunnel, (7) 12-foot pressure wind tunnel, auxiliaries building, (8) 12-foot pressure wind tunnel, (9) Fluid mechanics laboratory, (10) Supersonic free-flight wind tunnel, (11) Pressurized ballistic range, (12) Flight operations laboratory, (13) Airplane hangar and shop, (14) Structural fabrication shop, (15) Instrument research laboratory, (16) Model finishing shop, (17) 7- by 10-foot wind tunnel no. 1, (18) 7- by 10-foot wind tunnel no. 2 (19) 1- by 3½-foot high-speed wind tunnel, (20) 14-foot transonic wind tunnel, (21) Electrical services building, (22) Technical services building, (23) 40- by 80-foot wind tunnel, (24) 2- by 2-foot transonic wind tunnel, (25) Hypervelocity ballistic range, (26) Atmosphere entry simulator, (27) Substation, (28) 6- by 6-foot supersonic wind tunnel, (29) Unitary Plan wind tunnels building, (30) 11-foot transonic wind tunnel, (31) 9- by 7-foot supersonic wind tunnel, (32) 8- by 7-foot supersonic wind tunnel, (33) Unitary Plan wind tunnels, auxiliaries building, (34) Hypervelocity airflow laboratory.

Part III

THE LEAP TO SPACE

1959–1965

1959–1962

1

....

The Environment

SPACE ACT

THE Space Age brought vast changes in the general environment of the former NACA laboratories. The National Aeronautics and Space Act was signed into law on July 29, 1958.[1]

The Act established, within the Executive Office of the President, the National Aeronautics and Space Council to advise and assist the President in matters relating to the establishment of space policy and to the administration of the Nation's space program. The Council was to be headed by the President (in 1961 changed to the Vice President) as chairman and was to include the Secretary of State, the Secretary of Defense, the Administrator of the National Aeronautics and Space Administration, and the Chairman of the Atomic Energy Commission.

The Act also created the National Aeronautics and Space Administration (NASA), the specified functions of which were to—

1. Plan, direct and conduct aeronautical and space activities.
2. Arrange for the participation by the scientific community in planning scientific measurements and observations to be made through the use of aeronautical and space vehicles, and conduct and arrange for the conduct of such measurements and observations.
3. Provide the widest practicable and appropriate dissemination of information concerning its activities and the results thereof.[2]

The Act called for the termination of the National Advisory Committee for Aeronautics and the transferral of its assets, duties, and powers to NASA. It also provided for the early transferral to NASA of any facilities, functions, officers, or organizational entities of any other Government

---

[1] Public Law 85–568, 85th Cong., H.R. 12575, July 29, 1958.
[2] *Ibid.*

agency which related primarily to the functions of the new Administration.[3]

The transmutation of NACA into NASA was to take place 90 days after the passage of the Act or at any earlier date as determined and appropriately proclaimed by the new Administrator of NASA. It had quite generally been assumed that Dr. Hugh L. Dryden, Director of NACA, would be appointed Administrator of NASA. However, there were those who, though respecting Dr. Dryden's integrity and scientific abilities as everyone did, felt that his pursual of the space task would not be as bold as the occasion required. The matter was settled on August 8, 1958, when President Eisenhower nominated Dr. T. Keith Glennan, president of Case Institute of Technology, to be Administrator of NASA and Dr. Dryden to be Deputy Administrator. The nominations were quickly confirmed by the Senate and the two men were sworn in on August 19, 1958. Shortly Glennan gave notice in the *Federal Register* that, as of October 1, 1958, NASA would officially be in operation.[4]

TRANSFERS

Once NASA was in operation, certain transfers of functions, facilities, and organizational units from other Government agencies were quickly effected. These included:

1. Department of Defense responsibilities for the International Geophysical Year (IGY) scientific satellite program. Project Vanguard and the Naval Research Laboratory (NRL) Vanguard Division which involved about 150 men. Also transferred was a group of nearly 50 NRL men who had been associated with the NRL Upper Atmosphere Sounding Rocket group.
2. Several lunar-probe and satellite projects which were being carried out for the Advanced Research Projects Agency (ARPA) by the Army Ballistic Missile Agency (ABMA), the latter located at Huntsville, Alabama.
3. Air Force program for the development of the F–1 single-chamber rocket motor capable of developing up to 1.5 million pounds of thrust.
4. Together with the Army's space projects, Glennan sought to acquire the organizational units that were working on these projects. These units included the ABMA Development Operations Division, headed by the well-known Wernher von Braun, and the Jet Propulsion Laboratory at Pasadena, which was being operated for the Army by the California Institute of Technology. The Army readily relinquished JPL to NASA but fiercely resisted the

---

[3] *Ibid.*

[4] Proclamation executed by Glennan on Sept. 25, 1958; published in *Federal Register* on Sept. 30, 1958 (23 F.R. 7579).

surrender of the ABMA unit. Increasing pressure was brought to bear on the Army and early in 1960 the transfer was effected. The transfer included about 4000 men, facilities at Huntsville and Cape Canaveral, and also the Saturn rocket-development project. The Saturn rocket was a cluster of eight "conventional" liquid rocket motors which together provided a total thrust of 1.5 million pounds.

New Centers

The Army group and facilities which NASA acquired at Huntsville were augmented, to some extent reorganized, and in July 1960 given a new name: the NASA George C. Marshall Space Flight Center. In designating its research establishments, NASA chose to use the term "Center" instead of "Laboratory." The primary function of the Marshall Center was the development, assembly, and launching of large rocket-powered space vehicles.

Considerably earlier—in 1958—plans had been laid to establish a new space-projects center near Washington, D.C. The resulting organizational entity, at first largely composed of NRL groups occupying scattered temporary facilities, was in May 1959 named the NASA Goddard Space Flight Center and in 1960 was moved into new facilities built for it near Beltsville, Maryland. The assigned functions of the Goddard Space Flight Center were the planning and construction of vehicles and payloads for scientific applications and manned-space-flight programs and the conducting of flight operations relating thereto. The Center would also have a major responsibility in the establishment and operation of a global tracking and data-acquisition network.

In 1961, in view of the growing magnitude and importance of the manned space flight program, plans were laid for the construction of a Manned Spacecraft Center near Houston, Texas. The intended functions of this Center were to conduct research and development in manned spacecraft and to plan and carry out manned space flight missions.

NASA at first depended on the military for launching operations but in 1960 established a Launch Operations Directorate to assume general responsibility for NASA launchings at both the Atlantic and the Pacific Missile Ranges. Originally connected with the Marshall Center, the Directorate in 1962 became a separate entity known as the NASA Launch Operations Center. The new Center, located at Cape Canaveral, Florida, soon had a staff of well over 1000 and was participating in the design of some immense assembly, checkout, and launching facilities which NASA was planning to build at the Cape for future manned space flight operations.

NASA Organization and Growth

In building and administering NASA, Glennan had many people and agencies to satisfy. He operated under intense public and political pressures while coping with monumental organizational problems. Never before had a major Government agency been fabricated so quickly out of so many diverse elements. The task, moreover, was made vastly more difficult by the public's expectation that the new agency should immediately perform miracles in a new and highly sophisticated field of endeavor about which a notable state of ignorance prevailed. Glennan attacked the problem with intelligence and vigor, but the organizational turbulence that developed in NASA Headquarters reached substantial dimensions and persisted throughout the period 1959–1962.

By the time, late 1960, that presidential elections were at hand, NASA's staff had risen to about 16,000 from the 8000 originally inherited from NACA. Glennan attempted to avoid unnecessary growth of NASA personnel. Following the practice of the Atomic Energy Commission, on which he had once served, he chose to deal with NASA's expanding research needs by letting research and development (R&D) contracts with outside agencies rather than by expanding in-house capabilities. As a result, the old NACA laboratories did not share in the growth of NASA's staff.

NASA's annual operating budgets had, prior to the election, also risen considerably. The approximate figures were: $340 million in fiscal year (FY) 1959; $500 million in FY 1960; $965 million in FY 1961. For FY 1962 NASA had asked for something over $1200 million but Mr. Eisenhower's Bureau of the Budget had reduced the amount to about $1100 million. At this stage the growth of NASA appeared to have reached a plateau at which it might remain. Despite the recognized importance of space research, there was obviously a limit to the amount of money the U.S. Government could prudently devote to it. Such a limit, the Eisenhower administration seemed to feel, lay between $1000 million and $1500 million per year. Moreover, the NASA administration was apparently willing, without too much struggle, to accept this limitation.

The presidential election in 1960 brought John F. Kennedy into office and Glennan, following earlier plans, submitted his resignation. He was soon replaced by James E. Webb, a very persuasive individual who, though lacking the technical background of Glennan, was a highly experienced and very powerful administrator. As a matter of form, Dr. Dryden also resigned but his resignation was not accepted.

During the transition from Mr. Eisenhower to Mr. Kennedy, there was a period of uncertainty concerning NASA's progress and fate. Then, on April 12, 1961, the Russians launched *Vostok I* carrying a man, for the first time, into space. The mortification which the people of the United States felt over this "defeat" in the undeclared space race was almost as keen as it had been in the case of *Sputnik I*. Pressure for more rapid action quickly arose. In his State of the Union message on March 25, 1961, Mr. Kennedy declared that the time had come for the country to take longer strides in space and he thereupon set as a national goal, to be accomplished before the end of the decade, the task of landing a man on the moon and returning him safely to earth. A similar task was indeed already on NASA's tentative agenda but scheduled for some indefinite period after 1970.

Mr. Kennedy's declaration, followed quickly by the flight of *Vostok II,* provided a powerful stimulus which galvanized the Nation into action. NASA's FY 1962 budget was quickly increased by 60 percent to about $1800 million and the FY 1963 budget, prepared in 1962, was in the neighborhood of $3500 million. Correspondingly, the agency's personnel complement increased to over 25,000 by the end of 1962. The rapid growth was, of course, accompanied by another period of organizational turmoil. An additional result of the Kennedy impulse, over which there was considerable complaint in scientific circles, was that more than 50 percent of the huge NASA budget was being spent on the man-on-the-moon "space spectacular."

Clearly, the great surges of U.S. effort in the space field were reactions to Russian achievements. Aside from launching payloads of impressive size, the Soviets had, in space, realized a number of important "firsts." These had included:

- First to launch satellite: *Sputnik I,* October 4, 1957
- First to put animal in orbit: *Sputnik II,* November 3, 1957
- First satellite to orbit sun: *Lunik I,* January 2, 1959
- First to impact moon: *Lunik II,* September 12, 1959
- First to photograph back of moon: *Lunik III,* October 4, 1959
- First to put man in orbit: *Vostok I,* April 12, 1961

The United States, of course, was not standing still while the U.S.S.R. was accomplishing its "firsts" in space. During this period, NASA and the U.S. military services performed many outstanding space feats and U.S. efforts rose to an awesomely magnificent peak of scientific achievement at the end of 1962 with the Venus rendezvous of *Mariner II.*

EXTERNAL RELATIONS

The activities of NASA impinged on the interests of people and agencies throughout the world as NACA's activities never had. In respect to the military services, NASA was in the position of an equal rather than a mere technical adviser. NASA not only engaged in research but also actively competed with the military in the field of operations. While in earlier years the military had not hesitated in stepping into NACA's assigned field of aeronautical research, it was now reluctant to share with NASA any part of its operational role. Indeed in 1957–1958, when the space task assignment was being considered, it had fought very hard, though unsuccessfully, to maintain this traditional monopoly.

The Space Act declared the peaceful intentions of the United States in space but, while giving the major assignment to a civilian agency, did, nevertheless, limit that assignment through the statement:

> . . . except that activities peculiar to, or primarily associated with the development of weapons systems, military operations or the defense of the United States (including the research and development necessary to make effective provision for the defense of the United States) shall be the responsibility of, and shall be directed by, the Department of Defense. . . . [5]

Also arrangements were made for giving the needs of the military due consideration in NASA plans and for integrating the military into NASA space operations, particularly in the fields of policy making, broad technical planning, booster-rocket development and procurement, launch operations, tracking and data acquisition, and spacecraft recovery.

The military was never wholly satisfied with its somewhat limited space role and took every opportunity to enlarge it. This attitude was especially true of the Air Force which in March 1961 was assigned responsibility for all research engineering and flight testing in connection with DOD space projects.

NASA became a partner of the Atomic Energy Commission in the Rover nuclear rocket project which had been initiated by AEC and the Air Force. In August 1960 a joint NASA–AEC office was established to coordinate the activities of the two agencies in the field of nuclear-rocket applications in space flight.

The universities and the scientific community were also thoroughly integrated into NASA activities. The National Academy of Sciences and other scientific and technical bodies provided counsel and assistance to NASA while NASA undertook, on a large scale, the sponsorship of space-related studies in universities throughout the country. Many university groups, operating under contract with NASA, developed space experiments to be carried aloft in NASA satellites. NASA also sought advice and assistance from scientific groups abroad and collaborated with many countries in space projects. NASA activities were thus of worldwide scope and interest.

NASA's relations with industry were notably different than those of NACA had been. NACA had had no business to offer and its relations with industry were thus of a straightforward technical nature unaffected by considerations of money. NASA, on the other hand, had vast amounts of money to pay to industry for research, development, and manufacturing services. The advice it received from industry on R&D matters had thus to be scrutinized with care, and the welcome now given by industry to a NASA visitor would, unhappily, be a little suspect.

One of the more significant changes accompanying the transformation of NACA into NASA occurred in the field of public relations. NACA was

---

[5] See footnote 1.

known to but a few people and its activities were relatively obscure. NASA, however, became widely known as its spectacular exploits appeared on the television screens of the world. Everyone from schoolchildren to corporation heads offered advice and passed judgment on NASA operations. Never before had day-to-day progress in the exploration of a new field been so accessible to public observation. Aside from the hundreds of millions who were merely interested in NASA activities, there were also large numbers who were actively involved in its functions. Estimates indicated that as many as 2 million people were participating, in some degree, in the man-in-space program and this estimate, of course, did not include the 190 million people each of whom was contributing about $10 per year to pay for the program.

NATURE OF NASA RESEARCH

A basic difference between the operations of NACA and NASA was in the nature of the research undertaken by the two agencies. The work of NACA fell almost exclusively in the field of applied research—research aimed directly at improving the performance and reliability of military and commercial aircraft. Pure research, aimed simply at satisfying man's endless curiosity about nature, was an activity which Congress had heretofore been unwilling to fund. But the end objective of much of NASA's research was pure in character; no one expected any early practical rewards for landing a man on the moon or for determining the temperature and the magnetic fields of Venus. The revolution in man's thinking produced by the Space Age was perhaps best revealed by the actions of congressmen in appropriating vast sums of money for pure research.

Congressman Albert Thomas of Texas, member of House Appropriations Committee from 1941 to 1965 and Chairman of the Independent Offices Subcommittee from 1949 to 1952 and 1955 to 1965.

There were many who questioned the wisdom of spending so much money for such operations as going to the moon or to Venus and there were some who tried to rationalize the action by devious arguments of questionable validity. Still others appeared willing to accept without question or hindrance man's unique urge to learn more about the universe in which he lives. This great urge, like the one to procreate, is not benefited by attempts at explanation. The philosophy behind such feelings was well expressed in a statement attributed to the Arctic explorer Fridtjof Nansen: "The history of the human race is a continuous struggle from darkness toward light. It is therefore to no purpose to discuss the uses of knowledge—man wants to know and when he ceases to do so he is no longer man."

Still unsettled, however, was the question of how much a man or a nation can afford to spend to satisfy human curiosity. About all that could be said on this point was that past investments of effort and funds in such activities had, on the whole, paid off handsomely for they account in large part for the difference in status between man and the lower animals.

INFLUENCE ON AMES

This then was the nature of the organization and activity of which the Ames Research Center found itself an increasingly smaller part. Fortunately, the organizational commotion attendant on the formation of NASA was largely centered in the East. Ames was thus substantially isolated from these disturbing activities, and the transition from NACA to NASA was all the easier for Ames because it, together with the other former NACA centers (Langley, Lewis, and the High Speed Flight Station), continued, as before, to report to the same old NACA Headquarters group. This group was headed by Ira S. Abbott who in February 1960 was Director of the Office of Advanced Research Programs which, together with the Office of Space Flight Programs and the Office of Launch Vehicle Programs, comprised the main technical divisions in the NASA Headquarters organization.

The four former NACA centers were able to maintain some semblance of their old and close relationship and, as under NACA, their work received the coordination and advisory benefits of a group of technical committees. Coordination of activities was, of course, a much more complex function for NASA than it had been for NACA and required an effort of which the technical committees provided only a part. Likewise the executive function of a Headquarters technical division under NASA was the more difficult because it had to adjust to a more complex, heterogeneous, and fluid pattern of agency management than NACA had ever known or imagined.

Ames relationships with those NASA centers which were concerned with operations were not particularly close. Nevertheless, these centers were interested in the basic research being conducted by Ames and occasionally asked Ames to carry out specific research projects in support of their spaceflight missions. Such support was, of course, arranged through Headquarters. NASA was a larger, looser, and more impersonal organization than NACA. Increasingly, as time went on, the people employed within the agency's far-flung boundaries found themselves strangers to each other—both in person and in function. The intimacy that had characterized NACA's operations was forever gone.

NACA people had long felt that there was a basic incompatibility between research and operations and that whenever the two competed for attention, manpower, and funds, research was at a severe disadvantage. Thus as NASA got under way, concern quickly developed over the unfair competition the Administration's glamorous space operations would provide for the basic laboratory research upon which any successful space operations would surely depend. Dr. Dryden sincerely felt that basic laboratory research must be preserved and protected. Dr. Glennan seemed to agree but, despite their good intentions, a serious question remained as to whether it would be humanly possible to protect NASA's laboratory research from a starvation arising from public and political pressures for spectacular space achievements.

Ames management was steeped in the traditions of laboratory research and had little interest in undertaking space operations or space-project management. Indeed its attitude toward such activities was slightly disdainful. Within the Center, however, there were people who had a definite interest in space-project management and who, despite top-level resistance, pressed their point of view. Such divergent views had small effect and during the first year or two under NASA, Ames proceeded very much as it had under NACA. Money for facilities came a bit easier but from 1958 to the end of 1960 the Center was allowed no increase in manpower.[6] The growth of manpower in NASA was largely concentrated in the area of space operations and space-hardware development, neither of which was significantly represented in the Ames program.

Research at Ames was little benefited by the Space Age transformation —at least in the early years. In fact it received a sharp setback in 1959 when NASA Headquarters decided that NASA flight research should be concentrated at the Administration's Flight Research Center at Edwards, California. The only flight-research activity left at Ames was that associated with the development of vertical takeoff and landing (VTOL) and short takeoff and landing (STOL) aircraft. These projects were allowed to remain at Ames because it was felt that their prosecution would be greatly facilitated by the proximity of the 40- by 80-foot tunnel. The removal of Ames flight projects was regarded at Ames as an act of questionable wisdom. It was in any case a poor reward for the outstanding flight research which the Center

---

[6] See app. A.

had carried out. Headquarters allowed Ames to retain one F–86 airplane so that the Center's pilots might maintain their flying proficiency and thus their ability to contribute to flight-simulation programs.

As earlier indicated, NASA was a Government entity having powerful acquisitive rights. When first formed, it had the authority to take over almost any Government property, facility, or activity for which it could prove a legitimate need. One of its smaller acquisitions at this time was the 76-odd acres of Navy-owned land on which the Ames Research Center rested.[7] Prior to the takeover, NASA had been allowed to occupy this land on the basis of a "use permit" granted by the Navy. Now the land became NASA property but, inasmuch as it still lay within the Naval Base reservation, Ames administrative procedures had to be coordinated with Navy requirements. From past experience, this necessity presented no serious problem.

---

[7] 75.6 acres transferred from Navy on April 2, 1962, combined with 39.4 acres obtained from several purchases of adjacent privately owned land brings total owned by NASA, on April 2, 1962, to 115 acres.

2

People and Events

ALTHOUGH Ames was fairly well isolated from the organizational turmoil in Washington, it was obliged to reorganize and redirect its
efforts to cope with space-age responsibilities. New areas of space-related
research had to be covered and, inasmuch as no increase in staff had been
allowed, it was necessary to consolidate and reduce some of the Center's
older, aeronautical activities. It was not, however, until December 31, 1959,
more than a year after NASA was founded, that the first major organizational change was made at the Center. This organizational event was preceded by certain important personnel shifts of a localized character.

On August 31, 1959, Harry Goett, Chief of the Full Scale and Flight
Research Division, left Ames to become Director of the new Goddard Space
Flight Center. His going, though a big gain for Goddard, was a great loss for
Ames. Fortunately there had developed at Ames a cadre of extremely able
young men from whom vacancies could be filled. Goett's former position
was filled by Charles W. (Bill) Harper, who had been chief of the 40- by
80-Foot Wind Tunnel Branch. Bill, a sports-car racer by avocation, had displayed a high level of technical ability and leadership at Ames. In research
he readily distinguished the kernel from the chaff and pressed on toward the
target with exemplary vigor. The success of his leadership was further assured by his pleasant, debonair, personality. Harper's former position, in
the 40-by-80, was taken over by Woodrow Cook.

Another loss to the Center, fortunately temporary, occurred in the summer of 1959 when Dean Chapman left Ames for a year of study at the University of Manchester in England. This opportunity was afforded by the
Rockefeller Public Service Award which Chapman won for his outstanding
work on spacecraft reentry trajectories.

The major organizational changes made at the end of 1959 were principally concerned with the research divisions. The changes included (1) the
appointment of Harvey Allen to the position of Assistant Director, parallel-

Charles W. Harper.

ing that held by Russell Robinson; (2) elimination of the Theoretical and Applied Research Division; (3) the granting of divisional status to aerothermodynamics research; and (4) the formation of a new Vehicle Environment Division, under Alfred Eggers, to deal exclusively with problems of spacecraft design and operation.

As noted, the assumption, by Ames, of new space-research responsibilities necessitated a consolidation and a curtailment of some of the older aeronautical research activities. Moves in this direction by early 1960 included the following:

(1) In November 1959, the 10- by 14-Inch Supersonic Wind Tunnel Branch was disbanded and the tunnel reassigned, for use as required, to the 3.5-Foot Hypersonic Wind Tunnel Branch.

(2) The 14-Foot Transonic Wind Tunnel Branch also was disbanded late in 1959 and the tunnel reassigned, for use as required, to the 11-Foot Transonic Wind Tunnel Branch (Unitary Plan Wind Tunnel Division).

(3) The 7- by 10-Foot Wind Tunnels Branch was disbanded earlier and the two tunnels reassigned on a standby basis to the 40- by 80-Foot Wind Tunnel Branch.

(4) The remaining six non-Unitary wind tunnels were combined into three branches.

Most of the changes so far mentioned are reflected in the abbreviated organizational chart for January 1960. The chart, however, does not reveal the formation, in December 1958, of the Ames Manned Satellite Team, headed by Alfred Eggers. The responsibilities of this team were (1) to consider the design problems of a manned satellite, (2) to propose a practical

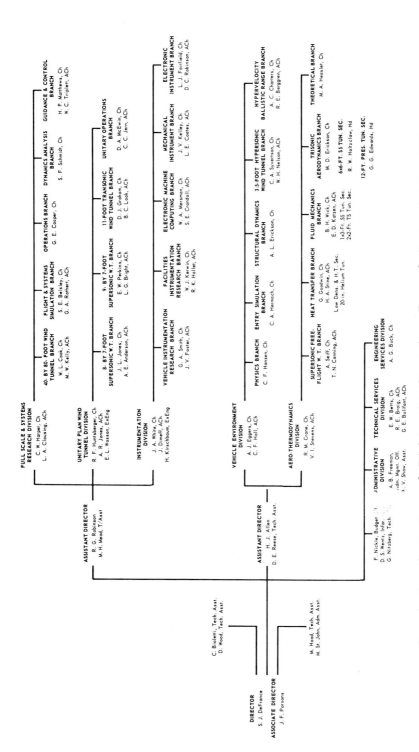

Organization chart (Research Division details) of Ames Research Center, October 1960.

system for such a satellite, and (3) to recommend research programs necessary for the development of the proposed system. This very influential group, which in June 1960 was reconstituted under the leadership of Alvin Seiff as the Ames Manned Lunar Mission Team, was instrumental in setting the manned lunar mission [1] as a NASA goal. As reconstituted, the team was organized as follows:

A. Seiff, Chairman; C. A. Syvertson, vice chairman; M. H. Mead, guidance and control; G. A. Rathert, piloting, simulation, bioengineering; A. L. Erickson, launch vehicles; G. G. Edwards, landing; B. Look, parachutes; H. Hornby, rendezvous, propulsion; G. A. Smith, guidance techniques; S. F. Schmidt, trajectories, control; G. Goodwin, heat transfer; C. A. Hermach, materials; A. C. Charters, meteoroid damage; and C. F. Hansen, physics.

LATER DEVELOPMENTS

Once the excitement over the initial Space Age developments at Ames began to fade, a certain restlessness in the Center's staff became evident. Don Wood retired and Alex Charters resigned in March 1961. Alex's position as chief of the hypervelocity ballistics range was filled by Tom Canning. A little later Fred Hansen, chief of the Physics Branch, resigned and the vacancy thus created was filled by Michel Bader, who had come to Ames from Caltech.

On April 19, 1961, Don Heinle, Ames test pilot, was killed in the crash of an F–101 at Edwards. Reportedly, his plane got into a flat spin from which he was unable to effect a recovery. Don was well liked at Ames and had made many contributions to the Center's flight research. His passing was a sad loss.

In August 1962 Bradford Evans replaced Dan Wentz as Information Officer. A month later Red Betts retired and his position was filled by Raymond Braig. Also, late in 1962, R. T. Jones departed from Ames on an extended leave of absence to work with an eastern research group on the development of an artificial heart.

The period 1961–1962 was also marked by a number of organizational changes. Early in 1962 Arthur Freeman was given the title "Assistant Director for Administration," but his task remained essentially unchanged. He had held the same position longer than anyone else at the Center except Smith DeFrance. NASA management was impressed with the need for ensuring that new devices and ideas developed for space operations be quickly brought to the attention of industry for possible application in other nonspace fields. To further this purpose, an Applications Officer was appointed at each NASA center. At Ames the position was assigned to George Ed-

---

[1] The team proposed a series of manned flights reaching ever closer to the moon but not an actual lunar landing.

320

Daniel S. Wentz and Bradford A. Evans, Public Information Officers.

wards, who for a time thereafter carried on the applications work while continuing to act as head of the 12-Foot Pressure Wind Tunnel Section.

The scope of the Ames research operation was considerably enlarged in August 1962 when a Space Sciences Division was formed. The new division, assigned to Harvey Allen's directorate and headed by Dr. Charles P. Sonett, was the first Ames unit established primarily for the purpose of carrying out experiments in space. Sonett had perhaps had as much experience in devising space experiments and instruments as anyone else in the country. As an employee of the Space Technology Laboratories, Sonett had worked for a number of years on Air Force space probes. More recently, he had been connected with the NASA Headquarters Office of Space Sciences. Because of manpower limitations, the Space Sciences Division at Ames grew much more slowly than Dr. Sonett had hoped, or expected, and by the end of 1962 had not increased much in size. First member of Sonett's staff was John Wolfe, who had been working with Michel Bader, in the Physics Branch, on solar-plasma probes. Another early staff acquisition was John Spreiter, who was appointed head of the Theoretical Studies Branch of the new division.

FORMATION OF LIFE-SCIENCES ACTIVITY

One of the most important organizational changes at Ames was the starting of a life-sciences activity in February 1961 with the arrival of Dr. Richard S. Young. Two weeks later Young was joined by Dr. Jiro Oyama. Dr. Young was then connected with the new Office of Life Sciences Programs which, under Dr. Clark Randt, had been established in NASA Headquarters. Randt's office had developed an interest in biological experiments to be carried out in space by means of satellites (e.g., Project Bios) and a laboratory was needed in which some ground experimentation could be performed prior to flight. Such work, they decided, could be done at Ames. This was the mission of Drs. Young and Oyama. They established their first

John H. Wolfe and Richard W. Silva (top left), *Dr. Charles P. Sonett* (top right), *Dr. Richard S. Young* (bottom left), *and Dr. Webb E. Haymaker* (bottom right).

biological research facilities in a small penthouse atop the instrument research building. At this stage, Dr. Young was not a part of the Ames organization. He received administrative support from the Center but reported to Dr. Randt.

Prior to Dr. Young's arrival at Ames, NASA Headquarters considered

322

the establishment of a major NASA life-sciences activity at Ames Research Center and other sites. Ames was of interest because of the well-known biological centers and scientists located in the San Francisco Bay region; another reason for the tide's turning in favor of Ames may have been the human-factors aspect of the Center's flight-simulation activities. This item might not have been effective had it not been for the enlightenment and persuasion which reportedly was offered to Dr. Randt by his friend Dr. Harald Smedal. Dr. Smedal, a captain in the U.S. Navy Medical Corps, had earlier become interested in the flight-simulation work at Ames and had joined the Center's staff.

The decision to establish a life-sciences research activity at Ames was made in November 1960,[2] but further action was delayed until the next spring when Drs. Young and Oyama became the first members of the Ames life-sciences organization. Walter Peterson, the first Ames staff member to be associated with the new activity, was appointed Administrative Assistant to the Assistant Director for Life Sciences. The latter position (Assistant Director for Life Sciences) was filled in July 1961 by Dr. Webb Haymaker, internationally known neuropathologist who at one time had been president of the American Association of Neuropathologists. Appointed as Dr. Haymaker's deputy was Dr. G. Dale Smith. A month before Dr. Haymaker's actual arrival at Ames, in November 1961, the Biotechnology Division of the Life Sciences Directorate was formed under the direction of a new man at Ames, Dr. Siegfried J. Gerathewohl. Its task was related quite closely to the flight-simulator work at Ames, and members of the Center's staff were available to form an operating nucleus for the new unit.

Despite the fairly good start made in organizing the Biotechnology Division, the Life Sciences Directorate was in a continuous state of turmoil for the next 2 years. As is often the case with new research organizations, little was accomplished during this period. The October 1962 Organization Chart is representative of the conditions prevailing.

MANPOWER PROBLEMS

Manpower problems at Ames were acute. The Center had not been permitted to augment its staff to handle the new research responsibilities that had been thrust upon it. Some of the new fields of research required training and experience of a kind which the old NACA staff at Ames did not possess. Disciplines involved in life-science research were obviously outside of NACA's experience and, even with respect to the physical space sciences, training of one kind or another would be required.

The Government Employees Training Act of 1958 was of some help. This Act allowed selected Government employees time off from their work

---

[2] Decision cited in letter from Dr. Clark T. Randt, Director, Office of Life Sciences Programs, to Dr. S. J. DeFrance, Director, Ames Research Center, dated Nov. 15, 1960.

Walter O. Peterson.

to attend university courses when these would significantly improve their ability to serve their employer. In pursuit of this opportunity, Ames staff members took courses at local schools. At Stanford University, the Center's longstanding cooperative arrangement remained in force and, as before, a number of Ames employees, notably John Spreiter, Harvard Lomax, and W. J. Kerwin, taught courses at the university in the aeronautical and space sciences.

Ames found some small relief from its manpower miseries in the postdoctoral fellowship program of the National Academy of Sciences. This program, funded by a grant from NASA, was not intended to solve NASA's staffing problems. Its purpose, rather, was to allow selected scientists from the international community to work in NASA space-research centers and thus gain experience that would be useful to them and the countries from which they came. The candidates were carefully screened and given assignments for one year which under favorable conditions might be extended to a second or a third year. The postdoctoral fellows, as they were called, were mostly very able men who often made substantial contributions to NASA's research effort and who, in some cases, later accepted regular employment at the Center. Dr. Cyril Ponnamperuma, the first postdoctoral fellow to serve at Ames, arrived in the summer of 1961. An extremely able research man, Dr. Ponnamperuma later joined the permanent staff of the Center's Life Sciences Directorate.

Still another arrangement that provided some slight relief for Ames' manpower shortage was an agreement reached between NASA and the military services whereby graduating college students in ROTC were allowed to

324

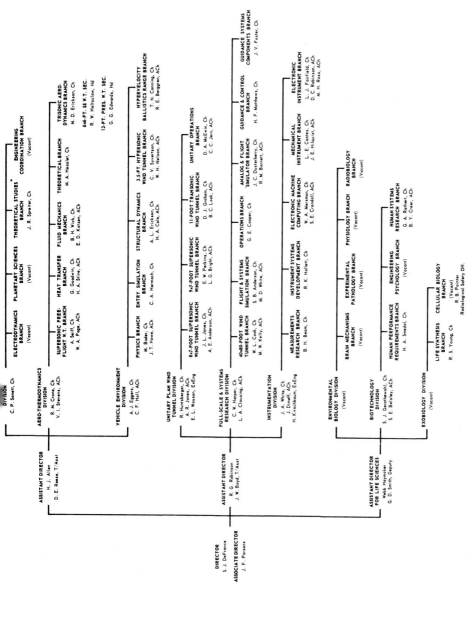

DIVISION
C. P. Sonett, Ch

DIRECTOR
S. J. DeFrance

ASSOCIATE DIRECTOR
J. F. Parsons

ASSISTANT DIRECTOR
H. J. Allen
D. E. Reese, T/Asst

AERO-THERMODYNAMICS DIVISION
R. M. Crane, Ch
V. I. Stevens, ACh

ELECTRODYNAMICS BRANCH
(Vacant)

PLANETARY SCIENCES BRANCH
(Vacant)

THEORETICAL STUDIES BRANCH
J. R. Spreiter, Ch

ENGINEERING COORDINATION BRANCH
(Vacant)

SUPERSONIC FREE-FLIGHT W.T. BRANCH
A. Seiff, Ch
W. A. Page, ACh

HEAT TRANSFER BRANCH
G. Goodwin, Ch
H. A. Stine, ACh

FLUID MECHANICS BRANCH
B. H. Wick, Ch
E. D. Katzen, ACh

THEORETICAL BRANCH
M. A. Heaslet, Ch

TRISONIC AERO-DYNAMICS BRANCH
M. D. Erickson, Ch

6x6-FT. SS W.T. SEC.
R. W. Holtzclaw, Hd

12-FT. PRES. W.T. SEC.
G. G. Edwards, Hd

VEHICLE ENVIRONMENT DIVISION
A. J. Eggers, Ch
C. F. Hall, ACh

PHYSICS BRANCH
M. Bader, Ch
J. T. Howe, ACh

ENTRY SIMULATION BRANCH
C. A. Hermach, Ch

STRUCTURAL DYNAMICS BRANCH
A. L. Erickson, Ch
H. A. Cole, ACh

3.5-FT. HYPERSONIC WIND TUNNEL BRANCH
C. V. Syvertson, Ch
W. H. Nelson, ACh

HYPERVELOCITY BALLISTICS RANGE BRANCH
T. N. Canning, Ch
R. E. Bergeron, ACh

UNITARY PLAN WIND TUNNEL DIVISION
R. Huntsberger, Ch
A. R. Jones, ACh
E. L. Wasson, ExEng

8x7-FOOT SUPERSONIC WIND TUNNEL BRANCH
J. L. Jones, Ch
A. E. Anderson, ACh

9x7-FOOT SUPERSONIC WIND TUNNEL BRANCH
E. W. Perkins, Ch
L. G. Bright, ACh

11-FOOT TRANSONIC WIND TUNNEL BRANCH
D. J. Graham, Ch
B. C. Look, ACh

UNITARY OPERATIONS BRANCH
D. A. McEwin, Ch
C. C. Jern, ACh

ASSISTANT DIRECTOR
R. G. Robinson
J. W. Boyd, T/Asst

FULL-SCALE & SYSTEMS RESEARCH DIVISION
C. W. Harper, Ch
L. A. Clousing, ACh

40x80-FOOT WIND TUNNEL BRANCH
W. L. Cook, Ch
M. W. Kelly, ACh

FLIGHT & SYSTEMS SIMULATION BRANCH
S. B. Anderson, Ch
M. D. White, ACh

OPERATIONS BRANCH
G. E. Cooper, Ch

ANALOG & FLIGHT SIMULATOR BRANCH
J. C. Dusterberry, Ch
R. M. Barnett, ACh

GUIDANCE & CONTROL BRANCH
H. F. Matthews, Ch

GUIDANCE SYSTEMS COMPONENTS BRANCH
J. V. Foster, Ch

INSTRUMENTATION DIVISION
J. A. White, Ch
J. Dimeff, ACh
H. Kirschbaum, ExEng

MEASUREMENTS RESEARCH BRANCH
B. H. Beam, Ch

INSTRUMENT SYSTEMS DEVELOPMENT BRANCH
R. K. Hallert, Ch

ELECTRONIC MACHINE COMPUTING BRANCH
W. A. Mersman, Ch
S. E. Crandall, ACh

MECHANICAL INSTRUMENT BRANCH
L. E. Coates, Ch
J. E. Hilquist, ACh

ELECTRONIC INSTRUMENT BRANCH
L. J. Fairfield, Ch
D. C. Robinson, ACh
M. H. Ross, ACh

ASSISTANT DIRECTOR FOR LIFE SCIENCES
Webb Haymaker
G. D. Smith, Deputy

ENVIRONMENTAL BIOLOGY DIVISION
(Vacant)

BRAIN MECHANISMS BRANCH
(Vacant)

EXPERIMENTAL PATHOLOGY BRANCH
(Vacant)

PHYSIOLOGY BRANCH
(Vacant)

RADIOBIOLOGY BRANCH
(Vacant)

BIOTECHNOLOGY DIVISION
S. J. Gerathewohl, Ch
S. E. Belsley, ACh

HUMAN PERFORMANCE REQUIREMENTS BRANCH
H. A. Smedal, Ch

ENGINEERING PSYCHOLOGY BRANCH
(Vacant)

HUMAN SYSTEMS RESEARCH BRANCH
G. A. Rathert, Ch
B. Y. Creer, ACh

EXOBIOLOGY DIVISION
(Vacant)

LIFE SYNTHESIS BRANCH
R. S. Young, Ch

CELLULAR BIOLOGY BRANCH
(Vacant)
R. B. Painter
Radiological Safety Off.

Organization chart (Research Division details) of Ames Research Center, October 1962.

spend their required two years of service in NASA rather than in the military. Quite a few men came to Ames under this arrangement.

These programs were valuable but unfortunately did little to solve the pressing manpower problems at Ames. The remaining avenues for dealing with these problems were: (1) curtailment of some of the less important work at the Center, and (2) the letting of contracts with outside agencies to carry out both routine and research tasks. Contracts could certainly be let for some of the routine services that absorbed the Center's manpower. Such services included training, routine computing, equipment maintenance, architectural design, and operation of the mechanical and electrical auxiliaries of the research facilities.

The letting of contracts for research was another matter. NACA and Ames had always favored the development of in-house capability for research work. But times had changed. Through oral persuasion and manpower squeeze, Headquarters was forcing Ames to move in the direction of research contracting. The Life Sciences Directorate clearly and with good reason would use contracting to accomplish many of its research objectives. The Space Sciences Division, which, because it was new, suffered most keenly from the manpower shortage, would also be forced to follow the contract route, at least for routine services such as computing and for supporting research and development work. A new day for Ames was in the making.

DISSEMINATION OF INFORMATION

With the founding of NASA, all of the old NACA report series were discontinued, as was NACA's practice of holding frequent inspections and technical conferences. Numerous meetings were held by NASA but few bore much resemblance to the old NACA technical conference. The establishment of a new report series was undertaken soon after NASA was founded but was not implemented until July 1959. In the interim, research reports issued by NASA were given a simple designation consisting primarily of the date of issue and a letter symbol indicating the Center of origin. A typical designation for a report issued during this period was: Memo 2–19–59A, where the A stood for Ames.

Of the several report series established in July 1959, the three main ones were designated by three letters followed by a serial number. The assigned designations were:

TM X–000   (replacing NACA RM series)
TN D–000   (replacing NACA TN series)
TR R–000   (replacing NACA TR series)

TM X series reports, like those of the old RM series, were classified if required but those of the other two series were unclassified. In addition to these three report series, there was a CR series for contractors' reports and an SP (Special Publication) series of NASA publications.

While NASA clearly held the right to publish the work of its staff and its contractors, it generally denied neither group the privilege of first publication of unclassified information in non-NASA media. And since outside publication often satisfied the agency's requirements, the results of NASA-financed research often did not appear under NASA report covers. Many NASA research men, particularly those operating in the new life-science and space-science fields, preferred to publish their papers in professional journals. Often new NASA test results were first presented at a meeting of some technical society. NASA men were in much demand as speakers at such meetings and some NASA research men made their way in London, Istanbul, New Delhi, and Tokyo as easily as they did in San Francisco. Within the world's scientific community, space research was providing the bonds of a common interest and a vehicle for increasing international collaboration.

The stigma which NACA once attached to public-relations activities was, in the new NASA environment, completely missing. Brad Evans thus entered Ames employ as a first-class citizen with a very important job to do. The job required a man with a broad knowledge encompassing, at once, a reasonably good understanding of the technically complex work being done by the Center and an understanding of the almost equally complex aspects of information transmission. Moreover, the job required political "savvy" and a fine sensitivity in human relationships. Often the blunt, obscure language of research engineers had, through Brad's good offices, to be softened and clarified for public consumption. The contributions of the public-relations man, the information specialist, were appreciated in these days.

3

Facilities

COMPLETIONS

THE hypervelocity research laboratory was completed in 1961 at a cost of about $1 million. This laboratory became the home of the Physics Branch, which carried on with ion-beam studies begun in 1957–1958 by Michel Bader and with the investigation into the properties of gases at high temperatures earlier initiated by Fred Hansen. This work was becoming increasingly important, and was both fundamental and applicable to current practical design problems.

The 3.5-foot tunnel, also completed in 1961, was equipped with interchangeable nozzles for operation at Mach numbers of 5, 7, 10, and 14. No longer was it considered feasible to provide variable-geometry nozzles for wind tunnels designed to operate at high speeds and temperatures. In the 3.5-foot tunnel a tremendous pebble-bed heater had been incorporated with the expectation that it would preheat the air to 4000° F and thus prevent liquefaction in the test section. Unfortunately, the heater was able to provide air temperatures of only 3000° F and the use of the Mach 14 nozzle was thus precluded.

The unexpected limitation on the performance of the pebble-bed heater arose, in part, from a chemical and structural instability of the refractory material (various mixtures of zirconia, alumina, calcia, etc.) produced, at high temperature, by a migration of its constituents. Additionally, the relative motion of the pebbles arising from thermal expansion produced refractory dust that sandblasted the finely polished tunnel throat and test model. Different refractory materials were tried as were also various arrangements and combinations of these materials. By the end of 1962 no solution to the problem had been found other than to accept, for the time being, the lower operating temperature and speed.

The item which had been proposed in 1958 as a 12- by 12-inch helium tunnel was completed late in 1960 and actually turned out to be a 20-inch-square helium tunnel. At the same time, a 14-inch helium tunnel was built

3.5-foot tunnel and 20-inch helium tunnel with hypervelocity research laboratory in foreground.

in the 3.5-foot-tunnel building. The 14-inch tunnel was built at very little cost inasmuch as the 3.5-foot tunnel was already equipped with a helium processing plant, helium storage facilities, and much of the piping required. All that was required were some simple nozzles.

Both the 14-inch and the 20-inch helium tunnel were equipped with alternate nozzles for operating at Mach numbers of approximately 10, 15, 20, and 25. Such high Mach numbers were easily achievable with helium inasmuch as heating was not required to avoid liquefaction. Because of the ease with which the helium tunnels could be operated, they were often used to run tests that would simplify and shorten test programs scheduled for the more cumbersome and expensive 3.5-foot tunnel. The limitations of helium for simulating air in a wind tunnel were also examined. It developed that helium test results are highly questionable in cases where: (1) a complex pattern of intense shock waves is present, (2) an occluded pocket of subsonic flow exists in an otherwise supersonic flow pattern, and (3) the ratio of skin friction to pressure drag is high.

Another facility completed and put into use in 1960 was the 1-foot hypervelocity shock tunnel on which Bernie Cunningham and his colleagues had spent so much development time. This tunnel was originally intended to be a part of a new hypervelocity atmosphere-entry simulator named the parabolic entry simulator, or PES. The PES was assembled but inasmuch as the need for the device was disappearing and the difficulties of operating it were great, the project was abandoned before the simulator was ever used.

330

The shock tunnel, however, was felt to be useful for other test purposes and thus it was installed in an old Quonset hut construction shack, which was glorified by the name of "hypervelocity airflow laboratory," just north of the 6- by 6-foot tunnel.

Described in TN D–1428 by Cunningham and Kraus, the shock tunnel consisted of a driver tube which was separated by a diaphragm from a shock tube which in turn was separated by a second diaphragm from a nozzle and supersonic throat. The throat was connected to a large evacuated vessel which received the gases flowing from the tubes. In operation, the driver tube was filled with an explosive mixture of hydrogen and oxygen gas together with a certain amount of helium for softening the explosion. The shock tube was filled, under pressure, with air or any other test gas which might be required to simulate the atmosphere of, for example, Mars or Venus. The combustible gases, ignited by an electrically heated wire, built up a pressure that burst the first diaphragm and caused an intense shock wave to race down the shock tube. The shock waves, both direct and repeatedly reflected, heated and pressurized the test gas to such a degree that it burst the second diaphragm and flowed past a test model mounted in the supersonic throat.

The 1-foot shock tunnel was capable of producing flows lasting up to 100 milliseconds or more at Mach numbers up to 14. Enthalpies ranged up to about 4000 Btu per pound. Operation of the tunnel required considerable preparation and only one shot could be made in an 8-hour shift. Adding to the operating time and difficulties was the mess caused by the water generated during a shot. This water was, of course, the condensate of the steam produced by the combustion gases.

HYPERVELOCITY FREE-FLIGHT FACILITIES

The use of a shock tunnel in counterflow arrangement with a light-gas gun had been pioneered in 1958 with the somewhat reluctant approval of Ames management by Tom Canning and Al Seiff. The pilot hypervelocity free-flight facility (pilot HFF facility), as the first device of this kind was called, was built of spare parts from around the Center and was fairly crude; but it demonstrated the soundness of the principle. There had been much questioning of the feasibility of such a device in view of the timing problems involved in making successful measurements. The principle of the HFF facility having been proved, Tom Canning and a few others at Ames wished to proceed immediately with the development of larger and more sophisticated HFF facilities capable of providing speeds, densities, and enthalpies corresponding to those encountered by a spacecraft returning from an earth orbit, a trip to the moon, or even a voyage to one of the planets. The HFF principle seemed the most likely of any yet developed to satisfy these simulation requirements. It appeared, however, that Ames management was not sufficiently well sold on the HFF idea to embark on this expensive enterprise without additional preparatory work. As a result Ames invested about $350,000 in a prototype HFF facility which was completed in 1961. This facility, which like the pilot HFF facility was located just south of the 1- by 3-foot tunnel, was approximately 200 feet long—much larger than the pilot facility. It incorporated a two-stage shock-compression gun that produced speeds of more than 20,000 feet per second and a shock tunnel that produced an air pulse having a speed of up to 15,000 feet per second. The maximum relative speed between air and model approached 40,000 feet per second, while the achievable stagnation enthalpy was greater than 30,000 Btu per pound and the Reynolds number per foot was over 1 million. The tunnel was designed for a modest Mach number of 7 in order to maintain the air density at a fairly high level. It will be recalled that a high density as well as a high enthalpy is necessary for the simulation of aerodynamic heating.

The performance of the prototype HFF facility proved satisfactory and shortly Seiff and Canning submitted a proposal for a huge new HFF facility that would cost about $5 million.

Prototype hypervelocity free-flight facility.

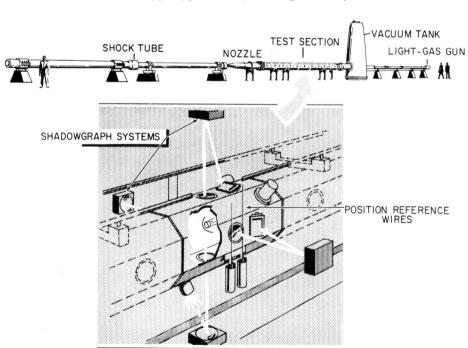

B. Pat Denardo and impact range.

IMPACT RANGE

The Ames Research Center was now taking a substantial interest in the effects of meteoroid strikes on spacecraft. Although Ames had already built three ballistics ranges in which such studies could be made, it was decided that a fourth range should be designed specifically for terminal ballistics work. The principal requirement for a range of this nature would be a gun of such size and power as to generate the highest possible launching speed. As in the other ranges, the gun, target, and test section would be enclosed in a single tubular chamber that could be evacuated to represent high-altitude conditions or filled with gases typifying various atmospheres.

The new range, named "impact range," was built in 1961 and first put to use in 1962. It was located with the other three (Janus, pilot, and main) ranges in the range building which had been constructed along the western border fence. The impact range thus became a part of a complex of four facilities that together were known as the hypervelocity ballistics range (HBR). The HBR was operated by the HBR Branch originally headed by Alex Charters and, after Charters left in February 1961, by Tom Canning.

GUN DEVELOPMENT

Inasmuch as the gun was perhaps the most important element in a range or a hypervelocity free-flight facility, it became the subject of an intensive and continuing development program. The Bioletti-Cunningham

333

shock-driven gun was relatively simple and generated launching speeds of around 20,000 feet per second but unfortunately it was not really suitable for launching heavy models. The Charters-Rossow-Denardo piston-compressor gun could launch heavier models, but launching speeds were limited to about 13,000 feet per second and, in any case, the gun was mechanically and otherwise impracticable in its existing form. The practicability of the gun could be increased, of course, by closing the breech and eliminating the reaction piston which, most disconcertingly, flew out of the rear end. This change would get rid of some of the more serious complications but even so the gun just did not have enough "zock" to produce the desired high launching speeds.

The main problem of the piston-compressor gun was that a small pocket of gas had to be left at the end of the driver tube to act as a shock absorber for the heavy metal piston. Otherwise the piston would slam into the end of the smaller launch tube with a devastating wallop. The pocket of gas, though useful as a shock absorber, introduced a thermodynamic, or volumetric, type of inefficiency that took the edge off the piston's thrust. It softened the blow as does the clearance volume in the cylinder head of an automobile engine. What was needed was a means for closing out that volume while still obtaining shock absorption.

The solution to this problem was found by a young man named John Curtis who had recently joined the Ames staff. Curtis decided that what was needed was a semisoft plastic piston that deformed on impact and thus acted as its own shock absorber. He believed, moreover, that the shock-absorbing action could be made still smoother if the last portion of the driver tube was made slightly conical (tapered) so that the soft-nosed piston, while coming to rest, would squeeze down and completely fill the cone. The nose of the piston, Curtis believed, would actually "squirt" forward, generating the highest possible pressure and driving the last bit of gas into the launching tube.

The idea proposed by Curtis was tried and proved immensely successful. The deformable-piston gun quickly demonstrated its ability to generate launching speeds as high as, or higher than, those of the shock-driven gun. John Curtis had really saved the Charters gun from extinction. The new Charters-Curtis deformable-piston, light-gas gun was destined to become the standard at Ames and, good though it originally was, its performance was continually increased by later refinements. Also, its efficiency was found to increase with its size. In the course of the gun's development, many different piston shapes and materials were investigated, with polyethylene becoming the favored material. Some of the pistons were made with an internal cavity containing water. The gun design ideas originated by Curtis are described in his report TN D–1144 (ref. C–1), "An Accelerated Reservoir Light-Gas Gun."

June 25, 1965, deformable-piston gun applied to main range. Used plastic pistons are under gun at left.

ABLATION RESEARCH REQUIREMENTS

The HFF Facility could, perhaps more accurately than any other device, simulate the aerodynamic and heating conditions experienced by reentry spacecraft. Nevertheless it had a number of faults, one of which was the short period of time over which the simulated conditions prevailed. Not only did this fault introduce severe operational difficulties but, even worse, it precluded the use of the facility for simulating certain aerodynamic and heating processes that required more than a few milliseconds to reach an equilibrium stage. One of these processes, unfortunately, was the thermochemical process of ablation, which at this time was regarded as the most promising means for protecting spacecraft from the ravages of reentry heating.

Ablation was a mass-transfer cooling process, like sweat cooling, in which a solid material with which a spacecraft could be coated would absorb heat by the physical processes of melting, evaporation, and sublimation; the material thus transformed would gradually be dissipated into the surrounding airstream. The choice of ablation material depended on the rate and duration of the heating pulse, and materials such as plastics (e.g., Teflon), quartz, and graphite appeared useful for this purpose.

The physical processes of ablation had been found to proceed with sufficient rapidity to allow them to be investigated in counterflow devices such as the atmosphere-entry simulator; indeed, that was the main function of the AES and the intended function of the abandoned parabolic entry simulator. Often, however, there were chemical reactions between the ablator

335

and the boundary layer that proceeded rather slowly and could not be investigated in short-period test devices of the HFF or the AES type. These reactions were prevalent in ablators that formed a surface char layer through the pores of which the vaporized ablation material percolated. It was for the investigation of charring ablators that a special test device was needed. That device was the arc-jet tunnel.

ARC-JET DEVELOPMENT

The development of the arc-jet at Ames was a complex and very important process that began in 1956, rapidly increased in intensity during the early years of NASA, and continued thereafter at a high level. It began with the preliminary study and applications of the few available commercial arc heaters (such as Plasmadyne) and continued with the development of a series of increasingly refined arc-jets that represented a major contribution both to arc-jet technology and to aerothermodynamic research. Early contributors to this work have already been named. Others who contributed in the 1959–1962 period included Glen Goodwin, Howard Stine, Charles Shepard, Velvin Watson, Roy Griffen, Ernie Winkler, Warren Winovich, and Brad Wick.

The arc-jet, or arc-jet tunnel, though sometimes of the continuous-flow type, is typically a supersonic blowdown tunnel in which air, or any other gas, from a pressure vessel is released to flow through a supersonic throat, over a test model, and into an evacuated receiving chamber. Running time is usually from one to several minutes. On its way to, or through, the supersonic throat, the air is heated by a powerful electric arc. One of the major problems in the design of an arc-jet is to arrange an intimate mingling of the airstream with the arc so that the heat of the arc is transferred to the air. The problem is difficult because the air seems to want to avoid the arc. Another critical problem in arc-jet design is to keep the whole unit, particularly the sonic nozzle and the electrodes, from melting. Water cooling, sweat cooling, and other means are used. Contamination of the airstream by vaporized electrode material must also be minimized. Such partial solutions to these problems as were available had required years of imaginative development work.

The first arc-jet units developed at Ames were completed in 1960. Their electrodes were in the form of hollow, water-cooled concentric rings over which the air passed on its way to the sonic nozzle (constriction) of the supersonic throat. A magnetic field was used to move the arc around the rings so that it would not cause excessive heating and erosion at any one point. One of these concentric-ring arc-jets was able to add 1500 Btu to each pound of air passing through it while operating at 100 atmospheres air pressure with an arc power of 2 megawatts. At low pressures (less than 1 atmosphere), the heat, or enthalpy, added to the airstream was as much as 9000

Btu per pound. The first published information on Ames concentric-ring arc-jet development work was the paper "Electric Arc Jets for Producing Gas Streams with Negligible Contamination," by C. E. Shepard and Warren Winovich. This paper was presented in 1961 at a meeting of the American Society of Mechanical Engineers and published as ASME Preprint 61–WA–247.

The enthalpy of 9000 obtained with the concentric-ring arc-jet did not, of course, represent spacecraft reentry conditions. A much more efficient transfer of heat from arc to air was needed. Howard Stine and Glen Goodwin bent their minds to this problem. The heat-transfer efficiency would be much higher, they figured, if the air and the arc were forced to commingle by passing them both through a narrow constriction in the airflow passage. The cathode would thus be upstream of the constriction, the anode downstream, and the arc would pass lengthwise through the constriction. This device was known as the "constricted arc."

The constricted arc was not new in principle but its successful development, as carried out by Howard Stine with the help of Charles Shepard and Velvin Watson, was a major accomplishment and produced a revolution in arc-jet design. With this work the potentiality of the arc-jet for simulating intense aerodynamic heating was much enhanced. Stine's classical work on the constricted arc represented a beautiful blending of theory with experiment. The theory is contained in TN D–1331 (ref. C–2), "The Theoretical Enthalpy Distribution of Air in Steady Flow Along the Axis of a Direct-Current Electric Arc," by Howard A. Stine and Velvin R. Watson.

In the first constricted arc-jet, initially operated in the fall of 1961, the arc was made to pass through a short constricted throat which was installed in the airflow passage ahead of the sonic throat. This unit, as described in a paper which Glen Goodwin delivered in Paris in 1962, produced enthalpies

From left to right: *Bradford H. Wick, Max A. Heaslet, Howard A. Stine, and Howard K. Larson.*

up to 12,000 Btu per pound with an arc power of 2.5 megawatts at an air-flow of 0.1 pound per second and 7 atmospheres pressure. The tests confirmed the theory of Stine and Watson, yet it appeared that the performance of the unit was handicapped by the fact that the heat, in effect, was being trapped in the plenum chamber ahead of the sonic nozzle. If the heat could be added to the air as it passed through the sonic nozzle, it was believed a better result could be achieved. If then the sonic nozzle were lengthened to prolong the contact between the arc and the air, a large improvement in performance might be expected. One problem, of course, was to prevent the arc current from passing through the walls of the elongated sonic throat rather than through the air passage. This problem could be solved, it was found, by constructing the nozzle of thin, transverse, water-cooled segments or laminations separated from each other by insulating material in the form of boron nitride washers. Boron nitride was a good electrical insulator yet provided some thermal conduction.

The principles just mentioned were incorporated in a new unit called the supersonic arc plasma jet, which was designed and built in 1962. Preliminary tests with this unit indicated that enthalpies of 30,000 Btu per pound could be obtained. The arc-jet had now proved itself ready for research use; in fact, some research had already been performed with Plasmadyne and concentric-ring units. At this stage, late in 1962, a number of papers on arc-jet technology were being prepared by such authors as Howard Stine, James Jedlicka, Charles Shepard, and Velvin Watson. An earlier Ames paper, presented in 1962 at the Second Symposium on Hypervelocity Techniques, was entitled "A Wind Tunnel Using Arc-Heated Air for Mach Numbers of 10 to 20," by Forrest E. Gowen and Vaughn D. Hopkins.

GASDYNAMICS LABORATORY

A Plasmadyne arc heater was incorporated in 1959 or 1960 into the 8-inch low-density wind tunnel and later two complete arc-jets, of the concentric-ring type, were installed in the 1- by 3-foot wind-tunnel building, now called the fluid mechanics laboratory. Later, two constricted-arc units were installed in flow channels in the old low-density heat-transfer building, now called the space technology building. These installations were small and mostly of an experimental character, but Glen Goodwin and Dean Chapman had come to the conclusion that the arc-jet offered sufficient promise to justify the construction of a major facility to exploit the device for studies of ablation and other heating phenomena. Glen and Dean each prepared specifications for the facilities they had in mind and when later these were combined and submitted to Ames management, the estimated cost of the proposed "mass transfer and aerodynamics facility," as it was called, was $15 million. Smitty DeFrance was not very enthusiastic about the proposal, and Jack Parsons knocked the allowable price down to $5 million. The proposal

Constricted arc-jet.

was then submitted to NASA Headquarters, where Ira Abbott, head of OART at the time, cut the price to $4 million, at which level it was approved. The facility, now called the "gasdynamics laboratory," was put under construction in 1960–1961 and completed in 1962. It was located just north of the Unitary Plan wind tunnels.

The gasdynamics laboratory designed for the exploitation of the arc-jet consisted not so much of the arc-jets themselves as of the mighty auxiliaries necessary to operate arc-jets of any reasonable kind or size. Positions were provided in the facility for the installation of three separate arc-jet units. Of the $4 million spent on the gasdynamics laboratory, approximately $1.7 million went for air-handling auxiliaries (evacuator and collector), another $1.36 million was spent on the 15-megawatt electrical power supply, and the remainder, nearly $1 million, was invested in wind-tunnel controls, data-handling facilities, and building. The facility so constructed had a great deal of operational flexibility and was well suited for the purpose intended: the further development of arc-jets, fundamental studies of ablation, and the effects of ablation on the aerodynamic characteristics of reentry bodies. It was not long before concentric-ring and constricted-arc-jets were installed and operating in the new laboratory.

Gasdynamics facility and 20-inch helium tunnel.

FLIGHT SIMULATORS

Flight simulators were at this time beginning to take on the character of major facilities. The analog-computer elements associated with the simulators already had become quite extensive. In 1960 it was found desirable to assign responsibility for these elements, and all of the other simulator hardware, to a special group. This group, headed by John Dusterberry, was the Analog and Flight Simulator Branch of the Full Scale and Systems Research Division. Research to be conducted with the equipment, however, was planned by other branches.

Of the several elements of which a flight simulator was composed, the most difficult to develop, and most costly, was the motion generator. Owing to development difficulties and costs, the motion generator was omitted from early simulators; in fact, it was not always felt to be needed. In 1957–1958, Ames built the pitch-roll chair, a relatively crude device which provided motions about either the pitch or the roll axis. In 1960 this device was improved somewhat to allow, in flight-simulation exercises, any combination of two angular accelerations to be impressed on the pilot. The motions were produced by an amplidyne-controlled, 10-horsepower, electric motor. Two other devices for generating angular motion, one in which a large sphere was freely floated on an air bearing, were built but were not especially successful.

Harry Goett was the main driving force in getting Ames started in the flight-simulator business; when he departed for Goddard, Bill Harper car-

John C. Dusterberry.

ried on the movement with equal or greater vigor and with the effective support of George Rathert. It was, however, under Goett's direction that the pitch-roll chair was built and it was also owing to his persistent efforts that action was initiated in 1959 on the construction of what was called the "five-degrees-of-freedom motion simulator." This simulator incorporated a centrifuge of 30-foot radius. The simulated cockpit, located in a hooded cab at the end of the centrifuge arm, was driven by motors, as required by the simulation, about each of its three axes (pitch, roll, and yaw). The cab was also driven through a limited range of motion along the vertical axis and of course was driven by the centrifuge arm along a curved path of fixed radius in the horizontal plane. Thus the motions that could be simulated in the cab were three angular motions, one translational motion, and a curvilinear combination of the remaining two translational motions. The curvilinear motions, and associated accelerations, were, of course, fairly representative of airplane flight.

The motion simulation achieved by the new facility was quite good except that the rates of motion were limited by power, the range of motion was limited by structure, and the accuracy of movement was limited by precision of the controls. To have greatly reduced any of these weaknesses would have cost much more money than was available to Goett for this project. The five-degrees-of-freedom simulator was built largely of spare parts scrounged from all possible sources, and the fact that a successful device of such complexity could be built in this manner was in no small way attributable to the ingenuity of Sam Davidsen and others of the Engineering Services Division. The simulator was placed in operation early in 1961.

In the design of flight simulators, an interesting substitute had been developed for the costly and complicated motion generator. This arrange-

341

ment made use of optical trickery to give the pilot the impression that he was moving while in actuality he was at rest. Such a scheme was employed in a landing-approach simulator built at Ames in 1961–1962. The simulator had a stationary transport-airplane-type cockpit incorporating more or less conventional controls and instruments. Apparent motion was provided by a commercially developed device known as the Dalto Visual Simulator. With it, a TV picture of a model moving-belt runway was projected on a screen in front of the windshield. The image thus presented gave the impression of an actual landing situation in which the attitude, elevation, and approach speed of the airplane were indicated. The landing-approach simulator was the usual closed loop consisting of pilot, controls, programed analog computer, motion generator, and cockpit instruments except that in this case the generated motion, controlled by the computer, was applied to the TV camera rather than to the cabin itself. The pilot was thus visually able to go through a landing maneuver with any airplane for which the computer had been programed. All six degrees of motion were simulated in the picture.

Another unusual, but useful, flight simulator built at Ames in 1961 was the "height control test apparatus." This device, which was attached to an exterior wall of the 40- by 80-foot tunnel building, was designed to simulate the vertical motions of an airplane, helicopter, or V/STOL aircraft. The device consisted of a cab, simulating a two-man cockpit, which by means of a motor-driven winch was moved vertically through distances of up to 100 feet at speeds as high as 22 feet per second and accelerations as high as ±1.5g. Arrangements were made whereby a TV monitor could be used to present an artificial landing scene in lieu of the real view of an open field. The height control test apparatus, which cost about $170,000, was put into use in 1962.

In none of the flight simulators built so far had motion in each of the six degrees of freedom been independently provided. In the five-degrees-of-freedom simulator, for example, the translational motions along the two axes in the horizontal plane were not independent and the motion in the vertical direction was limited to only ±2 feet. What was really needed, Ames engineers felt, and this particularly for V/STOL work, was a truly six-degrees-of-freedom simulator that would provide a reasonably large range, say ±10 feet, of translational motion along each axis. Such a simulator would obviously be rather large and expensive; but Bill Harper, feeling that the need was urgent, applied enough pressure to get the project under way in 1962. It would be ready for use in 1963.

←

Top left: *the fixed-cab landing simulator. The Dalto visual simulator is used for runway simulation.* Top right: *The height-control test apparatus, the flight simulator provides extensive vertical motion.* Below: *The 5-degrees-of-freedom flight simulator.*

343

Digital Computer Facilities

The use of digital electronic computers for theoretical computations and data workup had become so extensive as to require a separate building for that purpose. A proposal for the construction of such a building, at a cost of about $2.5 million, was approved in 1959. The approved facility, named the "data reduction building," was constructed in 1960–1961 and occupied early in 1962.

In 1961 the Center's IBM 7040 was replaced by an IBM 7090 (later modified to 7094), and during the same year a Honeywell H 800 machine was leased. The H 800 had hard-wire connections to the 6- by 6-foot, the 14-foot, and the Unitary wind tunnels and was used exclusively for data workup. With the procurement of the H 800, the Electrodata machines were retired.

The use of electronic computers for administrative work at the Center was increasing steadily, and in 1962 an IBM 1401 machine was leased to handle this load. Additionally, the IBM 7094 was used for certain administrative tasks.

4

···

Research

Pattern

BY the end of 1962 it was apparent that, although most of the Ames Center's research continued to fall in the "applied" category, a small but growing part of it could be called "pure"—performed mainly to satisfy human curiosity with no immediate practical objective in mind. Some work on meteors fell in this category, for example, as did some in the field of space science.

Work on aircraft and airplane flight problems was not neglected, but certainly the work on spacecraft and space flight predominated. While the space research, for the most part, followed the familiar pattern of experimentation and theoretical analysis conducted in the laboratory, it nevertheless also introduced two new forms of activity. One of these was the planning of specific space experiments (including the design of the required instruments) to be carried out by some other group. The other new activity was the management of space-flight research projects which were intended to carry out experiments designed by others.

Notable features of Ames research during this period were (1) the emphasis on reentry aerothermodynamics, particularly on the phenomena of radiation and ablation; (2) the acceleration of the movement toward the development and use of flight simulators; (3) the work on V/STOL aircraft; and (4) the beginning of work in the fields of human factors, biology, meteors, and space physics.

Aircraft Configurations and Airflows

Boundary-Layer Transition. It had long been recognized that the maintenance of a laminar boundary layer was of great benefit to the performance of both subsonic and supersonic airplanes, and that a laminar-flow condition could be maintained more easily in an accelerating flow than in a decelerating flow. The flow over an airplane wing and fuselage involved both accelerating and decelerating flows but more of the latter, since the net

345

reaction of these components in the line of motion was drag. There was a question, however, as to the degree of flow deceleration a boundary layer could tolerate without going turbulent, and there was also a question of the effects on transition of sweepback. Dr. Werner Pfenninger of the Northrop Aircraft Co. was of the opinion that the installation of carefully designed suction slots at many points over the whole surface of a wing would make possible the maintenance of laminar flow over the whole wing. The same result might also be achieved with the fuselage although in this case 100 percent laminar flow was perhaps too much to expect. The benefit of such an installation, if the system were light and efficient, would clearly be great. The speed of an airplane so equipped would be enhanced and, in the case of a bomber, a tremendous increase in range could be achieved.

The Ames 12-foot tunnel was the ideal instrument in which to check out some of Dr. Pfenninger's theories as well as to investigate boundary-layer transition. Ames worked closely with Dr. Pfenninger on his project and at the same time pursued the matter of boundary-layer transition on a more general level. Gary Chapman of the SSFF tunnel undertook in TN D–1066 and TN D–1075 to demonstrate and analyze the generally deleterious effects of wing sweep on transition at supersonic speed. At about the same time, Fred Boltz, George Kenyon, and Clyde Allen of the 12-foot tunnel were demonstrating (e.g., TN D–338) that the bad effects of sweep on transition also prevailed at high subsonic speeds. It appeared from the tests that the lateral component of flow caused by wing sweep produces boundary-layer vortices which precipitate transition. As a matter of related interest, Don Jillie and Edward Hopkins of the 8- by 7-foot Unitary tunnel investigated the combined effects of Mach number, leading-edge bluntness, and sweep on transition. This work, reported in TN D–1071, confirmed the adverse effects of sweep for Mach numbers from 2.0 to 4.0 and further revealed that, for straight wings with blunt leading edges, an increase of Mach number favors the maintenance of laminar flow.

Basic Configurations. Many of the airplane-configuration studies undertaken during this period were concerned with the design of the North American B–70 Mach 3 bombing airplane and with preliminary designs for a commercial supersonic transport (SST). The SST had become of interest as a national development project and it was felt to be the responsibility of NASA to take the lead in determining the most promising general configurations from which a successful SST might be developed. Toward this end, the NASA Langley Research Center sponsored what was known as the SCAT (supersonic commerical air transport) program to investigate four basic SST configurations designated SCAT 4, 15, 16, and 17. SCAT designs 4 and 15 were quickly disposed of, leaving SCAT 16, having a wing with controllable sweep, and SCAT 17, having a canard configuration with a fixed delta wing. These two design arrangements were studied intensively both by NASA, in its wind tunnels, and by certain major aircraft companies. Ames, because of its long-standing interest in delta-wing and canard configurations, gave most of its attention to SCAT 17; whereas Langley, for similar reasons, devoted most of its efforts to SCAT 16. The Boeing and the Lockheed aircraft companies were later awarded Government contracts for SST designs based essentially on the SCAT 16 and the SCAT 17 configurations.

Ames studies of both the B–70 and the SST (SCAT 17) represented largely a continuation of earlier work on canard and delta configurations. Numerous reports issued from this effort. There were, for example, TM X–363 by Richard Petersen and TM X–392 by Victor Peterson and Loren Bright, which determined the extent to which the stability of a delta-wing airplane would be benefited by deflecting downward a portion of the wing tips. There were also TM X–651 and TM X–781 by LeRoy Fletcher, which reported on the static and dynamic stability of delta-wing canard configurations at Mach numbers up to 3.50. In addition, TN D–690 by Victor Peterson and Gene Menees, revealed the adverse aerodynamic interference produced by a horizontal canard control surface on the wing and vertical tail surfaces. The slow-speed performance of SST configurations was established in the 40- by 80-foot tunnel by the team of Jim Brady, Dave Koenig, and Virgil Page. Typical reports from this work are TM X–643 and TM X–644. The work by the Ames staff on the SCAT 17 configuration is best indicated, perhaps, by the paper (ref. C–3) entitled "A Critical Study of Delta Wing Configurations for the Supersonic Transport Application," by J. L. Jones, L. W. Hunton, T. J. Gregory, and W. P. Nelms.

Inlets. This period saw a continuation of research directed toward the development of efficient supersonic inlets. Inlet work was conducted in the 8- by 8-inch, the 1- by 3-foot, and the Unitary tunnels and some of it was specifically intended to develop an inlet for the B–70 airplane. Among the contributors to this effort were Norman Sorenson, Tom Gregory, John Gawienowski, Richard Kurkowski, Earl Watson, William Peterson, John Lundell, Richard Scherrer, and Lewis Anderson. In TN D–584, the latter three described work conducted in the 1- by 3-foot tunnel on an idealized form of circular internal-compression inlet. A pressure recovery of nearly 90 percent was obtained with this inlet at a Mach number of 3.8. This was perhaps the highest recovery ever obtained at that Mach number and demonstrated the possibilities of internal-compression inlets. Despite the high performance theoretically possible with internal-compression inlets, an inlet combining external and internal compression was generally regarded as being more practicable.

Vortex Flows. The wings, bodies, and control surfaces of aircraft produce vortices which interact strongly with the general airflow pattern

Above: *A North American XB–70 in flight.* Below: *The canard configuration in 40- by 80-foot tunnel.*

around the aircraft. Over the years these interactions were the subject of numerous theoretical studies at Ames by such men as William Pitts, Jack Nielsen, George Kaattari, Max Heaslet, John Spreiter, and Al Sacks. Those early studies produced very useful results but did not, by any means, exhaust the field. Thus, during this period, J. Richard Spahr of the Fluid Mechanics Branch was able to make a very real contribution in developing a general method for calculating the paths of vortices generated by wing-body combinations and for determining the effects of such vortices on the load distribution and stability of aircraft. This work, which was performed in 1960, was reported in TR R–101 (ref. C–4).

Aircraft Flight Studies

As earlier noted, NASA Headquarters in late 1959 ruled that flight research involving the flying of airplanes would be conducted exclusively at the NASA Flight Research Center at Edwards, Calif. One exception to this rule was to be flight research on V/STOL aircraft. The Headquarters ruling in this matter accelerated Ames efforts in the application of ground-based flight simulators to flight research. Variable-stability airplanes were also flight simulators but, since they were not ground-based, they too were transferred to Edwards. The transferral of the variable-stability airplanes was a painful blow to Ames since the Center had pioneered in the development and application of these highly useful devices. The original variable-stability airplane developed by Ames was a Grumman F6F–3. Following that development were the North American F–86 variable-stability and the F–86 variable-control airplanes. Finally during 1958 and 1959, a North American F–100 had been converted into one of the most elaborate and fully automated variable-stability airplanes ever built. Much of the responsibility for the development of the F–100 variable-stability airplane fell on John Foster

Wingtip vortices revealed by vapor-screen technique.

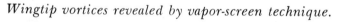

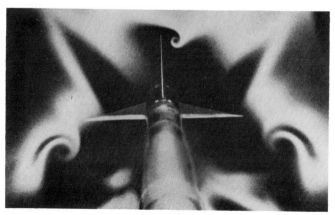

of the Instrument Research Division. Some of the basic design principles for the F–100, and earlier, variable-stability airplanes are given in the paper "Servomechanisms as Used on Variable-Stability and Variable-Control-System Research Aircraft," which Foster presented in October 1957 at a meeting in Chicago of the National Electronics Conference. Unhappily, the just-completed F–100, along with the other research airplanes, was shipped off to Edwards.

Shortly before the airplanes were moved to Edwards, a rather interesting study was made with the F–86 variable-stability and variable-control airplanes by Norman McFadden, Richard Vomaske, and Don Heinle. At this stage, the design features and operational ranges of airplanes were so extreme that one could scarcely expect an airplane to have adequate inherent static and dynamic stability under all flight conditions. It was clear that certain "black boxes" in the form of stability-augmentation devices would be required. Such devices were fine as long as they worked, but forever lurking in the designer's mind was the question of what would happen if they failed. An airplane would have to be designed so that the failure of a black box would not be catastrophic; the airplane in that event must at least be manageable even though its flying qualities were far from ideal. It was now necessary to determine the worst control and stability characteristics that could be accepted from a safety standpoint. The variable-stability airplane was the best available instrument for such a study and was used for this purpose in the just-mentioned investigation by McFadden, Vomaske, and Heinle; the results are presented in TN D–779, "Flight Investigation Using Variable Stability Airplanes of Minimum Stability Requirements for High-Speed, High-Altitude Vehicles." Pilot opinion was, of course, a vital element of this study.

Ground-Based Simulations. The study by McFadden, et al., of minimum acceptable stability under emergency conditions (black-box failure) could, of course, have been accomplished with a ground-based simulator. However, Ames did not have a ground-based simulator in which all motions of an airplane could be simulated, and thus the perennial question arose as to the importance of incomplete or imperfect motion simulation in such a study. Considerable enlightenment on this question came from a cooperative research program jointly undertaken by NASA and the Navy using the huge centrifuge of the U.S. Naval Air Development Center at Johnsville, Pennsylvania. One of the reports emanating from this program was TN D–348, "A Study of Longitudinal Control Problems at Low and Negative Damping and Stability with Emphasis on Effects of Motion Cues," by Melvin Sadoff, Norman M. McFadden, and Donovan R. Heinle.

The cab of the centrifuge, as used in the study, was equipped with an airplane cockpit with control stick and instruments; the rotor motion was controlled by an analog computer that had been programed with the dynamic characteristics of some selected airplane. The centrifuge was thus the motion-generator portion of a simulator which simulated motions imperfectly but nevertheless did provide normal accelerations in accordance with stick motions. Pilot opinion of tolerable emergency stability limits was determined, for a simulated airplane, in the centrifuge and these data were compared with similar results from simulators (fixed cab, pitch-roll chair, and variable-stability airplane) having different motion-generating characteristics. From such comparisons, it was possible to determine the stability ranges in which motion simulation was necessary and which kinds of motion simulation were of most value.

The study also investigated the interesting possibility, in a simulation, of replacing the pilot with his response equation programed into the computer. It was recognized that if the response of a pilot to the usual flight stimuli could be expressed in mathematical form, flight problems could then be solved with a computer alone. While the development of an accurate human-response equation was too much to hope for, this study of the matter produced some useful results.

SST Studies. The use of ground-based simulators for flight studies not only eliminated the hazard to life and property inherent in flight testing but also made possible the acquisition of important design information applicable to an airplane prior to its construction. Flight simulators were thus extremely useful for studying critical flight problems to be expected in the operation of the projected supersonic commercial transport airplane. Such studies were pursued at Ames by the team of Maurice White, Richard Vomaske, Walter McNeill, and George Cooper. The work was undertaken with the new five-degrees-of-freedom (centrifuge) simulator at Ames as well as with a simulator providing only angular motions, i.e., the cab portion of the five-degree simulator with centrifuge inoperative. Of particular interest to

Maurice D. White.

the investigators was the determination of the need for stability augmentors in the SST. Of equal interest was the effect of the failure of a stability augmentor as a separate emergency, or combined with the failure of an engine. In such emergencies, the airplane is momentarily out of equilibrium if not out of control and, before control can be restored, may achieve speeds and attitudes from which recovery is impossible.

The SST simulator work carried out by White, Vomaske, McNeill, and Cooper during this period is reported in two papers, one TN D-1888 and the other (ref. C-5) a paper entitled "Assessment of Critical Problem Areas of the Supersonic Transport by Means of Piloted Simulators," which was published in the May 1962 issue of *Aerospace Engineering*.

The authors concluded from their investigation that motion simulation provided by available flight simulators left much to be desired and that, for representing the emergency flight upsets that might be encountered by the SST, a simulator providing substantial translational as well as angular motions would be required.

V/STOL STUDIES

A rather deep chasm had long existed between aircraft which derived lift and control force from their motion through the air (airplanes) and aircraft which derived these forces largely from the direct application of engine power to special lifting surfaces (helicopters). Efforts to bridge the gap, to build a craft that would fly with the efficiency of an airplane yet be capable of vertical takeoffs and landings (VTOL), were now meeting with some success as a result of the growing sophistication of airplane and powerplant designers. More commonly, the gap was not wholly bridged and the resulting craft was capable only of short takeoff and landing (STOL). The general class of V/STOL aircraft was of growing interest to aircraft users, particularly the military, and both the Army and the Air Force had let contracts with industry for the development of prototype V/STOL configurations. The old NACA laboratories (Ames and Langley) had been drawn into this work and when in 1959, under NASA, all flight research at the laboratories, except V/STOL research, was proscribed, their interest and efforts in V/STOL research greatly increased.

Ames was in a particularly favorable position to pursue research on V/STOL aircraft because of the availability of the 40- by 80-foot tunnel in which V/STOL aircraft could be tested at full scale. The Center's background of handling-qualities research as well as its experience with variable-stability aircraft and other flight simulators was also helpful. Ames' earlier boundary-layer-control work provided a natural entry into V/STOL research; indeed, BLC was the first practical step toward achieving a V/STOL airplane. The downward deflection of the propeller slipstream by means of elaborate multicomponent flaps was perhaps the next step. Another

Seth B. Anderson.

approach might be to have the engines, and perhaps also the wings on which the engines were mounted, capable of being rotated in flight so that the propellers could lift more effectively for takeoff. Still another possibility might be to install separate lifting engines and propellers in the wings or fuselage, to be used only for takeoff and landing; for this system, special types of engines would be needed. All of these schemes and many more were under investigation and the whole field was wide open for inventive genius. At this stage, only the simpler V/STOL arrangements were ready for application. The more radical ones were still very much in the study stage of development.

Ames concerned itself mainly with the slow-speed aspects of V/STOL research and particularly with the control and handling qualities of such craft. No one really knew what handling qualities were required for V/STOL aircraft and one of the first tasks undertaken by Ames was, on the basis of its large experience with such matters, to analyze the situation and establish tentative V/STOL handling-qualities criteria. This worthwhile task was undertaken by Seth Anderson, whose work on this subject was published as TN D–331 (ref. C–6), "An Examination of Handling Qualities Criteria for V/STOL Aircraft."

There was much to be done in actually determining the flying qualities of V/STOL airplanes and the ability of the pilot to take full advantage of such slow landing and takeoff potential as the airplane might have. The piloting technique for a V/STOL aircraft was definitely more difficult than for conventional aircraft owing in part to the more complicated controls and the low inherent stability of the airplane at a very slow speed. The flying problems of STOL aircraft were investigated quite extensively at Ames by the team of Hervey Quigley and Robert Innis. Bob Innis was an engineering test pilot who had joined the Ames staff in 1954. The work of Quigley and Innis in this field was first concerned with two large cargo airplanes which were capable of STOL operation by virtue of boundary-layer-control installations. One was the two-engine Stroukoff YC–134A on which the suction type of BLC was applied to the flaps and also to the ailerons, which moreover were drooped, in landing, to give additional lift. The other airplane was a four-engine Lockheed C–130 airplane on which BLC and high lift were obtained by blowing air over the flaps and drooped ailerons. In the C–130, the air for BLC was provided by two jet engines mounted in outboard wing pods.

As reported in TN D–862, Innis and Quigley investigated the lift, drag, and stalling characteristics of the YC–134A as well as its stability and control characteristics—the latter particularly in approach and landing operations. Among other things, the airplane, at slow speed, was observed to have a bad stall characterized by an uncontrollable rolloff and large sideslip angles. In the tests of the C–130, reported in TN D–1647, the lateral-directional handling characteristics were closely observed and were found, under landing conditions, to be so poor as to render the landing of the airplane at a speed of less than 65 knots very difficult. Several special techniques for operating the airplane under STOL conditions were developed.

The flight tests of the BLC cargo-type airplanes were correlated with information obtained in the 40- by 80-foot wind tunnel and from flight simulator tests. Of the wind-tunnel tests, typical results for a four-engine tilt-wing model with blowing BLC are described in TN D–1034 by James Weiberg and Curt Holzhauser. The simulator tests, described in TN D–1773 by Hervey Quigley and Herbert Lawson, constituted a study of the C–130 lateral-directional characteristics which were known to be deficient. This study, which was made on the fixed-cockpit landing-approach simulator incorporating the DALTO visual (TV) simulating device, revealed much about the stability and control characteristics of the airplane and suggested ways in which the lateral-directional stability faults of the airplane might be corrected.

The BLC cargo airplanes represented an important, but conservative, approach to the V/STOL airplane development problem. Much interest had developed in more radical types such as the X–14A VTOL test-bed (prototype) vehicle built for the Air Force by the Bell Aircraft Co. and flown extensively by Fred Drinkwater in Ames flight research programs. The X–14A was a rather small, fixed-wing, jet-propelled aircraft in which the jet slipstream could, by means of a cascade of flaps, be diverted downward as required to produce any desired combination of thrust and lift. By controlling the flaps, the pilot could make the airplane rise vertically and then move off horizontally. Air jets were required for control at speeds below that at which conventional lifting-surface controls became effective.

The X–14A represented a type of airplane for which stability, control, and handling characteristics were largely unknown. It was for the purpose of studying these factors that the airplane was turned over to the Ames Research Center. To increase the extent and usefulness of the information obtained from the X–14A, Ames modified the airplane's control system to provide variable-stability and variable-control characteristics. The first flight study made with the X–14A is reported in TN D–1328 (ref. C–7), "A Flight Determination of the Attitude Control Power and Damping Requirements for a Visual Hovering Task in the Variable Stability and Control X–14A Research Vehicle," by L. Stewart Rolls and Fred J. Drinkwater III. The X–14A was a very versatile aircraft and was used at Ames not only for V/STOL flight studies but also for simulating the flight of a spacecraft landing on the moon.

Still more radical designs of V/STOL airplanes envisioned the use of lifting propellers built into wings and fuselage. Such applications had become more practical as a result of the development by the General Electric Co. of gas generators and turbine-driven fans especially designed for the purpose. As a joint project, the Army, NASA (Ames), and General Electric made conceptual designs and preliminary evaluations of a number of differ-

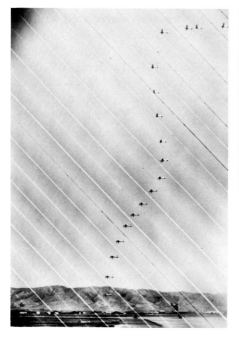

Two views of the Bell X–14A VTOL airplane.

ent lifting-fan V/STOL configurations. Models of the configurations were evaluated aerodynamically in the 40- by 80-foot tunnel. Several test reports were written, but the results of the whole project were summarized in the paper "Characteristics of Aircraft with Lifting-Fan Propulsion Systems for V/STOL," by Robert H. Goldsmith (GE) and David H. Hickey (Ames). This paper was presented at the annual meeting of the Institute of the Aerospace Sciences in New York in January 1963.

PILOT ADAPTATION TO FLIGHT ENVIRONMENT

Numerous experiments had been made to determine the tolerance of animals and humans to acceleration forces but in general these tests had not been particularly informative with respect to the effect of acceleration on the ability of experienced pilots to perform piloting tasks. The latter question, however, was one of several related matters investigated in a cooperative research program undertaken by the NASA Ames Research Center and the Aviation Medical Acceleration Laboratory of the Naval Air Development Center, Johnsville, Pennsylvania. In this program, the Navy's centrifuge at Johnsville was incorporated as a motion generator within the control loop of a flight simulator.

Several reports resulted from the joint program, one of which (TN D–348) has already been mentioned. Two additional reports (TN D–337 and TN D–345) dealt more specifically with the human-factors aspects of the program. These were authored by Brent Creer and Rodney Wingrove of Ames and Captain Harald A. Smedal of the USN Medical Corps. Captain Smedal, as earlier noted, eventually joined the staff of the Center and favorably influenced the decision to establish the NASA life sciences activity at Ames. A fourth report generated by the joint program (TN D–91) described a special restraint system which greatly helped a pilot maintain control of his craft while subjected to high and varying accelerations. This report was authored by Captain Smedal and two Ames test pilots, Glen Stinnett and Robert Innis.

The two human-factors reports revealed that a well-trained pilot could adequately carry out a control task during moderately high accelerations for prolonged periods of time; however, his ability to precisely control a vehicle of marginal dynamic stability deteriorated rapidly at accelerations over 4 g. The pilots could nevertheless tolerate accelerations of 6 g for as much as 6 minutes. Physiological measurements were made during the tests, and it was found that the respiratory function was one of the more limiting factors with respect to acceleration tolerance. This factor, however, was less critical when the direction of the acceleration was such as to tend to throw the eyeballs out of the head. The "eyeballs out" acceleration, to use the vernacular of the trade, is in contrast to the reverse "eyeballs in" acceleration and the most common "eyeballs down," or normal, acceleration.

RESEARCH

DYNAMIC LOADS AND MATERIALS

The Ames Research Center was now taking an increasing interest in the dynamic loads to which aircraft and spacecraft structures were subjected and thus also to the materials and structures used in such craft. Aerodynamic loads continued to be of primary interest, but loads caused by the sloshing of liquid fuel in a booster rocket or by the impact of landing on the moon were also under consideration. The use of such materials and structures in spacecraft as best to resist the impact of meteoroids had become a problem for research, as had also the erosion of spacecraft surface materials by the steady flux of fragmented atoms (ions) in space. In the materials field, the study of substances for use in ablation heat shields was, of course, of primary interest.

The long-standing problem of wing flutter received some attention during this period, as best indicated by reports TN D–344 by Henry Lessing, John Troutman, and Gene Menees, and TN D–1206 by Reuben Bond, Barbara Packard, Robert Warner, and Audrey Summers. The first report, from the 6- by 6-foot tunnel, demonstrated a rather clever technique for measuring pressure distributions on a wing while it was undergoing forced bending oscillations at supersonic airspeeds. The second provided some useful analytical tools for dealing with flutter and gust-response problems.

Bond and Packard also, in TN D–859, provided an analytical method for calculating the elastic-dynamic behavior of a launch vehicle in flight. This report was useful not only for calculating structural loads but also for determining the effects of missile bending on the design of the control system. The unsteady airloads on ascending missiles were generally greatest at the point in the trajectory where the missile passed through the transonic range, and these loads unfortunately were aggravated by the blunt-nosed "hammerhead" shape of the missile. The bulbous, hammerhead nose shape was often unavoidable because the diameter of the spacecraft (payload) sitting atop the booster was greater than that of the booster. Certain nose shapes caused an unsteady separating flow that excited a longitudinal bending vibration (flutter) of the missile. This vibration could, depending on the damping characteristics of the missile, be quite destructive. A study of the dynamic-load problem of hammerhead missiles was undertaken in the 14-foot tunnel. Charles Coe and Henry Cole were important contributors to the study; one of the more notable reports resulting from it was TN D–1982 (ref. C–8), "Dynamic Response of Hammerhead Launch Vehicles to Transonic Buffeting," by Henry Cole, who was well recognized at the Center for his accomplishments in the field of structural dynamics.

In any study of the structural dynamics (flutter) of a launch vehicle, the structural or internal damping of the missile was a critical factor. An important element of the internal damping, it had been found, was the sloshing of the liquid fuel in the fuel tanks of the missile. The effect of fuel sloshing, and the design of baffles to control the sloshing, thus became a rather important subject for study. Here again the abilities of Henry Cole came into play. As reported in TN D–694, he and Bruno Gambucci made a very useful study of fuel sloshing and baffle design.

The simulation in the laboratory of conditions existing in space was always difficult and in many cases impossible. The zero-g condition, for example, could not be simulated for any very useful period of time on earth, and the interacting radiation and magnetic fields in space could not be simulated at all or at least not until their basic nature had been determined through actual spaceflight tests. On the other hand, the flux of ions that prevailed in space, and their erosive effect on spacecraft materials could on a small scale be simulated in the laboratory. The first task here was to develop a facility for generating ions and for accelerating them in a narrow beam of uniform speed or energy. Ion beams of different energy levels could then be allowed to impinge on specimens of spacecraft materials to determine the erosive effect. The test specimens could thus be exposed at various angles and for different periods of time to ion beams having different energy levels. The resulting erosion, called "sputtering," was a function of angle, exposure time, and energy level. The energy level of the ions, as represented by their mass and speed, was expressed in the electrical units of electron-volts (eV) or more often in units of thousands or millions of electron-volts (keV or MEV). Sputtering effectiveness, or yield, was measured by the number of atoms of the target material that were knocked out by each ion that hit the target. The bombardment had to be carried out in a near vacuum, of course, and delicate measurements were obviously involved.

The development of an ion-beam apparatus was one of the projects undertaken by Michel Bader not long after he arrived at the laboratory from Caltech in 1955. His objective was a device of a type not built before which would produce a beam containing many particles of relatively low speed and energy. The energy level ranged from 0 to 8 keV. A description of how this device was developed and used in sputtering research is given in TR R–105 (ref. C–9), "Sputtering of Metals by Mass-Analyzed N_2^+ and N^+," by Michel Bader, Fred C. Witteborn, and Thomas W. Snouse.

The sputtering that occurred in space flight was known to be a slow process not likely to endanger the structural integrity of a spacecraft. Nevertheless its roughening effect could seriously alter the performance of surfaces intended to absorb, transmit, reflect, or emit radiation. Power-generating solar cells, for example, would be affected, as would the surfaces of optical instruments and radiating elements. In space flight, the temperature control of the spacecraft was often a critical matter and the only method for disposing of unwanted heat was to radiate it to cold outer space. Special radiation surfaces were often provided for this purpose and it was obviously necessary for the radiating efficiency (emissivity) of these surfaces to remain

RESEARCH

constant, at the design value, during flight. Such surfaces were usually smooth at the beginning of a flight but sputtering soon roughened them and changed their emissivity.

The effect of sputtering on the emissivity of surfaces was clearly an important matter, so its investigation was undertaken by the Ames Research Center. The results of this work are contained in TN D–1646, "Effects of Sputtering with Hydrogen Ions on Total Hemispherical Emittance of Several Metallic Surfaces," by Donald L. Anderson and George J. Nothwang. Following a different tack in the emissivity study, Carr Neel prepared an experiment by means of which the thermal radiation characteristics of several surfaces were measured in an actual space flight. The experiment which Carr devised was carried in the S–16 Orbiting Solar Observatory launched in March 1962 and was one of the first Ames experiments to be conducted in space. Some of the results of Carr's work are contained in a paper which he read in May 1963 before the Ninth Aerospace Instrumentation Symposium in San Francisco. It was subsequently published by NASA as TM X–51,196.

SPACECRAFT CONFIGURATIONS AND AIRFLOWS

Spacecraft configuration and airflow studies at Ames during this period were largely concerned with (1) blunt nonlifting reentry bodies, (2) lifting reentry bodies including boost-glide-vehicle configurations, and (3) dynamic stability of reentry bodies.

Nonlifting Bodies. In the blunt-body area, the analytical and numerical methods for calculating the flow existing between blunt bodies and the bow shock waves they produced were extended by a number of Ames research men. The resulting reports included TN D–791 by Frank Fuller and TN D–1426 by Mamoru Inouye and Harvard Lomax. Also included in this group of reports were TN D–1423, "Predicted Gas Properties in the Shock Layer Ahead of Capsule-Type Vehicles at Angles of Attack," by George E. Kaattari, and TN D–1979, "Experimental and Theoretical Pressures on Blunt Cylinders for Equilibrium and Nonequilibrium Air at Hypersonic Speeds," by Donald M. Kuehn.

Kaattari's paper notably considered the case of the blunt body at an angle of attack; in this situation the shock wave is not symmetrically disposed with regard to the body and this adds to the difficulty of calculating the shape and position of the resulting shock wave and of determining the character of the airflow behind it. The experimental portion of the study reported by Don Kuehn was carried out in a 6-inch arc-jet facility in the 1- by 3-foot wind-tunnel building. The tests were run at a nominal Mach number of 15 and at a stagnation enthalpy of 1000 Btu per pound. The results were correlated with a number of available theories and found to be represented best by a theory (blast wave) that had been developed to explain the aerodynamic effects of explosions.

359

One of the blunt-body configurations that received attention at Ames during this period consisted of a blunt-nose cylinder the rear end of which flared suddenly into a conical skirt. The flare was intended to stabilize the body in flight; but Ames research men found that within the general blunt-nose flow pattern, the flare produced an occlusion of alien flow the effects of which, on drag and stability, had not been anticipated. Within the occlusion, the flare produced oblique shock waves and sometimes boundary-layer separation. Although, as just noted, the blunt-nose flare configuration introduced a flow peculiarity, it was nevertheless considered worthy of study as a promising shape for the Polaris ballistic missile warhead and perhaps for other applications.

The stability characteristics of blunt-nose flare configurations were investigated quite extensively in the Unitary (11-foot) and the 6- by 6-foot tunnels. The principal contributors to this effort were Phillips Tunnell, David Reese, William Wehrend, Victor Peterson, and Willard Smith. At about the same time, Don Kuehn of the Fluid Mechanics Branch reported in TR R–117 and TR R–146 on studies he had made of boundary-layer separation caused by flares mounted on both blunt-nose and sharp-nose reentry bodies. Additionally, a rather extensive series of experimental and theoretical investigations of blunt-nose flare configurations was conducted by Alvin Seiff and Ellis Whiting of the SSFF tunnel. From the latter program, came a series of important reports including TM X–377, TN D–1147, TN D–1148, and TN D–1304. In general, Seiff and Whiting found that the stabilizing effects of flares on cylindrical bodies was less than had been expected and, also unexpectedly, varied with speed. On the other hand, the effectiveness of flaps or flares on conical bodies was greater than had been anticipated.

Aside from the studies just mentioned, many other investigations of nonlifting bodies were made during these years. Among them was the interesting undertaking described in TN D–1300, "Effects of Simulated Retrorockets on the Aerodynamic Characteristics of a Body of Revolution at Mach Numbers From 0.25 to 1.90," by Victor L. Peterson and Robert L. McKenzie. This study provided an insight as to what happens to the flow over a reentry body when it is being decelerated by forward-firing retrorockets.

Still more important were the studies undertaken during this period of the effects of gas mixtures representing the atmospheres of Mars and Venus on the aerodynamic behavior of various spacecraft configurations. This pioneering work was initiated by a 6- by 6-foot-tunnel group which included Jack Boyd, W. Pat Peterson, and Willard Smith.

Lifting Reentry Bodies.   Although the relative simplicity of nonlifting reentry bodies gave such configurations an initial priority in spaceflight operations, the numerous advantages of lifting reentry bodies were well recognized and the investigation of lifting bodies at Ames was intensively pur-

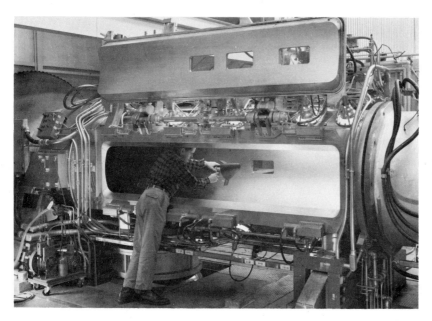

Model of reentry body in 3.5-foot tunnel throat.

sued. As uncertainty existed regarding the optimum shape for such bodies, a variety of configurations was investigated at subsonic, transonic, and supersonic speeds. Among the configurations tested were slender, blunt-edge delta wings and lenticular or disk-shape bodies equipped with fins and control flaps. Perhaps the most promising configuration, which had been suggested by Al Eggers and his associates in the 10- by 14-inch tunnel, was a blunted, flat-top semicone with control flaps and vertical stabilizing fins. Eggers, whose design conceptions were now appreciated more than ever, was given the AIAA Sylvanus Albert Reed Award in 1961.

Numerous investigations of lifting-body configurations were undertaken in the Unitary, the 6- by 6-foot, and the 12-foot tunnels. Semicone configurations were studied in the Unitary tunnel by Jack Tunnell and in the 6- by 6-foot tunnel by Ralph Holtzclaw. At the same time, disk-shape, or lenticular, configurations were investigated at transonic and supersonic speeds by Fred Demele and Frank Lazzeroni. In the 12-foot tunnel, semicones were investigated by George Kenyon and Fred Sutton, lenticular configurations by Fred Demele and Jack Brownson, and blunt deltas by George Edwards. A useful summary of the lifting-body test work, authored by David Dennis and George Edwards, was published in TM X–376 (ref. C–10).

The lifting bodies so far mentioned were designed to develop only low values of L/D and were thus expected to provide but a small amount of reentry-path control. Also investigated were configurations representing boost-glide vehicles which were to be rocket-boosted to the fringes of space and then glide long distances on airplane-like wings. The Air Force's new research vehicle, Dynasoar, then in the study phase of development, was of the boost-glide type. Dynasoar-type configurations received a considerable amount of research attention at Ames, and resulting reports included TN D–341 by Al Seiff and Max Wilkins, TM X–659 by George McCullough, and TM X–656 by Horace Emerson, John McDevitt, and John Wyss. The investigation by Seiff and Wilkins provided information on drag and boundary-layer transition on a complete glider model at Mach 6.0 and at full-scale Reynolds number. The significance of TM X–656 was that it proposed an original design for a folding-wing vehicle which would be rocket-launched but would thereafter use four jet engines to fly and land like an airplane. This project was said to have inspired the formation of a mission-analysis group at Ames.

Dynamic Stability. In most of the reentry-body studies just mentioned, the static-stability characteristics of the body were determined and in some cases, through the use of techniques invented by Ben Beam and Henry Lessing, their dynamic-stability characteristics were also evaluated. Still other investigations, to be mentioned, were largely concerned with dynamic stability.

Static stability, the tendency of the body to return to some preferred attitude when displaced, was of course an essential characteristic of a reentry body; but, since the body was thermally protected for flight in but one direction, it was unfortunate when it had two "preferred" attitudes about which it was stable. Unhappily some of the reentry bodies with square-cut rear ends were statically stable rear-end forward as well as front-end forward. Thus an initially tumbling body might well choose the rear-end-forward attitude for reentry and burn up for lack of thermal protection on that end. It had been found, however, that the rear-end-forward flight regime could be rendered unstable, and thus eliminated, by adding a conical projection to the flat base of the reentry body. A useful evaluation of this benefit was reported in TN D–1327, "Static Aerodynamic Characteristics of Short Blunt Cones with Various Nose and Base Cone Angles at Mach Numbers From 0.6 to 5.5 and Angles of Attack to 180°," by Stuart Treon.

Dynamic stability, the tendency of an oscillation once started about the statically stable attitude to damp out, was another important requirement for reentry bodies, since violent, large-amplitude oscillations could not be tolerated in most cases. However, as demonstrated by Allen, Tobak, and others, the dynamic-stability problem was eased considerably by the fact that a reentry vehicle was accorded a degree of pseudodynamic stability throughout that portion of its reentry path in which air density and dynamic pressure were increasing. This period of grace often carried the body past the peak of aerodynamic heating but, for bodies containing people or instruments to be recovered intact, an inherent dynamic stability was desirable.

Dynamic-stability investigations of reentry bodies were conducted in several wind tunnels as well as in the new pressurized ballistic range, which was ideally adapted for such work. Among the wind-tunnel investigations was one on the damping in pitch of blunt-nose flare models reported in TM X–648 by James Monfort and Jack Tunnell. This study was conducted in the Unitary Plan tunnels, as was an investigation of the static and dynamic stability of a flat-top wing-body model reported in TM X–361 by Bedford Lampkin and Kenneth Endicott of the 8- by 7-foot-tunnel staff.

The free-flight facilities at Ames were very useful for stability investigations and during this period were used quite extensively for this purpose. The pressurized ballistic range, owing to its high Reynolds number capabilities, was particularly applicable to stability research and was used for the investigation of the static and dynamic stability of blunt-cone bodies reported by Peter Intrieri in TN D–1299. Similarly, the supersonic free-flight tunnel was used by Simon Sommer and Barbara Short (TM X–373) to examine the stability characteristics of the Mercury capsule and by Ellis Whiting (TM X–657) to investigate the stabilizing effect of fins mounted on blunt-nose missiles. Important work of the same kind was carried out by Don Kirk and Robert Carros of the SSFF Tunnel Branch.

The static and dynamic stability of a model tested in a free-flight facility had to be deduced from its motions. If the motions of the model could be described by a mathematical formula, the stability coefficients were thus generally defined. In the dynamic-stability formulas devised for this purpose, it was usually assumed that the static stability of the test body—its tendency to return to the preferred attitude—varied linearly with the angle of pitch; but at the higher angles of pitch encountered by a reentry body, the relationship was definitely not linear and the dynamic-stability formulas

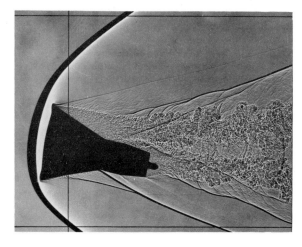

Shadowgraph of Gemini capsule model in flight-stability tests.

were thus not accurate. It remained for Maurice Rasmussen, a Stanford man temporarily employed at Ames, to develop a mathematical method for dealing with these nonlinearities in stability analyses. Rasmussen's work, a very useful contribution, is contained in TN D–144 (ref. C–11), "Determination of Nonlinear Pitching-Moment Characteristics of Axially Symmetric Models From Free-Flight Data."

SPACECRAFT FLIGHT STUDIES

The theory of satellite orbits was a subject which fitted in well with Bill Mersman's interests and with the electronic computing facilities of which he was in charge. Out of these interests and facilities came two erudite reports of which the titles offer as much information as can readily be absorbed by the layman. The first of these reports was TR R–99, "Theory of the Secular Variation in the Orbit of a Satellite of an Oblate Planet"; the second was TR R–148, "The Critical Inclination Problem in Satellite Orbit Theory." Studies such as these made possible the prediction of satellite orbits.

Dean Chapman followed his classical, 1958, study (TR R–11) of entry into planetary atmospheres with a second important entry study, reported in TR R–55 (ref. C–12), "An Analysis of the Corridor and Guidance Requirements for Supercircular Entry Into Planetary Atmospheres."

Spaceflight trajectories, it might be mentioned, could generally be described in terms of conic sections—circles, ellipses, parabolas, and hyperbolas—and each trajectory so described was associated with a range of launching and reentry speeds. The lowest speed range was associated with circular satellite orbits. The circular speed had to be increased to produce an elliptical orbit and increased still more for parabolic and hyperbolic trajectories. The ellipse, moreover, was the path requiring minimum-energy expenditure and least fuel consumption for travel between two circular orbits—such as those of the earth and Mars—but unfortunately for long trips the minimum-energy route was too time consuming to be useful. The speed associated with a parabolic trajectory was unique in that it represented escape speed—the lowest launching speed for which the spacecraft would leave the earth never to return unless power was exerted to bring it back. Escape speed for launchings from the earth [1] was about 36,000 feet per second (25,000 miles per hour).

It was clear from the title of TR R–55 that Chapman was concerned with speeds higher than those encountered in ordinary circular orbits. Dean showed in his study that the corridor in space through which a spacecraft must enter the earth's atmosphere, if it is to return safely to earth, is very narrow and rapidly becomes narrower as entry speed increases. On one side

---

[1] From the moon, about 7800 fps; from Mars, about 16,500 fps; and from Jupiter, about 196,500 fps.

of the corridor is the undershoot boundary, beyond which the spacecraft will be destroyed by excessive deceleration or heating. On the other side lies the overshoot boundary, beyond which air drag will be insufficient to keep the spacecraft from shooting completely past the earth. Thus a nonlifting spacecraft returning, say, from Mars must be guided with sufficient precision to hit a layer of the earth's atmosphere that, relative to the earth's diameter, might correspond in thickness to the skin of an apple. If the spacecraft has some lifting capabilities, can generate a lift-drag ratio of as much as 1.0, the entry corridor—though still narrow—is considerably widened. Thus, for spacecraft returning from deep-space missions, the ability to generate a positive lift-drag ratio is very valuable. Chapman pointed out that additional benefit from lift might be available if the values of lift (L), drag (D), or the ratio L/D could be modulated or varied throughout the entry process.

The critical heating, deceleration, and corridor problems of supercircular reentry arose directly, of course, from the use of air drag as the sole braking mechanism. While it was fully appreciated that these problems could be greatly relieved by killing off the supercircular velocity with retrorockets prior to entering the atmosphere, such a procedure involved weight and cost penalties too severe to contemplate except as a last resort.

Following Chapman's work, other entry studies, aimed at showing the benefits of modulating L, D, or L/D, were undertaken at Ames. Among these were the studies reported in TR R–80 by Tom Wong and Robert Slye, in TN D–1145 by Elliott Katzen and Lionel Levy, and in TN D–1427 by Lionel Levy. Another reentry study which gave particular attention to the heating problem was reported in TN D–334 by Tom Wong, Glen Goodwin,

Reentry corridor for supercircular velocities.

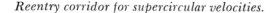

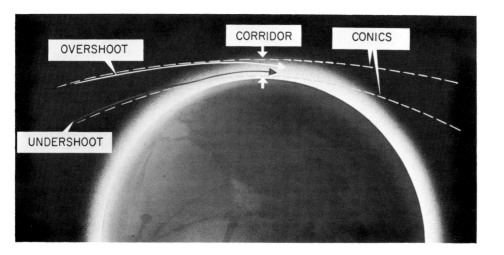

and Robert Slye. All of these studies dealt with supercircular reentry speeds such as those encountered by spacecraft returning from deep space.

One of the more outstanding studies of reentry at supercircular velocities was made by Rodney Wingrove and reported in TR R–151 (ref. C–13), "A Study of Guidance to Reference Trajectories for Lifting Reentry at Supercircular Velocity." His study provided the detailed analytical basis for the design of guidance systems capable of dealing with exceedingly critical guidance problems involved in lift-controlled reentry from supercircular orbits. A steppingstone to Wingrove's analysis was an earlier study which he and Robert Coate had reported in TN D–787, "Piloted Simulator Tests of a Guidance System Which Can Continuously Predict Landing Point of Low L/D Vehicle During Atmospheric Re-Entry."

The report just named represented one of the early uses at Ames of a flight simulator for spaceflight research and also one of the first spaceflight guidance-system studies attempted at the Center. Soon to be undertaken, however, were other space-guidance-system studies, representative of which was the one reported in TR R–135, "Application of Statistical Filter Theory to the Optimal Estimation of Position and Velocity on Board a Circumlunar Vehicle," by Gerald L. Smith, Stanley F. Schmidt, and Leonard A. McGee.

A certain amount of effort was expended during this period on mission, or system, studies. Of these the titles of the resulting reports are sufficiently descriptive. There was, for example, TN D–1207, "An Analytical Study of Orbital Rendezvous for Least Fuel and Least Energy," by Harold Hornby. There was also TN D–1143, "Orbital Payload Reductions Resulting From Booster and Trajectory Modifications for Recovery of a Large Rocket Booster," by Alan D. Levin and Edward J. Hopkins. Levin and Hopkins produced a second report, TN D–1295, which also dealt with the problem of recovering the first-stage rocket booster. Booster recovery was, indeed, a matter of great economic significance inasmuch as the one-shot use of costly first-stage rockets appeared to be a tremendously wasteful practice.

AERODYNAMIC HEATING: PHYSICS AND CHEMISTRY

General Problem. The speeds of interest to Ames engineers in the Space Age were much higher than those they had been concerned with in earlier years. The ballistic-missile warhead, for which Allen had suggested a blunt-nose configuration, had a reentry speed of 18,000 feet per second or less. Spacecraft, however, had reentry speeds of about 25,000 feet per second when returning from circular orbits or as much or more than 36,000 feet per second—earth parabolic speed—when returning from deep-space missions. Inasmuch as aerodynamic heating was known to vary as some multiple power (≈ 3) of velocity, it was obviously much higher for returning spacecraft than for returning missile warheads.

It was in the layer of air between the body and the bow shock wave—a

Heating of a reentry body. M–2 blunt half cone.

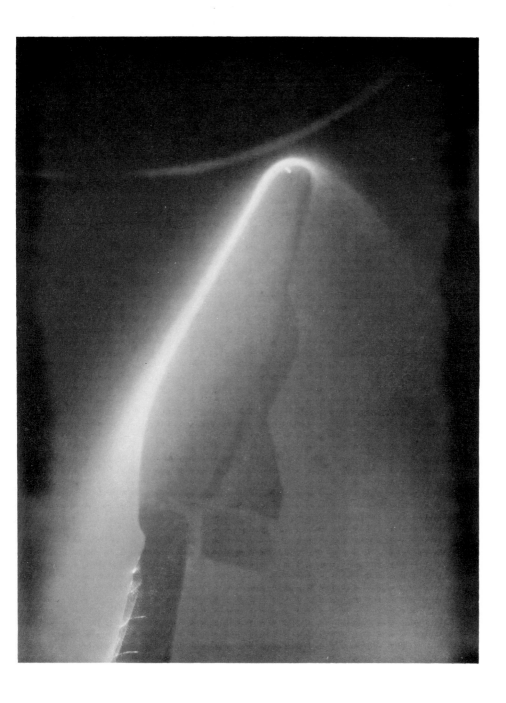

layer commonly called the gas cap or shock layer—that aerodynamic-heating phenomena were most strikingly evident. At parabolic reentry speeds, this layer reaches temperatures much higher than that of the surface of the sun. As a bell, when struck by a hammer, jangles for a moment before settling into its fundamental tone, so also a mass of air, slugged by a shock wave, jangles in brief but violent discord before relaxing into a more orderly state of activity. Strange things happen to the air molecules during this transient but hectic period of disequilibrium. First, the molecules are set in violent motion, bouncing back and forth, hitting each other and raising the temperature and pressure of the gas to a sharp peak. Then their energy penetrates the molecules, setting up various natural modes of vibration by and between the atoms. In consequence of their relative motion, the atoms of some molecules break the chemical bonds which tie them together and fly apart in the process called dissociation. Then, if the shock is severe enough, the very electrons which circle the nucleus of the atom become so agitated that they break away from their parent nucleus and fly away on their own in the process called ionization.

Following the initial pressure and temperature rise, each of the processes that successively takes place absorbs energy and decreases temperature. Quickly the molecules and fragments settle down to an equilibrium state of activity and temperature but, even in the equilibrium state, their activity and temperature are very high. The time required for the air to relax to the equilibrium state depends on the frequency with which the molecules collide with one another, thus with the air density, and thus with the flight altitude. Whether or not the relaxation process is completed before the air reaches the body which produced the shock wave depends on the distance of the shock wave ahead of the body, which in turn depends on the size and shape of the body. If the relaxation process is not completed by the time the out-of-equilibrium air reaches the body, the body will obviously be exposed to an unusually high air temperature. This condition, it has been found, is likely to occur only at high altitude during the early, usually uncritical, stage of spacecraft reentry heating.

A flow which remains in a constant state of dissociation is said to be "frozen," but ordinarily the forces of recombination, tending to heal the shattered molecules, are dominant. Moreover, recombination is sometimes precipitated by the catalytic action of the body surface. Inasmuch as the recombination process itself generates heat, the air temperature to which a catalytic body surface is exposed is unusually high.

Allen's blunt-body principle was based on the assumption that the heat generated by the shock wave, some distance from the body, could not reach the body through the normal process of convection. The assumption was demonstrably correct, but convection was not the only mode of heat transfer: there was also radiation. Radiation varies with the fourth power of the absolute temperature and, in the case of ballistic missiles, the gas cap does not get hot enough for radiation to be a significant factor. But as reentry speeds increase, the highly heated, dissociated, and ionized gas cap radiates intensely and the body is no longer isolated from the heat of the shock wave.

Radiation affected the aerodynamic heating process as the forward pass affected football—it changed the whole game. The heat of the shock wave no longer had to buck the line to reach the body; it was passed directly to this receiver largely unhindered by the intervening gas. But the effects of radiation were not quite that simple. The intervening gas did not transmit the radiation without some resistance. It absorbed radiation in proportion to its density and thus altered its own convective and radiative heat-transfer properties. Moreover, the incandescent gases of the shock layer radiated forward as well as backward. Thus, though the body was traveling at hypersonic speed, the air along its path could feel its hot presence before either the body or its preceding shock wave arrived. Indeed, the air ahead of the shock wave absorbed some of this radiated heat and carried it back to the body. On the other hand, the energy of the incandescent gas suffered a depletion or decay of its energy as a result of radiation; thus the gas had less heat to transport by convection. Radiation intensity also depended on the chemical composition of the radiating gas. Owing to the high carbon-dioxide content of the atmosphere of Mars and Venus, a spacecraft descending for a landing on either of these planets would suffer more intense radiation than one landing on the earth.

Radiation was recognized as a serious aerodynamic-heating threat in spacecraft design and considerable effort was spent at Ames, and elsewhere, in determining the earth reentry speed at which it became a significant factor. Research engineers were relieved to find that radiation became of serious consequence only at earth parabolic speeds and higher, but they noted with some awe the rapidity with which its effect developed, once started. Following onset, the radiative factor for blunt bodies was found to increase at something like the 15th power of the velocity, quickly becoming the dominating influence in aerodynamic heating. Inasmuch as a body could not be shielded from the radiated heat of the bow shock, it was obviously essential to reduce the intensity of the shock by changing its shape from normal to inclined. This objective, it was realized, could only be accomplished by making the body pointed. The point of the body, in contact with the inclined shock, would be subjected to terrific convective heating and would certainly melt, but this was a problem that would have to be faced if the devastating effects of radiation were to be avoided.

It was clear that the phenomena of dissociation, ionization, and radiation had added tremendously to the problem of comprehending and analyzing reentry aerodynamic heating. It was also clear that very effective thermal protection for spacecraft must be provided. Sweat cooling was known to be very effective, but the problems of providing a porous nose, of carrying fluid in the spacecraft, and of forcing the fluid through the pores at the proper rate were extremely troublesome. How much simpler it would be if the cooling material were a solid, such as a plastic, which could be coated over the front face of the spacecraft and allowed to melt, evaporate, or sublime with attendant cooling! A material passing from a solid to a gaseous state could normally be expected to absorb more heat than one (sweat-cooling fluid) passing only from a liquid to a gas. Moreover, the solid material would insulate the spacecraft structure from the convected and radiated heat. The insulation might, indeed, be so effective as to allow its surface temperature to be elevated to such a level that a substantial portion of the body's heat load would be disposed of by radiation to outer space.

Considerations of this kind led to the belief that the ablation heat shield, as the protective layer was called, was the most promising means for providing thermal protection for spacecraft. Much remained to be learned, however, about the physical-chemical processes of ablation and about the selection of specific ablation materials for applications involving a variety of thermal exposure patterns. It seemed possible that optimum ablation materials might be obtainable only through synthetic development.

Nonequilibrium Flows. The aerodynamic and heat-transfer properties of nonequilibrium airflows, and the chemical processes of dissociation and recombination, were subjects for numerous studies at Ames during this period. Among those who made contributions to these efforts were Paul Chung, Aemer Anderson, Ernest Winkler, Roy Griffin, Glen Goodwin, John Howe, and Jack Stephenson. One of the outstanding reports in this field is TR R–109 (ref. C–14), "Hypersonic Viscous Shock Layer of Nonequilibrium Dissociating Gas," by Paul Chung. Chung had earlier joined with Aemer Anderson in a study of "Dissociative Relaxation of Oxygen over an Adiabatic Flat Plate at Hypersonic Mach Numbers," which was reported in TN D–140. These two studies were purely analytical in character. Also analytical was the paper, by Glen Goodwin and Paul Chung, on "Effects of Nonequilibrium Flows on Aerodynamic Heating During Entry Into the Earth's Atmosphere From Parabolic Orbits." This paper was presented in Zurich at the Second International Congress for Aeronautical Sciences. In still another paper the authors, Goodwin and Howe, introduced the similarity parameter $\dot{q}_0/\sqrt{P_0}\ r$, where $\dot{q}_0$ and P_0 are respectively, the rate of heat transfer and the pressure at the nose of a body and r is the nose radius. This parameter proved very useful in correlating heat-transfer data obtained experimentally, in nonequilibrium, gas-cap flows.

Experimental studies of dissociation and recombination phenomena were also undertaken at this time. One was conducted in an arc-jet facility and reported by Ernie Winkler and Roy Griffin in TN D–1146, "Effects of Surface Recombination on Heat Transfer to Bodies in a High Enthalpy

370

Stream of Partially Dissociated Nitrogen." The purpose of this study was to investigate the effect of surface catalysis on recombination and heat transfer. Another study, of experimental character, had to do with the development of a technique for determining relaxation time in free-flight model tests. It was carried out by Jack Stephenson and reported in TN D–327.

Radiation Studies. Radiation and its effects on heat transfer to reentry bodies was the subject of numerous research investigations at Ames. One of the major contributors to this effort was John Howe of the Heat Transfer Branch of the Aero-Thermodynamics Division. One of John's interesting studies was an analytical investigation of the possibility of blocking the radiation from the gas cap to the body by injecting an opaque gas into the boundary layer. As reported in TR R–95, he found that the technique was effective in some cases and that its overall effect on the heat transfer to the body varied somewhat with the reflectivity of the body surface. Howe also produced TN D–1031, "Radiation Emission Effects of the Equilibrium Boundary Layer in the Stagnation Region," but his most noteworthy contribution, perhaps, was the analytical study he carried out with the help of John Viegas, which is reported in TR R–159 (ref. C–15), "Solutions of the Ionized Radiating Shock Layer, Including Reabsorption and Foreign Species Effects, and Stagnation Region Heat Transfer."

A notable experimental study of radiation effects was carried out in the pilot hypervelocity free-flight facility during this period. It is described in a paper (ref. C–16) entitled "Measurements of Radiation From the Flow Fields of Bodies Flying at Speeds up to 13.4 Kilometers per Second," by Thomas N. Canning and William A. Page. This paper was presented at an AGARD [2] meeting in Brussels in April 1962. The velocities (13.4 kps$\approx$ 44,000 fps) at which the tests of this investigation were conducted were perhaps the highest yet attained at Ames. Photographs of the model, itself speeding at 10 kilometers per second, were taken with a camera the exposure time of which was limited by a Kerr cell to 50 billionths of a second.

Radiation from the gas cap was measured by special instrumentation involving the use of photomultiplier tubes. It was learned, among other things, that the vaporized material from the ablation heat shield was itself a source of radiation, particularly in the model wake. Later the radiation from ablation by-products was more specifically investigated by Roger Craig and William Davey, whose work is reported in TN D–1978.

At the previously mentioned AGARD meeting in Brussels, Bradford Wick presented a paper (ref. C–17) entitled "Radiative Heating of Vehicles Entering the Earth's Atmosphere." Brad's paper was concerned with the prediction of radiation heating effects. The latest research results were utilized in the analysis and special attention was given to two spacecraft, one assumed to be returning from the moon at a speed of 37,000 feet per second

---

[2] Advisory Group on Aeronautical Research and Development (NATO).

Bradford H. Wick.

and the other from a trip to Mars at a speed of about 50,000 feet per second. The extreme conditions represented by these examples brought out all aspects of the radiative-heating problem.

A fairly basic analytical study of radiative heat transfer was produced by Kenneth Yoshikawa and Dean Chapman and reported in TN D–1424 (ref. C–18), "Radiative Heat Transfer and Absorption Behind a Hypersonic Normal Shock Wave." This study, which considers the emission, absorption, and decay of radiant energy in the shock layer for gas temperatures up to 15,000° Kelvin (centigrade absolute), provides useful analytical methods and data. Temperatures of the degree mentioned, it was indicated, could be encountered by spacecraft at earth entry speeds of from 40,000 to 60,000 feet per second.

It was surprising how many of the current heat-transfer studies at Ames made use of Fred Hansen's report (ref. B–55) on the thermodynamic and transport properties of high-temperature air. For its all-around usefulness, Hansen's report deserves special mention in the Ames hall of fame. Originally published as TN 4150 in 1948, it was subsequently republished in more permanent form as TR R–50. John Viegas and John Howe performed the useful service in TN D–1429 of converting Hansen's tabular data into analytical forms that could readily be handled by computing machines.

The efforts of Max Heaslet and Frank Fuller in theoretical aerodynamics ceased with the formation of NASA. Their attention turned to equally abstruse radiation theory, a subject which they proceeded to attack with the support of their colleagues, Barrett Baldwin and W. Prichard Jones. An example of the work of Heaslet and Baldwin is their paper, "Predictions of the Structure of Radiation-Resisted Shock Waves," which in June 1963 was published in the *Journal of the Physics of Fluids*. Another example of work in this field is TR R–138, "The Propagation of Plane Acoustic Waves in a Radiating Gas," by Barrett Stone Baldwin, Jr.

Ablation. Although research on ablation heat shields may have had little bearing on the conception of the Ames atmosphere-entry simulator, it became the principal function of the facility soon after the simulator was put to use. One of the early reports issuing from the AES group was TM X–394, "The Ames Atmospheric Entry Simulator and Its Application to the Determination of Ablative Properties of Materials for Ballistic Missiles," by Frank M. Hamaker. As time went on, the capability of the AES for ablation studies was continually increased through the incorporation of improved guns. The original one-stage gun was replaced by a two-stage gun, which in turn was replaced by a three-stage gun capable of firing projectiles at speeds up to 25,000 feet per second.

Among the men active in ablation research in the AES were Raymond Savin, Gary Bowman, Hermilo Gloria, and Richard Dahms. Typical of their work is the study reported in TN D–1330, "The Determination of Ablative Properties of Materials in Free-Flight Ranges," by Savin, Gloria, and Dahms. In this study, small blunt conical models, made of various thermoplastic (ablation) materials, were launched at speeds of 15,000 feet per second and were caught after decelerating to about 1000 feet per second. The erosion of the front face was observed and the loss of material through ablation was determined from the difference in their weights before and after launching. The weight-loss data and other test information were introduced into analytical formulas to provide a better quantitative definition of ablation as well as to provide a comparison of the several materials tested.

Plastic ablation materials were adopted for the models tested in the AES because such materials had earlier been found to have promising ablation characteristics. Such materials as Teflon, ethyl cellulose, and high-density polyethylene, which in flight appeared to go quickly from the solid to the gaseous state (sublime), were investigated. For each, a quantity known as the "heat of ablation"—the amount of heat necessary to ablate one pound of material—was determined.

Other free-flight facilities were used for ablation and aerodynamic-heating studies and a number of ingenious techniques were developed for such investigations. In one, for which Layton Yee and William Kerwin were largely responsible, the temperature at some critical point on the model was measured by a tiny thermocouple carried in the model. The thermocouple in the speeding model in effect transmitted its readings by radio by generating a magnetic field that was picked up by a coil surrounding the flight path. An example of the use of this device is given in TN D–777, of which Yee was coauthor. Still another clever device developed by the SSFF staff was a technique in which the model was quickly slowed, then caught in a special calorimeter which measured its heat burden. This technique was originally

Ablation of Mercury capsule model.

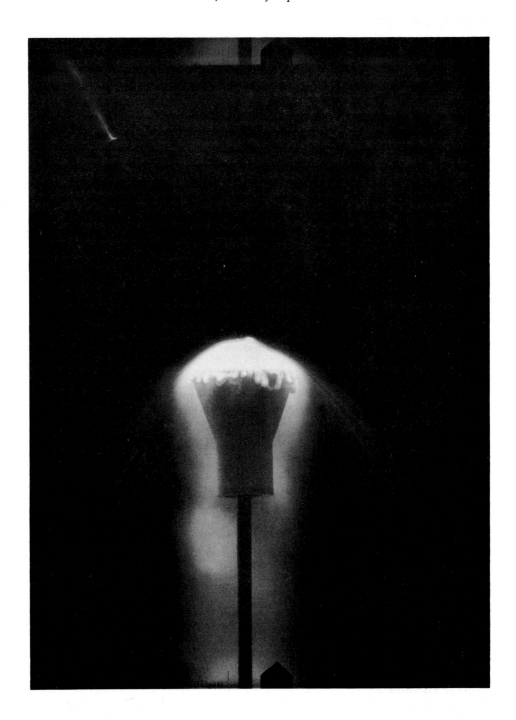

suggested by Al Seiff, but Gary Chapman exercised much skill in developing it to a practical stage. The technique is described in TN D–1890 (ref. C–19), "Measurement of the Heat Transfer to Bodies of Revolution in Free Flight by Use of a Catcher Calorimeter," by Gary T. Chapman and Charles T. Jackson, Jr.

The arc-jet, which had been under continuous development at Ames, became a more useful tool for ablation studies than the AES. It provided more manageable test conditions, its heat was delivered over a longer period of time, and the test model was held firmly in place. By the end of 1962, the AES was essentially passé, its mission largely taken over by the arc-jet.

Among the ablation studies conducted with the arc-jet was the analytical-experimental investigation reported in TN D–1205, "The Performance of Ablative Materials in a High-Energy, Partially Dissociated, Frozen Nitrogen Stream," by Nick S. Vojvodich. This study, made with teflon, nylon, and polyethylene ablative materials, was aimed at determining the effect of recombination, as promoted by surface catalysis, on ablator performance. Rather incidentally, but quite importantly, the tests revealed that, at low heating rates, the nylon and polyethylene materials remained in the liquid phase so long that the liquefied material was swept off the ablator surface by the airstream before it evaporated. Under these conditions, the effectiveness of these two materials, as ablators, was much reduced.

Another ablation study in which an arc-jet was used was reported in TN D–1332 (ref. C–20), "Measurements of the Effective Heats of Ablation of Teflon and Polyethylene at Convective Heating Rates from 25 to 420 Btu/Ft² Sec," by Dale L. Compton, Warren Winovich, and Roy M. Wakefield. This study confirmed the liquid-phase problem of polyethylene at low heating rates. Teflon, on the other hand, seemed to go directly from the solid to the gaseous phase and thus maintained its ablation cooling effectiveness even at low heating rates. It appeared that ablation materials having a prolonged liquid phase would not be suitable for applications where the heating occurred at low intensity but for relatively long periods of time. These conditions could occur on the nose of a reentry vehicle which used lift to reduce heating intensity and they could also occur on the afterbody of any reentry vehicle.

For applications in which the heat load was prolonged, the insulating qualities of the ablation material became important as did also the ability of such materials to avoid structural failure as a result of softening or embrittlement. It was also recognized that, to insulate against radiation heating, the ablation material must be opaque. A study of the insulating qualities of several ablation materials was reported in TN D–1889, "The Influence of Heating Rate and Test Stream Oxygen Content on the Insulating Efficiency of Charring Materials," by Nick S. Vojvodich and Ernest L. Winkler. This study took cognizance of the oxidation or combustion of ablation material that might occur during entry into an atmosphere containing oxygen. The combustion problem would presumably not be present for entry into the atmospheres of Venus and Mars, which are believed to be composed largely of nitrogen and carbon dioxide.

Projections. For 10 or 15 years, Harvey Allen had concentrated much of his attention on the problems of aerodynamic heating as affecting missile and spacecraft design. He not only guided the research work of his division or directorate but also made use of all available new knowledge in analytical projections aimed at uncovering and solving future design problems relating to aerodynamic heating. The projection process was continuous and one which exercised his extraordinary abilities for finding hidden pathways through confusing masses of physical evidence. Harvey's projections were of much interest to the scientific community and he was in great demand as a speaker at technical meetings. His numerous papers often overlapped one another in content, but each new one carried his projections a little farther.

One of Allen's papers, on "Problems in Atmospheric Entry from Parabolic Orbits," was presented in 1961 to the Japanese Society for Aeronautical and Space Sciences. Another notable paper (ref. C–21), entitled "Hypersonic Aerodynamic Problems of the Future," was presented at a NATO specialists meeting in Belgium in 1962. Allen also joined with two of his colleagues in producing one of the outstanding Ames reports of this period. This report, TR R–185 (ref. C–22), was entitled "Aerodynamic Heating of Conical Entry Vehicles at Speeds in Excess of Earth Parabolic Speed," by H. Julian Allen, Alvin Seiff, and Warren Winovich. TR R–185 was reminiscent of the original blunt-body report by Allen and Eggers as it dealt with the optimum nose shape for a reentry vehicle and made use of the mathematical stratagems for which Allen was well known. In contending with a problem as tremendously complex as aerodynamic heating, an instinct for tolerable approximations was a wonderful asset.

In their report, Allen and his colleagues deliberately chose to deal with the reentry speed range, above 37,000 feet per second, in which radiation effects were important. Allen had long ago shown that the heating of a reentry body by convection could be minimized by using a blunt nose. However, the normal shock wave produced by a blunt body generated very high temperatures in the gas cap and thus, at high reentry speeds, very intense radiation. At speeds well above parabolic, it would clearly be essential to reduce radiation to the body even at the expense of increasing convection. The question was: How could this objective be best accomplished?

It was known that the heat, and particularly the radiation, produced by a shock wave decreased rapidly with the backward inclination of the shock wave. Indeed, radiation intensity was believed to vary by as much as the 15th power of the sine of the angle of shock inclination—the angle being referred to body axis. The shape of the reentry body required for operating

H. Julian Allen explaining aerodynamic heating.

in a radiation environment was clearly one that produced an inclined shock wave and the cone was a rather obvious choice. With such a shape, the shock inclination and radiation intensity could be controlled by varying the cone angle. The cone shape also offered the advantage of being readily applicable to lifting-body configurations—much more so, in fact, than a blunt shape. The authors of TR R–185 found that the optimum cone angle (included angle) for the entry-speed range from 37,000 feet per second (parabolic) to 74,000 feet per second (twice parabolic) varied from about 110° to about 55°. With these optimum, radiation-reducing configurations it was found, rather surprisingly, that the heat burden imposed on the body still came largely (85 to 90 percent) via the convective route.

One of the more serious problems in the application of conical noses to reentry bodies arose from the fact that the sharp point was quickly melted and flattened by convection heating. Once the nose was rounded to any significant degree, a normal shock wave would form in front of the rounded area and the radiation in this region would become extremely intense. Somehow, Allen and his partners concluded, the shape of the cone must be maintained. This objective might be accomplished, they decided, if the point of the cone could be cooled in some fashion or continuously renewed. The use of ablation materials (Teflon or quartz) was contemplated, of course, but unless a long projecting spike of the material were mounted on the nose of the cone, the flattening would still occur. And the spike seemed impractical. A better way, it was felt, was to renew the point continuously, like the lead of a mechanical pencil, by propelling a rod of ablation material through a hole in the nose of the body.

377

These then were some of the conclusions arrived at by Allen, Seiff, and Winovich. They are simply stated but were reached only with great effort and the services of a huge IBM 7090 computer.

IMPACT PHYSICS AND METEORS

The hypervelocity ballistic ranges were obviously well suited for impact research, but the reasons Ames originally entered this field of research are slightly obscure. Explanations involving practical applications appeared a little thin; indeed, the reasons may have been more deeply based in the inherent urge of boys to throw rocks at things and see them smash. With the coming of the space age, an excuse fortuitously appeared in the need to study the effects of meteoroid impacts on spacecraft. Later, in view of NASA's liberal attitude toward pure research, even this reason was largely abandoned and the impact work accelerated on the basis of sheer interest. One could hope that fun, as it often does, might become profitable.

One of the first NASA impact studies was reported in TN D–94 (ref. C–23), "Investigation of High-Speed Impact: Regions of Impact and Impact at Oblique Angles," by James L. Summers. In this investigation, small metal spheres of widely varying densities were fired into lead and copper targets at speeds up to 11,000 feet per second. At low impact speeds, it was found that a sphere of hard, strong material (tungsten carbide) would enter the target and remain largely intact. At higher speeds, it would penetrate and shatter into pieces. Finally, as the impact speed increased still further, both it and the target material would melt and splash. The resulting crater would be large and its surface would be plated with the material of the sphere.

One of the first investigations of the effect of meteoroid impact on a space vehicle is reported in TN D–1039 (ref. C–24), "Preliminary Investigation of Impact on Multiple-Sheet Structures and an Evaluation of the Meteoroid Hazard to Space Vehicles," by C. Robert Nysmith and James L. Summers. Though some meteoroids are composed of metal, most are formed of stony material. Meteoroid velocities in general range from 36,000 to 236,000 feet per second and fortunately most of the meteoroids are very small. In the design of spacecraft structures best calculated to resist the effects of meteoroid hits, a question had arisen as to whether to use a skin composed of one thick sheet or of two or more thin sheets, perhaps with a filler of some kind in between. It was a question that had to be answered in the laboratory. From their study of this problem, Nysmith and Summers found that, for resisting meteoroid impacts, a multiple-skin structure was much better than a single-skin structure of the same weight though even it was not proof against penetration.

As gun development advanced, higher launching speeds were available for impact tests. In a study reported in TN D–1210 by Pat Denardo, plastic projectiles were launched at speeds up to 25,600 feet per second at massive

Impact at 19,500 fps of 20-mm blunt-nosed polyethylene model on an aluminum target at a pressure altitude of 100,000 ft.

The moon with the crater Tycho at lower left, 43° south latitude, 11° east longitude. (Lick Observatory photograph)

aluminum targets mounted on a ballistic pendulum. The use of the ballistic pendulum in this case allowed measurements to be made of the transfer of momentum from the projectile to the target. The penetration, crater volume, and material splashed from the crater were also observed. The basic character of the crater changed noticeably with the impact speed. In general, the crater rapidly increased in size and irregularity with speed as the materials in the impact area became more fluid and, at the highest speeds, quantities of fluid material were ejected clear of the target.

The best source of evidence on impact cratering was, of course, the moon. Through a telescope, the breadth and depth of lunar craters could be readily measured and the radial rays of ejected material easily observed. It was appropriate therefore that Ames, as part of its impact research program, should undertake a study of the mechanics of meteor impacts on the moon. From this study, it was hoped, might come information useful in the preparations for man's first lunar visit. The investigation was undertaken as a joint project with the U.S. Geological Survey. Principal investigators were Donald E. Gault for NASA and E. M. Shoemaker and H. J. Moore for USGS.

The first phase of the joint program was to conduct, in Ames range facilities, several series of impact tests using assumed lunar material (sand and rock) as the target. Such investigations were duly carried out and their results published in various technical journals. Finally the results of these experimental investigations were used as the basis for the analysis reported in TN D–1767 (ref. C–25), "Spray Ejected From the Lunar Surface by Meteoroid Impact," by Donald E. Gault, Eugene M. Shoemaker, and Henry J. Moore. This study made use of available statistical data on the size, frequency, and velocity of impacting meteoroids to determine the mass and size distribution, the velocities and trajectories of solid material ejected from the crater on impact. It was shown that, although the bulk of the material splashed from the craters reaches an altitude of no more than 6 miles, some relatively small portion is ejected at sufficiently high velocity (7800 feet per second) to escape from the moon's gravitational field.

In the impact tests they had conducted on rock and sand, Gault and his colleagues had been astonished at the volume of material ejected from the craters. In their subsequent lunar analysis, they estimated that the mass of rock and sand thrown up by a meteor striking the moon might be as much as a thousand times that of the meteor itself. Thus they conceded the possibility that the lunar surface might be permanently shrouded in a very thin dust cloud arising from its continuous bombardment by meteorites and falling lunar debris. Gault also estimated that as much as 10 tons of ejected material escapes from the moon each day. Of this, about 85 percent goes into orbit around the sun while the remainder forms a "cloud" of lunar material circling the earth.

Harvey Allen's interest in aerodynamic heating had led him, quite early, to a study of the heating and ablation of meteoroids as they ripped into the earth's atmosphere at speeds ranging from 7 to 50 miles per second. One of his early studies of this subject was recorded in a paper entitled "On the Motion and Ablation of Meteoric Bodies," which he presented at the Durand Centennial Conference at Stanford in August 1959. In this paper he attempted to correlate the information on meteors that astronomers and astrophysicists had collected with what had been learned in the relatively new, laboratory-developed science of aerodynamic heating. Allen's continuing interest in meteors was evidenced by his inclusion of a discussion of the subject in his 1962 paper on "Hypersonic Aerodynamic Problems of the Future" (ref. C–21).

In one of the last uses of the 1- by 3-foot blowdown tunnel before it was dismantled, Dean Chapman in early 1959 exposed a ball of "glycerin glass" (frozen glycerin) to the tunnel's Mach 3 airstream. As confirmed by photographs, the glass quickly softened and, as its surface melted into a viscous fluid, a system of surface waves appeared that were concentric about the stagnation point. Shortly after this, Dean departed for England for the year at the University of Manchester that constituted the Rockefeller Public Service Award with which he had been honored.

En route to England, Dean stopped off at the U.S. Museum of Natural History in Washington and while there told the Museum's curator, Dr. E. P. Henderson, about the wave patterns he had observed on the glycerin-glass models. Henderson immediately recognized the likeness between the wave pattern Dean described and the wave pattern on certain buttonlike pellets of black glass which, over several centuries, had been picked up at various places, notably Australia, on the surface of the earth. Even though the tektites, as the pellets were called, had been observed for hundreds of years, their origin was still most uncertain and the subject of much speculation in scientific circles. The Australian aborigines pointed to the sky when asked where the pellets came from. The Museum had a collection of meteorites which Dean examined with interest, and Henderson mentioned a fine collection of tektites in the British Museum in London. Dean's interest was vastly aroused. Although he did not recognize it at the time, these events had brought him to a major turning point in his scientific career. It was for the purpose of learning the nature and origin of tektites that Chapman at this point set forth on a scientific sleuthing task that would occupy his full attention for years. The hunt was an exciting exercise in pure research.

During his year at Manchester, Dean took the opportunity to study tektite collections in the museums of Europe, and a couple of years later he and Howard Larson, his colleague at Ames, went around the world visiting tektite collectors, obtaining specimens, and making measurements and molds of specimens in existing collections. The tektites found in different parts of the world were not all of the same shape, but those found in Australia were commonly of a small (½-inch diameter) button shape and some of these, despite millenniums of weathering and erosion on the earth's surface, still revealed annular, or ring, waves similar to those which had appeared on the glycerin-glass models.

An important part of Chapman's detective work on tektites was performed with the arc-jet facilities of the Ames Research Center. Earlier tektite studies, of which there had been many, had been made by chemists, geologists, naturalists, geochemists, petrologists, mineralogists, and physicists —but none by aerodynamicists and none by scientists equipped with the special knowledge of aerodynamic heating and ablation that only recently had been developed at Ames. To Dean it was fairly obvious that one face of the button tektites had been melted by aerodynamic heating and the viscous liquid surface thus formed had been swept back, like the waves of the sea, by aerodynamic forces. Indeed, in an arc-jet tunnel, using actual tektite material, he was able to produce a tektite button, complete with ring waves, that was almost identical with the better preserved of the natural specimens found in Australia. Natural tektites, cut in half, revealed flow lines in the surface material from which flight speed could be deduced; and it also became clear that, for the most part, the buttons had originally been spheres, a shape acquired following a previous melting.

Quite early, Chapman began to suspect an extraterrestrial origin for tektites and later, by systematically eliminating each alternate posssibility, he concluded that the most likely origin was the moon. Tektites were composed, he believed, of material splashed from the moon's surface many thousands of years ago by one or more huge meteors. The material splashed

Above: *Tektite on top specimen made in Ames arc-jet facility; bottom well-preserved natural specimen.* Below: *A cross section of a natural tektite specimen.*

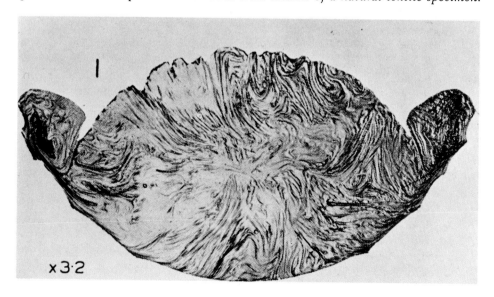

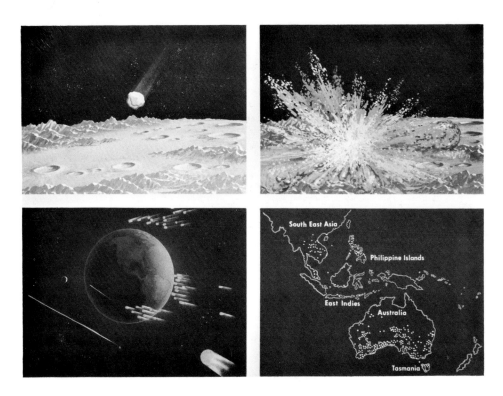

Postulated lunar origin of tektites.

up in such an impact would be molten, and the hotter and faster-moving portions would tend to break up into spherical drops. Some drops would escape from the moon, harden in the cold of outer space, and be drawn into orbit around the sun. Others, ejected from the moon with just the right speed and angle, would be captured by the earth's gravitational field and land on the surface of the earth. On entry into the earth's atmosphere, their front face would melt and flow back, thus forming the shape and surface waves of the Australian button tektite. The buttons, flattened-face forward, would be statically stable and the pseudostability, provided by increasing air density, would damp out oscillations during the ablation (heating) period.

Dean Chapman and Howard Larson prepared a number of scientific papers on tektites during this period, one of which was the fascinating document (ref. C–26) entitled "On the Lunar Origin of Tektites," which in 1963 was published in the *Journal of Geophysical Research*.

A few of the scientists who had earlier studied tektites were in agreement with Dean concerning the origin of these geological curiosities. More of them, however, including one Nobel Laureate, were strongly opposed to Chapman's theory. Among the prevalent ideas regarding the source of tek-

384

tites were the ones that they had been produced by lightning or volcanoes, had come from comets, or had been splashed over Australia by a huge meteor which long ago had impacted in Antarctica. Indeed the years of speculation on the subject had allowed time for many experts to go out on limbs from which retreat was embarrassingly difficult.

Some of the more serious objections to Chapman's theory were based on preconceived opinions or, in Dean's words, "intuitive expectations" regarding the origin, structure, and materials of the moon. In these cases, the sweeping approach of the cosmologist was at odds with the ability of a research specialist to wring the truth out of tiny scraps of physical evidence.

The opinions of world-famous scientists in the objecting group were not to be taken lightly: but neither was the carefully studied opinion of Dean Chapman. Dean had the temerity to disagree with the "experts" and proceeded with penetrating analytic power to disassemble their arguments one by one. As 1962 ended, the matter was far from settled; but the Ames staff, at least, was backing Dean Chapman.

SPACE PHYSICS

Space research after 1958 was notably augmented by direct on-the-spot observations made by instruments sent aloft in spacecraft. The simulation of spatial phenomena in earthbound laboratories was difficult, if not impossible, and would remain so at least until much more had been learned about the phenomena from direct observation. This technique was a frightfully expensive one, it was appreciated, and the greatest care had to be exercised in planning the experiments, designing the instruments, and, of course, in recovering and analyzing the data. All these activities were the assigned function of the new Space Sciences Division, headed by Dr. Charles P. Sonett, at the Ames Research Center. The first member of the Ames staff to transfer to the new division was John Wolfe, who later became chief of the Electrodynamics Branch. However, one of the first units of the division to commence operations, late in 1962, was the Theoretical Studies Branch under John Spreiter.

Spreiter and Wolfe had, in fact, been working in the space-science field well before the division was formed. In the course of this work both had developed a considerable interest in the interaction between the earth's magnetic field and the continuous flow of charged particles (nuclei of hydrogen and helium atoms and electrons) emanating from the sun. It had been suggested that, at a distance of about 10 earth radii, the geomagnetic field formed a blunt-nosed, egg-shaped boundary that fended off the oncoming particles. The limited experimental evidence then available revealed no sign of a boundary at 10 earth radii but did show a termination of the geomagnetic field at about 14 earth radii. A question thus remained concerning

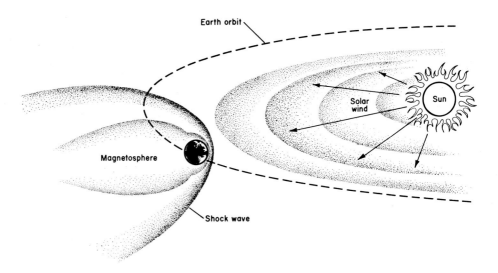

Interaction of solar wind with Earth's magnetic field.

the location and nature of the boundary that defined the limits of the magnetic field, or magnetosphere.

John Spreiter and Ben Briggs decided that this problem was a good one on which to exercise their analytical abilities. Their first studies of the subject are contained in the paper, "Theoretical Determination of the Form of the Boundary of the Solar Corpuscular Stream Produced by Interaction with the Magnetic Dipole Field of the Earth," by John R. Spreiter and Benjamin R. Briggs, published in the January 1962 issue of the *Journal of Geophysical Research* (henceforth, for convenience, to be designated *JGR*).

The theoretical study by Spreiter and Briggs also indicated a boundary at from 8 to 10 earth radii. Efforts were made in scientific circles to explain the discrepancy between theory and space measurements. The existence of a weak interplanetary magnetic field working perhaps at cross purposes to the geomagnetic field was postulated. Theoretical studies of this possibility suggested that a tenuous collision-free shock wave would form at some distance ahead of the geomagnetic boundary, and between the shock wave and the boundary the magnetic field would be irregular. The situation would thus be similar to the blunt-body flow patterns encountered in conventional aerodynamics except that the flow would be extremely tenuous. The interplanetary-field idea was investigated theoretically by a number of people including John Spreiter and William Prichard Jones, whose paper (ref. C–27), "On the Effect of a Weak Interplanetary Magnetic Field on the Interaction Between the Solar Wind and the Geomagnetic Field," was published in the June 1963 issue of the *JGR*.

While Spreiter and his colleagues were carrying on their initial theoretical attack on the space flow-field problem, Michel Bader of the Physics Branch was also investigating the problem through the Center's first space experiment, carried out in 1961. With the help of T. B. Fryer of the Instrument Research Division and F. C. Witteborn of the Physics Branch, Bader developed an instrument for measuring solar-particle flux. The instrument was carried aloft as one of the experiments in the *Explorer XII* satellite, which was launched on August 16 of that year. The data obtained with the instruments aboard *Explorer XII* revealed no sharp boundary between the geomagnetic field and the "solar wind" but did suggest the existence of a broad interference zone between the two. This indication seemed reasonably compatible with the shock-wave concept. The results of Bader's experiment are contained in his paper, "Preliminary Explorer 12 Data on Protons below 20 KEV," which was published in the *JGR*, December 1962. After this work had been completed, the Space Sciences Division was formed and solar-wind experimentation was taken over by Charles Sonett and John Wolfe.

It might be mentioned that during this period, Bob Jones was dabbling in relativity theory. Typical of his work was the paper "Conformal Coordinates Associated with Uniformly Accelerated Motion," which in 1961 was published in the *American Journal of Physics*. Another fairly abstruse study, relating perhaps to space physics, was made by Vernon Rossow and published as TR R–161, "Theoretical and Experimental Study of the Interaction of Free-Surface Waves on Liquid Metals with Transverse Magnetic Fields (One Dimensional Unsteady Waves)."

5

::

Space Project Management

S PACE-RESEARCH undertakings were tremendously complex operations requiring the close cooperation of many diverse groups, each with its own interests and responsibilities in the project. Inasmuch as the task of coordinating these operations for a particular project was enormous, it is not surprising that a form of activity called "project management" was brought into use. Project management could only loosely be called research; and during the early days of NASA, important people in the management of NASA felt that project management was not a proper activity for Ames. Nevertheless, at both Headquarters and Ames there were many who felt differently and under the pressure of these individuals the Center moved into the project-management field. The movement was at first very gradual and slightly traumatic.

Ames' first space-project work, led by Harry Goett and Bob Crane, was a study of the possibility, or feasibility, of meeting the precision requirement (1/10 second of arc) of an attitude-stabilization system for the proposed Orbiting Astronomical Observatory, OAO. The study was later extended to the proposed Nimbus meteorological satellite, which also required a precise pointing system. These studies resulted in the preparation by Ames of specifications for the stabilization systems for both OAO and Nimbus.

While the OAO work was under way, Ames asked NASA Headquarters for permission to assume technical responsibility for the OAO project. The request must have been made with the strong urging of Goett and Crane for it was known that both DeFrance and Allen were opposed to the Center's undertaking project work; Robinson was neutral toward it, and Parsons was only mildly favorable. In any case, the Ames proposal was not well received in Washington. With the full concurrence of Dr. Dryden, Ira Abbott of Headquarters replied with a strong suggestion that Ames stick with research and leave project work alone.[1]

---

[1] Stated in a report prepared by Crane for presentation at Pioneer seminar at Ames on Nov. 24, 1965. Report describes early history of some of the Center's project-management activities.

One might have imagined the project-management matter to be settled by Abbott's instructions but by 1960 Alfred Eggers, who had recently been made chief of a new Vehicle Environment Division, had become very much interested in the research possibilities of a solar probe. At the same time, Charles Hall, his assistant division chief, was promoting the solar probe as a project to be managed by Ames. In June 1960 Eggers formed a committee of Ames research men to consider and make proposals on the solar-probe project; and late in 1961, backed by the committee's findings, Hall on two occasions discussed the project with Headquarters groups. Headquarters thought the project too ambitious and, according to Crane, recommended as an alternative the development of a small, cheap interplanetary probe. A few years later the adjectives used in this connection seemed a little naive.

The Space Technology Laboratories, having heard of Ames' interest in a small interplanetary probe, submitted a proposal for such a device. Ames considered the proposal and early in 1962, with the concurrence of Headquarters, awarded STL a 3-month study contract on the probe. In June 1962, armed with material obtained from the STL study, an Ames group headed by Smith DeFrance and John Parsons headed for Washington to sell the project to Headquarters. The attitude of Ames management toward such work had obviously changed considerably—whether from internal or external pressure, it was not clear. In any case, DeFrance and Parsons requested permission to undertake the management of the interplanetary-probe project. Approval was not immediately forthcoming but was granted, in November, with the proviso that the Ames manpower outlay for the project be limited to 25 or 30 people. The first name chosen for the project was PIQSY (Pioneer International Quiet Sun Year), but this was soon reduced to "Pioneer."

In 1961 Ames engineers had become interested in still another project, this one having to do with the effect of the environment of space on living animals. The interest arose out of a study, made by Ames at the request of Headquarters, on the feasibility of sending primates (monkeys) aloft for periods of 14 days in leftover Project Mercury capsules. At this time, it should be noted, Dr. Richard Young had but recently arrived at Ames to conduct certain biological studies in preparation for the launching of Project Bios. Bios was an early NASA space biological experiment the launching of which, as it later developed, was unsuccessful. Although NASA had in November 1961 included a monkey named Enos in its second Mercury orbital flight (MA–5), the United States was substantially behind Russia in space biological research, at least as far as orbital-flight operations were concerned. There was thus, at this time, an obvious need for the United States to expand its efforts in this field.

Carl Bioletti had assembled a group of 10 or 12 people at Ames to make the monkey-flight study that Headquarters had requested. The results were submitted to Headquarters early in 1962, at which time an intense argument broke out between the Air Force and NASA as to whether NASA should now be allowed to enter the human-factors or life-sciences area of aerospace research which heretofore the military services had so thoroughly dominated. This argument, in which Bob Crane was involved for several months, was finally resolved in a favorable way for NASA, and NASA then proceeded to establish its Life Sciences Directorate at Ames.

By the time the jurisdictional argument was settled, NASA had received numerous proposals for space biological experiments from universities and other research agencies. Bioletti's group was asked to review these proposals and to determine the feasibility of incorporating them in a space-flight program designed specifically for biological research. In carrying out this mission, Carl and some of his group visited all of the 30-odd people, or agencies, who had made the proposals to see exactly what was required. He found that the most of the proposals involved small test specimens or short test periods and were incompatible with the 14-day monkey test. If the proposed additional tests were to be carried out, it appeared that a second satellite-booster system, selected especially for these tests, would be required. A search for the system best adapted to the new requirements was undertaken in the fall of 1962.

In October 1962, Ames was officially assigned responsibility for Project Biosatellite.[2] This project encompassed the first biological research work which Bioletti's group then had under consideration. With the establishment of Project Biosatellite and Project Pioneer in the fall of 1962, the Center was well launched in a project-management activity.

Even before the establishment of Project Biosatellite, Ames had become involved in flight biological research. The Center in 1961–1962 had assumed payload responsibility for certain flight tests aimed largely at determining the effect of cosmic rays on the brains of animals. The animals in these tests were monkeys, hamsters, and beetles that were carried in balloons to altitudes of up to 25 miles. Four launchings were made, the first in July 1962.

---

[2] As stated in letter from NASA Headquarters to Ames Research Center, attention Dr. Smith J. DeFrance, Oct. 26, 1962. Letter signed by Edgar M. Cortright for Homer E. Newell, Director, Office of Space Sciences.

1963–1965

6

The Environment

IN 1963 space exploration was a game for giants and the United States and Soviet Russia dominated the scene. Each had performed feats of astonishing scientific and technical virtuosity in the new field, but the exploits of the United States had been accomplished much more openly than those of Russia and the quantitative results were more voluminous and widely distributed. The Soviet Union in its space research had operated largely alone and secretively, whereas the United States in fostering space research had sought the collaboration of other countries—even Russia—and soon had cooperative space programs with as many as 50 countries.

NASA, commonly referred to as the Space Administration, had become known the world over. Its operations, which in 1961 appeared to be leveling out at an annual budget of about $1200 million, received a tremendous upward impulse from the Russians' first manned orbital flight in April 1961 and from the simultaneous declaration of national intent, by President Kennedy, to land a man on the moon and return him safely to earth before 1970. Under the stimuli of the Russian feat and the Kennedy declaration, NASA's budget in 1964 and 1965 shot up to over $5 billion, and its staff, which in mid-1961 had been 18,000 rapidly grew to 30,000 in mid-1963 and to 34,000 in 1965. At this time, in 1965, the Space Administration appeared to have reached a new plateau of activity and expenditure above which President Johnson and the Congress were reluctant to have it go. From its very beginning, NASA had been in a continuous and extremely rapid state of growth. Truly efficient operation under these conditions was too much to ask for; all that could be expected, and what was actually realized, was a good degree of effectiveness achieved through the blunt instrument of dollars.

The Kennedy impulse gave high priority to the manned-lunar-landing effort and by 1964 it was absorbing something like 65 percent of NASA's total annual appropriations. Many scientists felt that the priority assigned to the lunar-landing program was too high—that the program was in the nature of a stunt and would not yield information in proportion to the money spent. Indeed, not a few scientists, and many laymen, suggested that the space program as a whole was overblown and that the greater part of the money devoted to it could be spent with much more benefit to man on research in such fields as biology, medicine, earth sciences, or sociology. The cited fields of research, however, had never possessed the peculiar deep-seated appeal [1] required to command financial backing in the amounts their proponents desired or in the amounts they undoubtedly deserved. Until such time, if ever, as a more rational distribution of Federal research funds might be arranged, some comfort could be taken from the fact that the space program was so broad in scope that it carried many of the other fields along with it. And probably true was the often-heard remark that, if space research were wiped out, the other fields of research would surely lose by it— not gain. This line of reasoning, however, had limited appeal for workers in the more traditional fields of scientific research who looked with a jealous eye on NASA's $5 billion annual appropriation and who considered the offer of a ride on the coattails of space research a rather poor solution to their problems. Better, they felt, that the widely flying coattails should be trimmed.

Ames by 1963 was caught up in the growing swirl of organizational and operational turbulence centered in NASA Headquarters. Long since, the Center had lost the warmth and intimacy of its early NACA days and now, as a part of a very large organization, it was subjected to the many trying rules and regulations which organizations of such size must establish to survive. Moreover, NASA Headquarters had gone through repeated reorganizations, all having the unsettling effects on the field centers. Originally the field centers reported to specific program offices in Headquarters—the old NACA centers, to the Office of Advanced Research Programs manned by a familiar group of former NACA people.[2] In November 1961, however, the old arrangement was abandoned and all field centers, while continuing to receive technical guidance from the program offices, were required to report administratively to the Associate Administrator. Ames thus lost a familiar and useful intermediary in Washington and its relations with Headquarters became more complicated. The new arrangement lasted until November 1963 when, in a major reorganization, the field centers were reassigned to Headquarters technical divisions, or offices.

Following the reorganization of 1963, the research activities of NASA were carried out under the general direction of three program offices in Headquarters: the Office of Advanced Research and Technology (OART), which concerned itself largely with the operation of the old NACA labora-

---

[1] Space exploration is aptly described by Wernher von Braun as having sex appeal; but its appeal, fundamental and inexplicable though it may be, is surely less durable than that of sex. Clearly, also, the appeal applies far more to space exploration by man than to space exploration with instruments, and more to either than to laboratory space research.

[2] See ch. 1.

tories; the Office of Space Science and Applications (OSSA) and the Office of Manned Space Flight (OMSF), which were largely concerned with space-flight operations. DeFrance and the directors of the other old NACA laboratories reported to OART, but important segments of Ames activities were managed and funded by OSSA and considerable work was done for OMSF and the various research centers. The lines of management and control were thus somewhat tangled. Since the days of NACA, the Headquarters staff had mushroomed by over 1000 percent [3] and numerous individuals of uncertain position and vaguely defined authority were now issuing instructions to Ames, some even bypassing the Director and going directly to the Center employee. To Smitty DeFrance, whose whole management philosophy was built on running a tight, efficient operation, these developments were scarcely appealing.

Ames had long been a Center devoted exclusively to research in the physical sciences. The life scientists represented a distinctly foreign element at Ames. Their disciplines, their mode of operation, and their very language were sharply different from those of the Ames physical scientists and engineers. These factors had certainly, in some degree, been evaluated by the Ames management when it made its decision to seek to acquire the life-sciences activity. Indeed it had been expected that certain interdisciplinary benefits would spring from the arrangement. Both, at least, were intramural, laboratory-type activities sharing the normal aversion of their kind to anything called "operations." The integration problem was in no way insuperable and, in a spirit of cooperation, both sides made sincere efforts to adjust to each other. Nevertheless, complete compatibility between the Ames body and the new graft seemed unachievable and the bonds of attachment between the two were rather slow in developing.

while glamorous space operations increasingly dominated NASA's activities, Ames, perhaps better than any of the old NACA laboratories, resisted pressures to indulge in such operations and maintained its position as a research laboratory. But in 1963 pressures from both outside (Headquarters) and inside became too great to resist. The Center thus moved into the field of project management even though, in the minds of some, the quality of the Center's product must thereby be diluted. Those in the activity, however, regarded it merely as another form of research.

During this period it also became clear that NASA's policy of doing more of its work by contracting and less by in-house effort was having an impact on Ames. NACA had always run an in-house operation, but NASA Headquarters, by assigning more work while withholding personnel complement, was forcing Ames into an ever-growing contracting business. The danger of becoming mere contract monitors rather than research men was of

---

[3] Compared with 400 percent for the NASA staff in the field.

San Francisco Bay region circa 1964. Buildings reveal population density.

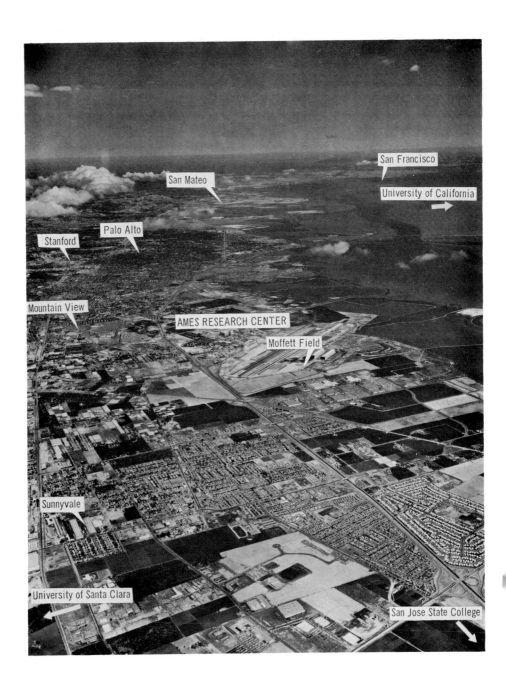

concern to most, but not all, members of the Ames staff. Some were sure that the practice degraded the staff and there were individuals who declared that, if Ames let a contract for research work they were presently doing, they would quit NASA and go to work for the contractor.

The environment to which Ames was exposed during this period was one which undoubtedly produced considerable internal strain. Moreover, the role of the Center, once well understood and supported by every member of the Ames staff, had now become so ramified and diffuse as to tax the comprehension of the management itself. Under these circumstances it was natural that Ames research men should become increasingly preoccupied with personal or group achievement in specific fields of endeavor and should show less concern for the performance and vaguely defined goals of the Center as a whole. Largely missing in the Center's staff therefore was that element of pride and esprit de corps which formerly had arisen from the feeling of being, collectively, a self-reliant and vital organ of a clearly directed enterprise.

The internal strain to which the Ames organization was now being subjected was accompanied by irritations of more common origin—the traffic and congestion arising from a rapid growth of population in the San Francisco Bay area. The pleasant fruit orchards with which Moffett Field had once been largely surrounded had given way to close-packed housing developments. Travel on the local highways and byways, once a happy experience, had become an exasperating fight with traffic. The density of population in the area had indeed provided considerable justification for the earlier transferral of the Center's airplane flight testing to the more remote and secure environment of the NASA Flight Research Center at Edwards, California.

7

··

People and Events

EARLY ORGANIZATIONAL CHANGES

IN January 1963 a major revision of the Ames organization was announced. Necessitated by changing missions and requirements, it
established two new management offices, or directorates, each of which
like the previous four was headed by an Assistant Director of the Center.
One of the new directorates, headed by Robert Crane with the title of Assistant Director for Development, was obviously needed to deal with the
project-management responsibility which the Center had recently assumed.
The second was headed by an Assistant Director for Research & Development Analysis and Planning in the person of Alfred Eggers. It was formed
specifically to provide a channel for Al to exercise his talents and interests
which for the past few years had focused on mission studies. The move
was well justified by the leadership and personal productivity which Eggers
had demonstrated.

These major changes in January 1963, together with minor changes
that took place later in the year, are reflected in the chart which shows the
Ames organization as it existed on January 1, 1964. The Life Sciences Directorate was at this time headed by Dr. Harold P. Klein, who formerly had
been chief of the Exobiology Division. An expert in the field of microbiol-
ogy, he had for 7 years prior to his arrival at Ames been professor of biology
and subsequently chairman of the biology department at Brandeis University in Massachusetts. Dr. G. Dale Smith, who had once been Deputy Assistant Director of Life Sciences, had become Manager of Experiment and Life
Support Systems in Project Biosatellite. Dr. Richard S. Young, the first life-
sciences man to appear for duty at Ames, was at this time Acting Chief, and
in 1965 became Chief of the Exobiology Division. Also Steve Belsley was
now Acting Chief, and was soon to become Chief, of the Biotechnology Division. The Biotechnology post assumed by Belsley had been vacated by Dr.
Siegfried Gerathewohl when, late in 1963, Dr. Gerathewohl accepted an assignment at Headquarters. It will also be noted in the chart that the third

Organization chart of Ames Research Center, January 1964.

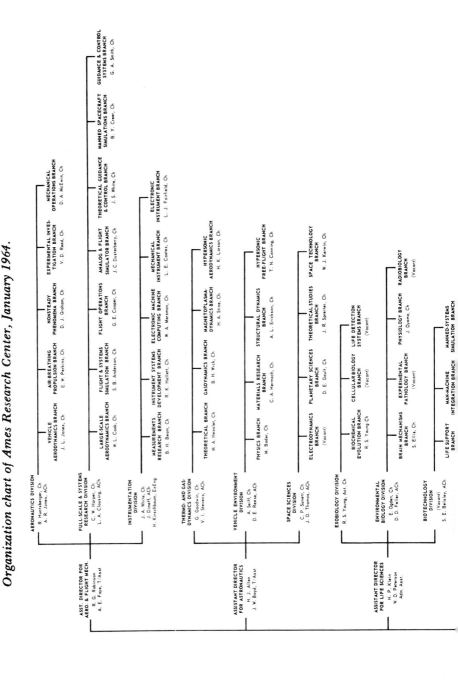

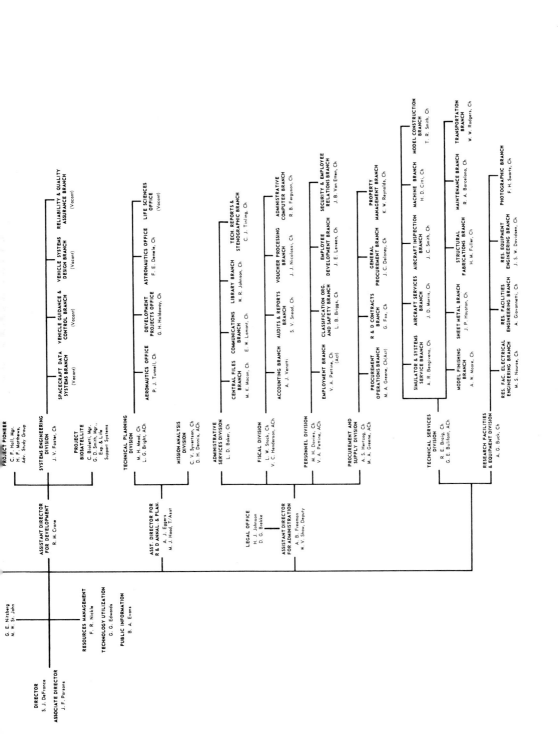

DIRECTOR
S. J. DeFrance

ASSOCIATE DIRECTOR
J. F. Parsons

G. E. Nittberg
M. W. St. John

RESOURCES MANAGEMENT
F. R. Nickle

TECHNOLOGY UTILIZATION
G. G. Edwards

PUBLIC INFORMATION
B. A. Evans

PROJECT PIONEER
C. F. Hall, Mgr.
H. F. Matthews,
Adv. Study Group

SYSTEMS ENGINEERING DIVISION
J. V. Foster, Ch

PROJECT BIOSATELLITE
C. Bioletti, Mgr.
G. D. Smith, Mgr.
Exp. & Life
Support Systems

SPACECRAFT DATA SYSTEMS BRANCH
(Vacant)

VEHICLE GUIDANCE & CONTROL BRANCH
(Vacant)

VEHICLE SYSTEMS DESIGN BRANCH
(Vacant)

RELIABILITY & QUALITY ASSURANCE BRANCH
(Vacant)

ASSISTANT DIRECTOR FOR DEVELOPMENT
R. M. Crane

TECHNICAL PLANNING DIVISION
M. H. Mead, Ch
L. G. Bright, ACh

MISSION ANALYSIS DIVISION
C. V. Syvertson, Ch
D. H. Dennis, ACh

AERONAUTICS OFFICE
P. J. Tunnell, Ch

DEVELOPMENT PROJECTS OFFICE
G. H. Holloway, Ch

ASTRONAUTICS OFFICE
F. E. Dennis, Ch

LIFE SCIENCES OFFICE
(Vacant)

ASST. DIRECTOR FOR R & D ANNAL. & PLAN.
A. J. Eggers
M. J. Hood, T/Asst

ADMINISTRATIVE SERVICES DIVISION
L. D. Baker, Ch

CENTRAL FILES BRANCH
M. K. Macon, Ch

COMMUNICATIONS BRANCH
E. W. Lamont, Ch

LIBRARY BRANCH
W. R. Johnson, Ch

TECH. REPORTS & STENOGRAPHIC BRANCH
C. J. Timling, Ch

FISCAL DIVISION
L. W. Stock, Ch
V. C. Henderson, ACh

ACCOUNTING BRANCH
A. J. Venoti

AUDITS & REPORTS BRANCH
S. V. Snead, Ch

VOUCHER PROCESSING BRANCH
J. J. Nicolosi, Ch

ADMINISTRATIVE COMPUTER BRANCH
R. B. Ferguson, Ch

LEGAL OFFICE
H. J. Johnson
D. G. Brekke

PERSONNEL DIVISION
M. H. Davies, Ch
V. A. Pettine, ACh

EMPLOYMENT BRANCH
V. A. Pettine, Ch
(Act)

CLASSIFICATION ORG. AND SAFETY BRANCH
L. B. Briggs, Ch

EMPLOYEE DEVELOPMENT BRANCH
J. E. Leveen, Ch

SECURITY & EMPLOYEE RELATIONS BRANCH
J. B. Van Etten, Ch

ASSISTANT DIRECTOR FOR ADMINISTRATION
A. B. Freeman
W. V. Shaw, Deputy

PROCUREMENT AND SUPPLY DIVISION
A. S. Hertzog, Ch
M. A. Greene, ACh

PROCUREMENT OPERATIONS BRANCH
M. A. Greene, Ch (Act)

R & D CONTRACTS BRANCH
G. Fox, Ch

GENERAL PROCUREMENT BRANCH
J. C. Deloney, Ch

PROPERTY MANAGEMENT BRANCH
K. W. Reynolds, Ch

TECHNICAL SERVICES DIVISION
R. E. Braig, Ch
G. E. Builtani, ACh

SIMULATOR & SYSTEMS SERVICE BRANCH
A. R. Bengivena, Ch

AIRCRAFT SERVICES BRANCH
J. D. Morris, Ch

AIRCRAFT INSPECTION BRANCH
J. C. Smith, Ch

MACHINE BRANCH
H. D. Cirri, Ch

MODEL CONSTRUCTION BRANCH
T. R. Smith, Ch

TRANSPORTATION BRANCH
W. W. Rodgers, Ch

MODEL FINISHING BRANCH
A. W. Moore, Ch

SHEET METAL BRANCH
J. P. Houston, Ch

STRUCTURAL FABRICATIONS BRANCH
H. M. Fuller, Ch

MAINTENANCE BRANCH
R. A. Barcelona, Ch

RESEARCH FACILITIES & EQUIPMENT DIVISION
A. G. Buck, Ch

RES. FAC. ELECTRICAL ENGINEERING BRANCH
M. S. Nourse, Ch

RES. FACILITIES ENGINEERING BRANCH
A. Giovannetti, Ch

RES. EQUIPMENT ENGINEERING BRANCH
J. S. W. Davidsen, Ch

PHOTOGRAPHIC BRANCH
F. H. Swartz, Ch

*Dr. Harold P. Klein, member of
Life Sciences staff.*

life-sciences division—the Environmental Biology Division—was at this time headed by Dr. Eric Ogden with Dr. David D. Feller serving as Assistant Chief. The staff of the Life Sciences Directorate had been carefully selected and all the key men were of the highest repute, known nationally, if not internationally, for their work.

The work of the Life Sciences Directorate had no direct connection with Project Biosatellite and there was surprisingly little interchange between the two activities. This situation was said to be a source of regret to both the life-sciences and the project-management people. It could also be said that the three life-sciences divisions were quite individualistic and their work was only tenuously related. Additionally, the modes of operation of each of the three divisions, especially regarding contracting, were considerably different as were also their means of financial support. The Exobiology Division was funded by OSSA [1] in Headquarters, whereas the other two divisions were funded, as was most of the remainder of Ames, by OART. A degree of financial inflexibility thus arose from the inability of the Life Sciences Directorate to transfer funds freely between its several divisions. Moreover, the situation left room for one or another of the divisions to feel that it had been slighted with respect to financial support. A divisive influence was thus unfortunately present.

One of the outstanding features of the organizational change in January 1963 related to the organization of the research divisions; they were now organized around disciplines rather than around specific research facilities. This change, which actually had begun a few years earlier, represented a complete reversal of the old NACA practice of organizing a research group around each major facility. While there was something to be said for each

---

[1] The Headquarters Life Sciences Programs Office, to which all three Ames life-sciences divisions might otherwise have been responsible, was eliminated in 1961 and its functions were split up between the remaining Headquarters program offices.

method, the shortage of personnel and the trend of research had made organization according to discipline seem desirable.

Inasmuch as many of the wind tunnels were now used much more for development work than for fundamental research, it was feasible to assign these facilities to a single group which would operate them as a service to development or research groups located either within or outside of the Center. Also, since the Unitary Plan tunnels had been built to serve a similar function, they too were included in the facility group just mentioned and the name "Unitary Plan" was dropped. Thus within the Aeronautics Division there was established, under the leadership of Loren Bright (later assigned to Verlin Reed), an Experimental Investigations Branch to manage and operate a group of wind tunnels which included the 8- by 7-foot, the 9- by 7-foot, the 11-foot, and the 14-foot, the 12-foot, the 6- by 6-foot, and the 2- by 2-foot tunnels. Later the 1- by 3-foot tunnel, which had established an enviable record in the field of research, was added to the list.

TRANSFERS AND ORGANIZATIONAL REPERCUSSIONS

In June 1964 Al Eggers was transferred to Washington to become Deputy Associate Administrator in OART. His departure represented a serious loss to Ames and left the directorate created especially for him without a permanent head. In his place, Clarence Syvertson became Acting Assistant Director while continuing his permanent assignment as Chief of the Mission Analysis Division. David Dennis retained his position as Assistant Chief of the Division.

The mission-analysis work at Ames had been Al Eggers' primary inter-

David H. Dennis.

est and, when he went to Washington, he apparently sought to persuade Ray Bisplinghoff, his immediate superior, that OART should have its own mission-analysis group and that the proposed group might best be located at one of the OART-controlled Centers, specifically Ames. As usual, Eggers' arguments were convincing; in January 1965 a Headquarters (OART) Mission Analysis Division was established at Ames with the staff of the Ames Mission Analysis Division becoming, on a tour-of-duty basis, the nucleus of the OART Division and with Clarence Syvertson becoming its Chief. It was expected that the staff nucleus thus acquired would be augmented by men temporarily assigned by other OART-controlled Centers such as Langley, Lewis, and the Flight Research Center at Edwards; but, as time went on, the realization of this expectation seemed increasingly remote. Ames, in any case, was to furnish administrative support for the OART division, but management responsibility was to rest with OART.

The function of the original Ames Mission Analysis Division had been to make studies to determine research areas in which Ames could most effectively use its time and money. The function of the OART division would be essentially the same, except that the studies would be extended to encompass the broader interests of OART. The Division was also given responsibility for coordinating the OART advanced-study program. The planned complement of the Division for 1965 was about 50, but here again hopes were not realized.

The formation of the OART Division at Ames left in a rather fractured state the Directorate for Research and Development, Analysis and Planning that had been created for Eggers. Thus as 1965 ended, plans were in hand for eliminating the Directorate, leaving only the OART Mission Analysis Division headed by Syvertson. The planning function which had been carried out by Eggers' directorate was at the beginning of 1966 to be transferred to a new Programs and Resources Office under Merrill Mead who had but recently returned from a tour of duty in Washington. Mead's new office was also to absorb the functions of Ferril Nickle, the Resources Management Officer, who retired at the end of 1965. Nickle and Parsons, it may be recalled, were the first Ames employees and also the first to arrive at the Moffett Field site. Nickle had made important contributions to the early construction program at Ames and subsequently, as Budget Officer and later as Resources Management Officer, had served with great ability. Reporting to the Office of the Director, Nickle each year led the "battle of the budget," a rather thankless task but one of vital consequence to the Center.

In September 1964, three months after Eggers departed, Bill Harper was transferred to Headquarters to become Chief of the Aeronautics Division in OART. Here again the loss to Ames was keenly felt. Harper was badly needed at the Center at this time and fortunately it appeared that his assignment to Washington might be temporary. Accordingly, Larry Clous-

From left to right: *George H. Holdaway, Frederick A. Demele, Dr. Seymour N. Stein, and Phillips J. Tunnell, members of Technical Planning Division staff.*

ing was made Acting Chief of the Full Scale and Systems Research Division with Woodrow Cook and Norman Johnson as Assistant Chiefs.

OTHER LATE DEVELOPMENTS

Before the end of 1965 there was one more major change in the Ames organization, but this will be described at a later time. There were also a few smaller but individually important developments during this period. One was the retirement in March 1965 of Carlton Bioletti, who for 33 years had served in NACA and NASA. The position he vacated as Chief of Project Biosatellite was filled by Charles Wilson. To be happily reported was the return to Ames in July 1965 of the exceptionally able Morris Rubesin, who had satisfied his earlier craving to be an entrepreneur. Rubesin was shortly appointed Chief of the Physics Branch, filling a position earlier relinquished by Michel Bader, whose interests had turned to airborne astrophysical research. Another organizational change, made in September 1965, was the appointment of Dr. John Billingham as Assistant Chief of the Biotechnology Division. Also to be mentioned was the honor earned by John

William R. Johnson (left) *and Carol J. Tinling and Harry J. DeVoto* (right).

Boyd, technical assistant to the Assistant Director for Astronautics, who in 1965 was named to receive the 1965–1966 Stanford-Sloan Executive Fellowship. A similar award, the 1962–1963 MIT-Sloan Executive Fellowship, had earlier been won by Merrill Mead, Chief of the Ames Technical Planning Division.

Flight-simulator work was growing apace and the facilities had become so complex and extensive that it was deemed desirable to establish a separate division, in Russ Robinson's directorate, to manage, further develop, and operate these facilities as a service to the several research groups that had need for them. The new organizational unit, known as the Simulation Sciences Division, was founded in September 1965 with George Rathert as Chief and John Dusterberry as Assistant Chief. The function of the new division was noticeably similar to that of the Experimental Investigations (wind tunnel) Branch earlier mentioned. It was not expected to carry on research, except that required for the improvement and fullest exploitation of flight simulators.

Also to be mentioned was the formation within the Administration Directorate of a Technical Information Division headed by William R. Johnson. Included in this Division were a Library Branch under John W. Pollock, a Graphics and Exhibits Branch under Harry J. DeVoto, Jr., and a Manuscript Branch under Carol Tinling.

The less happy events occurring in the 1963–1965 period included the deaths of Dr. Harald Smedal in the spring of 1963, of Ray Braig in October 1964, and of Ralph Huntsberger in June 1965. Dr. Smedal, extremely popular, was a man of the highest ability. Ray Braig, one of the charter members of the Ames staff, was very well liked and his performance had always been of the highest quality. His position was subsequently filled by Frank Lawrence.

Ralph Huntsberger was a competent performer whose work on the design, construction, and operation of the Unitary Plan tunnels was quite outstanding. In 1964, together with Bill Harper, Jay Christensen, and Earl Keener, Ralph won the NASA Group Achievement Award for contributions to the X–15 program. Lloyd Jones was selected in December 1965 to take over Ralph's position.

Another death affecting Ames was that of Dr. Hugh L. Dryden on December 2, 1965. Once Director of NACA, Dr. Dryden had since the beginning of NASA held the position of Deputy Administrator of the latter organization. Above all other men, he had given character to the huge, sprawling, tumultuous organization that NASA had become. The feeling for Dr. Dryden among his many acquaintances was one of deepest respect while among those who knew him best, it bordered on the reverential. In him a gentle, humane spirit had cloaked a driving intellectual force. President Johnson, in eulogy of Dr. Dryden, said:

> Hugh Dryden's death ended nearly 50 years of single-minded devotion and effort by one of the most distinguished civil servants this country has ever known. Beloved by all his associates and respected throughout the world, Dr. Dryden more than any other man led us into the age of jet aircraft and space exploration.

Manpower Shortage and Contracting

With regard to the supply of manpower, the Ames Research Center was being squeezed unmercifully. Through the first 3 years of NASA, the Ames staff had remained constant at the final NACA level of about 1475.[2] Then with the Kennedy impulse of 1961–1962, it rose quickly to a new plateau of about 2200.[3] The personnel growth was about 50 percent, but the responsibilities assigned to the Center increased by 100 percent or more. The squeeze was on manpower rather than on money and, although there was a national shortage of scientists and engineers at the time, its imposition on Ames appears to have represented deliberate Headquarters policy. Ames was being "encouraged" to carry on more of its work by contracting rather than in-house.

Ames management had resisted pressures encouraging the Center to undertake project management and space operations. Other NASA Centers, such as Lewis, had yielded more quickly to these pressures and during the Kennedy impulse had acquired the staff needed for such activities. By the time Ames was prepared to enter the game, the manpower allocations resulting from the Kennedy impulse had been completed and the lid on personnel recruitment had again been clamped down tightly. At Ames the pangs arising from manpower shortage were thus very acute and new activities in

---

[2] See app. A.
[3] *Ibid.*

the fields of space sciences, life sciences, and project management were especially hard hit. All possible means were used to relieve the situation but none except contracting was very effective.

Some improvement in the manpower picture at Ames was achieved by decommissioning certain low-productivity wind tunnels and by grouping others under a single operating branch. An important additional benefit came from the National Academy of Sciences postdoctoral fellowship program, which provided a number of very able research men who were not counted in the Ames personnel quota. Of somewhat less help was the annual faculty summer fellowship program under which 10 to 15 university faculty members would spend 10 weeks in the summer working, for mutual benefit, at the Ames Center. The latter program was jointly sponsored by NASA and the American Society for Engineering Education. Some indirect benefits were also achieved by improving the competence of existing staff through cooperative training arrangements with local colleges and universities. The Stanford-Ames program, begun many years earlier, was still in effect though operating at low ebb. In the past, such programs had enabled Ames employees to acquire skill in the new disciplines evolving in the general fields of aeronautical and space science. But while such "retreading" operations had been useful in the past, many of the newer disciplines were of such fundamental complexity as to place them beyond the reach of a retreaded wind-tunnel engineer. Recently graduated Ph. D.'s were needed.

In the solution of the Ames manpower bind, the remedies just cited were quite inadequate. Contracting, with all its disadvantages, was the only way out. Contracts were let for the maintenance of major mechanical auxiliaries, for computing services, for maintaining and operating some of the now-extensive electronic computing equipment and architectural and engineering services in connection with facilities design, for staff training and, in 1965, for wind-tunnel operation. As a result of needs expressed for the services of the 12-foot tunnel, which had been largely dormant since 1963, Ames, in March, let a contract for the operation of the tunnel to ARO, Inc., a subsidiary of Sverdrup & Parcel & Associates, Inc., of St. Louis. The work of the tunnel, as operated by ARO, was still coordinated by Verlin Reed's Experimental Investigations Branch. By the end of 1965 the arrangement with ARO had proved so successful that thought was being given to the letting of contracts for the operation of the 6- by 6-foot and the 14-foot tunnels.

In a similar move, NASA, in February 1965, completed arrangements with the U.S. Army whereby that agency was granted permission to use, for its own purposes, with its own staff and largely at its own expense, the Ames 7- by 10-foot tunnel No. 2. This tunnel had been idle for a number of years and required a considerable investment by the Army in its restoration and in the updating of auxiliary equipment. Not only were the Army's uses of the tunnel of interest to Ames but there were additional benefits from the

410

arrangement which accrued to the Center. These benefits arose from the fact that the Army agreed to provide not only the operating staff for the tunnel but also additional personnel to assist Ames in carrying out research and development projects of particular interest to the Army. To accomplish these purposes, the Army established a group of about 45 people at Ames in what was known as the Army Aeronautical Activity at Ames (AAA–A). The head of AAA–A was Colonel Cyril D. Stapleton, USA, while the technical director, a former Ames employee, was Paul Yaggy. The relationship between Ames and the Army proved very friendly and mutually profitable.

Such were the measures taken to deal with the manpower squeeze at the Ames Research Center; but they were not enough. Contracting, it was clear, must be extended to the design and construction of research instruments, to the planning and execution of research projects, and even to the analysis of the resulting data and the writing of research reports. In the life-sciences activity at Ames, a large part of the research was performed by agencies to whom NASA contracts or grants had been given. The contract research for the Exobiology Division amounted to only a few percent of the total; but that for the Environmental Biology Division represented about 70 percent of the total, and that of the Biotechnology Division also loomed rather large. The Space Sciences Division of the Astronautics Directorate likewise became involved in an extensive contracting operation, but its contracts were largely restricted to the procurement of services and to supporting research and development. The research experiments themselves were mostly conceived, and often carried out, by the Space Sciences staff. The project-management activity at Ames was largely a contract operation. Its funds for the most part were spent on contracts for booster hardware, spacecraft design, research planning, instrumentation, and analysis of data. In addition to the cases cited, almost all of the physical research divisions at the Center carried out certain research and development projects by means of contracting.[4]

In the matter of research contracting, the interests of the Center differed considerably from those of NASA as a whole. To NASA, the practice gave access to talent, facilities, and a sheer volume of technical manpower that could not feasibly be assembled within the confines of a Government laboratory. It was probably the only way the huge task confronting the agency could be accomplished. From the standpoint of the Center, whose interest lay mainly in basic research, such contracting was in many respects debilitating. It would, of course, inhibit the full development of the Center and would dilute the quality and reduce the morale of the staff. It would render more difficult the problem of acquiring and retaining research men of the highest quality and would be particularly harmful if it reduced the Center's best research men to mere contract monitors—assuming that they

[4] See app. A re costs of contracting.

would accept such a role. Moreover, if contracting were undertaken in areas of research in which the Center's staff members were acknowledged leaders, the results would surely be an inferior substitute for the product that might otherwise have been obtained. As with mercenary soldiery, there was in any case a question of the quality of "bought" research.

What was happening was fairly obvious. To handle its vast responsibilities, to achieve the necessary speed and volume of output, NASA was deliberately paying the associated penalty. The penalty was a deterioration at least of its research centers and probably also of the quality of its research product; and of course the cost of the product, good or bad, was shockingly high. The process was earlier referred to as the "shotgun" approach—effective but costly. These then were some of the influences operating at Ames during this period.

8

Facilities

SERVICE FACILITIES

THE rapid growth of personnel and activities at Ames during 1962–1963 produced severe strains on service facilities, some of which were already overburdened. A new cafeteria was built in 1963–1964, and construction of a large addition to the instrument research laboratory was undertaken in 1964 and completed in February 1965. The old cafeteria, under the auditorium, was converted to office space. At the same time the administrative responsibilities of the Center had grown as a result not only of the increase in personnel but also of the multiplicity of directives emanating from a mushrooming Headquarters organization, and in 1964 a large administrative management building was put under construction. This new structure, completed late in 1965 at a cost of $1,200,000, was located on Bush Circle and in design and location was almost the mirror image of the data reduction building. In the meantime an extension of the administration building annex was being made to house the OART Mission Analysis Division.

WIND TUNNELS AND WIND-TUNNEL TECHNIQUES

The 10- by 14-inch tunnel was disassembled in 1962–1963 and crated up for transplantation into the 3.5-foot-tunnel building. The transplantation was not completed, and throughout this period the tunnel remained crated with no prospect of reassembly.

In September 1963 the failure of a fan blade in the 14-foot tunnel compressor resulted in a decision to replace all 96 blades. Although contracting was the rule of the day, the replacement of the blades eventually turned out to be another job for Red Betts' blade-carving machine. At the end of 1965, however, the reblading task was still not completed and would not, it was expected, be finished before May 1966. Since its completion in 1955 at a cost of $11 million, the 14-foot tunnel had been used considerably; but now, with the long layup due to blade failure, one might be led to recall Carl

413

Bioletti's remark, "a damned waste of money," made in 1950 when construction of the tunnel was being considered. Carl, of course, had not foreseen Space Age situations in which some bit of essential design information obtained in the tunnel could readily mean the difference between success and failure of a space shot costing $50 million or more. Owing to the huge financial gamble of space exploration, supporting laboratory research facilities, at whatever cost, represented a prudent investment. In what it had revealed concerning hammerhead missiles alone, the 14-foot tunnel had easily paid for itself.

The 3.5-foot tunnel shared with the 14-foot the distinction of being one of the two most expensive tunnels ever built at Ames.[1] It had made important contributions in the field of spacecraft aerothermodynamics, yet it was rather new and still in the process of justifying itself. The realization of its considerable potential for testing large models at high speeds had been somewhat hindered by the rather unsatisfactory performance of its pebble-bed heater. A search for a more satisfactory material for the "pebbles" had been undertaken in a pilot heater located in a small addition to the 10- by 14-inch tunnel building. From such studies a cored brick made of yttria-stabilized zirconia seemed promising, but the cost and difficulty of rebricking the huge 3.5-foot pebble-bed heater were large and Ames management was reluctant to make the necessary investment of time and money without more assurance regarding the superiority of the new material.

Another modification of the 3.5-foot, however, seemed desirable. This modification, undertaken in 1963–1964 and completed in 1965, made it possible to operate the tunnel with gases (nitrogen, carbon dioxide, etc.) representing the atmospheres of certain other planets[2] in our solar system. The modification represented a practical substitute for a "hypersonic planetary gas test facility" (HPGTF) which in 1961 was in preliminary design and considered as a possible auxiliary for the new gas-dynamics facility. As a result of this substitution, the HPGTF was never completed.

At this time numerous facilities had been built for investigating reentry heating, but only the hypervelocity free-flight facilities lent themselves to studies of the purely aerodynamic factors of extreme speed, and in these severe restrictions were imposed by the requirements of small, simple models and short operating time. The idea thus arose at Ames of building a very fast, Mach 50, helium tunnel in which models of reasonable size could be tested for fairly long periods. Although preheating had not heretofore been used in helium tunnels, it was nevertheless necessary in the Mach 50 helium tunnel which, at a cost of $1.5 million, was built at Ames during 1965. The tunnel had just been completed as the year ended and not much was known about its operating characteristics except that it had so far attained a Mach

---

[1] Unitary cost more but constituted three tunnels.
[2] For example, Mars and Venus.

414

number of 45. Even while the Mach-50 helium tunnel was under construction, the interest of Ames engineers in helium tunnels continued to wane, and by the end of 1965 it was at fairly low ebb. The use of helium was accepted as being tricky and some felt it impractical except perhaps for checking out certain theoretical concepts. The monatomic character of the helium molecule, with all of its thermodynamic implications including the absence of chemical dissociation, was generally believed to limit the usefulness of helium for simulating the aerothermodynamic environment of high-speed reentry. Thus, while retaining a tantalizing potential for achieving high Mach numbers, the helium tunnel, at Ames, remained a concept of somewhat dubious overall practicality.

Here it should be said that the development of new research facilities is an integral part of any research effort and is thus subject to the same risks and gambles as the research itself. A perfect record of success in research-facility design carries with it the strong implication that the agency making the record has been guilty of conservatism quite unbefitting a research institution.

A problem regarded as inherent in wind-tunnel testing arose from the flow interference produced by the structure (sting) that supported the model. This problem was, of course, not present in facilities using gun-launched models and during this period the idea developed that it might also be avoided in conventional high-speed wind tunnels, especially since the techniques for making free-flight measurements were now highly developed. For example, in a vertical tunnel, with the airstream going upward, a model, originally supported, could be dropped and its weight might thus nearly balance the upward air force. The model would thus remain for some time, in free flight, in front of the viewing window. This scheme had been used in the Langley spin tunnels in the 1930's. Alternatively, in a horizontal tunnel, the model might at first be held just downstream of the test section and then, at the right time, propelled forward in front of the viewing window with just enough force to balance the air drag for a few seconds. Drag and stability could be determined, as in the case of a gun-launched model, by observing the motions of the model. At the same time information on pressures and temperatures could be obtained, Ames engineers found, by telemeter. The idea for the technique as applied to supersonic wind tunnels had come from Caltech; but at Ames it was developed to a state of practicality through tests in the 6- by 6-foot tunnel, in the 14-inch helium tunnel, and in a vertical arc-jet tunnel located in the fluid mechanics building. This ingenious development was carried on by a number of men including John McDevitt, Joseph Kemp, Ronald Hruby, and Lionel Levy and is reported in such papers as TN D–3319 (ref. C–28) by Hruby, McDevitt, Coon, Harrison, and Kemp, and TM X–1154 by Kemp. A paper on the subject by Levy,

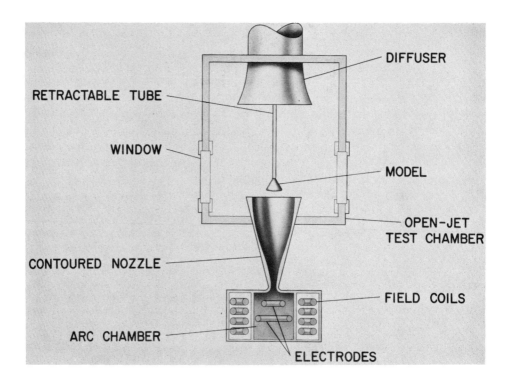

RETRACTABLE TUBE

WINDOW

CONTOURED NOZZLE

ARC CHAMBER

DIFFUSER

MODEL

OPEN-JET TEST CHAMBER

FIELD COILS

ELECTRODES

Arc-heated free-flight wind tunnel.

McDevitt, and Fletcher was also presented at an AGARD meeting in Brussels in September 1964.

GUNS, RANGES, AND ARC TUNNELS

Gun development as a science in itself had advanced continuously and at Ames, perhaps, had reached a higher level of refinement than anywhere else in the world. Most of the guns at Ames were now of the deformable-piston type. Their speed had been raised to an impressive 37,000 feet per second; this peak speed, a world's record, was obtained in 1965 with a gun used in the impact range.[3] Notably, it was also earth-escape speed and thus the Ames gun was theoretically capable of firing a bullet so fast that it would leave the earth forever.

Further increases in the speed of guns would not come easily. Nevertheless, despite anticipated design difficulties, there was still hope that guns having higher speeds—perhaps as high as 50,000 feet per second—could be developed. Perhaps if an inner wall of the driver tube could, by an exploding charge, be collapsed sideways, higher gas pressures and velocities could be ob-

---

[3] Later to be described in this work.

tained than by pushing the gas lengthwise from rear to front. The problem was being studied by the Stanford Research Institute under an Ames contract.

Material and structural limits were being pushed in gun design. In the case of air guns—more commonly known as shock tunnels or shock tubes—the diaphragm separating the driving from the driven gas had become a particularly troublesome design problem. Such diaphragms were expected to burst at the design pressure with the pieces, held at the periphery, bending backward and thus providing the minimum resistance to the flowing gas. Above all, they must not shatter with the pieces flying downstream. Difficulties increased as the diaphragms were made thicker to resist higher operating pressures and the problem was particularly difficult in the case of the shock tunnel. To achieve the desired bursting performance in the shock tunnel, it was necessary to score the diaphragm along the desired bursting lines and then to initiate the bursting by means of an explosive charge placed in the scored grooves. A study of the diaphragm design problem was reported by Robert Dannenberg and David Stewart in TN D–2735.

Don Gault, of the Space Sciences Division, had been using the impact range to study the pattern of material ejected from an impact crater. One problem he had encountered arose from the fact that the force of gravity was at right angles to the line of fire and thus it was not possible to reproduce the ejecta patterns that were evident around the craters of the moon. What was needed was a range in which the gun could be fired downward toward a horizontal target surface. In 1964 this need was met by the construction of the vertical impact range. It was located in the old 10- by 14-inch wind-tunnel building, which had been largely taken over by the Space Sciences Division and renamed the space technology building annex.

The vertical impact range was designed to use any of several guns which could shoot at the target at selected angles ranging from the vertical to the horizontal. First operation, with conventional power guns, occurred late in 1964. Light-gas guns were later installed and the most advanced of these, the deformable-piston gun, was installed and ready for operation in November 1965. To study ejecta trajectories and the sequential phases of crater formation, a special camera capable of taking pictures at the rate of 4 million frames a second and capable also of taking stereographic pictures was provided for use with the vertical impact range. The effect of reduced gravity, such as prevailed on the moon, was obtained by dropping the target at the time of impact.

Research interest at Ames was moving toward increasingly higher reentry speeds and thus much design attention was being given to the means by which extreme reentry conditions could be simulated in the laboratory. The man-carrying Apollo spacecraft, returning from its planned trip to the

Vertical impact range—the gun is shown in a horizontal position but may be raised in several steps to a vertical one.

Donald E. Gault.

moon, was expected to reenter the earth's atmosphere at a speed of about 35,000 feet per second. Reentry from missions to nearby planets such as Mars and Venus could, by the use of special techniques, be accomplished at speeds of no more than 50,000 feet per second; and reentry from a trip to a more remote planet such as Jupiter could possibly, through the use of similar techniques, be accomplished at speeds of 65,000 feet per second. Such speeds appeared to represent the maximum that might be encountered for some time to come. Flights to celestial bodies beyond our solar system seemed likely to be of such long duration[4] that return and reentry were only of far-out academic interest.

Thus at Ames there existed an urge to develop facilities capable of simulating entry speeds of 50,000 feet per second or more. The pilot hypervelocity free-flight (HFF) facility came closest to filling this need but still fell far short of the goal. By 1963, however, guns and shock tunnels, as well as free-flight testing techniques, had reached a state of development and sophistication which made possible the planning of a very advanced HFF facility having speed potentialities well beyond that of the pilot HFF facility. What

---

[4] Dryden had estimated that it might take 160,000 years for a round trip to the nearest star.

418

was actually designed in 1963 was a laboratory building housing three large and powerful test devices. This complex, which was to cost over $5 million, was put under construction in 1964 and was largely completed in 1965. It was named the hypervelocity free-flight facility which, somewhat confusingly, was the name of the individual test devices of which it was composed. The test devices incorporated in the main facility were:

> An aerodynamic hypervelocity free-flight facility.
> A radiation hypervelocity free-flight facility.
> A gun-development hypervelocity free-flight facility.

The aerodynamic HFF facility, the largest of the test units, was a counterflow arrangement capable of generating relative speeds between air and model of 50,000 feet per second and stagnation enthalpies of 50,000 Btu per pound. Test Reynolds numbers up to 80 million per foot of model length could be reached. As indicated by its name, the aerodynamic facility was to be used for aerodynamic studies, the measuring of forces and moments; whereas the radiation HFF facility, also a counterflow device and having the same performance as the aerodynamic HFF facility, was to be used for studying radiation in the gas cap and wake. The gun-development facility, as its name implies, was to be used for gun-development tests and did not include a counterflow shock tunnel. The aerodynamic facility had a total length of about 400 feet, a test-section length of 75 feet, a test-section diameter of 3.5 feet, and a gun length of 145 feet. Corresponding figures for the radiation facility were 260, 18, 3.5, and 145. The radiation and gun-development facilities became operational in 1965, but the larger and somewhat more complicated aerodynamics facility would not be ready for use until early 1966.

As the speed of HFF facilities increased, testing techniques became painfully difficult. Arranging a meeting, at a prescribed point in the test section, of a model traveling at 30,000 feet per second with a short pulse of air traveling in the opposite direction at 20,000 feet per second required controls that were fantastically precise and photographic devices that had shutter speeds of only a few billionths of a second. Moreover, the boundary-layer thickness and the pressure of the air pulse continuously varied as it passed along the test section and thus the Reynolds number of a test was dependent on where, along the test section, the model intercepted the air pulse. All of this technical complication was endured, however, as the HFF was the only facility at Ames, or elsewhere, in which both the aerodynamic and the heating phenomena of extreme reentry speeds could be truly represented.

The possibility of using the shock tunnel for the testing of fixed models had been demonstrated through the development and operation, at Ames, of the 1-foot shock tunnel. As earlier mentioned, the operation of this facility was a slow and messy business—the mess resulting from the condensation of steam generated by the burning of hydrogen and oxygen in the driver tube.

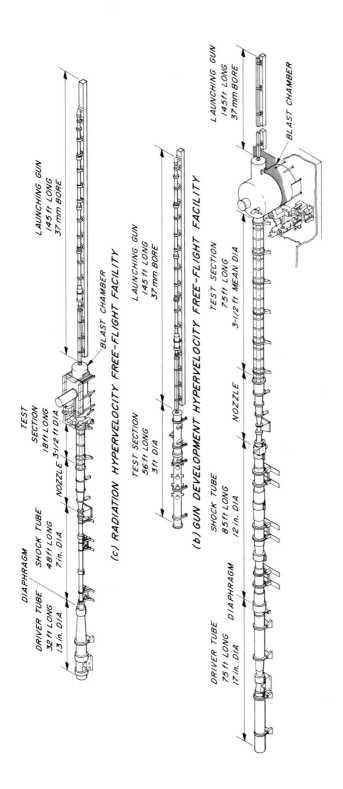

LAUNCHING GUN
145 ft LONG
37 mm BORE

BLAST CHAMBER

TEST
SECTION
18 ft LONG
NOZZLE 3-1/2 ft DIA

SHOCK TUBE
48 ft LONG
7 in. DIA

DIAPHRAGM

DRIVER TUBE
32 ft LONG
13 in. DIA

(c) RADIATION HYPERVELOCITY FREE-FLIGHT FACILITY

LAUNCHING GUN
145 ft LONG
37 mm BORE

TEST SECTION
56 ft LONG
3 ft DIA

(b) GUN DEVELOPMENT HYPERVELOCITY FREE-FLIGHT FACILITY

LAUNCHING GUN
145 ft LONG
37 mm BORE

BLAST CHAMBER

TEST SECTION
75 ft LONG
3-1/2 ft MEAN DIA

NOZZLE

SHOCK TUBE
85 ft LONG
12 in. DIA

DIAPHRAGM

DRIVER TUBE
75 ft LONG
17 in. DIA

Schematic drawing of hypervelocity free-flight facility.

Light-gas gun. Thomas N. Canning holds model that is fired down range. Plastic pistons are seen stacked against wall at left.

Above: *Shock tunnel (air gun) composed of driver and shock tubes. At left: Test section of aerodynamic facility; this is the "counterflow" region where the test model and the air jet, traveling in opposite directions, meet.*

Consideration had been given by the 3.5-foot-tunnel staff to the development of a new shock tunnel which would have a higher performance than the old tunnel and be cleaner and easier to operate. These worthy goals were to be accomplished by eliminating combustion as a source of power. In the new tunnel, which was under construction in 1965, the driver gas, helium, was to be heated by a tremendous surge of electric-arc power. The electrical energy, equivalent to over 10 million horsepower acting for 1/10,000 second, was to be obtained through the discharge of a bank of capacitors. The new facility, which might be called an electric-arc shock tunnel, was believed to have potentialities for generating air speeds up to 40,000 feet per second. Unfortunately the duration of the air pulse produced would only be a couple of milliseconds and the air as it passed over the model, having just received such a frightful shock, would likely be completely out of chemical and thermal equilibrium. The device was thus considered unsuitable for use in a counterflow, HFF, arrangement.

The arc-jet, in which an arc heats the airstream but is not its primary driving means, continued in a rather rapid state of development during this period. The arc-jet installations by the end of 1965 included three in the fluid mechanics building, two or three in the space technology building, two in the gas dynamics laboratory, and one in the Mach 50 helium wind-tunnel facility. The one in the Mach 50 facility, known as the 1-inch constricted-arc supersonic jet, was perhaps the most sophisticated of all and had the highest performance of any arc-jet yet built at Ames. It could be operated with any desired mixture of air, nitrogen, and carbon dioxide; and, while the Mach number of the gas stream was only 3, its temperature was so high that enthalpy values of up to 200,000 Btu per pound were potentially obtainable. One of the newer units in the fluid mechanics building, a unit called the entry heating simulator, was particularly notable because in it the test model was to be exposed not only to the heat of the arc-heated airstream but also to a separate source of radiative heat produced by arcs and focusing mirrors. The auxiliary radiation source was to be used to simulate the radiating gas cap which the arc-jet, owing to its low Mach number, was itself unable to produce.

The use of a separate source of radiation in the entry heating simulator was, indeed, evidence of a basic weakness of all arc-jet facilities. In such facilities it had not been possible to obtain high enthalpy and high Mach number at the same time. Howard Stine, who together with Charles Shepard and Velvin Watson had received a NASA award in 1965 for his major contributions to arc-jet development, freely admitted this weakness of the arc-jet as a research tool. As yet, he said, no one had fully learned how to control the vast amount of electric power that is poured into an arc-jet—how to keep the power from reducing the arc-jet structure to a puddle of molten metal. In the operation of arc-jets, to avoid overheating the structure

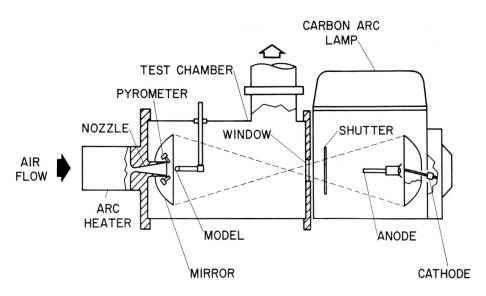

CARBON ARC
LAMP

TEST CHAMBER

PYROMETER

NOZZLE

AIR
FLOW

ARC
HEATER

WINDOW

SHUTTER

MODEL

ANODE

MIRROR

CATHODE

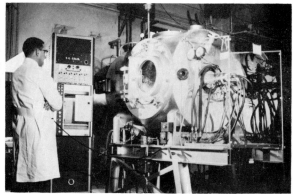

Above: *Entry-heating simulator with combined convective
and radiative heating. At
right: Planetary-entry ablation arc-jet facility.*

it had been necessary to reduce the pressure (thus the density) of the airstream as its temperature (enthalpy) was increased. In other words, extremely hot air molecules were tolerable if they were sufficiently few in
number. One may recall having held one's hand in the shower of sparks emanating from a Fourth of July sparkler and feeling nothing more than a
mild warmth—because the sparks, though white hot, were relatively few
and small. The sparkler flux was obviously of high enthalpy (Btu per
pound), but inasmuch as the density was low not many pounds struck the
hand and little heating resulted.

In the most critical heating phase of spacecraft reentry, the air in the
gas cap is both hot and fairly dense and the resulting heating condition lasts
for seconds, if not minutes. Owing to the low density of its airstream, the
arc-jet had not been able to duplicate the high heating rate of the gas cap

but had, nevertheless, been able to maintain a very high heating rate for a prolonged period of time. The HFF facility, on the other hand, could duplicate the high heating rate of the gas cap but could not maintain the heating long enough to represent actual reentry flight conditions. Thus it was clear that, in the simulation of reentry heating, the arc-jet and the HFF facility represented two imperfect, and distinctly different, approaches which by virtue of their differences possessed advantages that were complementary.

Further comparisons of the arc-jet with the HFF facility might be noted:

1. The arc-jet with a running time of several minutes or more provides more time for force measurements and photography and sufficient time for development of the charring ablation process.
2. The arc-jet allows the testing of larger models which more accurately represent the flight article. Models tested in the HFF facility are small, tend to be of oversimplified design, and, since small models are more sensitive to the effects of roughness, must be made with great precision. Also the HFF facility models must be designed to resist extremely high launching loads.
3. The arc-jet models are firmly supported, a condition which facilitates instrumentation and makes it possible to obtain a wider variety of test data. Also the models are not lost, as they are in the HFF facility.
4. Unlike the arc-jet, the HFF facility can simulate the Mach numbers, Reynolds numbers, and gas-cap heating conditions of actual reentry flight, but not the flight duration.

It might be added, as an incidental note, that Stine's work on arc-jets, while aimed at the development of a research tool, had revealed certain possibilities for the application of the arc-jet as an efficient power plant for spacecraft. In 1965 experimentation was under way on the use of a transverse magnetic field to accelerate the flow of plasma issuing from an arc-jet.

SPACE ENVIRONMENTAL RESEARCH FACILITY

In the design of space vehicles, engineers were continually encountering problems arising from the limitations of materials. At Ames, research that bore on the subject of materials began in 1959–1960. In early 1963 a Materials Branch was formed under Charles Hermach and Bernard Cunningham, and in 1964 construction commenced on a materials research laboratory. This laboratory, called the space environmental research facility, was completed at a cost of $3,530,000 and put into use in March 1965. The new facility was provided with excellent equipment, including spectroscopes, an electron microscope, and several ion accelerators. Among the latter were instruments that the Physics Branch had developed for sputtering research—an activity which had now been taken over by the Materials Branch.

FACILITIES

Under construction within the new space environment research facility late in 1965 was a test chamber in which certain important aspects of the environment of space could be simulated. This device, called a combined environment chamber, consisted of a large vacuum chamber incorporating three proton accelerators having beam energies ranging from 2 to 300 MeV. Through the use of a combination of oil-diffusion pumps and condensers cooled by liquid nitrogen and liquid helium, it was expected that the chamber could be evacuated to the extremely low pressure of 10^{-10} millimeters of mercury. A smaller vacuum chamber, thought to be capable of reproducing the low pressures existing between earth and moon (about 10^{-13} mm mercury), already had been completed but no way had been found for measuring that degree of vacuum.

STRUCTURAL DYNAMICS LABORATORY

Ames' long-standing interest in wing flutter was transferred early in the Space Age to an interest in the dynamic structural loads of spacecraft and their launching vehicles. A Structural Dynamics Branch, which had been created in 1960 under Al Erickson and Henry Cole, undertook research on a number of problems such as launch-vehicle instability, landing-impact attenuation, and fuel-sloshing loads. This work had so expanded by 1963 as to

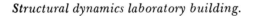

Structural dynamics laboratory building.

require a new facility. Construction of this facility, known as the structural dynamics laboratory, began in 1964 and was largely completed by the end of 1965. Its cost was about $1,650,000.

The new structural dynamics laboratory provided a wide array of conventional and special structural research equipment as well as some badly needed office space. The most imposing element of the laboratory, however, was a 100-foot-tall concrete tower to be used principally for tests of launch vehicles but additionally for drop tests of spacecraft landing gears. A launch vehicle tested in the tower could be exposed to an environment simulating in many structurally important respects what the vehicle would normally encounter as it ascended through the earth's atmosphere. The environment would include a moderate vacuum (10 mm mercury or less), heating (infrared radiation sources totaling $12\frac{1}{2}$ megawatts), vibration (by means of variable-frequency shakers), and noise such as produced by a rocket motor. The tower was given a pentagonal cross section, to preclude the development of a strong standing wave pattern, and was separately mounted on a 6-foot-thick block of concrete floating, without benefit of piles, in the rather mucky soil of Moffett Field. This manner of mounting was expected to isolate the tower from external vibrations, but certain congenital skeptics on the Ames staff could not refrain from speculating that it might create a leaning tower rivaling the one in Pisa.

BIOLOGICAL RESEARCH FACILITIES

Soon after the Space Sciences Division and the Life Sciences Directorate were formed, they found themselves severely hampered for lack of office and laboratory space. Both made extensive use of trailers and the Life Sciences Directorate was forced to find temporary housing for some of its activities, in the nearby town of Mountain View. While the Space Sciences Division continued to have a housing shortage, steps were initiated in 1963 to relieve the more critical need of the Life Sciences Directorate.

The first building created for the biological interests at Ames was a bioscience laboratory built in 1963–1964 and located just north of the 6- by 6-foot tunnel. Although this facility provided office and laboratory space in a two-story building, its main feature was a vivarium—more commonly known as an animal shelter—providing accommodation for experimental animals such as monkeys, apes, and dogs. Accommodations for smaller animals (cats, rabbits, rats, etc.) were provided in air-conditioned trailers adjacent to the bioscience laboratory.

The animal shelter served both the Life Sciences and the Biosatellite interests at Ames. By the end of 1965, the shelter, in behalf of the Biosatellite project alone, cared for several hundred *Macaca nemestrina* (monkeys) which, because of their short tails, were called "pig-tailed" macaques. Caring for the monkeys was Don Warner, manager of the clinical, biochemistry,

426

and vivarium section of Project Biosatellite. The animals were treated with all due consideration; Dr. Dale Smith to whom Warner reported was, indeed, a member of the National Animal Care Panel whose function it is to assure the humane treatment of experimental animals. The bioscience laboratory had a surgery, a recovery room, and isolation wards, and its stainless-steel animal cages were scrupulously cleaned with superheated steam at frequent intervals.

The monkeys arriving from southeast Asia were suspected of harboring germs of possibly dangerous tropical diseases. Extreme precautions were taken to avoid transmittal of disease germs from monkey to handler and also from handler to monkey. Before working with the monkeys, the handler was required to shower and change into a freshly laundered and sterilized uniform. On finishing the handling task, he was required to shower and disinfect himself carefully before changing into street clothes. Food for the monkeys consisted of no less than Purina Monkey Chow, a relative of the dog and cat chows with which pet lovers are familiar. Surplus or over-age animals were turned over to National Institutes of Health centers, such as the National Center for Primate Biology run by the University of California at Davis, California.

Although the main purpose of Project Biosatellite was to conduct biological experiments in space, there was, nevertheless, a need for certain preliminary, ground-based investigations to assure the success of the flight experiment. For example, it was considered desirable to subject the flight experimental packages to a realistic simulation of the longitudinal accelerations and noise levels anticipated during launch and recovery. The facility needed for such a simulation—a centrifuge—was put under construction in 1963 and completed in 1964. This facility, known as the Biosatellite centrifuge, was located under the return passage of the 40- by 80-foot tunnel. Its 50-foot-diameter rotating arm could provide accelerations up to 15 g, reached at a controlled rate of up to 2 g per second, for payload packages of up to 1200 pounds located at either or both ends of the arm. Arrangements for providing a noise environment for the payload were also available.

It was recognized during 1963, or before, that the Life Sciences Directorate would require a major office-laboratory facility quite beyond anything of the kind that the bioscience laboratory might provide. Such a facility was put under construction in 1964 and completed in 1965. On December 30, 1965, it was dedicated in a special ceremony attended by Congressmen Miller and Gubser of California, Dr. Mac C. Adams who was the new head of OART, Professor Harold Urey of the University of California, Professor Joshua Lederberg of Stanford, and other notables.

The new facility, called the life sciences research laboratory, was a three-story, well-equipped unit costing over $4 million. In appearance it was strikingly different from the other Ames buildings. From the first, Ames architecture had been characterized by two-story arrangements, simple horizontal lines, and flat unpainted concrete surfaces. This was the pattern originally established by NACA designers and later carried on at the Center's request by contracting architectural firms. In the case of the life sciences research laboratory, however, the architect was not bound by the usual requirement of style conformance and perhaps felt there was some advantage in making more intensive use of the diminishing building space available at the Center. He shunned the traditional long lines and used instead a not unattractive arrangement of rectangular masses, the external surfaces of which were dimpled like a lunar landscape.

It was the interior, not the exterior, of the life sciences research laboratory that was, in any case, important. The research facilities were outstanding. The exobiology laboratory on the third floor, for example, contained in addition to the usual laboratory instruments a mass spectrometer and a rather large collection (a dozen or more) of gas chromatographs. It contained a separate enzyme laboratory and on the whole was regarded by the Chief of the Exobiology Division as being the best equipped laboratory in the world for detecting traces of organic elements.

Still uncompleted at the end of 1965 was a "high bay" building associated with the life sciences research laboratory. This building, it was planned, would provide space for some of the larger items of research equipment including, in particular, biological research simulators required by the Biotechnology Division. One of the simulators, under construction in 1965 but not scheduled for completion until 1966, was a man-carrying rotation device in which investigations could be made of human reactions to angular accelerations and velocities about any selected axis.

The Life Sciences Directorate, in 1962–1963, had built a small centrifuge in the basement of the instrument research building. This centrifuge was mainly used by Dr. Ogden's Environmental Biology Division for small-animal investigations.

FLIGHT SIMULATORS

The 1959 Headquarters ruling transferring all flight testing, except that involving V/STOL aircraft, to the Flight Research Station at Edwards accelerated the steps Ames was already taking in the development and use of flight simulators. The ruling, however, was not wholly practicable, and by 1963–1964 some of the proscribed airplanes were being returned to the Center. Among these was the F–100 variable-stability airplane for which, in 1965, a flight-research program was being readied. Other airplanes arriving at Ames were a Douglas F5D required for a special wing test, a Lockheed C–130 partially adapted for variable-stability work, a Convair 340 adapted for a blind-flying study, and a Convair 990 four-engine transport purchased by NASA for use by the Center as a flying research laboratory. There was

Life sciences research laboratory building.

also a small LearJet which the Center owned and used for both research and research support.

Although the airplanes were returning to Ames, the Center continued to press its flight-simulator development work and by the end of 1965 the simulator facilities in use and under construction were quite impressive. No longer was it necessary for Center engineers to build simulators, without Headquarters knowledge, out of spare parts scrounged from wherever obtainable. Many millions of dollars were now being spent on the construction of some very sophisticated devices. These expenditures appeared prudent in view of the possible saving of human lives and the tremendous cost of the aircraft (such as the SST) and the spacecraft (such as the Apollo) for which the simulators were to provide essential design information.

It had been found, moreover, that in the solution of stability and control problems of specific aircraft, the groundbased simulator and the wind tunnel worked well as a team, enhancing each other's effectiveness. First, the aerodynamic coefficients of the original airplane configuration, as obtained in the wind tunnel, would be programed into the computer of the simulator. Simulator runs would then suggest desirable changes in the configuration. These changes would then be checked out in the wind tunnel and the new coefficients obtained. This cycle, repeated, would rapidly home in on an optimum configuration.

Ames' simulator equipment had become very extensive by 1965 and completely filled the original NACA hangar, which now was called the space flight simulation laboratory. Simulators were normally composed of a num-

429

ber of basic units: the computer, the cockpit display and controls, the motion generator, and now, in the newer simulators, the device for providing the external visual cues simulating the external scene that the pilot would normally see through the windshield of his airplane. The heart of the simulator was, of course, the computer, which was programed to represent the dynamics of the aircraft or spacecraft being simulated and which controlled the cockpit instruments, the motion generator, and the external-visual-cue device.

The computer equipment was expensive, but fortunately the same equipment could often be made to serve alternately more than one simulator. Such equipment was usually composed of analog units of which by 1965 Ames had assembled a vast array including over 1000 amplifiers. In a recent simulation, an attempt had been made to augment the analog equipment with an IBM 7094 digital computer tied in through a long cable reaching to its remote location. Also, combined analog and digital computing equipment was to be provided for some of the sophisticated simulators which, at the end of 1965, were under construction.

The motion generator was usually the largest and most expensive component of a simulator and as time went on more and more realistic motion simulation was demanded. To satisfy the simulation requirements of V/STOL aircraft, there was built, in 1963, at a cost of $640,000, a motion generator providing six degrees of freedom including large (±10 feet) translational motions along each axis. This facility was called the all-axes

6-degrees-of-freedom flight simulator.

Brent Y. Creer.

motion generator or, when combined with other simulator elements, the six-degrees-of-freedom simulator.

Among other smaller simulators built during the 1962–1964 period were the moving-cab transport simulator—a refined version of an earlier device —and a midcourse navigation simulator. The latter device, intended for use in spaceflight navigation studies, consisted in part of an Apollo-sized crew compartment mounted on an air bearing in such a way as to allow small angular motions in pitch, roll, and yaw. The compartment contained appropriate instrumentation; and an externally simulated star field, made visible by room darkening, provided the visual reference points required for navigational exercises. The cabin motion could be controlled manually by air jets or automatically, in a closed loop, by a computer.

While the simulators just mentioned were being put to use, plans were in preparation for the design and construction of much more pretentious facilities for simulating the flight of both aircraft and spacecraft. Bill Harper had in 1962 proposed the construction of a large centrifuge for simulation work at Ames, but the proposal was rejected by Headquarters on the basis that the request should have been for a more comprehensive, spaceflight guidance facility of which the centrifuge was a part. When, the following year, a suitably augmented proposal was submitted to Headquarters, it was approved. A further augmentation was later approved, with the result that the final plan encompassed a complex of four facilities. These facilities were being designed during the latter half of 1963, were being built and checked out at the factory during 1964–1965, and were scheduled for installation at Ames in 1966.

The new simulators were to be installed in a building especially constructed for the purpose on a site bordering the airfield near the existing space flight simulation laboratory. Named the space flight guidance research laboratory (SFGRL), the building and its complement of four facilities cost over $13 million. The facilities comprising the SFGRL were:

- Flight simulator for advanced aircraft.
- Man-carrying motion generator.
- Midcourse navigation simulator.
- Satellite attitude control facility.

All four were designed to make use, as needed, of a common analog-digital computer system. All, it was planned, would ultimately be used for space-flight simulation purposes, except that the flight simulator for advanced aircraft would for several years serve the development needs of the Nation's supersonic jet transport.

The flight simulator for advanced aircraft, costing about $2.6 million, was expected to be the largest and most sophisticated airplane flight simulator ever built. Unfortunately the delay entailed by the long process of procurement would curtail its contributions to the supersonic transport project. Within its three-man cabin (replica of transport cabin), the crew would be subjected, in simulated form, to all of the meaningful sensations they could expect to encounter in the flight of the supersonic transport. The simulator was designed to provide all six degrees of angular and translational motion. Moreover, the range of lateral motion was made unusually large (± 50 feet) to properly simulate the extensive sweeps of sidewise motion which the crew would experience in their location far ahead of the wing in the long nose of the airplane.

The equipment for providing the external visual cues—the external scene as viewed from the cabin—was rather elaborate and expensive ($285,000). By means of a projector mounted atop the cabin, the simulated external scene would be projected in color on a screen mounted in front of the cabin. The projected scene would be obtained from a color television camera moving, as controlled by the computer, over a model landscape. The computer-controlled camera would follow the motions of the computer-controlled cabin, thus giving the proper picture orientation and distance.

The man-carrying motion generator, costing about $9.8 million, was the most expensive item of equipment to be located in the space flight guidance research laboratory. It was a huge centrifuge which, when coupled with the computer, with the visual-cue apparatus, and with other auxiliaries,

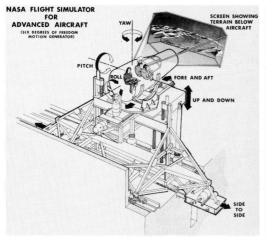

Upper left: *Schematic drawing of flight simulator for advanced aircraft.* Upper right: *The redifon visual cue generator.* Below: *View of simulated runway and landscape from simulator cockpit.*

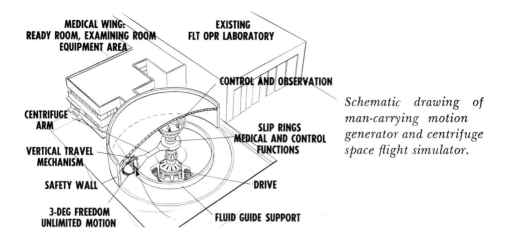

Schematic drawing of man-carrying motion generator and centrifuge space flight simulator.

was capable of providing a spacecraft crew with all of the sensations, except weightlessness, they would experience in a flight from the earth to the moon or to Mars. In particular, it would simulate not only the accelerations of takeoff and landing but also the angular and vertical motions, the external scene, solar radiation, and cabin environment—temperature, pressure, gas composition, and vibration, all of which were to be controllable.

At the end of a 50-foot arm, driven by an 18,600-horsepower dc motor, the three-man cabin could be accelerated by the centrifuge to a level of 20 g at rates up to $7\frac{1}{2}$ g per second. An alternate, one-man cabin which was being provided could be accelerated up to 50 g, if unmanned, or otherwise to the limit of human tolerance. In addition to the rotation provided by the centrifuge, the cabin was to have unlimited motion about the roll, pitch, and yaw axes, as well as a vertical motion of ± 2 feet. It was expected that the cabin motions would normally be controlled by the computer, in a closed-loop system, but manual control without benefit of computer—except possibly for a small on-board computer—would also be possible.

The midcourse navigation simulator, the third facility in the space flight guidance research laboratory, was to be a refined version of the one earlier described. Its cost is included with that of the centrifuge. The device was a manned-flight simulator, either computer or manually controlled, in which it would be possible to conduct deep-space navigational exercises on earth. Its three-man cabin, or capsule, mounted on a spherical air bearing, would allow limited (up to $\pm 13°$) angular motion about all three axes. For the use intended, the simulation of translational motions was unnecessary. The environment provided in the cabin was to include the same variety of controlled conditions as were available in the cabin of the centrifuge. Also to be provided were celestial screens on one of which simulated stars, precisely located, would realistically transmit their light in narrow beams of parallel rays.

FACILITIES

The satellite attitude control facility, the fourth item in the space flight guidance research laboratory, was a device to be used in studying attitude-control, or stabilization, systems such as are required by certain types of unmanned satellites. One such satellite is the Orbiting Astronomical Observatory, the attitude of which must be very precisely controlled to allow the telescope it carries to be pointed at the star, or other heavenly object, to be observed. In other cases, spacecraft are required to keep their solar panels pointed at the sun or their radio antennas or instruments pointed at the earth or their payload pointed in some prescribed direction. The devices that provide the stabilization derive their power from such sources as air jets, reaction wheels, gravity, gyroscopic forces, or geomagnetism and refer their actions mainly to celestial bodies, including the earth and its gravitational and magnetic fields.

In the Ames facility, it was planned that the stabilizing devices to be investigated would be mounted on an 8-foot-diameter table floating friction-lessly on a spherical air bearing inside an evacuated 22-foot-diameter sphere. The motions of the simulated satellite (table) around the earth

Artist's drawing of satellite attitude-control simulator.

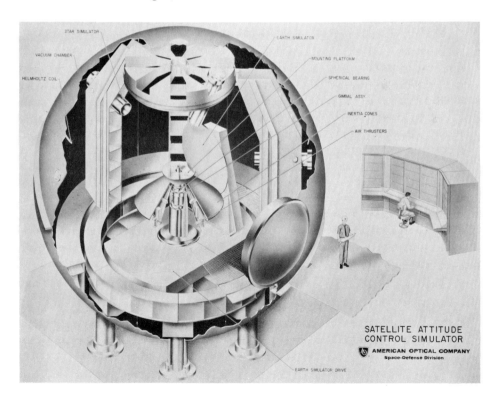

were to be represented by moving an earth model around the table in circular or elliptical paths according to the orbit desired. Other external references or influences would include a star screen, coils for producing a magnetic field corresponding to that of the simulated earth, and a heater for simulating earth infrared radiation. A simulated sun was also to be provided at a later date. As in the case of the other three facilities in the laboratory, the attitude-control facility was designed so that it could be operated in a closed loop with a computer. Its cost, incidentally, was about $1.2 million.

LONG-PATH GAS CELL

Much had been, and much remained to be, learned about the atmospheres and the surface characteristics of solar-system planets from the spectrographic analysis of radiation emanating from the planets. However, accurate interpretation of the spectrographic data required a knowledge of the absorption and emission characteristics, at various pressures and temperatures, of the planetary atmospheres. These were matters of great concern to the Ames Space Sciences Division and were matters about which much could be learned in a ground-based laboratory if proper facilities could be provided. One such facility, conceived by Ames scientists in 1964, was a long, enclosed chamber through which a beam of selected radiation could repeatedly be passed to obtain the absorption characteristics of the gas with which the chamber was filled.

The device just mentioned, called the Ames long-path gas cell, was completed early in 1965. Although only 25 meters long, the chamber was equipped with a system of mirrors by means of which the beam of radiation, introduced at one end, could be bounced back and forth for a total path length up to 1 kilometer before it fell on the detector. The chamber was so designed and equipped that it could be charged with any gas, or combination of gases, at any pressure in the range from 10^4 to 10^{-5} millimeters of mercury. As 1965 ended, the long-path gas cell was being used to obtain infrared absorption spectra of gases known or suspected to be present in extraterrestrial planetary atmospheres. Such information, it was expected, would be utilized in later spectrographic studies aimed at determining the pressure and temperature of planetary atmospheres and the abundance of the various gases of which they are composed.

CAPITAL GROWTH

The capital equipment of the Ames Research Center had greatly expanded during the NASA regime.[5] In October 1958, Ames contributed to the new agency a plant valued at about $80 million. By the end of 1965, the

---

[5] See app. A.

cost value of Ames facilities, including the space flight guidance research laboratory, had grown to about $175 million. As a result of modifications and improvements, the value of many of the facilities had risen far above the original cost. For example, the 1- by 3-foot tunnel, which originally cost $1.2 million, had by 1965 increased in value to $4.1 million. Corresponding figures, in millions, for other facilities are: supersonic free-flight tunnel ($0.23 to $1.7) ; 6- by 6-foot tunnel ($4.5 to $6.4) ; 12-foot tunnel ($3.8 to $5.1) ; 40- by 80-foot tunnel ($7.1 to $8.9) ; Unitary Plan tunnels ($24.8 to $32.2) . Some of the facilities, of course, were obsolete by 1965 and their true value had fallen to essentially zero.

The accelerated building program of the Ames Research Center during the period 1963–1965 required more land than the 115 acres which, at the end of 1962, were owned and occupied by NASA. On being apprised of this problem, the Navy granted Ames a license [6] to use an additional 110.7 acres of land at the base. The ownership of this parcel was permanently transferred to NASA on January 22, 1965, bringing the Administration's holdings at Moffett Field to a total of approximately 226 acres.

---

[6] License No. NOy (R) 65159, dated May 1, 1964.

9

....

Research

PATTERN

THE in-house research at Ames was becoming increasingly fundamental and an increasing proportion was of the pure variety aimed principally at satisfying human curiosity and having little relation to practical applications. Research objectives were, in fact, often intermingled. For example, applied aerothermodynamic research provided the practical knowledge required for the design of spacecraft to be used for the pure objective of exploring some foreign planet. Applied research thus represented the pillars on which pure research was mounted and often found useful applications beyond its original objective. Indeed these related practical benefits were frequently used as justification for the costs of the pure research, though such costs seemed much too heavy to be amortized by this means.[1] It is also of interest to note that a strong element of "pure" motivation existed behind much of the applied research—indeed behind the work of any man worthy of the appellation of research scientist or engineer.

The pattern of research at the Center had become very complex. The life-sciences, space-sciences, and project-management activities were getting into full swing. Aeronautical research represented no more than 20 percent of the total effort; the remaining 80 percent was devoted to a diversity of space problems. The interest in aerodynamic heating, ablation, and radiation continued strong during this period but the speed range of interest was outrunning the capacity of the test facilities. Aerodynamicists had turned to meteors as a source of information on aerodynamic heating at extremely high speeds. Indeed, for this and other reasons, a surprising interest had developed in these celestial bodies.

---

[1] See ch. 10 re Technology Utilization.

AIRCRAFT DESIGN STUDIES

Research relating to aircraft, although a fairly small percentage of the Ames research effort during the period 1963–1965, still constituted a substantial volume. A significant amount of this research was in the nature of development studies of advanced military aircraft undertaken in behalf, and at the request, of the military services. This work, dealing with such aircraft as the Dynasoar, the B–70, the F–111, the YF–12A, and various other airplane and missile types, was generally classified. The Dynasoar, which as the X–20 was to have been the next major step beyond the X–15 in the research-airplane program, was canceled in December 1963 when the interests of the Air Force turned to a manned orbiting laboratory (MOL). The research-airplane program carried on with the X–15 and before the end of 1965 that airplane had attained speeds of over 4000 miles per hour and altitudes of over 65 miles.

Aside from the development work just mentioned, the remaining aircraft research conducted at Ames during this period was focused on the supersonic transport, on large subsonic transports several of which were being designed, and on various types of V/STOL vehicles.

Although airfoil research was a bit old fashioned in these days, certain specialized aspects of the airfoil problem invited study. One example was a theoretical study, made by Joseph Cleary and John Axelson and reported in TR R–202, of sharp and blunt airfoils in hypersonic flow; another was an analysis (TR R–201) by James Der of the performance of airfoils operating in air that, as a result of a shock wave, was in a state of disequilibrium.

Despite the vast amount of earlier work on wing planforms, there was still something to be learned on this subject. One of the more important wing-design concepts arising at this time, a scheme involving a nonlinear (S-curve) leading edge, came from Britain. The distinguishing feature of the OGEE wing, as it was called, was the leading edge of the inboard portion which not only was rather sharp but, more noticeably, swooped forward as it approached the fuselage. At the same time the leading edge of the tip section was rounded backward, thus completing the S-curve. The result was a planform not unlike that which was found in the vertical tail surfaces of earlier airplanes but which, surprisingly, had not before been applied to a wing. The action of the sharp, highly swept inboard sections (cf. dorsal) was to produce a strong vortex extending spanwise over the forward portion of the wing. Unexpectedly, perhaps, the vortex stabilized the flow over the wing and provided, in a simple efficient way, the benefits sought but not always achieved through the use of heavy, complicated lift-control devices. The OGEE wing was in 1965 applied experimentally to a Douglas F5D–1 airplane which was then tested by Ames engineers both in the 40- by 80-foot wind tunnel and in flight. The modification so improved the stability and control characteristics of the airplane that the pilot felt

440

Above: *North American X–15 in flight.* Below: *OGEE wing on Douglas F5D–1 airplane.*

safe in lowering the landing approach speed by 10 knots. The results of the F5D–1 tests were reported in TN D–3071 by Stewart Rolls, David Koenig, and Fred Drinkwater.

Design studies of the supersonic transport (SST) made by NASA and industry had by 1964 revealed two promising configurations: one a canard arrangement incorporating a delta wing, and the other having a wing the sweep of which could be varied as required in flight. Ames gave some attention to the variable-sweep configuration but much more to the develop-

441

ment of the canard-delta design. In fact, Ames engineers were largely responsible for the successful development of the canard-delta SST configuration, an accomplishment for which they received some acclaim.

In 1963, as part of the SST program, the Ames Vehicle Aerodynamics Branch undertook a study of the effect of spanwise variations of leading-edge sweep on wing performance. This work, reported by Ray Hicks and Ed Hopkins in TN D–2236, led to considerations first of the OGEE planform and then of a more practical substitute—the "double-delta" wing. The double-delta, which provided the principal benefits of the OGEE planform, represented, in effect, the superposition of two delta planforms having different amounts of sweep. The double-delta planform was adopted by the Lockheed Aircraft Corp. for use in its SST proposal.

To provide the designers of the SST with requisite information, it was necessary to try to anticipate the flying qualities of the airplane. For this purpose, flight simulators were extremely useful. Flight-simulator studies of the SST, made during an earlier period by White, Sadoff, Cooper, and others, have already been mentioned. Further work of this kind, on the landing characteristics of a canard-delta SST configuration, was carried out and reported by Richard Bray in TN D–2251. In this study the known performance of the Boeing 707 was used as a reference for judging that of the SST.

Inasmuch as the SST was expected to involve a tremendous national investment, the need was evident for the utmost care in evaluating SST design proposals. The Federal Aviation Agency (FAA) established a Supersonic Transport Evaluation Team composed of specialists in all of the many aspects of aircraft design and operation. Heavily represented on this team were several NASA Centers including Ames. The work of the team won high praise from FAA and, for their contributions, certain NASA representatives, including several men from Ames, won honors from their own agency. Among those at Ames so honored were Edward W. Perkins, George E. Cooper, Maurice D. White, Adrien E. Anderson, Mark W. Kelly, and Norman E. Sorensen.

The Ames flight simulators also found use during 1963–1965 in studies of a number of special airplane flight problems. In one of these, reported by Tom Wempe in TM X–54,063, the Ames height control apparatus (attached to the side of the 40- by 80-foot tunnel) was used to investigate the problems of a pilot who, as required by some military missions, attempts to fly very low over irregular terrain. The pilots performing the simulated mission "crashed" a number of times, thus demonstrating the importance of simulator studies. Another useful application of flight simulators at Ames during this period was a study of the serious situation that had occasionally occurred in the operation of commercial jet transports when severe turbulence was encountered, particularly during the climb to altitude. Under such conditions, a momentary loss of control arising from a burst of turbulence can lead to rather wide excursions of airplane attitude and possibly to

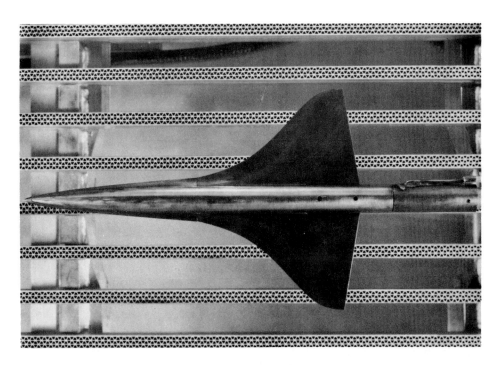

Above: *OGEE wing model in transonic tunnel.* Below: *Double-delta supersonic transport model in 40- by 80-foot tunnel.*

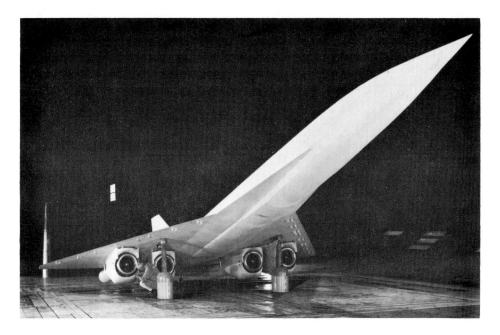

structural failure during attempted recovery. The technique for handling the airplane safely in such circumstances obviously can be studied much more safely in a flight simulator than in flight. The work of Ames pilots and engineers on this problem was very constructive. It was reported at an AIAA meeting in July 1965 in a paper (ref. C–29) entitled "Summary of NASA Research on Jet Transport Control Problems in Severe Turbulence," by Melvin Sadoff, Richard S. Bray, and William H. Andrews. From the study of this problem it became clear that a simulator providing wide ranges of translational, as well as angular, motion would be of much value.

V/STOL aircraft were becoming of increasing interest both at home and abroad and for commercial as well as for military applications. While normally thought of as applying to craft having only modest top-speed capabilities, VTOL principles had been used in some cases, such as the British Hawker P–1127, for high-speed fighter-type aircraft.

V/STOL aircraft offered a tremendous range of design possibilities— many, assuredly, no good but few so bad that they could be abandoned without wind-tunnel prototype flight tests. The diversity of V/STOL design was especially great with respect to the powerplant and the means by which engine power was used to produce both thrust and lift. The powerplant was far more important than in an ordinary airplane; indeed, it was the very heart of any V/STOL design. In VTOL types, other than helicopters, a power failure in flight almost inevitably spelled catastrophe. Ames pilots, it should be noted, were shocked by the ease with which glib proponents of dangerous and impractical VTOL devices were able to sell their ideas.

Owing to the complexity, diversity, and in many cases impracticality of the design of V/STOL aircraft, their development seemed permanently to remain in the prototype stage. By 1965 a few of the simpler V/STOL schemes appeared ready for application to operational aircraft but the more radical ideas continued to be limited to highly experimental craft. In the development of V/STOL aircraft, analysis had played its part but there was no substitute for experimental confirmations obtained in wind tunnels and simulators and through prototype flight tests. A new V/STOL science had to evolve and in the generation of this science NASA played a leading role, working closely with the military services, the FAA, the industry, and even with foreign development agencies.

Ames, in particular, had by 1965 become a world authority on V/STOL aircraft. Its elevation to this role resulted in some degree from its interest in the V/STOL field but even more from its impressive background of flight-research experience and from its possession of a large wind tunnel and advanced simulator facilities. The counsel and assistance of Ames engineers and pilots were regularly sought by domestic and foreign agencies engaged in the development of V/STOL aircraft. Seth Anderson of Ames was in 1965 made chairman of a new international committee that was

Left: *Tandem, dual ducted-fan model, mounted for test in 40- by 80-ft tunnel.* Below: *Breguet 941 airplane landing.*

formed for the purpose of dealing with the establishment and standardization of V/STOL handling requirements.

An example of the international cooperation provided by Ames was the Center's joint program with the French Air Ministry and the Breguet Aircraft Co. to investigate the handling qualities, stability and control and operational characteristics of the Breguet 941 (deflected slipstream) transport. One phase of this program was reported by Hervey Quigley, Robert Innis, and Curt Holzhauser in TN D–2231 (ref. C–30). As reported in TN D–2966 by Holzhauser, Innis, and Vomaske, Ames also collaborated with certain Japanese national and private organizations in a flight and simulator study of an experimental Japanese STOL seaplane.

On the domestic front, Ames investigated numerous V/STOL configurations in the 40- by 80-foot wind tunnel. These included types involving ducted fans, propellers-in-wing, jet-helicopter rotors, deflected slipstream, complicated jet flaps, and tilt wings. An example of this work was the tests of a large model of the four-engine, tilt-wing, Ling-Temco-Vought XC–142 reported in TN D–1857 by Wallace Deckert, Robert Page, and Stanley Dickinson.

In flight research the Bell X–14A variable-stability VTOL airplane proved very useful, as did the Lockheed C–130 equipped with boundary-layer control. The value of the C–130 for STOL stability research was considerably increased by the incorporation of certain variable-stability features in the airplane—a modification performed by Lockheed under contract with Ames. Though the powerplant may have been the heart of any V/STOL design, stability and control were certainly the crux of its operation. Inherent stability under landing and takeoff conditions was found very difficult to obtain, with the result that electromechanical stability augmentors ("black boxes") came to be regarded by many V/STOL designers as a practical necessity.

The critical recirculation problem of V/STOL aircraft was investigated at Ames in a special, outdoor, static test rig which allowed the distance between the test model and the ground to be varied. Recirculation, one of the more serious problems of hovering VTOL aircraft, occurs when the hot downwardly deflected jet of the lifting engines finds its way back, through ground reflection or other influences, to the engine inlet. The recirculating

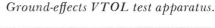

Ground-effects VTOL test apparatus.

air may carry debris from the ground to the inlet and, being relatively hot, will reduce the power of the engine and perhaps actually cause it to stall. Ames studies indicated that, as a result of recirculation, the use of the deflected-slipstream principle for VTOL aircraft was questionable.

Because of manpower limitations and other factors, Ames found it desirable, in the 1963–1965 period, to let contracts for certain V/STOL investigative work. Contracts were let with Boeing for a number of flight studies designed to exploit the special capabilities of the Boeing 367–80 prototype airplane. This airplane was one of the 707 class which had been so modified (BLC and special high-lift devices added) as to give it an unusually low landing speed and further so modified as to provide lateral-directional variable-stability characteristics. With this airplane, Boeing in 1965 undertook two studies for Ames. One was a study of the landing-approach characteristics of a large swept wing STOL transport; the other was an investigation of the flight characteristics of the huge C–5A cargo-transport airplane in which the Air Force had recently become interested.

In addition to carrying on its own V/STOL contracting work, Ames in 1964–1965 was collaborating with the FAA and industry in a design study aimed at the development of a short-haul, STOL commercial transport airplane. The general requirements of such an airplane were investigated at Ames and the results of the study were presented in 1964 at a meeting of the AIAA as a paper entitled "Design and Operating Considerations of Commercial STOL Transports," by Curt A. Holzhauser, Wallace H. Deckert, Hervey C. Quigley, and Mark W. Kelly. Additionally, Ames was proceeding on research leading to the ability to land aircraft under conditions of zero visibility which would have obvious application to STOL transports; flight investigations of a Convair 340 airplane, equipped for blind landings, began in this period. Following these efforts, NASA let contracts with Boeing, Ling-Temco-Vought, and Lockheed for feasibility studies of various V/STOL concepts applicable to the short-haul transport. These studies were under way as 1965 ended and were to be completed in time for results to be presented at a general V/STOL conference at Ames in 1966.

The importance of the pilots' role in the V/STOL work at Ames can scarcely be overemphasized. Their evaluations, in simulators and in flight, of the performance of V/STOL types were particularly valuable in view of the meagerness of existing knowledge and experience relating to the operation of such craft. In this pioneering work, there was obviously much danger. The Ames pilots most deeply involved were Fred Drinkwater and Bob Innis, both of whom luckily escaped serious injury in their flight tests of V/STOL aircraft. The staff at Ames was more than pleased when, in 1964, both pilots won the coveted Octave Chanute Award for their V/STOL work. For significant contributions to the safety and efficiency of flight testing, Fred Drinkwater also, in 1965, won the Richard Hansford Burroughs Test Pilot Award.

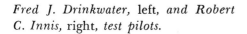

Fred J. Drinkwater, left, *and Robert*
C. Innis, right, *test pilots.*

DYNAMIC LOADS AND MATERIALS

The desire to land instrument packages and human beings safely on foreign celestial bodies stimulated an interest in the means for attenuating the landing impact. A primary requirement, of course, was that the weight of the shock-absorbing material be as small as possible. Thus the factor "specific energy absorption" (SEA)—energy absorption per pound of weight of the absorbing material—became an item of interest. In seeking the highest value of SEA, research engineers considered many forms of energy absorption. These included (1) gas compression (air bags), (2) acceleration of masses, (3) friction, and (4) cutting, crushing, extrusion of materials, or other forms of materials deformation. Processes resulting in a rebound were considered undesirable. One interesting method of energy absorption with which Ames engineers experimented was the pulling inside out of an aluminum tube. Another one was the cutting or crushing of a mass of plastic foam. The plastic (polystyrene) would be carried compactly as a fluid and then "blown up" in time to harden just before impact.

SEA, it was soon realized, was by no means the only important factor in the design of a lunar or planetary landing system. It was also necessary that the supporting elements of the landing gear provide stability, so the spacecraft would not tip over, and have broad feet so as not to sink into the lunar dust. The gear also had to be stowable in a small space for launching. With all these requirements, the design of a spacecraft landing system

448

offered room for the exercise of a great deal of ingenuity. It also represented a natural field of activity for the Ames Structural Dynamics Branch. The work of the Structural Dynamics Branch in this field is best represented, perhaps, by the paper published in 1965 by the American Society for Testing and Materials, entitled "Materials Needs for Energy Absorption in Space-Vehicle Landings" (ref. C–31), by R. W. Warner and D. R. Marble.

Although there had been earlier work on materials at Ames, the materials research effort began to take on significant proportions only in 1963–1965. The sputtering work, which had been instituted by Mike Bader and Fred Hansen, was continued during the early part of this period by Tom Snouse, whose work appeared as TN D–2235, "Sputtering at Oblique Angles of Ion Incidence." In the meantime, Ames materials research engineers had become interested in the effects on certain spacecraft materials of the hard vacuum and ultraviolet radiation encountered in space. One phenomenon investigated was the welding that sometimes takes place between two pieces of metal which are brought together in a high vacuum. This study was reported in TM X–56,334, "Solid Phase Welding of Metals under High Vacuum," by William Gilbreath and H. T. Sumsion.

Strangely enough, it was also found that the vacuum of space affected the mechanical properties of metals—particularly single crystals of certain metals. For example, it was possible to produce a single crystal of magnesium so large that it could be machined into a cylindrical tensile test specimen. When the specimen was pulled beyond the yield point in various degrees of vacuum, its cross section remained circular, as expected, as long as the air pressure was greater than 10^{-6} mm of mercury. At lower air pressures, however, the cross section became oval and the material showed increasing ductility. These characteristics suggested that under normal conditions the ductility of a test specimen is greatly affected by the oxide film which immediately forms on the surface of virgin test-body material as it is exposed by stretching. In a high vacuum, the oxide film does not form fast enough to lend its strength to the stretching material. The study of this phenomenon by Ames engineers was reported by Dell Williams and Howard Nelson in the paper, "Effect of Vacuum on the Tensile Properties of Magnesium Single Crystals," published in the *AIME Transactions* in July 1965.

In spacecraft design, plastics were used quite extensively for heat shields, thermal-control coatings, etc. Unfortunately, under a space environment, many plastic materials tend to evaporate, be clouded by ultraviolet radiation, be eroded by micrometeoroids, or suffer other detrimental effects. To study these effects in a fundamental way the Materials Branch undertook what it referred to as its "polymer program." Out of this program by the end of 1965 had come several research reports, one being TM X–54,030 by John Parker and Hermilo Gloria on "The Kinetics of the Vacuum Weight Loss of a Composite Comprising a Subliming Solid in an Inert

Polymer Matrix." There was also a series of papers on the mechanical properties of polymers, an example of which was TM X–54,020, "An Analytical Method for Evaluating the Effects of Radiation in Vacuum on the Mechanical Properties of Rigid Plastics," by Jerome J. Lohr and John A. Parker. Additionally, a study of the degradation of plastic materials exposed to ultraviolet radiation was being made in 1965 by Ronald Reinisch.

The Gasdynamics Branch was also much interested in certain materials problems. Carr Neel of that branch had for several years been investigating performance degradation, produced by the environment of space, of painted "thermal control" panels. The development of ablation materials was by 1965 becoming a rather sophisticated science, and it now seemed feasible to synthesize new ablation materials by altering the molecular structure of existing plastics in such a way as to make them more suitable for ablation purposes. So that such investigations could be pursued more effectively, a fine new chemical laboratory was being established in 1965, within the Gasdynamics Branch. John Parker, a well-known polymer chemist whose work has already been mentioned, was in charge of the new laboratory.

SPACECRAFT CONFIGURATION AND AIRFLOWS

The studies of spacecraft configurations and airflows undertaken at Ames during this period seemed to fall into four categories: theoretical or experimental studies of (1) basic airflows, (2) conical reentry bodies, (3) Apollo-type capsule configurations, and (4) lifting reentry bodies, in particular the M–2 configuration which originated at Ames.

In the first category, the analysis of the familiar blunt-body flow problem was continued in a study reported in TR R–204 by Harvard Lomax and Mamoru Inouye. At the same time, a less formal and very practical analytical approach to the blunt-body flow problem was made by Elliott Katzen and George Kaattari and reported in a paper entitled "Inviscid Hypersonic Flow around Blunt Bodies," which in 1964 was presented at a meeting of the American Institute of Aeronautics and Astronautics (AIAA).

In another phase of the basic-flow work, several studies were made of the effects of ablation on the aerodynamics of reentry bodies. This work is well represented by two important papers prepared in 1965 but not published until the following year. One of these, presented at an AIAA meeting in January 1966, was entitled "Free-Flight Aerodynamics of a Blunt-Faced Reentry Shape With and Without Ablation," by Lionel L. Levy, Jr., and Leroy S. Fletcher (ref. C–32). Special interest attached to this study because it employed the free-flight test method which had recently been developed by the Gasdynamics Branch for use in the vertical arc-jet tunnel. The second paper, prepared for an AGARD meeting in Brussels in May 1966, was entitled "Boundary Layer Separation and Reattachment With and Without Ablation," by Donald M. Kuehn and Daryl J. Monson. This work represented an extension of studies of boundary-layer separation on reentry bodies which Don Kuehn had been making for several years.

Also in the first category were two studies of a somewhat different type. One was TN D–2135 by Maurice Rasmussen and Don Kirk, which dealt with the pitching and yawing motions of a spinning symmetric missile. This study represented an extension of earlier work by both authors on the application of nonlinear analytical methods to the analysis of free-flight (HFF) model tests. The second study was TM X–54,045, "Electric Drag on Satellites—Theory and Experiment," by William C. Pitts and Earl D. Knechtel, which in April 1964 was presented at an AGARD meeting in Marseilles, France. This study evaluated the extremely small resistance to motion (drag) encountered by a satellite as a result of its passage through a flow (solar flux) of electrically charged particles. In determining the lifetime of a high-flying satellite, this "electric drag," though minute, may nevertheless be important.

The second category, the study of conical reentry bodies, is perhaps best represented by the work of Peter Intrieri and particularly his report TN D–3193 (ref. C–33) entitled, "Experimental Stability and Drag of a Pointed and a Blunted 30° Half-Angle Cone at Mach Numbers from 11.5 to 34 in Air." Another worthwhile study was made by Joe Cleary and reported in TN D–2969, "An Experimental and Theoretical Investigation of the Pressure Distribution and Flow Fields of Blunted Cones at Hypersonic Mach Numbers."

In the third category, the Apollo configuration, the work undertaken was quite extensive. Included in this effort was a study, reported by Louis Stivers in TM X–1081, in which measurements of forces and moments on an Apollo capsule were made at high air speeds and at angles of incidence ranging from −30° to +185°. There was also, as reported by Jack Mellenthin in TM X–1203, an investigation of an Apollo capsule model at Mach numbers up to 21.2 in a helium tunnel. Additionally, a particularly interesting study of the Apollo capsule was made in the 14-inch helium tunnel and reported by Joe Kemp in TM X–1154 (ref. C–34). This study, in which afterbody pressures of free-flying models were transmitted by telemetry, represented the first application of the free-flight testing technique in the helium tunnel. Out of the hypervelocity free-flight facility came another important study dealing with the Apollo capsule. Reported in TM X–1086 by Robert Sammonds, it was an investigation of the force and moment characteristics of the Apollo capsule at Mach numbers up to 35 in air. The effects of changing the corner radius of the capsule were investigated as one element of this study.

In the fourth—lifting-body—category, the work was a continuation of studies under way at the Center since 1957. Indeed, Ames from the first had been a major advocate of the lifting-body principle for spacecraft. In the press of competition the nonlifting body had been adopted for the first U.S.

451

man-in-space operation, but the advantages of the lifting reentry body became increasingly apparent and increasingly important as more advanced space missions came under consideration. It became clear that, as compared with a simple drag body, a lifting reentry body would widen the entry corridor, simplify the entry navigation task, and provide some control over entry heating and accelerations. It would also offer some latitude in choice of a landing site and permit a landing on solid earth, if desired, rather than at sea. The design of a lifting reentry vehicle was, however, a much more difficult and time-consuming task than the design of a nonlifting body and required a great deal of preliminary research. By the end of 1965, this research effort, being pursued elsewhere in the country as well as at Ames, had reached a fairly advanced state.

Among the major contributors to the lifting-body research work at Ames was the team of George Holdaway, Joe Kemp, and Tom Polek. As reported in TM X–1029 and TM X–1153, this trio investigated experimentally the control characteristics and horizontal landing capabilities of a variety of blunt, lifting reentry bodies. Among the many other contributors to the lifting-body studies during this period were John McDevitt, John Rakich, Gene Menees, Jack Mellenthin, John Axelson, Leland Jorgensen, George Kenyon, and Ronald Smith. In TN D–3218, Rakich and Menees reported on a series of tests in the 3.5-foot tunnel of flared bodies at incidence, while in TM X–950 Gene Menees and Willard Smith described reentry-body tests made alternately in air, carbon dioxide, and argon—the last two gases being regarded as likely constituents of the atmosphere of Mars.

The lifting-body configuration that Ames engineers considered most promising was one for which Al Eggers and his 10- by 14-inch-tunnel staff had laid down general design principles in 1957. This configuration—essentially a blunt, flat-topped semicone—was later, when fitted out with control and stabilizing surfaces, cockpit, and landing gear, given the name of M–2. Much effort was spent at Ames developing a practical configuration which would provide the necessary amount of lift, stability, and control while at the same time resisting the ravages of reentry aerodynamic heating. Toward this end development test work was conducted in the 11-foot, the 12-foot, the 3.5-foot, the 6- by 6-foot, and the 8- by 7-foot wind tunnels.

These tests provided the information required for the construction of a flying prototype, called the M2F1. The M2F1, made of plywood with a steel-tube frame, was a glider designed to be towed aloft by a DC–3 airplane and released. It, in large part, was built by the Briegleb Sailplane Corporation of America under contract with NASA. It was thoroughly tested in the 40- by 80-foot tunnel, and was then flight-tested at the NASA Flight Research Center at Edwards. The information gained from these and other tests was utilized in the design of a second, larger, more refined flight prototype, the M2F2, which the Northrop Aircraft Corp. built. The M2F2 was made of aluminum and, like the X–15, was designed to be carried aloft for

M2F2 reentry vehicle model in 40- by 80-foot tunnel.

launching by a B–52 airplane. In 1965 it was undergoing checkout tests in the 40- by 80-foot tunnel in preparation for later flight tests.

While Ames was concentrating its efforts on the M–2, considerably different reentry-vehicle configurations were being developed by the NASA Langley Research Center and the Air Force. Langley's design, called the HL–10, was shaped something like a high-prowed flat-bottom boat. In 1965 Northrop was building a flying model of the HL–10 for flight-testing at Edwards. It was planned that both the M2F2 and the HL–10 would later be fitted with 8000-pound-thrust engines. The flight tests of the M2F2 and the HL–10 were expected to provide a comparison of the low-speed, maneuvering, and landing characteristics of the two configurations but not of their high-speed reentry performance. The Air Force, however, was preparing to evaluate its design, called the SV–5D, at high speed by means of rocket-launched test flights.

Late in 1964 four members of the Ames research staff received special recognition from NASA Headquarters for their conception and development of the M–2 reentry vehicle. The four men were Alfred J. Eggers (who had recently joined the Headquarters staff), Clarence A. Syvertson, George G. Edwards, and George C. Kenyon.

SPACECRAFT FLIGHT STUDIES

Spacecraft reentry techniques and problems had been fairly well examined in earlier years; nevertheless, a few additional studies, relating to very high entry speeds, were made during this period. One of these, reported in TN D–2818 by Henry Lessing and Robert Coates, described an entry guid-

Contributors to M–2 development. From left to right: *George C. Kenyon, George G. Edwards, Dr. Alfred J. Eggers, and Clarence A. Syvertson.*

ance scheme appropriate for lifting-body entries made at speeds up to 50,000 feet per second. A second study was reported by Robert Carlson and Byron Swenson in a paper, "Maneuvering Flight within Earth-Entry Corridors at Hyperbolic Speeds" (ref. C–35), which in January 1965 was presented at a meeting of the AIAA. This study looked into the question of how much the entry corridor, already narrow because of the high entry speeds, might be further restricted by the probable imprecision of the onboard knowledge regarding entry angle, velocity, and altitude. It thus dealt with a very practical problem relating to manned spacecraft returning from interplanetary missions.

Devices that control the attitude of a vehicle in space generally utilize power generated by gas jets, inertia wheels, or other means. These devices may be made to operate automatically or, if a pilot is present, they may be controlled manually. The design and efficient use of a manually controlled jet system were matters of some interest to Ames engineers and there was a question of how well a pilot could control the attitude of his spaceship in the vacuum of space. Out of this interest came TN D–2068, "Simulator Studies of the Manual Control of Vehicle Attitude Using an On-Off Reaction Control System," by Armando Lopez and Donald W. Smith.

The possibility of using gravitational force to stabilize a space vehicle and keep it pointed at the earth was at this time well understood in principle, but much remained to be learned about the practical application of such a scheme. The problem was studied by Bruce Tinling and Vernon Merrick, who then prepared a paper on "The Status of Passive-Gravity-Gradient Stabilization" for presentation in June 1965 at the International Federation of Automatic Control Symposium in Stavanger, Norway.

RESEARCH

A substantial number of the spacecraft flight studies undertaken at Ames during this period were aimed at solving the guidance and control problems of the Apollo spacecraft. This work came under the surveillance of a special Apollo Guidance and Control Team established at Ames under the leadership of Merrill Mead in September 1961. The principal matters to be considered by this team were (1) the problems of midcourse navigation, and (2) how best to use a human pilot in reentry. Among the studies bearing on the problems was one reported in TN D–2697, "Application of Statistical Filter-Theory to the Interplanetary Navigation and Guidance Problem," by John S. White, George P. Callas, and Luigi G. Cicolani. Studies were also made of the feasibility of using handheld sextants for space-navigation purposes. Several important papers were written on this subject, one of which was TN D–2844, "Investigation of a Manual Sextant-Sighting Task in the Ames Midcourse Navigation and Guidance Simulator," by Bedford A. Lampkin and Robert J. Randle. The sextant used in this case was one which Ames scientists had modified and specially adapted for space navigation. Plans were being made in 1965 for experiments with the sextant in space during the projected flight of Gemini XII.

Early manned space flights had been controlled largely by automatic means but, as more experience was gained in such flight operations, an increasing interest was taken in the abilities of the pilot and crew to guide and control their spacecraft. The sextant sighting study just mentioned was one of many attempts to investigate this matter at Ames. One of these, amply described by its title, was TN D–2807, "Evaluation of Pilot's Ability to Stabilize a Flexible Launch Vehicle during First-Stage Boost," by Gordon H. Hardy and James West. In this study the Ames five-degrees-of-freedom flight simulator proved very useful. Another investigation of the same general character was reported in TN D–2467 (ref. C–36), "A Study of the Pilot's Ability to Control an Apollo Type Vehicle during Atmosphere Entry," by Rodney C. Wingrove, Glen W. Stinnett, and Robert C. Innis. This study, also performed with the five-degrees-of-freedom simulator, brought the reentry task down to a very personal and practical level. Wingrove's work in the reentry field had been quite outstanding and included the paper, delivered in June 1965 in Norway, on "Guidance and Control in Supercircular Atmosphere Entry."

Pilot performance under conditions of stress—such as might be encountered in space flight—was also investigated at Ames. Representative of this work is the study described in TN D–2710, "Effect of Combined Linear and Oscillatory Acceleration on Pilot-Attitude Control Capabilities," by C. B. Dolkas and John D. Stewart. The physical limitations of the pilot with respect to the withstanding of accelerations was a critical matter in space flight. Accordingly, a great deal of effort was spent in devising special restraining harnesses, or suits, that would enable the pilot better to withstand acceleration loads. At Ames a very promising restraining harness and suit were de-

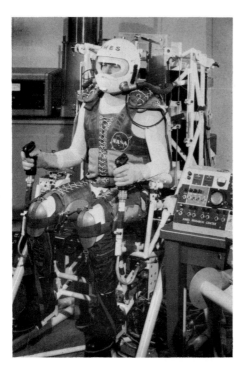

Pilot restraint suit developed at Ames, worn by Robert Innis.

Rodney C. Wingrove.

Ames researchers, left to right: *Norman S. Johnson, George E. Cooper, Dr. G. Allan Smith, Mark W. Kelly, Woodrow L. Cook, and John S. White.*

veloped by Hubert C. Vykukal and E. Gene Lyman. As 1965 ended, the evaluation of this equipment was about to begin. Vykukal had been working on such matters for years and in 1963 had been accorded recognition for the design and development of a "universal pilot restraint suit."

During this period a number of Ames engineers received honors and awards for their work in space-flight guidance research. In 1963, John White and Rodney Wingrove jointly won the Dr. Samuel Burka Award of the Institute of Navigation for their analysis of guidance and navigation problems connected with manned missions to the moon. In 1965, Rodney Wingrove was chosen to receive the AIAA Lawrence Sperry Award for his contributions to controlled reentry and precise landings of U.S. manned spacecraft. Also in 1965 Gerald L. Smith was honored by his agency for having developed a computer analysis which resulted in a NASA decision to give ground-based navigation a primary role during Apollo lunar missions.

MISSION STUDIES

Much interest existed during this period in the exploration of neighboring planets—particularly Mars, since that planet was reasonably accessible, had surface features which had long intrigued astronomers, and seemed more likely than any of the others to harbor some form of life. The Mars landing, it was felt, would probably be made first by an instrument package and, much later, by human beings. Before even an instrument package could be landed safely, it would be desirable, Ames engineers realized, to obtain much more information about the atmosphere of the planet.

Al Seiff, on giving thought to this matter, concluded that much could be learned about the structure and chemical composition of the atmosphere of a planet from the dynamic response and gas-cap radiation of an instrumented probe vehicle as it penetrated the planet's atmosphere in a crash landing. The structure (pressure-density-altitude relationship) of the atmosphere could be deduced from the motions of the probe—telemeterd back to earth—and the chemical composition might be revealed by the gas-cap radiation measurements—also telemetered back to earth. The technique as conceived represented a wholly new approach to the study of planetary atmospheres and Seiff realized that it might well provide the basis for a useful planetary probe mission. His thoughts regarding such a mission were developed in 1962 and published in April 1963 as TN D–1770, "Some Possibilities for Determining the Characteristics of the Atmosphere of Mars and Venus from Gas-Dynamic Behavior of a Probe Vehicle." This paper was followed by others, including one, "Defining Mars' Atmosphere—A Goal for the Early Missions" (ref. C–37), which Al Seiff and Dave Reese prepared in 1964 for presentation to the AIAA.

Seiff's enthusiasm for the Mars probe project aroused the interest of others and considerable research bearing on the project was undertaken. At-

David E. Reese and Alvin Seiff.

tempts to devise engineering models of the Mars atmosphere were made by the team of G. M. Levin, D. E. Evans, and V. I. Stevens,[2] and also by H. E. Bailey. These efforts were reported in TN D–2525 and SP–3014. Also, as reported by Victor Peterson in TN D–2669 and TR R–225, techniques for determining the structure of planetary atmospheres through probe operations were devised and evaluated for accuracy.

The application of the probe method of planetary atmosphere determination required more theoretical and experimental information on the flow properties of gas mixtures than was then available. Accordingly, tests involving the use of various gases were instituted in several facilities including the 1-foot shock tunnel and the 3.5-foot tunnel. Some of these tests have already been mentioned. Theoretical analyses were also instituted. One of these is reported in TR R–222, "Equations for Isentropic and Plane-Shock Flows of Mixtures of Undissociated Planetary Gases," by Victor Peterson.

The dynamic stability of the Mars probe was also a matter of serious concern to Ames engineers. This was investigated in a general way by Murray Tobak and Victor Peterson. This team produced two reports, one of which was TR R–210, "Angle of Attack Convergence of Spinning Bodies Entering Planetary Atmospheres." The other was TR R–203 (ref. C–38), "Theory of Tumbling Bodies Entering Planetary Atmospheres With Application to Probe Vehicles and the Australian Tektites." In addition, the general aerodynamics problem of the Mars probe was covered in a paper by Leland Jorgensen, "Aerodynamics of Planetary Entry Configurations in Air and Assumed Martian Atmospheres," published by the AIAA in 1966.

While the Mars atmosphere probe, owing to its early feasibility, ab-

---

[2] G. M. Levin of the Goddard Space Flight Center, D. E. Evans of the Manned Spacecraft Center, and V. I. Stevens of the Ames Research Center were members of an Ad Hoc Planetary Atmospheres Committee established by the NASA Office of Advanced Research and Technology.

sorbed much attention at Ames, interest continued at the Center in landing a man on Mars. The manned Mars mission was analyzed by the Ames staff and also, in greater detail, by several commercial aerospace companies operating under NASA contracts. One of the Ames studies is reported in TN D–2225 (ref. C–39), "A Parametric Study of Mass-Ratio and Trajectory Factors in Fast Manned Mars Missions," by Duane W. Dugan. Another study, which related to both the manned Mars and the Mars probe missions, was reported by Robert McKenzie in TN D–2584, "Some Effects of Uncertainties in Atmospheric Structure and Chemical Composition on Entry Into Mars."

Also to be mentioned was the development of the Venus Swingby technique, whereby the braking effect of the gravitational attraction of Venus would be used to slow the reentry speed of a space vehicle returning from a mission to Mars. Analysis had shown that Mars-mission reentry speeds, which might otherwise amount to 75,000 feet per second, could be reduced through the use of the Venus Swingby technique to 50,000 feet per second or less. Work on this important development was led by Harold Hornby of the Ames Mission Analysis Division and carried out under contract with Ames by the Thompson Ramo Wooldridge Corp.

Aerodynamic Heating, Ablation, and Radiation

Research in the general field of aerodynamic heating, radiation, and ablation continued in 1963–1965 to represent a substantial portion of the effort of the Ames Research Center. The work was quite diverse but seemed to fall roughly into four categories: (1) physics of gases, (2) convective heat transfer, (3) ablation, and (4) radiation. There was, of course, considerable overlapping between these categories.

The work on physics of gases was carried on by the Magnetoplasmadynamics Branch of the Thermo- and Gasdynamics Division as well as by the Physics Branch of the Vehicle Environment Division. The Magnetoplasmadynamics Branch was using the arc-jet in studies of the chemistry and thermodynamics of high-temperature gases. This work was of fundamental significance and also contributed to further arc-jet development. The efforts of the Physics Branch were concentrated by the end of 1965 in the fields of chemical kinetics, atomic collisions, and vacuum ultraviolet radiation. Ultraviolet radiation was now of interest to Ames research people inasmuch as the frequency of radiation produced by a reentry body moved into the ultraviolet range as reentry speeds increased and gas-cap disturbances became more violent.

Representative of the numerous technical papers that resulted from physics-of-gases work at Ames during this period was TN D–2611, "A Critical Evaluation of Existing Methods for Calculating Transport Coefficients of Partially and Fully Ionized Gases," by Warren F. Ahtye. There were also

TN D–2794, "The Vacuum Ultraviolet Radiation from N^+ Electron and O^+ Electron Recombination in High Temperature Air," by G. Hahne, and a paper by Leroy Presley and Charles Chackerian, "Chemical Kinetics Studies of CO in an Arc Discharge Shock Tube," which in 1965 was presented at a meeting of the American Physical Society. Additionally, there was TN D–2678, "Effects of Uncertainties in the Thermal Conductivity of Air on Convective Heat Transfer for Stagnation Temperatures up to 30,000° K," by John T. Howe and Yvonne S. Sheaffer.

The studies of convective heat transfer undertaken during this period were often concerned with the tremendously high reentry speeds of vehicles returning to earth from planetary missions or with the aerodynamic heating that would be encountered by a vehicle penetrating the atmosphere of a foreign planet such as Mars or Venus. Under consideration at this time were reentry speeds of up to 70,000 feet per second and stagnation temperatures of up to 24,000° K—up to four times the temperature of the surface of the sun. At these speeds and temperatures, the heating of a blunt reentry body would come primarily from radiation; but Allen and others had shown that the radiation component could be greatly reduced, and the aerodynamic heating confined largely to convective heating, if the front face of the reentry body was made in the shape of a cone the included angle of which was decreased as the entry speed increased. Thus, even at the highest reentry speeds, convective heating remained a very important factor as did also the condition of the boundary layer—laminar or turbulent—upon which convective heat transfer is strongly dependent. Moreover, it was now clear that, owing to the threat of radiation, convective heating could be controlled only by ablation and not, as in days of yore, by body blunting.

Among the many studies of convective heat transfer made by Ames engineers, those described in the following papers might be taken as representative: TN D–2463 (ref. C–40), "Theoretical Laminar Convective Heat Transfer and Boundary-Layer Characteristics on Cones at Speeds to 24 Km/Sec" (nearly 80,000 feet per second), by Gary T. Chapman; TR R–224 (ref. C–41), "Convective Heat Transfer in Planetary Gases," by Joseph G. Marvin and George S. Deiwert; TN D–3017, "Pressure and Convective Heat Transfer Measurements in a Shock Tunnel Using Several Test Gases," by Joseph G. Marvin and Clifford M. Atkin; TN D–2871 (ref. C–42), "Free-Flight Measurements of Stagnation-Point Convective Heat Transfer at Velocities to 41,000 Ft/Sec," by Dale L. Compton and David M. Cooper; and TM X–1096, "Free-Flight Measurement of Heat Transferred to the Apollo Afterbody With and Without Ablation," by Layton Yee. The measurement of heat transfer in free-flight facilities was difficult at best and novel methods were devised for its accomplishment. Thus Compton and Cooper in their study determined stagnation temperatures and corresponding heat transfer at test speeds higher than had ever before been obtained by observing the point in the trajectory at which melting of aluminum models began to occur.

Numerous studies of ablation were undertaken during this period. Ablation had become the generally accepted method of protecting spacecraft against the rigors of reentry heating; but the more the ablation process was studied, the more complex it appeared. The process was particularly difficult to treat analytically. Mathematical description of gas-cap conditions, at best almost impossible, became still more difficult with the addition of chemically reactive ablation products to the gases normally present. Moreover, the ablation process itself, and the thermal protection it provided, were quite complex. It was known that an ablation material changing in state, in a non-chemical reaction, from a solid to a liquid to a gas would absorb heat and that the relatively cool ablation gases flowing along the body would fend off the hot gases in the gas cap, thus reducing convective heat transfer to the body. It was also known that under certain conditions some of the melted ablation material would be swept away in waves and thus would fail to complete its cooling mission.

There was, however, much more to the ablation process than the effects just noted. In ablators of current interest, such as those which were made of phenolic nylon, the aerodynamic heating would cause a chemical reaction, a pyrolysis, in the plastic and the resulting vapor would then itself often react chemically (sometimes burn) with the gas-cap gases. The reaction, or pyrolysis, zone in the ablator would gradually work inward from the surface leaving a porous char layer through which the ablation vapors would percolate. If the gas-cap atmosphere contained oxygen (not present in the Mars atmosphere), the ablation vapors and the char-layer surface would tend to burn, thus adding to—not subtracting from—the heat load. However, the char-layer surface would get very hot and dissipate some of its heat by radiation. Thus the whole pattern of convective and radiative heating in the gas cap was materially affected by the ablation process as was also the character of the boundary layer.

The action of the ablator, in all of its ramifications, was difficult of comprehension, but experimentation had confirmed its effectiveness in protecting space vehicles. Of all of the beneficial actions of an ablator, the most important, perhaps, was the fending off of the hot gases by the ablation vapors. The radiation of heat by the char layer had also been found to be important.

A group of six research papers may be cited as representative of the ablation studies at Ames during the period 1963–1965. One was TR R–207 (ref. C–43), "Mass Addition in the Stagnation Region for Velocity up to 50,000 Feet per Second," by John T. Howe and Yvonne S. Sheaffer. In this paper, Howe and Sheaffer undertook the difficult analysis of gas-cap flow to which ablation by-products had been added. Another paper was TN

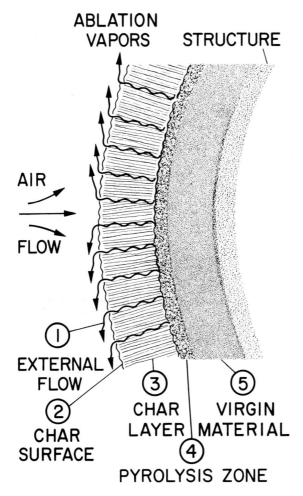

ABLATION VAPORS

STRUCTURE

AIR

FLOW

① EXTERNAL FLOW

② CHAR SURFACE

③ CHAR LAYER

④ PYROLYSIS ZONE

⑤ VIRGIN MATERIAL

Ablation heat-protection mechanisms. (1) External flow: (a) Blockage of convective heat by ablation vapors and (b) Heat produced by combustion of vapors. (2) Char surface: (a) Heat radiated by char and (b) Heat produced by char combustion. (3) Char layer: (a) Heat absorbed by char sublimation, (b) Heat absorbed by vapors, and (c) Heat absorbed by char. (4) Pyrolysis zone: Heat absorbed by pyrolysis. (5) Virgin material: Heat absorbed by material.

D–2437, "Heat Transfer Measurement for Binary Gas Laminar Boundary Layers with High Rates of Injection," by C. C. Pappas and Arthur F. Okuno. In the work described here, the authors injected gas into the boundary layer to evaluate the major benefit of ablation which arises from fending off the hot gases. This effect could not be determined in tests made with a solid ablator inasmuch as it would be obscured by chemical, and other, reactions produced by the ablator. Another paper in this group, one which was presented at an AIAA meeting in July 1965, was entitled "Generalized Ablation Analysis With Application to Heat Shield Materials and Tektite Glass," by Fred W. Matting and Dean R. Chapman. A useful computer program for ablation analysis was developed in this study.

Additional papers in the group on ablation included one, published in a 1964 issue of the *AIAA Journal*, entitled "Effect of Gas Composition on

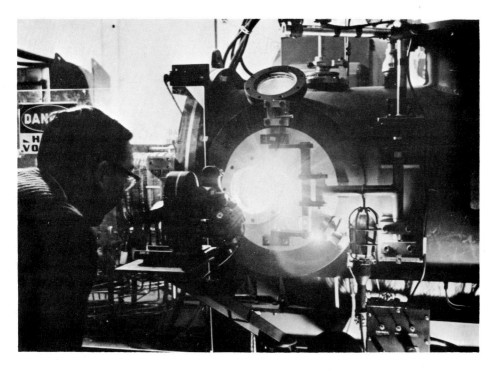

Arc-jet entry heating simulator in operation with John Lundell observing test.

the Ablation Behavior of a Charring Material," by Nick S. Vojvodich and Ronald Pope. Another paper published in the *AIAA Journal* in 1965 was "Experimental Investigation of a Charring Ablative Material Exposed to Combined Convective and Radiative Heating" (ref. C–44), by John H. Lundell, Roy M. Wakefield, and Jerold W. Jones. Finally, a review of Ames work on ablation was prepared by Brad Wick and presented in a paper entitled "Ablation Characteristics and Their Evaluation by Means of Arc Jets and Arc Radiation Sources." In June 1965 Brad delivered this paper before the Seventh International Aeronautical Congress held in Paris.

Radiation, as produced by reentry vehicles, also received much attention at Ames during these years. Radiative heating was known to decrease very rapidly with the backward inclination of the bow shock wave. Thus, by using a pointed conical body, which produced an inclined shock, it could be kept under control. The trouble was that the normal ablation processes rapidly blunted the conical point and when that occurred, a vertical (normal) shock would form in front of the blunted portion. Control of radiative heating thus depended on the designer's ability to ensure that all portions of the bow shock wave maintained a backward tilt.

While many radiation studies were made in the arc-jet facilities at

463

William A. Page.

Ames, gas-cap radiation could be truly represented only in the hypervelocity free-flight facilities. It was thus not surprising that much of the radiation research effort was concentrated in the HFF Branch headed by Tom Canning and Bill Page. Indeed, the HFF radiation team, headed by Page, was believed to be one of the most knowledgeable groups of reentry radiation experts in the country.

Although the HFF facility was able to reproduce gas-cap radiation phenomena, it did not, for obvious reasons, lend itself to easy radiation measurements. Much ingenuity was therefore exercised in devising methods for measuring the radiation, and the distribution of radiation, in the gas caps of fast-flying models. When it came to measuring ultraviolet radiation, which is absorbed by air, the problem of measurement in the HFF facilities seemed almost insurmountable. Almost it was, but not quite. Dale Compton, one of the clever chaps in the HFF radiation team, solved the problem by using the ultraviolet radiation detector as the target for the speeding test model. Thus the detector, in the barest instant before being struck by the model, was reading the true value of ultraviolet radiation.

A number of the technical papers resulting from the research performed by the HFF radiation group bear mentioning. Among these is TM X–852, "Measurements of Spatial Distribution of Shock Layer Radiation for Blunt Bodies at Hypersonic Speeds," by John Givens, Thomas N. Canning, and Harry Bailey. Another, published in the *Journal of Quantitative Spectroscopy and Radiative Transfer,* is entitled "Oscillator Strengths for the N_2 Second Positive and N_2^+ First Negative Systems From Observations of Shock Layers About Hypersonic Projectiles," by Victor H. Reis. Still another important document was TR R–193 (ref. C–45), "Shock-Layer Radiation of Blunt Bodies at Reentry Velocities," by William A. Page and James O. Arnold. In addition to these, there was a study, reported by Jack Stephenson in TN D–2710, of the radiation emanating from the glowing wake of ablating blunt bodies.

Some very fundamental theoretical studies of radiation phenomena were made by such men as Max Heaslet, Franklyn Fuller, Barrett Baldwin, W. P. Jones, and Walter Pearson. Out of their work came a number of reports of which two are representative: TN D–2128, "On the Direct Solution of the Governing Equation for Radiation-Resisted Shock Waves," by Walter E. Pearson; and TN D–2515 (ref. C–46), "Approximate Predictions of the Transport of Thermal Radiation Through an Absorbing Plane Layer," by Max A. Heaslet and Franklyn B. Fuller.

IMPACT PHYSICS AND METEORS

A surprising interest in meteors developed at Ames. It was related in part to practical matters but also to broad philosophical questions—such as the origin of the solar system. Meteor impact was of interest in connection with the damage it might do to spacecraft; meteor flight was of interest because it provided a means of studying aerodynamic heating and ablation at speeds (up to 50 miles per second) so far unattainable in the laboratory; and meteor composition and shape were of interest because of what they might reveal about the composition and origin of our solar system. All told, meteors provided Ames scientists with a very satisfying and rather open-ended field of study.

The meteors that had produced the large craters on the moon were obviously large as were also a few that had left evidence on the earth. It appeared, however, that the overwhelming majority of such bodies were small —their size ranging down to, or less than, that of a small marble. In substantial part, therefore, meteor studies were concerned with small objects, essentially cosmic dust.

Most meteorites,[3] it appears, fall into two broad classes depending on composition. Stony meteorites, the first and more common class, are composed of stony or rocklike materials. One variety, the chondrites, contain tiny globular occlusions (chondrules) which may have been formed by condensation from a primordial solar nebula. Iron meteorites, the second class, are in large part composed of iron and nickel and are about twice as dense as the stony variety. In addition to the two main classes, there are also tektites, composed of siliceous glass of somewhat lower density than the stones. Finally, although none has been found on earth, there is some evidence of the existence of a very low-density variety of meteoroid which at Ames was identified by the name "fluffy."

Although the speed of meteoroids was beyond the capabilities of Ames test facilities, Ames engineers had, as earlier reported, been able to use the Ames impact range to assess the threat to spacecraft arising from meteo-

[3] A meteorite is what remains of a meteor or meteoroid that has come to rest on earth.

roid impacts. During 1963–1965, the Ames impact range proved useful for investigating the impact characteristics of certain man-made meteoroids as well as for further generalized studies of the impact phenomena. Two papers relating to this work may be cited.

One of these reports is TN D–1981, "Investigation of the Impact of Copper Filaments into Aluminum Targets at Velocities to 16,000 Feet per Second," by C. Robert Nysmith, James L. Summers, and B. Pat Denardo. The filaments used in the experiments were very fragile threads of copper, a few thousandths of an inch thick and three-quarters of an inch long. They resembled the filaments which, as contemplated in the Air Force's "West Ford" project, were to be orbited by the billions into a radio-wave-reflecting band around the earth. The study reported in TN D–1981 suggested what might happen to a fast-traveling spacecraft that encountered such man-made projectiles in space. The copper filaments were far too fragile to be hurled down the impact range at the target. Instead, one was supported on threads in the range and the target, an aluminum sphere, was hurled at it. The tests showed that the filament, hit end on, would at speeds of 16,000 feet per second penetrate the aluminum sphere to a depth of about four-tenths of an inch.

The second report to be mentioned is TN D–3369 (ref. C–47), "Penetration of Polyethylene Into Semi-Infinite 2024–T351 Aluminum up to Velocities of 37,000 Feet per Second," by B. Pat Denardo. This study was parti-

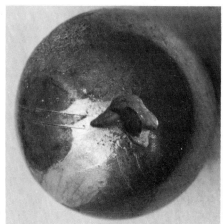

Left: cross section of an aluminum sphere penetrated by fine copper filament showing a penetration of over 0.4 inch. Right: Front view showing point of entry of the filament.

cularly notable because it established a world speed record for guns. Never before had a projectile been hurled so fast by a gun. The advances made by Ames in gun development were evident. In this case, the gun used a 125-gram powder charge exploding behind a 100-gram polyethylene deformable piston to compress hydrogen gas which drove the projectile out of the barrel. The projectile was photographed by cameras operating with exposure times, as controlled by Kerr-cell shutters, of 5 billionths of a second. The impact with the target was made at a speed well above that (25,000 fps) at which the target material became fluid and confirmed the earlier established relationship that the penetration of a spherical projectile into a target, and thus the volume of material ejected, varies as the two-thirds power of the projectile velocity expressed as a fraction of the speed of sound in the target material. This speed criterion was thus in the nature of an impact Mach number.

While the work just mentioned was going on in the impact range, Donald Gault and William Quaide of the Space Sciences Division were intently pursuing their studies of impact cratering in materials considered representative of the surfaces of the earth and the moon. The new vertical impact range proved very useful in these studies though it could not reproduce the highest meteor speeds and there were also some questions about scale effect. The speed of the vertical gun was, nevertheless, such that it could at least reproduce the lower end of the lunar primary impact velocities and the full range for the secondary impacts produced by ejecta from primary meteor impacts. Regarding scale effect Gault, Quaide, and Verne Oberbeck obtained reassuring evidence from craters produced at the White Sands Proving Ground by the impact of missiles.

The White Sands evidence also confirmed the impact-range observations that an impact in sand, regardless of the angle of missile approach, would produce a circularly symmetrical crater—in top view. Impact in rock, however, produced a different result which, at least at the lower speeds (of secondary impacts), depended very much on the strength of the target material. Owing to the natural fractures in rock, impacts in such material often produced a squarish crater.

In 1965, Gault and his colleagues were using a new technique for studying the flow of material in impact craters. In this technique, targets having strengths as desired are made from quartz sand bonded by thermosetting cement. The sand is laminated in thin horizontal or vertical layers, each layer being stained with a different color. After the target has been impacted, it is carefully sectioned by sawing. The distortion of the different strata can thus be easily observed and measured. Through the use of this technique, it has been possible at Ames to reproduce in the laboratory many of the peculiar structures found in natural craters. Credit for the method of building the targets goes to Andre Bogart and his coworkers of the Model Construction Branch.

Impact in stratified sand target. The sand is colored and bonded with thermo-setting cement.

In their cratering work, Gault and his staff had cooperated closely with people of the U.S. Geological Survey office in nearby Menlo Park. Together they had become a team of world authorities on impact cratering. In behalf of the International Astrophysical Union, three of this team—Don Gault, Bill Quaide, and Verne Oberbeck—undertook an interpretation of the photographs of the lunar surface taken by *Ranger* IX. The study was reported in a paper entitled "Interpreting Ranger Photographs from Impact Cratering Studies."

Gault's cratering studies had involved considerations of the physical nature of the cratering process as well as of the character and trajectories of the material ejected. He had concluded that material was regularly escaping from the moon as a result of impacts of meteor showers—remnants, perhaps, of comets—and that some of it, together with material from remoter origins, was reaching the earth. These considerations encouraged an interest among members of his staff in the nature of the extraterrestrial material and in the possibility that scientifically interesting information could be obtained from it. Interest in these matters led to a fairly intensive study of the composition, origin, and probable thermodynamic history of meteoritic materials.

In 1964–1965, the Space Sciences Planetology Branch participated in the Luster project, an operation in which meteoric particles in space were collected by means of a space probe. Part of the collected material was subjected to chemical analysis at Ames as were also certain meteorites that had been found years earlier on the surface of the earth. The particles examined were often very small, which would have made chemical analysis difficult had it not been for the recent commercial development of an instrument called an electron microprobe. This instrument was capable of nondestructive chemical analysis of a particle only a few thousandths of a millimeter in diameter. The technique was to bombard the specimen with a finely focused beam of high-energy electrons whereupon the specimen would emit X-rays in a pattern of wavelengths and intensities characteristic of the materials present. The emitted pattern was analyzed by means of an X-ray detection system.

Leader of the analytical work on meteorite composition was Dr. Klaus Keil, a brilliant NAS Fellow from Germany who later became a permanent Ames employee. While examining a stony meteorite (enstatite chondrite) which in 1926 had fallen near the Pakistanian village of Jajh deh Kot Lalu, Keil and his colleagues discovered within the meteorite an occlusion of a new material, silicon oxynitride (Si_2N_2O). The new mineral, which they chose to call "sinoite," had only recently been produced in a laboratory by a team of Swedish scientists; it had never before been discovered in a natural state on earth and presumably could not have been generated in any recent earth environment.

The finding was first reported in the October 9, 1964, issue of *Science* by its discoverers, Christian A. Andersen of the Hasler Research Center, Goleta, California, Klaus Keil of Ames, and Brian Mason of the American Museum of Natural History, New York. More details of the finding were given in a paper (ref. C–48) entitled "Electron Microprobe Study of the Jajh deh Kot Lalu Enstatite Chondrite," by Klaus Keil and Christian Andersen.

Keil's studies of chondrites led him to believe that they may have come from small planetary bodies which condensed directly from the solar nebula at about the same time—perhaps $4\frac{1}{2}$ billion years ago—that the earth was formed. Inasmuch as the earth's rocks have since remelted one or more times, the chondritic material appeared to be a billion or more years older than the oldest rocks discovered on earth. Meteorites thus provide clues, otherwise unavailable on earth, of the primordial materials and environment that existed during the formation of our solar system.

Keil and his associates also examined iron and stony meteorites to determine from their grain structure the rate at which the material cooled following the solidification process. The cooling rate suggests the depth to which they were buried in the planetary bodies of which, presumably, the meteorite was originally a part. For the meteorites examined, the indications of this analysis are that the burial depth was fairly shallow—150 miles or less.

In the meantime, and throughout the period 1963–1965, Dean Chapman continued his scientific search for the origin of tektites—those glasslike pellets which in great numbers had been discovered in the Australasian region from Tasmania to the Philippines. Dean's detective work had by 1965 become one of the most fascinating displays of scientific virtuosity in the annals of the Ames Research Center. Helping him in this work were Howard Larson, Fred Matting, Frank Centolanzi, and others. The best record of Chapman's tektite studies during this period exists in his paper (ref. C–49) entitled "On the Unity and Origin of the Australasian Tektites," published in *Geochimica et Cosmochimica Acta*, 1964.

Through careful measurements made on thousands of tektites, Dean and his colleagues determined that despite the variation in physical appearance of tektites from different parts of the Australasian area, they were nevertheless of common age and common origin—which he was convinced was the moon. Their age since last solidification, as determined by both the argon-potassium and the uranium-fission age-dating processes, was 700,000 years. These were by far the youngest tektites found on earth. Tektites found in Czechoslovakia were about 15 million years old and others found in the United States (Georgia and Texas) were still older—about 35 million years.

The youth of the Australasian tektites no doubt accounted for the fact that the ablation pattern, produced by their entry into the earth's atmosphere, had not been worn off in all cases by chemical and physical erosion occurring on earth. And from the ablation pattern and other clues, Dean was able to deduce their entry speed (about 7 miles per second) and entry angle. He was also able to explain the differences in shape of the Australasian tektites—why those that fell in southeast Australia were often nice round little buttons, while those from areas farther north tended to be irregular blobs. If the tektite material had been splashed from the moon, the buttons would come from the hotter, less viscous, central part of the splash and the stringy blobs from the cooler, more viscous, outer portions. The spray of Australasian tektites, Dean concluded, had moved from south to north.

Opponents of the lunar-origin theory pointed out that, from the moon, the earth blocks out only 1/15,000th of the celestial sphere; thus the probability that a splash from the moon would ever hit the earth would be very small, and if it did, they said, it would sweep over the whole earth and not just Australasia. But Dean, with the help of his colleagues at Ames, and an IBM 7094 computer, made trajectory studies which showed that, because of the earth's gravitational pull, the probability that a lunar splash might hit the earth was much greater than the 1 in 15,000 cited by the objectors and was indeed about 1 in 200—as an average for all possible points of origin on the moon.

Then from lunar photographs, Dean selected 10 of the youngest (700,000 years considered very young) craters—ones in which the rays of ejected material were still clearly visible—and made trajectory studies to determine whether some narrow stream of molten ejecta from any one of the craters could have reached the earth and, if so, what its landing pattern would have been. He found that the probability of an earth hit from most of the craters, including one on the back side, was quite high (as high as 1 in 60 in one case) but that from only one, Tycho, would the landing pattern correspond to the distribution of Australasian tektites. Tycho, a crater over 50 miles in diameter located in the lower left quadrant of the moon, had in some past millennium been formed by a cataclysmic event of such

Lunar crater Tycho. (Lick Observatory photo.)

appalling magnitude that it might be likened to the ramming several miles into the earth of the combined city and suburbs of Los Angeles.

The spurts of ejecta from a crater, as evidenced by the lunar rays and as observed in impact tests at Ames, are very narrow and the dispersion of those coming from a lunar crater would be further restricted by the focusing effect of the earth's gravitational field. It was clear from the trajectory analysis that the landing pattern of a stream of ejecta from the moon might well be restricted to a fairly small portion of the earth's surface. The analysis had, indeed, indicated the exact angle at which a spurt of ejecta would have had to emerge from Tycho if it were to produce the observed pattern of Australasian tektites. Chapman set his protractor at that angle and laid it on an enlarged photograph of Tycho. Under the protractor's edge lay a prominent ray!

Many simplifying assumptions had been required in making the trajectory analysis and Dean offered no assertions that the Australasian tektites came from Tycho. He remained firmly convinced, however, that they came from the moon. A few of the scientists who earlier opposed this view had yielded a little in the face of Chapman's convincing evidence. As 1965 ended, however, the Nobel Laureate appeared to be holding his ground in opposition.

In October 1963, at a ceremony in which Vice President Lyndon B. Johnson was principal speaker, Dean was presented with NASA's highest scientific award, its Medal for Exceptional Scientific Achievement. He was the first man at Ames to receive this award.

Harvey Allen shared in the general interest in meteors that prevailed at Ames during this period. His special concern with the subject, however, was to gain information on aerodynamic heating that might be useful in the de-

Dr. Dean R. Chapman and Vice President Lyndon B. Johnson examining tektite.

sign of some future space vehicle. That, at least, was the nominal objective; but scientific curiosity, unrelated to practical application, was certainly one of the influences which each year led him more deeply into the subject. By the end of 1965 he had become an authority on meteor flight and kept in touch with meteor observation groups in the United States, Canada, and Europe.

The difficulties of increasing the speed potentialities of laboratory test facilities had become so great that the thoughts of Ames engineers had turned to meteors as a possible source of information on high-speed heating effects. Meteors were known to travel at speeds from 7 to 50 miles per second, and their flashing entry into the earth's atmosphere was a common and readily observable occurrence. Astronomers had in fact been making photographic records of meteor trails for many years. Unfortunately for the purpose of their study, most meteors are very small and only a few of the larger ones reach the earth and are recovered for inspection. Moreover, as Allen pointed out, the visible flight of most meteors occurs at an altitude at which the air is too tenuous to act as a continuous medium or to form a shock layer, or gas cap, ahead of the meteor. Much of the meteor evidence is thus lacking in practical value for the aerodynamicist. Nevertheless, it was felt at Ames that useful information was obtainable from the evidence provided by the rather few large meteors that fall, and the Center encouraged the observatories to obtain more and better information on future events of this kind.

The evidence of meteor flight regularly obtained by the observatories consists of precisely timed photographs obtained by two cameras separated by a known distance, and also of photometric measurements of the luminous intensity of the meteor throughout its visible flight path. The camera data provide altitude, flight-path angle, and a time history of velocity and deceleration. Such data also allow the calculation of the rate of ablation—the change in diameter of the meteor—if the density is known. However, unless the meteorite is recovered, its density is difficult to determine. The luminosity data can be used to estimate the rate of mass loss; and Allen, through the use of a rather devious procedure, was able to show that the density could also be estimated. It was clear to Ames engineers that the interpretation of meteor observations could be greatly aided by a program of laboratory tests aimed at the evaluation of such factors as the luminous efficiency and the ablation characteristics of meteoritic materials.

Allen had gone into the meteor-analysis methods with some thoroughness in the report TN D–2068, "Prospects for Obtaining Aerodynamic Heating Results from Analysis of Meteor Flight Data," by H. Julian Allen and Nataline A. James. Along another tack, he and his colleagues, aided by a large electronic computer, calculated the performance of four series of hypothetical meteors, each series composed of a different material (stone, iron, pumice, and tektite glass) and covering a range of meteoroid diameters (0.4

to 0.000001 inch) and a range of entry speeds (7 to 45 miles per second). This very interesting study was reported in TN D–2872 (ref. C–50), "Effect on Meteor Flight of Cooling by Radiation and Ablation," by H. Julian Allen, Barrett S. Baldwin, Jr., and Nataline James. The report provided answers to a number of pertinent questions, such as: (1) At what size does melting occur and over what range of altitudes does the molten state exist? (2) Under what conditions will a nonrotating body with a molten front face have a solid rear face? (3) When will the dynamic pressure overbalance the surface tension and break up a molten drop? (4) How does the size of a meteorite vary with the initial size of the meteoroid? (5) At what altitude does the speed fall to a negligible value? And (6) what is the behavior of the luminosity of these bodies with respect to both maximum magnitude and magnitude variation with altitude?

Meteor evidence obtained by astronomers had revealed certain anomalies such as sudden changes in luminous intensity and sudden drastic reductions in density of the meteor body. Fragmentation of the meteor or peculiarities in surface radiation had been offered as possible causes. Why the density of a meteor of stone should suddenly fall by an order of magnitude was, nevertheless, rather difficult to explain. One possible answer appeared in the course of a major study which Howard Stine and his Magnetoplasmadynamics Branch staff in 1965 were making on meteors and their hazard to spacecraft. This study included measurements of radiation spectra from meteor models in arc-jet facilities and in particular it involved the determination of their luminous efficiency—a factor which heretofore had been largely guessed at but which was needed for an accurate interpretation of flight observations.

In the course of the study just mentioned, a stone meteorite model, containing some moisture, was tested in an arc-jet at very low pressure. In this high-enthalpy, low-pressure environment, the stone bubbled up, becoming frothy or fluffy. Its density fell quickly to a low value. The environment to which the test model was subjected corresponded to high-altitude meteor flight—but would moisture be present in a stone meteoroid? Possibly, Allen thought, if it were of cometary origin. No fluffy meteorite had yet been found on earth but an object of this kind would not, until this time, have been recognized as a meteorite. Henceforth, however, meteorite hunters would be on the lookout for such an object.

Space and Planetary Physics

The composition and structure of the planets were subjects which were open to a surprising degree of analytical treatment, and such studies received attention from Ames space scientists during the period 1963–1965. Representative of this effort is a paper (ref. C–51) entitled "Models of Uranus and Neptune," by Ray T. Reynolds and Audrey L. Summers, which was

Artificial fluffy meteorite ablated in arc-jet.

published in the January 1965 issue of the *Journal of Geophysical Research*. The major effort of the Ames space scientists during this period, however, was devoted to investigations of phenomena that were closer to home and more accessible to our spacecraft. These included the magnetic fields of the earth, moon, and nearby planets but related mostly to the flow of solar particles (solar wind) and its interaction with the earth's magnetic field.

The solar wind was known to be composed largely of hydrogen and helium nuclei, heated to a temperature of at least 100,000° K, which flow out from the sun in all directions sweeping over the earth and far beyond at speeds of a million, or more, miles per hour. The earth's magnetic field resists this earthward flow of charged particles and fends them off along a boundary which is about 10 earth radii out from the earth on the solar side but which trails backward, closing behind the earth far downstream. The enclosed, elongated area within the boundary, an area in which the magnetic field is dominant, is called the magnetosphere. The magnetosphere is obviously of vital consequence to human beings for it protects life on earth from damaging, if not deadly, radiation.

The boundary between solar plasma and the magnetosphere is never steady, for the defensive power of the magnetosphere is continually being tested by great surges of particle flux coming from the sun during "solar storms." It is a boundary of conflict between opposing forces, where temperatures rise to a million or more degrees Kelvin as the raging particles from the sun struggle to reach the earth. It is a boundary of great scientific as well as practical interest.

475

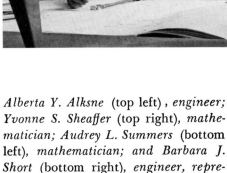

Alberta Y. Alksne (top left), *engineer; Yvonne S. Sheaffer* (top right), *mathematician; Audrey L. Summers* (bottom left), *mathematician; and Barbara J. Short* (bottom right), *engineer, representative of the women performing research at Ames.*

The theoretical attacks on the boundary problem which had begun earlier were continued during this period. Representative of the more recent work in this field was the study reported in TR R–206, "On the Stability of the Boundary of the Geomagnetic Field," by John R. Spreiter and Audrey L. Summers. A contribution was also made by Vernon Rossow in a paper,

RESEARCH

"Magnetic Compression of Collision-Free Plasmas with Charge Separation," which in 1965 appeared in the *Journal of the Physics of Fluids*. Additionally, the assaults on the boundary produced by solar storms were studied by Joan Hirshberg and reported in a paper, "Recurrent Geomagnetic Storms and the Solar Wind," which in November 1965 was published in the *Journal of Geophysical Research*.

The opportunities for carrying out experimental research in space were relatively few and the cost of such research was exceedingly high. Accordingly, there was much competition among scientists in the matter of devising experiments so promising that they would be chosen for inclusion in a spaceflight program. To be chosen, not only must the experiment be well conceived but the instruments with which the experimenter proposes to carry out his mission must also be of the highest quality and reliability. This was the sort of business in which Charles Sonett's Space Sciences Division was extensively engaged and much of it was the responsibility of the Electrodynamics Branch headed by John Wolfe. Wolfe had come to Ames in 1960, had become involved in spaceflight research while working in the Physics Branch, and then became the first Ames staff member to join the Space Sciences Division when it was formed. The Space Sciences Division had not long been in operation and had remained painfully short of manpower, yet its performance in the highly competitive field of space research had been noteworthy. Its experiments had been chosen for the following space missions:

Mission	*Ames Experiment*
Explorer IV	Plasma probe
IMP I, II, III	Plasma probe
OGO I	Plasma probe
EGO A and B	Plasma probe
Pioneer VI (A)	Plasma probe
Pioneer B and C	Plasma probe and magnetometer
Apollo lunar landing	Tri-axis magnetometer

Numerous papers were written by Space Sciences Division personnel on studies of magnetic fields and solar-plasma flows. Two papers may be cited as being representative of this work. One (ref. C–52), published in the March 1966 issue of the *Journal of Geophysical Research* is entitled "Observations of the Solar Wind During the Flight of IMP I," by John H. Wolfe, Richard W. Silva, and Marilyn A. Myers. The second was the paper entitled "Evidence for a Collision-Free Magnetohydrodynamic Shock in Interplanetary Space," by C. P. Sonett, D. S. Colburn, L. Davis, E. J. Smith, and P. J. Coleman, Jr. This paper, which was published in *Physical Review Letters* in August 1964, contained material included in the book *Solar Wind* (general editors: Robert Mackin, Jr., and Marcia Neugebauer), published in 1966 by Pergamon Press of New York.

Space-physics experiments were also being devised by individuals in other divisions of the Ames Research Center. Experiments to determine the effects of space radiation on thermal-control coatings had been prepared by Carr Neel of the Gasdynamics Branch and flown in 1962 in *OSO I*. Similar experiments prepared by Carr were flown in *OSO II*, which was launched in 1965. In both cases the experiments were successful, and those in *OSO I* yielded the additional information on reflected earth radiation reported in TM X–54,034, "Albedo and Earth Radiation From Emissivity Sensors on the First Orbiting Solar Observatory," by John P. Millard and Carr B. Neel.

In space research a tremendous premium was placed on the design of accurate, lightweight, reliable instruments, and much ingenuity was demonstrated in the development of such equipment. For his work in devising instruments for the *OSO I* and *II* flights, Carr Neel received an award of excellence from the Instrument Society of America. Among the other noteworthy space-research instruments devised by Ames research engineers were a plasma probe, originally developed by Mike Bader and Fred Hansen but later improved by Roger Hedlund, Tom Fryer, and others of the Instrument Research Division, and an excellent magnetometer in the design of which major contributions were made by Charles Sonett, William Kerwin, John Dimeff, and others.

Another useful instrument which attracted much interest was an impulse balance for measuring the momentum of micrometeoroids striking a spacecraft. This instrument, designed by Vernon Rogallo for use in Project Pioneer, was so sensitive that it could detect the heartbeats of a chicken embryo in an egg 4 days old. The instrument found numerous uses such as for measuring the thrust of laser and ion beams, and in 1965 it was being considered by the Food and Drug Administration as a possible means of evaluating the effects of drugs and chemicals on heart action.

BIOLOGICAL EFFECTS OF SPACE ENVIRONMENT

Of particular concern to the life-sciences people at Ames was the effect of the environment of space on the performance of the whole man and on the functioning of his organs. Of particular concern were the physiological and psychological stresses peculiar to space flight and the ability of a man to withstand these stresses. Human test specimens were used whenever feasible, but in many cases the severity of the test conditions dictated the use of animals, such as rats, mice, cats, dogs, chickens, and monkeys. Much of the work that related to the performance of man as a whole fell under the jurisdiction of the Biotechnology Division under Steven Belsley, while most of that concerned with the more detailed organic and physiological effects was the responsibility of the Environmental Biology Division under Eric Ogden.

The psychological part of the program had largely to do with the measurement of certain sensory perceptions which might well be important to

From left to right: *Dr. John Billingham, Melvin Sadoff, and Dr. R. Mark Patton, staff members of the Biotechnology Division.*

the crew of a spacecraft. The perceptions evaluated included the judgment of signal duration, pattern recognition, and visual responses to bright objects such as might be seen in space. For the exploration of the last-mentioned problem, a new high luminance vision laboratory was being installed in 1965 as a facility of the Biotechnology Division. Published papers representative of the psychological work at Ames include TM X–54,058, "Intersensory Judgments of Signal Duration," by Trieve A. Tanner, Jr., R. Mark Patton, and R. C. Atkinson; "Methods of Confusion in a Pattern Matching Task," by James A. Duke; and "Visual Problems of Space," by R. Mark Patton. Among other contributors in this particular field of endeavor were Ronald Kinchla and Richard Haines.

Effects of the immediate cabin environment on the mental and physical well-being of a spacecraft crew were also studied extensively. Some of this work was aimed specifically at the Apollo lunar mission and some also at longer space missions. One of these studies was an examination of the performance of two human beings (one being Ames test pilot Glen Stinnett) during confinement in an Apollo-size capsule for 7 days. Carried out in 1962, this investigation resulted in two reports, one of which, published in 1963, was TN D–1973 (ref. C–53), "Behavioral Testing During a 7-Day Confinement: The Information Processing Task," by Rollin M. Patton.

The nature of the cabin atmosphere—its composition and pressure—was a matter of grave importance in spacecraft design. In the Mercury and

Gemini flights, NASA had used an atmosphere of pure oxygen at about 5 pounds per square inch pressure and was planning to continue this practice in the Apollo. Questions arose about the physiological implications of prolonged exposure to a pure oxygen atmosphere, and this was the subject of at least two investigations conducted with animal subjects. One of these investigations was reported in a paper (ref. C–54), "Effects of Prolonged Exposure of Animals to Increased Oxygen Concentrations," by G. A. Brooksby, Robert W. Staley, and Robert L. Dennis, presented in November 1965 at the Third International Conference on Hyperbaric Medicine at Duke University. The second study, yet unreported, was made by Jorge Huertas. In this case a monkey was installed in a special "hypobaric hyperoxic chamber" where he was exposed for periods up to a month to an atmosphere of pure oxygen at 5 pounds per square inch pressure. During the prolonged exposure, observations were made of numerous physiological and behavioral factors to detect any abnormalities arising from the environment.

Aside from claustrophobia and the effects of an unusual atmosphere, there were many other stresses to which a spacecraft crew would be subjected during a long space journey. One was a tendency toward dehydration. A study of this matter at Ames, conducted on human subjects, was reported in the paper, "Voluntary Dehydration in Man," by John E. Greenleaf, published in the July 1965 issue of the *Journal of Applied Physiology*. Another important cabin stress would arise from the malfunction of the gastrointestinal system during the close and prolonged confinement in a spacecraft. A study of this problem made at Ames is reported by Carl J. Pfeiffer in a paper, "Space Gastro-enterology—An Appraisal of Gastro-Intestinal Func-

Hypobaric hyperoxic chamber.

tion as Related to Space Flight," published in the *Medical Times*, September 1965.

The metabolism of fats and carbohydrates, and food-energy sources for space flight, were the subjects of extensive investigations at Ames. A major contributor to this effort was Donald Young. Representative of the numerous papers published on the subject was "Carbohydrate and Fat Metabolism During Prolonged Physical Work" (ref. C–55), by Donald R. Young. This paper was presented in March 1965 at the Symposium on Survival Nutrition, at the Arctic Aeromedical Laboratory in Seattle.

Spacecraft-crew requirements for air, food, and water were all under study in 1965, as was the problem of gastrointestinal function and waste disposal. For very long flights such as a trip to Mars, closed ecological systems, involving the complete recycling of all wastes, were being considered. Leading the work on such systems was Phillip Quattrone.

Among the more obvious stresses to which spacecraft crews would be subjected were those which would arise from changes in the force of gravity. A constant gravitational force has been a basic factor in man's evolutionary history and thus, in anticipation of space travel, there was good reason to question his tolerance of changes in gravitational environment, particularly of prolonged exposure to unusual conditions. There was interest not only in the effects of altered gravitation on organic function but also on the processes of reproduction and the physical and behavioral characteristics of offspring conceived and born under such conditions.

At Ames a study of these matters was undertaken by a group of scientists headed by Jiro Oyama. The subjects used for the investigation were rats and mice, and the vehicle for simulating the gravity variations was the centrifuge. The rat cages were hinged so that the combined centrifugal and gravitational force acted normal to the bottom of the cage. The rats were whirled for periods of one or more years at speeds simulating gravity forces of 2.5, 3.5, and 4.7 g. They mated and the babies were born and grew to full maturity while whirling on the centrifuge. The effects of acceleration on behavior, mating practice (discouraging above 3.5 g), metabolism, body weight and size, food consumption, organ development, and other physiological factors were determined. The effects of reducing the acceleration to 1 g (removing rats from centrifuge) after long exposure to high acceleration were also noted. Numerous papers were written on this study, one of which, "Effects of Prolonged Centrifugation on Growth and Organ Development of Rats," by J. Oyama and W. T. Platt (ref. C–56), was published in April 1965 in the *American Journal of Physiology*. One interesting effect noted in the centrifugation of rats was the large deposits of fat in the livers of rats that had been exposed to fairly high (4.5 g) accelerations for as little as 3 hours. This phenomenon was examined in some detail and reported in a number of papers, among which was "Chemical and Metabolic Changes of

Dr. Jiro Oyama and 8-foot radius rat centrifuge.

Hepatic Lipids From Rats Exposed to Chronic Radial Acceleration," by D. D. Feller, E. D. Neville, J. Oyama, and E. G. Averkin (ref. C–57).

Space-cabin environment was expected always to be abnormal in some degree, and the effects on heart function of such conditions as high temperature and abnormal atmospheric-gas composition were considered worthy of study. Among the resulting papers was one by Eric Ogden entitled "Temperature Change and Oxygen Deficit as Determinants of Cardiac Power." It was presented at the 23d International Congress of Physiological Sciences in Tokyo in 1965.

Stresses such as those to which space crews are subjected were known to cause the breakdown of proteins in the body and the release of certain enzymes which might affect body functions. The Life Sciences Directorate had excellent biochemical and endocrinology laboratories and was thus well equipped for enzyme studies. Leaders in this work were J. Ken McDonald and Stanley Ellis. Representative of their work was the study reported in the paper "Properties of a Dipeptidyl Arylamidase of the Pituitary," by J. Ken McDonald, Stanley Ellis, and Thomas Reilly, published in September 1965 in the *Journal of Biological Chemistry.*

One of the major efforts of the Ames Environmental Biology Division was a study of the pathological effects, on animals, of radiation such as that to which space travelers might be exposed. This radiation included protons

482

(perhaps the most serious threat), alpha particles, X-rays, and gamma rays. The radiation work at Ames was carried on with the assistance of the University of California Radiation Laboratory by an exceptionally competent team headed by the internationally known neuropathologist, Webb Haymaker, and including Jaime Miquel, J. F. Estable-Puig, R. D. de Estable, Tom Taketa, and others.

The subjects used in the radiation studies included fruit flies, rats, cats, and rhesus monkeys; in some cases the whole body was exposed, and in others only the brain. In all cases, the animals were examined very carefully for pathological changes resulting from the radiation. Brain damage resulting from radiation was evidenced by many cellular changes and by an accumulation of glycogen in the brain. The fruit flies were used for studies of chromosomal changes produced by simulated cosmic ray primaries.

The papers issuing from the radiation studies at Ames, of which Haymaker is an author of a dozen or so, are rather large in number. An example is the paper, "Glycogen Accumulation in Monkey and Cat Brain Exposed to Proton Radiation," by J. Miquel and W. Haymaker (ref. C–58). It was presented at the International Congress of Neuropathology in Zurich in 1965. A second example of the radiation work at Ames is a paper entitled "Effects of Acute Doses of High Energy Protons on Primates," by S. Tom Taketa, C. A. Sondhaus, B. L. Castle, W. H. Howard, C. C. Conley, and W. Haymaker (ref. C–59).

Ames benefited from the services not only of Webb Haymaker but also from those of his wife, Dr. Evelyn Anderson, a distinguished endocrinologist who contributed greatly to the establishment of the Ames endocrinology laboratory. Dr. Anderson also headed a team which was responsible for developing a method for detecting a hitherto unknown stress hormone in the blood stream. In 1964 she was one of six recipients of the Fourth Annual Federal Woman's Award.

Although the life-science and the physical-science groups at Ames had little in common, mutual benefits occasionally arose from their being together. Along the common boundary of their activities, either group could benefit from the expertise of the other. One area in which the physical scientists were able to help the life scientists was in instrument design. Tom Fryer, Gordon Deboo, and Joseph Zuccaro of the Instrument Research Division were particularly active in this field. The work of Zuccaro is indicated by the title of a paper, "Pioneering Work in Bioinstrumentation for Flight Experiments and Flight Simulation," which in 1965 he presented at a national meeting of the IEEE. Fryer and Deboo wrote a number of papers on bioinstrumentation among which was one entitled "A High-Performance Miniature Biopotential Telemetry System" (ref. C–60). The instrument described in this paper had created widespread interest and had been used quite extensively by C. M. Winget of the Ames Life Sciences Directorate for studies of circadian rhythms in animals. It was particularly useful for mea-

Dr. Evelyn Anderson (top left), *Vance I. Oyama and Dr. Leonard P. Zill* (top right), *and Dr. Cyril A. Ponnamperuma* (left).

suring such physiological factors as body temperature, brain waves, and heart action under conditions in which direct wire connections to the subject were not feasible.

Aside from developing bioinstruments, Ames physical scientists occasionally undertook to apply their special knowledge of fluid flows to the solution of some life-science problem. An example of such application is reported in the paper (ref. C–61) by John Howe and Yvonne Sheaffer on "An Analysis of Recent Hypotheses of Plasma Flow in Pericapillary Spaces."

Evolution and Detection of Extraterrestrial Life

Perhaps the most stirring prospect in space research is the possibility that life may be discovered on some celestial body other than earth. One might suppose that if an intelligent manlike creature existed on some remote planet, his discovery by earth men would shake the foundations of our society. A much more likely discovery might be of some rudimentary form of life; but even this would be of tremendous scientific interest. The life form discovered might well, indeed, lie in that hazy zone between the inanimate and the animate through which life on earth, in its evolution, passed several billions of years ago. In their search for extraterrestrial life, space scientists, it is clear, must know what kind of evidence to look for, must know how to detect it in a foreign environment, must know how to recover it by means of a remote-controlled vehicle, must know how to nurture any life forms discovered to facilitate later studies and, if such discoveries are returned to earth, must know how to protect the foreign and the domestic life forms from each other. These, then, were some of the problems that faced the Exobiology Division of the Ames Life Sciences Directorate.

The Exobiology Division was headed by Richard Young, who had started the life-science activity at Ames in February 1961. The division in 1965 was comprised of a Chemical Evolution Branch directed by Cyril Ponnamperuma, a Biological Adaptation Branch directed by Robert Painter, and a Life Detection Systems Branch directed by Vance Oyama. The work of the division was of a very basic nature. Most of it was conducted in-house, none with human subjects, and little with animal subjects other than micro-organisms, eggs, and frogs. Indeed the evidence of life that was being sought was so subtle as to be easily obscured by the bacterial "filth" with which all humans and other animals on earth are laden. The experimental work of the Exobiology Division was mostly performed in its own, excellent laboratories though some of it was being carried out in space through experiments placed on space vehicles. Experiments devised by Richard Young and his colleagues were scheduled for inclusion in Gemini flights and the Biosatellite program.

If life forms have developed on other celestial bodies, it is assumed that they did so through a general evolutionary process which began with a primordial, hydrogen-rich environment,[4] and proceeded first through numerous organic chemical phases, then through biological stages of increasing sophistication. The crux of the process is the step, or steps, from the chemical to the biological stage, and it is assumed that this step would not take place

---

[4] An atmosphere presumably containing methane, ammonia, water vapor, and hydrogen, but no free oxygen.

unless the chemical environment were favorable. The nominal purpose of the Chemical Evolution Branch was to investigate some of the chemical steps in the evolutionary process; however, if this effort proved successful, the Branch staff could be expected to press on, with great joy and gladness, to the early biological phases. The prospective task was enormous, for it was recognized that in nature the crucial "step" from chemical to biological may well alone have occupied millions of years and been so subtle as to defy any subsequent human effort to demonstrate that, through it, life had truly been produced. Some workers in the field of molecular biology seemed to feel that life is but a property of matter in a certain state of organization and that, if the proper molecules and their organization could be arranged in a test tube, the awesome phenomenon of life would automatically appear. Much work had been done in this field by scientists around the world and, while amazing progress had been made, life had not yet been produced in the laboratory nor was there any solid basis for guessing when this objective might be achieved.

Living matter is largely made up of specialized proteins, each assembled from a variety of amino acids contained in the cells. The amino acids so assembled are connected together, chainlike, in a pattern which is specific for each particular protein. The pattern for the amino-acid chain comes from a gene, also a chain, contained in the cell nucleus. The gene chain is composed of nucleotides each composed of three chemical compounds—a sugar, a phosphate, and any one of four nitrogenous bases. It is, however, the pattern of the bases in the gene chain that determines the pattern of amino acids in the protein.

Clearly the sugars, phosphates, and bases of the gene chain are essential chemical building blocks of life. They are produced in living animals and plants by a chemical breakdown of food or by photosynthesis. The questions Dr. Ponnamperuma and his staff undertook to answer was whether the individual building blocks could be synthesized in the laboratory, whether they could then be combined into nucleotides, and finally whether the nucleotides could be induced to form a gene chain—hopefully self-replicating. If they could demonstrate in the laboratory the chemical steps which led to the origin of life on earth several billions of years ago, this development would then lend much weight to the common presumption that life has also evolved elsewhere in the universe. The results of such work might also suggest what to look for in the search for extraterrestrial life.

In proceeding toward the goals just mentioned, Dr. Ponnamperuma and his associates had, by the end of 1965, synthesized under conditions representing a primitive earth environment, some of the bases (adenine and guanine), sugars (ribose and deoxyribose), sugar-base combinations (adenosine and deoxyadenosine), and nucleotides (such as adenosine triphosphate) contained in the gene chain, as well as some of the amino acids used in protein construction. Still in the early stages, however, were their attempts, through the use of catalytic enzymes and other means, to encourage nucleotides to form a chain.

The work of Ponnamperuma and his associates was reported in numerous papers. One of these (ref. C–62) is entitled "Synthesis of Adenosine Triphosphate Under Possible Primitive Earth Conditions," by Cyril Ponnamperuma, Carl Sagan, and Ruth Mariner. Another, which in May 1965 appeared in *Science,* is entitled "Nucleotide Synthesis under Possible Primitive Earth Conditions," by Cyril Ponnamperuma and Ruth Mack.

Dr. Ponnamperuma had come to Ames in June 1961 as the first NAS Fellow stationed at the Center. He later became a permanent member of the staff. In recognition of his outstanding work, he was in 1964 presented with the NASA Sustained Superior Performance Award.

In the detection of life, extraterrestrial or otherwise, it is first necessary to establish the criteria by means of which the existence of life will be judged. Inasmuch as the boundary between the animate and the inanimate is rather hazy, there has been some disagreement in scientific circles as to what the criteria should be. Though not in full accord on the subject, scientists generally agree that living matter: (1) is of organic composition, (2) metabolizes (uses up energy and rejects a byproduct substance), (3) grows and reproduces. The first criterion is not conclusive in itself and, while the addition of the second is very reassuring, the matter is really clinched only when the third one is also present.

In view of our total ignorance of the life forms that may exist on foreign bodies, the Exobiology Division assumed that useful related knowledge might be obtained from an investigation of the tolerance of earth life forms to extreme conditions of temperature, pressure, atmosphere, moisture, radiation, salts, and gravity such as may be found naturally, or produced artificially, on earth. This work, which comes under the surveillance of the Biological Adaptation Branch, was still, in 1965, in an early stage.

The detection of life on celestial bodies other than the moon will presumably first be accomplished by remotely controlled, unmanned instrument packages (automated chemical laboratories) that are landed on the body. The development of life-detection procedures had, indeed, been studied extensively by the Exobiology Division as had also the design of automated chemical laboratories for life-detection purposes. Additionally, life-detection field studies were made in Death Valley in 1964.

A number of papers on life-detection problems had, by 1965, been written by members of the Exobiology Division. The best summary of the subject was perhaps to be found in NASA Special Publication SP–75 (ref. C–63) entitled "An Analysis of the Extraterrestrial Life Detection Problem," by Richard S. Young, Robert B. Painter, and Richard D. Johnson. The subject was also treated in Dr. Young's book, *Extraterrestrial Biology,* published by Holt, Rinehart & Winston in 1966.

10

Project Management and Other Technical Activities

THE common practice in laboratory research had been for the engineer who planned an experiment to serve as the project manager and the coordinator of required support activities. The support activities, however, were rather small in scope, involving mainly the branch and division, and seldom reached outside of the Center. In space-flight research, the supporting role became of such overwhelming magnitude, scope, complexity, and cost that a special NASA-wide project-management team was required to deal with it. The scientist-experimenter, who certainly could not be expected to launch his own spacecraft, was now freed of extraneous distractions and allowed to remain the specialist he generally preferred to be. But space-project management was a new class of activity—not exactly research, yet closely attuned to research requirements. Made to order for engineers, it was the kind of integrative, multidisciplinary task in which the engineer, as a professional type, often reached the peak of his achievement.

NASA space-research programs were planned and organized by the Headquarters program offices with the advice and counsel of the scientific community. When a decision had been made to proceed with a specific program or project, the research centers of the nation, or the world, would be invited to submit proposals for experiments to be undertaken in the program. The competition was keen and often 5 or 10 times as many experiments were proposed as could be carried in the spacecraft. The experiments to be carried would be selected by a scientific advisory panel or steering committee established by the program office at NASA Headquarters. Overall supervisional responsibility for the program would be retained in Headquarters, while active management would be assigned to a project-management team located, ordinarily, at one of the NASA research centers.

The general function of the project-management team was to organize and coordinate the diverse activities involved in (1) the selection and procurement of booster rockets, (2) the design and procurement of spacecraft, (3) the integration of the experiments with the spacecraft, (4) detailed mission planning, (5) the launching of spacecraft, (6) tracking and data acquisition by the worldwide NASA network, and (7) the recovery of spacecraft —if such was planned. The acquired data were ordinarily turned over to the experimenter for detailed analysis and publication largely as he saw fit.

Not only had each of the elements of support to be successfully completed, but all had to be brought together at exactly the right time for integration into a smoothly functioning whole. Timing was often an agonizingly frustrating matter especially, as in the Biosatellite project, where a diversity of carefully prepared plants and animals had to be assembled in the spacecraft at precisely the right moment and in exactly the right condition. Experiments with living creatures could easily be devalued or completely ruined by any significant delay in the hour of launch. Wheat seedlings and larvae, for example, had to be in the right state of development, and frogs' eggs had to be fertilized just hours before launch. In addition, of course, many of the life forms had to have their own special air-conditioning system, the animals had to be regularly fed, and means had to be provided to deal with, and possibly chemically analyze, the excreta. Attention had to be given even to such seemingly minor matters as to whether the teeth of the rats would grow so long during the tests that they would chew holes in the feeding nipples. It was not too much to say that the physical scientists at Ames were learning a great deal about animal research. The life scientists were a little amused.

Space-project management required broad experience, management ability, and very steady nerves. Robert Crane, a man eminently suited for the task, had earlier been appointed Assistant Director for Development, an office which held responsibility for most of the space-project management activity at Ames. Crane was calm and capable, quite equal to managing either the Development Directorate or the whole Center. He was ably supported by Charles Hall, manager of Project Pioneer, and Charles Wilson, manager of Project Biosatellite. When the Development Directorate was formed, the Ames management, always mindful of the unfair competition basic research would suffer at the hands of glamorous space operations, enjoined Crane from draining off the manpower and research effort of the research directorates at the Center. Crane therefore found it desirable to establish, within his own directorate, a systems-engineering division. John Foster became head of the new division. Although his staff was painfully limited in numbers, Foster, through the extensive use of contracting, was able to provide the often unique equipment systems required by the Development Directorate as well as the systems engineering effort needed for the design of such equipment.

In view of the attitude of Ames management toward hardware development and space operations, Bob Crane's new directorate began with something of a handicap. The handicap was augmented by the circumstance that

490

both the Pioneer and the Biosatellite projects came under the Headquarters Office of Space Science and Application (OSSA), whereas the Center as a whole came under the Office of Advanced Research and Technology (OART). Some degree of organizational incompatibility thus prevailed.

Bob Crane had expected that the project work being carried on at Ames would benefit not only his own Development Directorate but also the research directorates at the Center. He hoped that the space projects would provide something of a focus for the otherwise fairly indefinite pattern of basic research. And he felt that the technical support of the research directorates would be of great help to his activity. Bob's hopes had not in 1965 been fully realized. Within the Ames operation, the project work was treated with a friendly indifference. This attitude prevailed in Project Pioneer and particularly in Project Biosatellite. The indifference of the Life Sciences Directorate toward the Biosatellite project was somewhat surprising and rather disappointing to Crane. The only experiment the Life Sciences Directorate had proposed for the Biosatellite was a relatively minor frogs' eggs experiment and this had been submitted by the Exobiology Division, the activities of which also came under Headquarters OSSA. It appeared that the Life Sciences Directorate, in common with the other research directorates at Ames, was firmly wedded to the laboratory where one's research could proceed at the desired pace and be kept under close personal control. Some experiments, of course, had to be performed in space, but as long as the bulk of research remained to be done in earthbound laboratories, many scientists were reluctant to forsake these familiar and productive haunts for the glamorous but uncertain realms of space.

AIRBORNE RESEARCH PROJECTS

Not all project-management work at Ames came within the jurisdiction of Bob Crane and his Development Directorate. In 1963 a small group of Ames men had participated in an airborne (DC–8) research expedition to observe a solar eclipse along its path of totality, which lay in Canada. The group included Sheldon Smith, of the Physics Branch, and Ray Torrey, of the Guidance and Control Systems Branch. As participants in the expedition, this pair, with the aid of others at the Center, developed and built a rather unique gyro-stabilized camera for photographing the eclipse from the expedition's airplane. A description of the camera is given in the July 1964 issue of the *ISA Transactions* in a paper entitled "A Stabilized Automated Camera for Airborne Eclipse Photography," by S. M. Smith, M. Bader, R. A. Torrey, and M. E. Henderson.

The photographs of the eclipse obtained with the camera were quite good and the experience of the expedition gave Smith, Bader, and others the idea that Ames should have an airborne research laboratory of its own. Such a laboratory, it was felt, would provide ready observational accessibility to astronomical and other events occurring, sometimes on short notice, in remote parts of the world. The idea of the airborne research laboratory was approved by Ames and Headquarters management and was shortly implemented by the procurement of a Convair 990, four engine, jet transport airplane.

In May 1965, during the International Year of the Quiet Sun, a group of 38 scientists took off in Ames' new airborne laboratory to join other groups traveling by land, sea, and air to witness another solar eclipse—this one reaching totality in the South Pacific. The operation was coordinated and managed by Mike Bader. The airplane on this occasion carried the Ames eclipse camera as well as 13 other experiments provided by 4 foreign observatories or universities and 9 American organizations. The eclipse observations made on this occasion were very successful. As they were made from a high-speed airplane flying at high altitude, their value was the greater because (1) the period of totality was prolonged by following the path of total eclipse, (2) a greater range of wavelengths was observed owing to the altitude of the airplane, and (3) the background light around the eclipsed sun, normally produced by light diffusion in the atmosphere, was much reduced because of the altitude of the airplane. The reduced background light made it possible to observe the solar corona out to a distance of 12 solar radii, whereas from the ground the corona appeared to extend to only about 3 solar radii.

As the eclipse mission came to an end, the participants, by common agreement, selected the name "Galileo" for the airplane which had served them so well. The name was chosen in honor of the well-liked Dr. Guglielmo Righini who, on the mission, represented the Arcetri Observatory of Florence, Italy. NASA Headquarters quickly approved the name, and Brad Evans wrote a letter to the mayor of Florence.

Not long after the eclipse expedition, another occasion arose to use the *Galileo*. This occasion was the discovery, in October 1965, of the Ikeya-Seki comet. Hurriedly an expedition was arranged to observe the comet during perihelion, which was best observable in an area 150 miles northeast of Hawaii. Fred Drinkwater was pilot and Mike Bader was again project manager. Of the seven experiments carried on this expedition, four came from various NASA Centers and three from other American sources. The experiments involved a variety of spectrographic measurements as well as white-light photography. While some of the spectrographic observations suffered from a lack of light intensity, the white-light photographs were very good and were the only photographs obtained of the comet at perihelion.

The eclipse and the comet expeditions convinced Ames management of the value of an airborne research laboratory and, as 1965 ended, plans were being made to intensify the exploitation of the *Galileo*.

Above: *Sheldon M. Smith and eclipse camera on NASA 1965 Solar Eclipse Expedition.* At right: *Photograph of solar corona taken during NASA 1965 Solar Eclipse Expedition.*

PROJECT PIONEER

The eclipse and the comet expeditions represented but a small part of the project-management activity at Ames, which mainly centered in the Pioneer and the Biosatellite projects. The Ames group directing the Pioneer project numbered over 40 people, was headed by Charlie Hall, and in-

Dr. Michel Bader in Eclipse Expedition airplane.

Galileo astronautical research airplane, a modified Convair 990.

cluded Howard Matthews, in charge of flight operations and data processing; Ralph Holtzclaw, spacecraft systems manager; Herbert Cross, scientific experiments manager; and Robert Hofstetter, responsible for launch vehicles, launch operations, and trajectory analysis.

"Pioneer" was a name applied by NASA to a class of deep-space research vehicles to which numbers were assigned only after a successful launch. Most recent of the series, *Pioneer V* had in 1960 demonstrated NASA's ability to send commands to a spacecraft at distances of over 22 million miles. A block of four Pioneer space flights, designated A, B, C, and D, had been assigned to Ames management with the implication that more might later be added. The cost of completing the four missions was estimated at something over $40 million. These funds would mostly be spent on hardware contracts. Douglas and Aerojet-General would provide the Thor-Delta booster rockets, and the Space Technology Laboratories would build the spacecraft in which the experiments would be carried. The experiments would be provided by various scientific organizations, the launching would be managed by the NASA Goddard Space Flight Center, and the tracking and data acquisition would be accomplished by means of the NASA Deep Space Network operated by the Jet Propulsion Laboratory.

Pioneer A was scheduled for launching into an elliptical solar orbit having a period of about 310 days and a perihelion distance from the sun of about 77 million miles—just inside the orbit of the earth. Its 140-pound, spin-stabilized spacecraft, made up of 56,000 separate parts, would carry 35 pounds of instruments to implement six carefully selected experiments. Most of the experiments were concerned with studies of the sun and its emanations. The sun was, indeed, a very promising subject for study because, other than the earth, no celestial body was so important to man.

One of the experiments in Pioneer A was to be a solar-plasma probe provided by John Wolfe of the Ames Space Sciences Division. In addition, there would be a plasma cup detector provided by the Massachusetts Institute of Technology; a radio-propagation detector provided by Stanford University; a magnetometer supplied by the NASA Goddard Space Flight Center; and a cosmic-ray anisotropy detector provided by the Graduate Research Center of the Southwest. Inasmuch as faint interplanetary magnetic fields were to be measured, extreme care was exercised to ensure that the spacecraft was magnetically clean. Further precautions in this matter were taken by mounting the sensor of the magnetometer at the end of a 5-foot boom.

Finally, on December 15, 1965, after a heroic preparatory effort, Pioneer A was launched. The spacecraft, soon to be designated *Pioneer VI,* successfully achieved the planned orbit around the sun and shortly flight information began flowing into the Pioneer Control Center which had been established at Ames. The instruments appeared to be working very well; indeed, by the end of the year, it was clear that *Pioneer VI* was providing very important new knowledge about the sun and its emanations. Having demonstrated their competence, Charlie Hall and his associates were already turning their attention to Pioneer B, scheduled for launching in the summer of 1966.

Pioneer VI launch (left). *Artist's conception of spacecraft by Space Technology Laboratory* (below).

PROJECT BIOSATELLITE

The responsibilities of the Biosatellite project management group were generally similar to those of the Pioneer group. The Biosatellite group of more than 70 people was, in 1965, headed by Charles Wilson. Included in the group were Bonne Look, manager of spacecraft systems; Dale Smith, manager of experiments and life systems; and Don Warner, manager of the clinical, biochemistry, and vivarium section under Smith.

Contemplated in Project Biosatellite was the launching of a spacecraft, carrying living plants and organisms, into an earth orbit of from 160- to 180-mile altitude. The purpose was to determine the effects of a space environment, principally weightlessness and radiation, on living matter. The results, it was felt, would be scientifically interesting, if not practically useful, and hopefully might shed some light on problems that man will encounter

Charles A. Wilson, manager of Project Biosatellite.

in space. As of 1965, six Biosatellite flights had been scheduled: two of 3-day duration, the first to be launched late in 1966; two of 21-day duration, to be launched in 1967; and two of 30-day duration, to be launched in 1967–1968. Beyond that, the Biosatellite group hoped it might win approval from Headquarters to launch biology experiments in an Apollo-size vehicle—perhaps as an auxiliary payload on a regular Apollo flight.

The Biosatellite spacecraft and experiment hardware were being built by the General Electric Co. under contract with Ames. From Cape Kennedy, according to plan, the spacecraft would be launched into orbit by a thrust-augmented Thor-Delta booster. No attempt would be made to completely stabilize the spacecraft, but excessive rotational velocities would be nullified by gas jets. Inasmuch as a large part of the data would come from photographic records or postflight examinations, a serious attempt would be made to recover the spacecraft intact. Recovery, the responsibility of the military services, would be effected if possible by snatching the spacecraft from the air as it descended on parachute. Failing that, the specially equipped recovery airplane would attempt to snatch the spacecraft from the sea. A final recourse would be recovery by surface vessel.

The selected experiments, including one contributed by Richard Young of the Exobiology Division, were being provided by a variety of agencies including Dartmouth College, the University of California (both the Berkeley and the Los Angeles institutions), the University of Southern California, Colorado State University, Texas Woman's University, Texas Medical Center, the Institute of Cancer Research, Oak Ridge National Laboratory, Brookhaven National Laboratory, and North American Aviation, Inc. Over 170 experiments had been proposed but fewer than 20 were accepted. The two 3-day flights would carry 12 or 13 experiments; the two 21-day flights, three; and the two 30-day flights, also three but on a single animal subject.

The intended purpose of the 3-day flights was to determine the effect of weightlessness, radiation, or a combination of the two on plant and animal life. Inasmuch as the spacecraft was not expected to enter the Van Allen radiation belts, an artificial, strontium-85, radiation source was to be provided in the capsule. The radiation experiments were to be placed at appropriate distances from this source.

Answers were to be sought in the 3-day flights to such questions as whether the limbs of a pepper plant will continue to grow upward; whether the roots of a wheat seedling will grow downward; and whether frogs' eggs will hatch into normal frogs or two-headed monsters. The frogs' eggs experiment was one that Richard Young had tried, without much success, in *Gemini III* and was planning to try again in *Gemini VIII*. Frogs' eggs, it was believed, had a heavy end which, under the influence of gravity, established the orientation of the egg. If during a certain stage in the egg's development, the egg was deliberately turned heavy-end up, a two-headed frog would result. The question of interest therefore was whether this unfortunate condition might occur naturally in a weightless environment. The 3-day flights were also expected to show whether radiation, or the combined effects of radiation and weightlessness, would produce genetic changes in spores, larvae, wasps, fruit flies, or spiderwort herbs or would affect the rate of proliferation of virus in bacteria.

Of the three experiments to be carried on the 21-day flights, one was to observe the occurrence of histologic changes in human-liver tissue during an exposure to weightlessness. Another was to observe the effect of weightlessness on the growth pattern of a fast-growing plant of the cress family. Still another, the most difficult, was to determine the effect of weightlessness on the gross body composition and metabolic rhythms of rats. For this purpose, eight adult rats, wired for telemetry transmission of body temperature and muscular activity, would be carried in the spacecraft. At the same time, a larger control group of rats on the ground would be subjected as nearly as possible to the same environmental conditions—except for weightlessness—as those in space. Providing control groups and establishing baseline conditions for animal subjects used in research was no small task.

The sole test subject of each of the 30-day flights was to be a 15-pound pig-tailed macaque from southeast Asia. The tests were expected to show the effects of prolonged exposure to weightlessness on brain function, cardiovascular function, and bone density—a demineralization was expected. The monkey to be chosen for a particular flight would be selected from hundreds; his body composition and organ functions would be thoroughly documented before flight, and he would be trained to eat pellets pulled

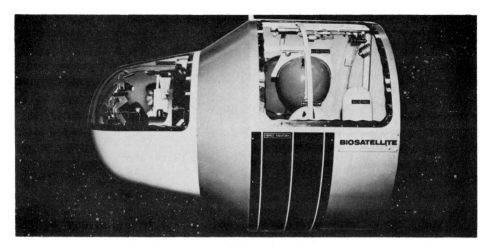

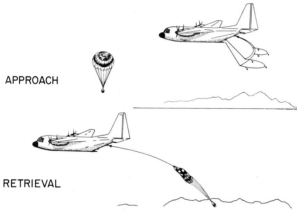

APPROACH

RETRIEVAL

Above: *Artist's conception of 3-day mission with monkey in Biosatellite spacecraft.* Left: *Air retrieval of Biosatellite performed by Air Force.*

from a tape on a rotating wheel, to suck fluids from a tube, and to carry out certain functional or psychological exercises.

Although a rather pampered animal, the monkey would, nevertheless, have to endure a number of indignities such as having his eyeteeth pulled out (to avoid bite hazard to handler), having several electrodes permanently embedded in his brain with clip-on terminals projecting from his skull, having catheters installed in his main blood vessels (as well as in his bladder for the removal of urine), and having a form-fitting "butt plate" attached by screws to his rump bones to hold him in place and to facilitate the collection of feces. In addition, there would be leads inserted between his ribs to transmit electrocardiograph readings, and thermocouples and pressure sensors would be attached at various points on his body. His food and fluid intake would be carefully metered, his excreta would be chemi-

499

cally analyzed, and he would be expected to sit still for 30 days carrying out psychological exercises for which he had been trained. The least of his worries, presumably, would be whether the Air Force would miss when they tried to snatch him from the air on his return to earth. A second trip would be too much to contemplate.

TECHNOLOGY UTILIZATION

The often-asked question of what good it would do to land a man on the moon was sometimes answered by proponents of the plan with the remark that the value might come less from landing on the moon than from learning how to get there. They were in such cases referring to the expectation that the tremendous outpouring of scientific and technical effort required to solve the practical problems involved in getting to the moon would result in the development of new materials, equipment, techniques, and processes which would have broad application throughout industry and a major impact on the economy of the Nation and the world. While one might be forgiven for believing that it was human curiosity rather than byproducts which accounted for our going to the moon, there was certainly much truth in the theory.

This was so clear in 1962 as to lead the NASA Administrator to take steps not only to facilitate the transfer of technology but also, and very importantly he felt, to document it for ready referral. He assigned the task of expediting the process to the Headquarters Office of Applications, which shortly arranged for the appointment of Application Officers at each of the research Centers. The activity was given a still higher priority in 1963, and made more pointed, when in the course of a major reorganization of the Headquarters establishment, a separate Office of Technology Utilization, reporting directly to the Administrator, was formed. Subsidiary Technology Utilization (TU) Offices were established at each of the Centers, and the whole spinoff operation was greatly accelerated. At Ames the appointed TU officer was George Edwards. He operated with a full-time professional staff of two or three, but with the assistance of individuals (numbering 50 or 60) in the research branches who served as TU representatives.

Formally stated, the objective of the NASA Technology Utilization program was to transfer to the public domain those scientific and technical results of the aerospace effort which potentially have other uses—in industry, business, medicine, education, and in the various agencies of Federal, State, and local governments. The specific tasks of the TU organization were: (1) to identify potentially useful innovations generated in NASA research centers or through the activities of its contractors; (2) to expedite the preparation of descriptive material, photographs, related and supporting evidence that would be helpful in the application of the innovation to other fields (here the patent status of the innovation would be determined

From left to right: *Darrell G. Brekke, patent counsel, and Hirschie J. Johnson, chief counsel.*

and indicated) ; and (3) to promptly bring the innovations to the attention of possible users by suitable publication of descriptive information.

In operation, the procedure might, for example, start with the development of a unique instrument, such as Vernon Rogallo's momentum balance, in one of the Ames research branches. The instrument would be noted by the local TU representative and identified as being potentially useful to others. The TU representative would bring the matter to the attention of George Edwards and his staff, who would examine the instrument with regard to its general usefulness, discuss the patent aspects of the case with a patent counsel at Ames, and then prepare a summary of the innovation and send it to the Headquarters TU Office in the form of a "flash sheet." The idea proposed in the flash sheet would be evaluated both by Headquarters and by a private technical agency retained for the purpose by NASA. If approved for dissemination, a thorough description of the innovation would be published in any one, or more, of several forms.

The forms adopted for TU publications include: a Technical Brief, dealing with items of small scope; a Technology Utilization Report, dealing with important single subjects; a Technology Handbook, describing processes; and a Technology Survey, reviewing a whole technical field. One example of the TU Report is SP–5007, which originated at Ames and is entitled "Measurement of the Heartbeat of Bird Embryos With a Micrometeorite Transducer." This report describes an instrument capable of measuring the thousandth part of the momentum of a grain of salt that has dropped half an inch. The published information about the instrument generated considerable interest in industrial and medical centers and it was not long before the commercial production of the instrument was being planned.

From all NASA Centers, the total number of flash sheets submitted to the Headquarters TU office for evaluation in 1965 was 2589. Of these, 1116 were accepted for publication. Comments on the NASA TU program in the technical press had earlier been critical but in 1965 were turning to praise.

The principal problem faced by George Edwards in his TU operations was a shortage of manpower. This problem had been aggravated by the necessity of digging out ideas from often indifferent contractors as well as by the heavy influx of inquiries about TU innovations. Also, Edwards and his staff were often major contributors to technical conferences such as the one on "Space, Science, and Urban Life" sponsored jointly by NASA and the Ford Foundation and, with the cooperation of the University of California, held in Oakland in March 1963.

11

A Change of Leadership

THE first generation of top management at Ames was approaching retirement age. A few had already retired and others, it was clear, would soon follow. Within another 5 years the management picture could change rather markedly. Some change in the outlook and policies of the Center would occur even if the new management team were chosen from the existing staff. The change would very likely be more drastic if a new Director from outside the Center were appointed. The opportunity for this arose late in 1965.

On October 15, 1965, Dr. Smith J. DeFrance, Director of the Ames Research Center since its founding, retired after 45 years of public service. He had been an effective leader, well liked by his staff and respected throughout the aerospace community. Coming to Moffett Field in 1940, on the eve of World War II, DeFrance had applied his long experience and characteristic driving energy to the construction of a new Laboratory which well served the country's wartime needs and grew, under his guidance, to a research center of international repute. The Laboratory which he founded bore the stamp of his integrity.

Dr. DeFrance was in 1964 one of 10 men to receive the Career Civil Service Award of the National Civil Service League and, on October 5, 1965, at a ceremony held in Washington, he was accorded NASA's highest award—the NASA Medal for Outstanding Leadership. He was further honored on October 19, 1965, with a retirement dinner, in San Jose, attended by 800 of his friends from all over the country. Also a portrait of Dr. DeFrance, executed in oil, was hung opposite that of Dr. Ames in the lobby of the Ames Administration Building.

When Dr. DeFrance's plan to retire was announced, there was much speculation as to who would replace him. There were, on the Center's staff, several worthy candidates for the position; nevertheless, qualms developed over the possibility that an "outsider" might be picked. It was therefore an occasion that brought relief as well as pleasure to the staff when the announcement was made that the new Director of the Ames Research Center

Oil painting of Dr. Smith J. DeFrance hanging in lobby of administration building of Ames Research Center.

H. Julian Allen.

John F. Parsons.

would be H. Julian (Harvey) Allen. This honor closely followed an earlier one. At the same Washington ceremony at which DeFrance had received his medal, Allen had been awarded NASA's highest scientific honor—the NASA Medal for Exceptional Scientific Achievement.

Harvey assumed his new duties with a certain air of resignation and quickly took steps to ensure that they would not infringe too heavily on his personal research work. He turned over a large segment of his administrative responsibilities to Jack Parsons who was, in fact, quite capable of managing the whole Center. Administrative responsibilities were also shifted to Loren Bright, for whom the position of Executive Assistant to the Director was established. Having thus substantially unburdened himself, Allen again picked up the threads of his aerodynamic-heating research while the work of the Center moved forward with scarcely a ripple.

Epilogue

AS the author considers the writing of this closing statement, the need for an epilogue to the Ames history is not very clear. True, the present ending is rather abrupt, but that is the way it is: the record of a mighty stream of activity suddenly disappearing like a cataract plunging over a cliff. Better, perhaps, than letting it dribble off to an unheroic end!

If the epilogue is to be a forward projection, a common objective of such literary devices, the writer is in trouble. In an area of activity that is changing with the rapidity of the field of aerospace science, forward projections are likely to lead only to argument, and later embarrassment. Perhaps, as a reversal of common practice, the epilogue can be put in the form of a retrospective view of certain salient factors in the evolution of the Ames Research Center. The author should, indeed, like to talk about human beings and their relation to research. Yes, that might be worth doing and the results may be regarded as one man's opinion.

The evolution of the Ames Research Center at first closely followed the evolution of its parent organization, NACA. But as the parent organization grew and changed into NASA, Ames became a relatively smaller, and somewhat divergent, part of the whole. Its physical growth was by no means phenomenal. Indeed, in that respect it did not keep pace with its sister centers. Why? One can only guess. Langley, of course, was NACA's senior aerodynamics laboratory and NACA's management always had an eastern bent. To some extent the same sectional influences prevailed as those which originally delayed the formation of the Ames laboratory. But there was more to the matter than that. Ames destiny was strongly influenced by the character of the Center's management. The term "conservative" can truthfully be applied to Ames managers, but the current implications of the word do them an injustice. They were brought up in the exceedingly frugal environment of NACA's early years and became permeated with the old-fashioned notion that there should be a maximum return to the country for every dollar spent. They were not great entrepreneurs nor were they bubble artists. They wanted to expand the Ames research operation but only as required by clear-cut missions and only with such rapidity as would allow them to maintain a high degree of control and efficiency.

In matters such as described, the Ames managers were conservative and they were even more conservative in their predilection for fundamental laboratory research as opposed to hardware construction, contract monitoring, and glamorous space operations. Their experience, professional principles, and tastes did not encourage their direct participation in some of the costly, highly publicized, spectacular events of the space age. They preferred activities closer to their fundamental interests—activities that could be pursued within Ames boundaries and over which they could themselves maintain control. In this they were somewhat isolationist—an attitude which, because of their detached western location and the continuing eastern bent of NACA management, may have been forced upon them. In any case they moved slowly into the nonresearch fields of space exploration; indeed they had to be pushed by NASA Headquarters and by a few of the younger members of the Ames staff.

The reluctance with which Ames managers moved into the new fields of space exploration undoubtedly resulted in smaller appropriations and personnel allocations for the Center. It was clearly impossible for NASA management, despite its good intentions, to protect Ames' basic laboratory research from a certain starvation arising from public and political pressures for spectacular space achievements.

While the Ames staff were slow in moving into non-, and extramural, research fields, they proceeded with brilliance and speed in their laboratory investigations of certain fundamental problems of aerospace science upon which the success of glamorous space missions often depended. Here there was no conservatism on the part of Ames management—only encouragement and support. At Ames there was, in laboratory research, a spirit of daring and adventure which enabled the Center to maintain its position at the forefront of a science that was developing with phenomenal speed.

Aerospace research has, since the founding of Ames, undergone tremendous growth both in magnitude and in sophistication. At the time Ames was established, NACA was "the" Government aeronautical research agency, accounting for most of the Nation's work in that field. This situation carried on to the end of World War II, at which time the field of aeronautical research literally exploded. With war's end came the realization that NACA could no longer, alone, handle the full burden of the Nation's aeronautical research. It would be necessary to seek appropriations much larger than NACA, typecast as a small agency, could command; it would be necessary to employ research facilities located elsewhere than in NACA laboratories; and it would be necessary to enlist research talent that preferred to operate in environments provided by universities, industry, and other Government agencies. Thus while NACA remained the single largest, most experienced, and best equipped agency devoted to aeronautical research, the burden of research after the war was shared by a growing number of public and private agencies largely financed, of course, by the Government. The beginning of the Space Age found NACA but one of many such agencies—and of that one, Ames constituted less than a quarter. The expansion accelerated during the space age and, under NASA, Ames became but a very small part

510

EPILOGUE

of an American aerospace establishment which stretched around the world.

More and more of NASA's research was now being performed under contract by private organizations. Such organizations, large and small, were generally not handicapped by civil service salary restrictions and were prepared and happy to undertake, at a moment's notice, research as desired on any subject in any field. As 1965, and this history, ended, one might well have asked, "Why does the Government continue to operate a small research center such as Ames? Why not let the research out on contract and allow private enterprise to do the laboratory's work?" To attempt an answer: perhaps the reason is to maintain the tradition of Government in-house research, or possibly it rests in the belief that such in-house research is more economical and controllable than is research conducted via contract. The answer may also lie in the obvious fact that contract research will yield results of the greatest value when it is administered and monitored by people who themselves carry on research.

But may not more subtle factors have been considered? Perhaps in the case of Ames, the reason is that over the years the Center has concentrated its efforts in certain important areas of aerospace research and in these particular areas its engineers and scientists have few, if any, equals and have provided themselves with unique facilities. Perhaps the reason is that Ames has, with care and attention, provided an environment which has attracted and held good men against the temptations of higher salaries offered from outside. Perhaps, more generally, the reason stems from the belief that a career Government research man, whose livelihood and activities are not subject to the vicissitudes and deadlines of contract procurement and completion, will be more likely than others less fortunate to find the relaxed, contemplative atmosphere which favors fundamental research. There is a continuity of effort in Government laboratories that often is not feasible or possible in private research centers. Such continuity may result in the development of a deeper understanding of scientific problems and a greater effectiveness in fundamental research.

I am speaking here of the work of the few at Government laboratories such as Ames. The work of the many could, indeed, be let out on contract with little loss of research quality though perhaps at considerably higher cost. But it is the work of the few exceedingly competent individuals, men who in the face of tempting offers from private industry choose to remain with their colleagues in the evocative environs of their own laboratories, that justifies the existence of the whole Center. A single original idea from one of these men may notably affect the world.

E. P. H.

APPENDICES AND REFERENCES

Appendix A

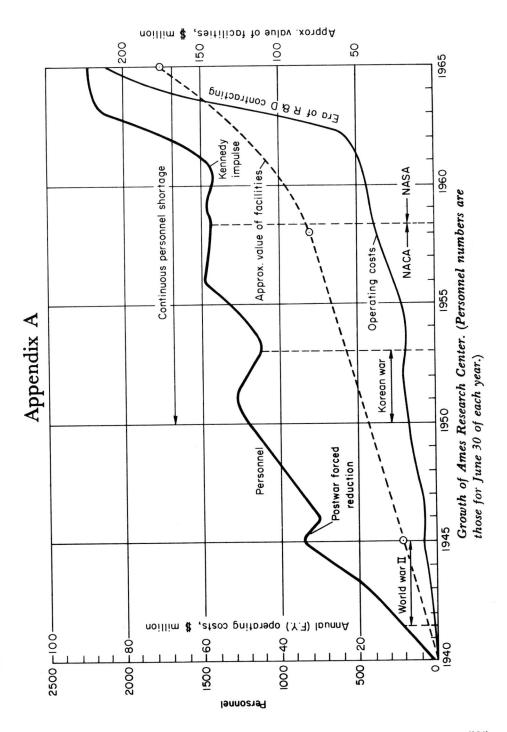

Growth of Ames Research Center. (*Personnel numbers are those for June 30 of each year.*)

515

Appendix B

Major Honors and Awards Won by the Staff of the Ames Research Center as a Result of Work Performed at the Center

Allen, H. Julian
  Sylvanus Albert Reed Award (Institute of the Aeronautical Sciences), 1955
  Distinguished Service Medal (NACA/NASA), 1957
  Wright Brothers Lecture (Institute of the Aeronautical Sciences), 1957
  Science Trophy (Air Force Association), 1958
  Exceptional Scientific Achievement Award (NASA), 1965
Anderson, Dr. Evelyn
  Fourth Annual Federal Woman's Award, 1964
Boyd, John W.
  The Stanford Alfred P. Sloan Fellowship in Executive Development, 1965–1966
Chapman, Dr. Dean R.
  Lawrence B. Sperry Award (Institute of the Aeronautical Sciences), 1952
  Rockefeller Public Service Award, 1959
  Exceptional Scientific Achievement Award (NASA), 1963
Christensen, Jay V.
  Group Achievement Award (NASA), 1964—with Ralph F. Huntsberger, Charles W. Harper, and Earl R. Keener
Clousing, Lawrence A.
  Octave Chanute Award (Institute of the Aeronautical Sciences), 1947
  Outstanding Achievement Award (University of Minnesota), 1954
Cooper, George E.
  Octave Chanute Award (Institute of the Aeronautical Sciences), 1954
  Arthur S. Flemming Award (Junior Chamber of Commerce, Washington, D.C.), 1954
DeFrance, Dr. Smith J.
  Presidential Medal for Merit, 1948
  Vice President, Institute of the Aeronautical Sciences, 1948 and 1951

Honorary Doctor of Law degree (University of California at Los Angeles),
1952

Honorary Doctor of Engineering degree (University of Michigan), 1953

Career Service Award (National Civil Service League), 1964

Outstanding Leadership Medal (NASA), 1965

Drinkwater, Fred J., III

Octave Chanute Award (American Institute of Aeronautics and Astronautics), 1964—with Robert C. Innis

Richard Hansford Burroughs Test Pilot Award (Flight Safety Foundation),
1966

Eggers, Dr. Alfred J., Jr.

Arthur S. Flemming Award (Junior Chamber of Commerce, Washington,
D.C.), 1956

Outstanding Alumni Award (University of Omaha), 1958

Sylvanus Albert Reed Award (American Institute of Aeronautics and Astronautics), 1961

Harper, Charles W.

Group Achievement Award (NASA), 1964—with Jay V. Christensen, Ralph
F. Huntsberger, and Earl R. Keener

Huntsberger, Ralph F.

Group Achievement Award (NASA), 1964—with Jay V. Christensen, Charles
W. Harper, and Earl R. Keener

Innis, Robert C.

Octave Chanute Award (American Institute of Aeronautics and Astronautics), 1964—with Fred J. Drinkwater III

Jones, Robert T.

Sylvanus Albert Reed Award (Institute of the Aeronautical Sciences), 1946

Kauffman, William M.

Arthur S. Flemming Award (Junior Chamber of Commerce, Washington,
D.C.), 1955

Keener, Earl R.

Group Achievement Award (NASA), 1964—with Jay V. Christensen, Charles
W. Harper, and Ralph F. Huntsberger

Lewis, William

Robert M. Losey Award (Institute of the Aeronautical Sciences), 1949

NOTE.—Mr. Lewis was a meteorologist employed by the U.S. Weather Bureau and was assigned to the Ames Aeronautical Laboratory from October 1, 1944, to May 6, 1949. During that assignment he did the research for which the award was made.

McAvoy, William H.

Octave Chanute Award (Institute of the Aeronautical Sciences), 1943

Mead, Merrill H.

The M.I.T. Alfred P. Sloan Fellowship in Executive Development,
1962–1963.

Neel, Carr H.
>The Award of Excellence (Instrument Society of America), 1965

Rodert, Lewis A.
>Collier Trophy (National Aeronautic Association), 1946

Syvertson, Clarence A.
>Lawrence B. Sperry Award (Institute of the Aeronautical Sciences), 1957

Van Dyke, Dr. Milton D.
>Fulbright Award for Research, 1954
>John Simon Guggenheim Award, 1954

Vincenti, Walter G.
>Gold Medal Award (Pi Tau Sigma), 1948
>Rockefeller Public Service Award, 1955

White, John S.
>Samuel Burka Award (Institute of Navigation), 1963—with Rodney C. Wingrove

Wingrove, Rodney C.
>Samuel Burka Award (Institute of Navigation), 1963—with John S. White
>Lawrence B. Sperry Award (American Institute of Aeronautics and Astronautics), 1965

Appendix C

List of References

Product Display

The principal product of a research laboratory is the technical report. The following list of reports is intended to serve more as a "product display" than as a conventional reference source. The listed reports represent but a small fraction of the total output of the Ames Research Center. They were selected by the author, somewhat arbitrarily, on the basis of their historical and technical significance and, as a group, are believed to be broadly representative of the Center's best research efforts during the period of this history. The list by no means includes all of the important reports produced by the Center. Nor does it document the Center's continuous and effective development-test effort by means of which the Nation's military and civilian aircraft have, during the past quarter century, been notably improved.

PART I

A–1. Rodert, Lewis A.; McAvoy, William H.; and Clousing, Lawrence A.: Preliminary Report on Flight Tests of an Airplane Having Exhaust-Heated Wings. NACA ACR, April 1941. (Issued as NACA WR A–53, 1941.)

A–2. Hardy, J. K.: An Analysis of the Dissipation of Heat in Conditions of Icing from a Section of the Wing of the C–46 Airplane. NACA Rep. 831, 1945.

A–3. Neel, Carr B., Jr.: An Investigation of a Thermal Ice-Prevention System for a C–46 Cargo Airplane. I—Analysis of the Thermal Design for Wings, Empennage, and Windshields. NACA ARR 5A03, 1943.

A–4. Jones, Alun R.: An Investigation of a Thermal Ice-Prevention System for a Twin-Engine Transport Airplane. NACA Rep. 862, 1946.

A–5. Goett, Harry J.; Jackson, Roy P.; and Belsley, Steven E.: Wind-Tunnel Procedure for Determination of Critical Stability and Control Characteristics of Airplanes. NACA Rep. 781, 1944.

A–6. Nissen, James M.; Gadeberg, Burnett L.; and Hamilton, William T.: Correlation of the Drag Characteristics of a Typical Pursuit Airplane

Obtained from High-Speed Wind-Tunnel and Flight Tests. NACA Rep. 916, 1948.

A–7. Frick, Charles W.; Davis, Wallace F.; Randall, Lauros M.; and Mossman, Emmet A.: An Experimental Investigation of NACA Submerged-Duct Entrances. NACA ACR 5I20, 1945.

A–8. Allen, H. Julian: General Theory of Airfoil Sections Having Arbitrary Shape or Pressure Distribution. NACA Rep. 833, 1945.

A–9. Graham, Donald J.; Nitzberg, Gerald E.; and Olson, Robert N.: A Systematic Investigation of Pressure Distributions at High Speeds Over Five Representative NACA Low-Drag and Conventional Airfoil Sections. NACA Rep. 832, 1945.

PART II

B–1. Heaslet, Max A.; Lomax, Harvard; and Jones, Arthur L.: Volterra's Solution of the Wave Equation as Applied to Three-Dimensional Supersonic Airfoil Problems. NACA Rep. 889, 1947.

B–2. Spreiter, John R.: The Aerodynamic Forces on Slender Plane- and Cruciform-Wing and Body Combinations. NACA Rep. 962, 1950.

B–3. Heaslet, Max A.; Lomax, Harvard; and Spreiter, John R.: Linearized Compressible-Flow Theory for Sonic Flight Speeds. NACA Rep. 956, 1950.

B–4. Jones, Robert T.: Estimated Lift-Drag Ratios at Supersonic Speed. NACA TN 1350, 1947.

B–5. Vincenti, Walter G.; Nielsen, Jack N.; and Matteson, Frederick H.: Investigation of Wing Characteristics at a Mach Number of 1.53. I—Triangular Wings of Aspect Ratio 2. NACA RM A7I10, 1947.

B–6. Vincenti, Walter G.: Comparison Between Theory and Experiment for Wings at Supersonic Speeds. NACA Rep. 1033, 1951.

B–7. Frick, C. W.; and Chubb, R. S.: The Longitudinal Stability of Elastic Swept Wings at Supersonic Speed. NACA Rep. 965, 1950.

B–8. Chapman, Dean R.; and Perkins, Edward W.: Experimental Investigation of the Effects of Viscosity on the Drag and Base Pressure of Bodies of Revolution at a Mach Number of 1.5. NACA Rep. 1036, 1951.

B–9. Chapman, Dean R.: An Analysis of Base Pressure at Supersonic Velocities and Comparison with Experiment. NACA Rep. 1051, 1951.

B–10. Allen, H. Julian; and Perkins, Edward W.: A Study of Effects of Viscosity on Flow Over Slender Inclined Bodies of Revolution. NACA Rep. 1048, 1951.

B–11. DeYoung, John; and Harper, Charles W.: Theoretical Symmetric Span Loading at Subsonic Speeds for Wings Having Arbitrary Plan Form. NACA Rep. 921, 1948.

B–12. Kauffman, William M.; Liddell, Charles J., Jr.; Smith, Allan; and Van Dyke, Rudolph D., Jr.: An Apparatus for Varying Effective Dihedral in Flight With Application to a Study of Tolerable Dihedral on a Conventional Fighter Airplane. NACA Rep. 948, 1949.

B–13. Chapman, Dean R.; and Rubesin, Morris W.: Temperature and Velocity Profiles in the Compressible Laminar Boundary Layer With Arbitrary Distribution of Surface Temperature. *Jour. Aero. Sci.*, vol. 16, no. 9, Sept. 1949, pp. 547–565.

B–14. Scherrer, Richard: Comparison of Theoretical and Experimental Heat-Transfer Characteristics of Bodies of Revolution at Supersonic Speeds. NACA Rep. 1055, 1951.

B–15. Stalder, Jackson R.; and Jukoff, David: Heat Transfer to Bodies Traveling at High Speed in the Upper Atmosphere. NACA Rep. 944, 1949.

B–16. Stalder, Jackson R.; Goodwin, Glen; and Creager, Marcus O.: A Comparison of Theory and Experiment for High-Speed Free-Molecule Flow. NACA Rep. 1032, 1951.

B–17. Seiff, Alvin: A Free-Flight Wind Tunnel for Aerodynamic Testing at Hypersonic Speeds. NACA Rep. 1222, 1955.

B–18. Huntsberger, Ralph F.; and Parsons, John F.: The Design of Large High-Speed Wind Tunnels. Presented at Wind-Tunnel and Model Testing Panel, Fourth General Assembly, AGARD, Scheveningen, Netherlands, May 4, 1954. AGARD publication AG15/P6, pp. 127–152.

B–19. Lomax, Harvard; Heaslet, Max. A.; Fuller, Franklyn B.; and Sluder, Loma: Two- and Three-Dimensional Unsteady Lift Problems in High-Speed Flight. NACA Rep. 1077, 1952.

B–20. Vincenti, Walter G.; and Wagoner, Cleo B.: Transonic Flow Past a Wedge Profile With Detached Bow Wave. NACA Rep. 1095, 1952.

B–21. Vincenti, Walter G.; and Wagoner, Cleo B.: Theoretical Study of the Transonic Lift of a Double-Wedge Profile with Detached Bow Wave. NACA Rep. 1180, 1954.

B–22. Spreiter, John R.: On the Application of Transonic Similarity Rules to Wings of Finite Span. NACA Rep. 1153, 1953.

B–23. McDevitt, John B.: A Correlation by Means of Transonic Similarity Rules of Experimentally Determined Characteristics of a Series of Symmetrical and Cambered Wings of Rectangular Plan Form. NACA Rep. 1253, 1955.

B–24. Chapman, Dean R.: Airfoil Profiles for Minimum Pressure Drag at Supersonic Velocities—General Analysis With Application to Linearized Supersonic Flow, NACA Rep. 1063, 1952.

B–25. Chapman, Dean R.; Wimbrow, William R.; and Kester, Robert H.: Experimental Investigation of Base Pressure on Blunt-Trailing-Edge Wings at Supersonic Velocities. NACA Rep. 1109, 1952.

B–26. Eggers, A. J., Jr.; and Savin, Raymond C.: A Unified Two-Dimensional Approach to the Calculation of Three-Dimensional Hypersonic Flows, With Application to Bodies of Revolution. NACA Rep. 1249, 1955.

B–27. Van Dyke, Milton D.: A Study of Hypersonic Small-Disturbance Theory. NACA Rep. 1194, 1954.

B–28. Perkins, Edward W.; Jorgensen, Leland H.; and Sommer, Simon C.: Investigation of the Drag of Various Axially Symmetric Nose Shapes of Fineness Ratio 3 for Mach Numbers from 1.24 to 7.4. NACA Rep. 1386, 1958.

B–29. Nielsen, Jack N.: Quasi-Cylindrical Theory of Wing-Body Interference at Supersonic Speeds and Comparison with Experiment. NACA Rep. 1252, 1955.

B–30. Pitts, William C.; Nielsen, Jack N.; and Kaattari, George E.: Lift and Center of Pressure of Wing-Body-Tail Combinations at Subsonic, Transonic, and Supersonic Speeds. NACA Rep. 1307, 1957.

B–31. Jones, Robert T.: Theory of Wing-Body Drag at Supersonic Speeds. NACA Rep. 1284, 1956.

B–32. Reynolds, Robert M.; Sammonds, Robert I.; and Walker, John H.: An Investigation of Single- and Dual-Rotation Propellers at Positive and Negative Thrust, and in Combination With an NACA 1-Series D-Type Cowling at Mach Numbers up to 0.84. NACA Rep. 1336, 1957.

B–33. Turner, Howard L.; Triplett, William C.; and White, John S.: A Flight and Analog Computer Study of Some Stabilization and Command Networks for an Automatically Controlled Interceptor During the Final Attack Phase. NACA RM A54J14, 1955.

B–34. Triplett, William C.; Brown, Stuart C.; and Smith, G. Allan: The Dynamic-Response Characteristics of a 35° Swept-Wing Airplane as Determined From Flight Measurements. NACA Rep. 1250, 1955.

B–35. Allen, H. Julian; and Eggers, A. J., Jr.: A Study of the Motion and Aerodynamic Heating of Ballistic Missiles Entering the Earth's Atmosphere at High Supersonic Speeds. NACA Rep. 1381, 1958.

B–36. Charters, A. C.; Denardo, B. Pat; and Rossow, Vernon J.: Development of a Piston-Compressor Type Light-Gas Gun for the Launching of Free-Flight Models at High Velocity. NACA TN 4143, 1957.

B–37. Eggers, A. J., Jr.: A Method for Simulating the Atmospheric Entry of Long-Range Ballistic Missiles. NACA Rep. 1378, 1958.

B–38. Spreiter, John R.; and Alksne, Alberta Y.: Thin Airfoil Theory Based on Approximate Solution of the Transonic Flow Equation. NACA Rep. 1359, 1958.

B–39. Eggers, A. J., Jr.; Resnikoff, Meyer M.; and Dennis, David H.: Bodies of Revolution Having Minimum Drag at High Supersonic Airspeeds. NACA Rep. 1306, 1957.

B–40. Holdaway, George H.; and Hatfield, Elaine W.: Transonic Investigation of Yawed Wings of Aspect Ratios 3 and 6 with a Sears-Haack Body and With Symmetrical and Asymmetrical Bodies Indented for a Mach Number of 1.20. NACA RM A58C03, 1958.

B–41.   Heaslet, Max A.; and Fuller, Franklyn B.: Drag Minimization for Wings and Bodies in Supersonic Flow. NACA Rep. 1385, 1958.

B–42.   Eggers, Alfred J., Jr.; and Syvertson, Clarence A.: Aircraft Configurations Developing High Lift-Drag Ratios at High Supersonic Speeds. NACA RM A55L05, 1956.

B–43.   Hall, Charles F.; and Boyd, John W.: Effects of Canards on Airplane Performance and Stability. NACA RM A58D24, 1958.

B–44.   Kelly, Mark W.; Anderson, Seth B.; and Innis, Robert C.: Blowing-Type Boundary-Layer Control as Applied to the Trailing-Edge Flaps of a 35° Swept-Wing Airplane. NACA Rep. 1369, 1958.

B–45.   Davis, Wallace F.; and Scherrer, Richard: Aerodynamic Principles for the Design of Jet-Engine Induction Systems. NACA RM A55F16, 1956.

B–46.   Beam, Benjamin H.: A Wind-Tunnel Test Technique for Measuring the Dynamic Rotary Stability Derivatives at Subsonic and Supersonic Speeds. NACA Rep. 1258, 1956.

B–47.   Douvillier, Joseph G., Jr.; Foster, John V.; and Drinkwater, Fred J., III: An Airborne Simulator Investigation of the Accuracy of an Optical Track Command Missile Guidance System. NACA RM A56G24, 1956 (Confidential).

B–48.   Cooper, George E.: Understanding and Interpreting Pilot Opinion. *Aero. Eng. Rev.*, vol. 16, no. 3, March 1957, pp. 47–51, 56.

B–49.   Cole, Henry A., Jr.; Brown, Stuart C.; and Holleman, Euclid C.: Experimental and Predicted Longitudinal and Lateral-Directional Response Characteristics of a Large Flexible 35° Swept-Wing Airplane at an Altitude of 35,000 Feet. NACA Rep. 1330, 1957.

B–50.   Chapman, Dean R.; Kuehn, Donald M.; and Larson, Howard K.: Investigation of Separated Flows in Supersonic and Subsonic Streams With Emphasis on the Effect of Transition. NACA Rep. 1356, 1958.

B–51.   Smith, Donald W.; and Walker, John H.: Skin-Friction Measurements in Incompressible Flow. NACA TN 4231, 1958.

B–52.   Tendeland, Thorval: Effects of Mach Number and Wall-Temperature Ratio on Turbulent Heat Transfer at Mach Numbers from 3 to 5. NACA TN 4236, 1958.

B–53.   Sommer, Simon C.; and Short, Barbara J.: Free-Flight Measurements of Turbulent-Boundary-Layer Skin Friction in the Presence of Severe Aerodynamic Heating at Mach Numbers from 2.8 to 7.0. NACA TN 3391, 1955.

B–54.   Canning, Thomas N.; and Sommer, Simon C.: Investigation of Boundary-Layer Transition on Flat-Faced Bodies of Revolution at High Supersonic Speeds. NACA RM A57C25, 1957.

B–55.   Hansen, C. Frederick: Approximations for the Thermodynamic and Transport Properties of High-Temperature Air. NACA TN 4150, 1958 (superseded by NASA TR R–50, 1959).

B–56. Rossow, Vernon J.: On Flow of Electrically Conducting Fluids Over a Flat Plate in the Presence of a Transverse Magnetic Field. NACA Rep. 1358, 1958.

B–57. Eggers, Alfred J., Jr.; Allen, H. Julian; and Neice, Stanford E.: A Comparative Analysis of the Performance of Long-Range Hypervelocity Vehicles. NACA Rep. 1382, 1958.

B–58. Allen, H. Julian: Hypersonic Flight and the Re-Entry Problem. Twenty-First Wright Brothers Lecture, Washington, D.C., Dec. 17, 1957 (published in *Jour. Aero. Sci.*, vol. 25, no. 4, April 1958, pp. 217–230).

B–59. Hansen, C. Frederick: The Erosion of Meteors and High-Speed Vehicles in the Upper Atmosphere. NACA TN 3962, 1957.

B–60. Spreiter, John R.: Aerodynamics of Wing and Bodies at Transonic Speeds. Presented at Eighth Japanese National Congress for Theoretical and Applied Mechanics, Tokyo, Japan, Sept. 6–8, 1958 (published in *Jour. Aero/Space Sci.*, vol. 26, no. 8, Aug. 1959, pp. 465–487 and 517).

B–61. Anderson, Seth B.; Cooper, George E.; and Faye, Alan E., Jr.: Flight Measurements of the Effect of a Controllable Thrust Reverser on the Flight Characteristics of a Single-Engine Jet Airplane. NASA Memo 4–26–59A, 1959.

B–62. Seiff, Alvin; and Short, Barbara J.: An Investigation of Supersonic Turbulent Boundary Layers on Slender Bodies of Revolution in Free Flight by Use of a Mach-Zehnder Interferometer and Shadowgraphs. NACA TN 4364, 1958.

B–63. Matting, Fred W.; Chapman, Dean R.; Nyholm, Jack R.; and Thomas, Andrew G.: Turbulent Skin Friction at High Mach Numbers and Reynolds Numbers in Air and Helium. NASA TR R–82, 1961.

B–64. Chapman, Dean R.: An Approximate Analytical Method for Studying Entry Into Planetary Atmospheres. NASA TR R–11, 1959.

B–65. Eggers, Alfred J., Jr.; and Wong, Thomas J.: Re-entry and Recovery of Near-Earth Satellites, With Particular Attention to a Manned Vehicle. NASA Memo 10–2–58A, 1958.

B–66. Van Dyke, Milton D.; and Gordon, Helen D.: Supersonic Flow Past a Family of Blunt Axisymmetric Bodies. NASA TR R–1, 1959.

PART III

C–1. Curtis, John S.: An Accelerated Reservoir Light-Gas Gun. NASA TN D–1144, 1962.

C–2. Stine, Howard A.; and Watson, Velvin R.: The Theoretical Enthalpy Distribution of Air in Steady Flow along the Axis of a Direct-Current Electric Arc. NASA TN D–1331, 1962.

C–3. Jones, J. Lloyd, Jr.; Hunton, Lynn W.; Gregory, Thomas J.; and Nelms, Walter P., Jr.: A Critical Study of Delta Wing Configurations for the

Supersonic Transport Application. Presented at 31st Annual Meeting, Inst. Aero. Sci., New York, Jan. 21–23, 1963. IAS paper 63–5.

C–4. Spahr, J. Richard: Theoretical Prediction of the Effects of Vortex Flows on the Loading, Forces, and Moments of Slender Aircraft. NASA TR R–101, 1961.

C–5. White, Maurice D.; Sadoff, Melvin; Bray, Richard S.; and Cooper, George E.: Assessment of Critical Problem Areas of the Supersonic Transport by Means of Piloted Simulators. *Aerospace Eng.*, vol. 21, no. 5, May 1962, pp. 12–21.

C–6. Anderson, Seth B.: An Examination of Handling Qualities Criteria for V/STOL Aircraft. NASA TN D–331, 1960.

C–7. Rolls, L. Stewart; and Drinkwater, Fred J., III: A Flight Determination of the Attitude Control Power and Damping Requirements for a Visual Hovering Task in the Variable Stability and Control X–14A Research Vehicle. NASA TN D–1328, 1962.

C–8. Cole, Henry A., Jr.: Dynamic Response of Hammerhead Launch Vehicles to Transonic Buffeting. NASA TN D–1982, 1963.

C–9. Bader, Michel; Witteborn, Fred C.; and Snouse, Thomas W.: Sputtering of Metals by Mass-Analyzed N_2^+ and N^+. NASA TR R–105, 1961.

C–10. Dennis, David H.; and Edwards, George G.: The Aerodynamic Characteristics of Some Lifting Bodies. NASA TM X–376, 1960.

C–11. Rasmussen, Maurice L.: Determination of Nonlinear Pitching-Moment Characteristics of Axially Symmetric Models From Free-Flight Data. NASA TN D–144, 1960.

C–12. Chapman, Dean R.: An Analysis of the Corridor and Guidance Requirements for Supercircular Entry Into Planetary Atmospheres. NASA TR R–55, 1960.

C–13. Wingrove, Rodney C.: A Study of Guidance to Reference Trajectories for Lifting Reentry at Supercircular Velocity. NASA TR R–151, 1963.

C–14. Chung, Paul M.: Hypersonic Viscous Shock Layer of Nonequilibrium Dissociating Gas. NASA TR R–109, 1961.

C–15. Howe, John T.; and Viegas, John R.: Solutions of the Ionized Radiating Shock Layer, Including Reabsorption and Foreign Species Effects, and Stagnation Region Heat Transfer. NASA TR R–159, 1963.

C–16. Canning, Thomas N.; and Page, William A.: Measurements of Radiation from the Flow Fields of Bodies Flying at Speeds up to 13.4 Kilometers per Second. AGARDograph 68: "High-Temperature Aspects of Hypersonic Flow," Proc. of AGARD NATO Specialists Meeting, Belgium, April 3–6, 1962 (Pergamon Press, New York, 1963, pp. 569–582).

C–17. Wick, Bradford H.: Radiative Heating of Vehicles Entering the Earth's Atmosphere. AGARDograph 68: "High-Temperature Aspects of Hypersonic Flow," Proc. of AGARD NATO Specialists Meeting, Belgium, April 3–6, 1962 (Pergamon Press, New York, 1963, pp. 607–627).

C–18.   Yoshikawa, Kenneth K.; and Chapman, Dean R.: Radiative Heat Transfer and Absorption Behind a Hypersonic Normal Shock Wave. NASA TN D–1424, 1962.

C–19.   Chapman, Gary T.; and Jackson, Charles T., Jr.: Measurement of the Heat Transfer to Bodies of Revolution in Free Flight by Use of a Catcher Calorimeter. NASA TN D–1890, 1963.

C–20.   Compton, Dale L.; Winovich, Warren; and Wakefield, Roy M.: Measurements of the Effective Heats of Ablation of Teflon and Polyethylene at Convective Heating Rates from 25 to 420 Btu/Ft² Sec. NASA TN D–1332, 1962.

C–21.   Allen, H. Julian: Hypersonic Aerodynamic Problems of the Future. AGARDograph 68: Proc. of AGARD NATO Specialists Meeting, Belgium, April 3–6, 1962 (Pergamon Press, New York, 1963, pp. 1–41).

C–22.   Allen, H. Julian; Seiff, Alvin; and Winovich, Warren: Aerodynamic Heating of Conical Entry Vehicles at Speeds in Excess of Earth Parabolic Speed. NASA TR R–185, 1963.

C–23.   Summers, James L.: Investigation of High-Speed Impact: Regions of Impact and Impact at Oblique Angles. NASA TN D–94, 1959.

C–24.   Nysmith, C. Robert; and Summers, James L.: Preliminary Investigation of Impact on Multiple-Sheet Structures and an Evaluation of the Meteoroid Hazard to Space Vehicles. NASA TN D–1039, 1961.

C–25.   Gault, Donald E.; Shoemaker, Eugene M.; and Moore, Henry J.: Spray Ejected From the Lunar Surface by Meteoroid Impact. NASA TN D–1767, 1963.

C–26.   Chapman, Dean R.; and Larson, Howard K.: On the Lunar Origin of Tektites. *Jour. Geophysical Res.*, vol. 68, no. 14, July 15, 1963, pp. 4305–4358 (NASA TN D–1556, 1963).

C–27.   Spreiter, John R.; and Jones, Wm. Prichard: On the Effect of a Weak Interplanetary Magnetic Field on the Interaction Between the Solar Wind and the Geomagnetic Field. *Jour. Geophysical Res.*, vol. 68, no. 12, June 15, 1963, pp. 3555–3564.

C–28.   Hruby, Ronald J.; McDevitt, John B.; Coon, Grant W.; Harrison, Dean R.; and Kemp, Joseph H., Jr.: FM Telemetry and Free-Flight Techniques for Aerodynamic Measurements in Conventional Wind Tunnels. NASA TN D–3319, 1966.

C–29.   Sadoff, Melvin; Bray, Richard S.; and Andrews, William H.: Summary of NASA Research on Jet Transport Control Problems in Severe Turbulence. Paper No. 65–330, Second AIAA Annual Meeting, San Francisco, Calif., July 26–29, 1965.

C–30.   Quigley, Hervey C.; Innis, Robert C.; and Holzhauser, Curt A.: A Flight Investigation of the Performance, Handling Qualities, and Operational Characteristics of a Deflected Slipstream STOL Transport Airplane Having Four Interconnected Propellers. NASA TN D–2231, 1964.

C–31. Warner, R. W.; and Marble, D. R.: Materials Needs for Energy Absorption in Space-Vehicle Landings. ASTM Spec. Tech. Publ. 379, 1965. Presented at Symposium on Newer Structural Materials for Aerospace Vehicles, Amer. Soc. for Testing and Materials, Sixth Annual Meeting, Chicago, Ill., June 21, 1964.

C–32. Levy, Lionel L., Jr.; and Fletcher, Leroy S.: Free-Flight Aerodynamics of a Blunt-Faced Reentry Shape With and Without Ablation. AIAA Paper 66–61, AIAA 3d Aerospace Sciences Meeting, New York, Jan. 24–26, 1966.

C–33. Intrieri, Peter F.: Experimental Stability and Drag of a Pointed and a Blunted 30° Half-Angle Cone at Mach Numbers From 11.5 to 34 in Air. NASA TN D–3193, 1966.

C–34. Kemp, Joseph H., Jr.: Telemetry Measurements of Afterbody Pressures on Free-Flying Models of the Apollo Capsule at Mach Numbers From 10 to 21 in Helium and 14 in Air. NASA TM X–1154, 1965.

C–35. Carlson, Robert W.; and Swenson, Byron L.: Maneuvering Flight within Earth-Entry Corridors at Hyperbolic Speeds. AIAA Paper 65–19. Presented at Second AIAA Aerospace Sciences Meeting, New York, Jan. 25–27, 1965 (published in *Jour. Spacecraft and Rockets*, vol. 3, no. 3, March 1966, pp. 353–358).

C–36. Wingrove, Rodney C.; Stinnett, Glen W.; and Innis, Robert C.: A Study of the Pilot's Ability to Control an Apollo Type Vehicle During Atmosphere Entry. NASA TN D–2467, 1964.

C–37. Seiff, Alvin; and Reese, David E., Jr.: Defining Mars' Atmosphere—A Goal for the Early Missions. *Astronautics & Aeronautics*, vol. 3, no. 2, Feb. 1965, pp. 16–21.

C–38. Tobak, Murray; and Peterson, Victor L.: Theory of Tumbling Bodies Entering Planetary Atmospheres With Application to Probe Vehicles and the Australian Tektites. NASA TR R–203, 1964.

C–39. Dugan, Duane W.: A Parametric Study of Mass-Ratio and Trajectory Factors in Fast Manned Mars Missions. NASA TN D–2225, 1965.

C–40. Chapman, Gary T.: Theoretical Laminar Convective Heat Transfer and Boundary-Layer Characteristics on Cones at Speeds to 24 Km/Sec. NASA TN D–2463, 1964.

C–41. Marvin, Joseph G.; and Deiwert, George S.: Convective Heat Transfer in Planetary Gases. NASA TR R–224, 1965.

C–42. Compton, Dale L.; and Cooper, David M.: Free-Flight Measurements of Stagnation-Point Convective Heat Transfer at Velocities to 41,000 Ft/Sec. NASA TN D–2871, 1965.

C–43. Howe, John T.; and Sheaffer, Yvonne S.: Mass Addition in the Stagnation Region for Velocity up to 50,000 Feet per Second. NASA TR R–207, 1964.

C–44.   Lundell, John H.; Wakefield, Roy M.; and Jones, Jerold W.: Experimental Investigation of a Charring Ablative Material Exposed to Combined Convective and Radiative Heating. Presented at AIAA Entry Technology Conference, Williamsburg/Hampton, Va., Oct. 10–12, 1964 (published in *AIAA Jour.,* vol. 3, no. 11, Nov. 1965, pp. 2087–2095).

C–45.   Page, William A.; and Arnold, James O.: Shock-Layer Radiation of Blunt Bodies at Reentry Velocities. NASA TR R–193, 1964.

C–46.   Heaslet, Max A.; and Fuller, Franklyn B.: Approximate Predictions of the Transport of Thermal Radiation Through an Absorbing Plane Layer. NASA TN D–2515, 1964.

C–47.   Denardo, B. Pat: Penetration of Polyethylene Into Semi-Infinite 2024–T351 Aluminum up to Velocities of 37,000 Feet per Second. NASA TN D–3369, 1966.

C–48.   Keil, Klaus; and Andersen, Christian A.: Electron Microprobe Study of the Jajh deh Kot Lalu Enstatite Chondrite. *Geochimica et Cosmochimica Acta,* vol. 29, 1965, pp. 621–632.

C–49.   Chapman, Dean R.: On the Unity and Origin of the Australasian Tektites. *Geochimica et Cosmochimica Acta,* vol. 28, 1964, pp. 841–880.

C–50.   Allen, H. Julian; Baldwin, Barrett S., Jr.; and James, Nataline A.: Effect on Meteor Flight of Cooling by Radiation and Ablation. NASA TN D–2872, 1965.

C–51.   Reynolds, Ray T.; and Summers, Audrey L.: Models of Uranus and Neptune. *Jour. Geophysical Res.,* vol. 70, no. 1, Jan. 1, 1965, pp. 199–208.

C–52.   Wolfe, John H.; Silva, Richard W.; and Myers, Marilyn A.: Observations of the Solar Wind during the Flight of IMP–I. *Jour. Geophysical Res.,* vol. 71, no. 5, Mar. 1, 1966, pp. 1319–1340.

C–53.   Patton, Rollin M.: Behavioral Testing During a 7-Day Confinement: The Information Processing Task. NASA TN D–1973, 1963.

C–54.   Brooksby, G. A.; Staley, Robert W.; and Dennis, Robert L.: Effects of Prolonged Exposure of Animals to Increased Oxygen Concentrations. Presented at Third International Conference on Hyperbaric Medicine, Duke University, Durham, N.C., Nov. 17–20, 1965.

C–55.   Young, Donald R.: Carbohydrate and Fat Metabolism During Prolonged Physical Work. Proceedings, Symposium on Arctic Biology and Medicine (ed., Lucile Vaughn), 1965, Arctic Aeromedical Laboratory, Fort Wainwright, Alaska, Mar. 22–24, 1965.

C–56.   Oyama, J.; and Platt, W. T.: Effects of Prolonged Centrifugation on Growth and Organ Development of Rats. *American Jour. of Physiology,* vol. 209, Sept. 1965, pp. 611–615.

C–57. Feller, David D.; Neville, E. D.; Oyama, J.; and Averkin, E. G.: Chemical and Metabolic Changes of Hepatic Lipids From Rats Exposed to Chronic Radial Acceleration. *Proc. Soc. Exper. Bio. Med.,* vol. 119, 1965, pp. 522–525.

C–58. Miquel, J.; and Haymaker, W.: Glycogen Accumulation in Monkey and Cat Brain Exposed to Proton Radiation. Proc. Fifth International Congress of Neuropathology, Zurich, Switzerland, Sept. 1965, pp. 792–797.

C–59. Taketa, S. Tom; Castle, B. L.; Howard, W. H.; Conley, C. C.; Haymaker, W.; and Sondhaus, C. A.: Effects of Acute Doses of High Energy Protons on Primates. *Radiation Research,* Supplement 7, 1967, pp. 336–359.

C–60. Fryer, Thomas B.; and Deboo, Gordon J.: A High-Performance Miniature Biopotential Telemetry System. Proc. 17th Annual Conference on Engineering in Medicine and Biology, Nov. 16–18, 1964, vol. 6, p. 39.

C–61. Howe, John T.; and Sheaffer, Yvonne S.: An Analysis of Recent Hypotheses of Plasma Flow in Pericapillary Spaces. Prepared for presentation at International Symposium on the Human Capillary Circulation, Jamaica, British West Indies, Jan. 1966.

C–62. Ponnamperuma, Cyril; Sagan, Carl; and Mariner, Ruth: Synthesis of Adenosine Triphosphate under Possible Primitive Earth Conditions. *Nature,* vol. 199, no. 4890, July 20, 1963, pp. 222–226.

C–63. Young, Richard S.; Painter, Robert B.; and Johnson, Richard D.: An Analysis of the Extraterrestrial Life Detection Problem. NASA SP–75, 1965.

INDEX

INDEX

INDEX

INDEX

INDEX

INDEX

INDEX

INDEX

Mead, Merrill H., 223–224, 224 (illus.), 255, 320, 406, 408, 455

Medical Times, 481

Mellenthin, Jack A., 209, 288, 451, 452

Menees, Gene P., 251, 288, 347, 357, 452

Menlo Park, Calif., 468

Menunketesuck Point, Conn., 20

Mercury, Project, 390

Mercury spacecraft, 479–480

Merrick, Robert B., 258, 290

Merrick, Vernon K., 454

Mersman, William A., 197 (illus.), 198, 244, 295, 364

Messerschmitt (aircraft), 15

Meteoroid, 270, 465–469, 472–474

Michigan, 26

Michigan, Univ. of, 26, 182

Migotsky, Eugene, 247

Miguel, Jaime, 483

Millard, John P., 478

Miller, Representative George P., 427

Minden, L. E., 28 (illus.)

Minneapolis, Minn., 74

Missile, ballistic (*see also* ICBM; IRBM), 263–264, 274

MIT-Sloan Executive Fellowship, 408

Mobilization Plan of the Aeronautical Board, 42

Moffett Field, Calif., ii (illus.), 23, 24 (illus.), 25, 26, 27, 29, 37, 40, 45, 293, 316, 399, 406, 426, 437, 503

Moffett, R/A William A., 23

Monfort, James C., 209, 363

Monson, Daryl J., 450–451

Monterey Bay, Calif., 37

Montgomery, Lawrence, Sr., 96

Moon, 311, 314, 382–384, 434

manned flight to. *See* Apollo, Project

Moore, H. J., 380–381

Morrill, Charles, 161

Moscow, U.S.S.R., 9

Mossman, Emmet, 93–94, 162, 254

Mountain View, Calif., 23, 426

Munk, Max, 155

Muroc Dry Lake, Calif., 82, 92, 123

Muroc Flight Test Unit, 123

MX-774 (project) (*see also* Atlas), 125

Myers, Marilyn A., 477

N9M-2 (aircraft), 104

NACA (National Advisory Committee for Aeronautics), xi, 31–32, 37, 45, 74, 148, 155, 175–176, 234, 246, 287

Aeronautical Intelligence, Office of, 5

budget, 126, 175–176, 221

Committees, 33–34

Director, 3, 129, 308, 409

Director of Aeronautical Research, 34

facilities expansion program ("Unitary Plan"), 150–152

Headquarters, 177–178, 188, 241, 242, 275, 285, 314

history, 1–30

inspections, 130

manpower crisis, 175–176, 222

mission, 153–154

pilots, 211, 252

public relations, 130, 179, 312–313

space research program, 274–275, 294

transfer to NASA, 275, 299–301, 307–308, 310, 311–315, 396–397

Unitary Wind Tunnel Programs, Project Office for the, 151–152, 178

Western Coordination Office, ix

Nansen, Fridtjof, 314

NASA (National Aeronautics and Space Administration), ix, xi

Administrator, 301, 307–308, 310, 500

Associate Administrator, 396

budget, 310–311, 315, 395

contracting, 310, 312–313, 397–399, 409–410

Deputy Administrator, 308, 409

establishment of, 274–275, 299–301, 308–310

external relationships, 311–313, 315–316, 350–351

Headquarters, 310, 314–316, 322, 349, 389–390, 396, 401, 413, 431, 489, 492, 497

Office of Advanced Research and Technology, xii, 339, 396–397, 404, 405–406, 427, 491

Aeronautics Div., 406

Mission Analysis Div., 405–406, 413

Office of Advanced Research Programs, 396

Office of Applications, 500

Office of Launch Vehicle Programs, 314

Office of Life Science Programs, 321–323

Office of Manned Space Flight, 397

Office of Space Flight Programs, 314

Office of Space Sciences, 321

INDEX

INDEX

INDEX

779763

NASA Historical Publications

HISTORIES

MANAGEMENT HISTORY SERIES:
  Robert L. Rosholt, *An Administrative History of NASA, 1958–1963*, NASA SP–4101, 1966, $4.00.*

PROGRAM HISTORY SERIES:
  Loyd S. Swenson, James M. Grimwood, and Charles C. Alexander, *This New Ocean: A History of Project Mercury*, NASA SP–4201, 1966, $5.00.
  Constance McL. Green and Milton Lomask, *Vanguard: A History*, NASA SP–4202 (1970).

CENTER HISTORY SERIES:
  Alfred Rosenthal, *Venture Into Space: Early Years of Goddard Space Flight Center*, NASA SP–4301, 1968, $2.50.

HISTORICAL STUDIES

Eugene M. Emme (ed.), *History of Rocket Technology*, special issue of *Technology and Culture* (Fall 1963); augmented and published by Society for the History of Technology (Detroit: Wayne State University, 1964).

Mae Mills Link, *Space Medicine in Project Mercury*, NASA SP–4003, 1965, $1.

Historical Sketch of NASA, NASA EP–29, 1965, and 1966.

Katherine M. Dickson (Library of Congress), *History of Aeronautics and Astronautics: A Preliminary Bibliography*, NASA HHR–29, for sale by the Clearinghouse for Federal Scientific and Technical Information, Springfield, Va. 22151, $3.

CHRONOLOGIES

Aeronautics and Astronautics: An American Chronology of Science and Technology in the Exploration of Space, 1915–1960, compiled by E. M. Emme, Washington: NASA, 1961.

Aeronautical and Astronautical Events of 1961, published by the House Committee on Science and Astronautics, 1962.

Aeronautical and Astronautical Events of 1962, published by the House Committee on Science and Astronautics, 1963, $1.

Astronautics and Aeronautics, 1963, NASA SP–4004, 1964, $1.75.

Astronautics and Aeronautics, 1964, NASA SP–4005, 1965, $1.75.

Astronautics and Aeronautics, 1965, NASA SP–4006, 1966.

Astronautics and Aeronautics, 1966, NASA SP–4007, 1967, $1.50.

Astronautics and Aeronautics, 1967, NAS SP–4008, 1969, $2.25.

Astronautics and Aeronautics, 1968, NASA SP–4010, 1969, $2.00.

Project Mercury: A Chronology, by James M. Grimwood, NASA SP–4001, 1963.

Project Gemini Technology and Operations: A Chronology, by James M. Grimwood and Barton C. Hacker, with Peter J. Vorzimmer, NASA SP–4002, 1969, $2.75.

The Apollo Spacecraft: A Chronology, vol. I, *Through November 7, 1962*, by Ivan D. Ertel and Mary Lou Morse, NASA SP–4009, 1969, $2.50.

---

*All titles with prices can be ordered from the Superintendent of Documents, Government Printing Office, Washington, D.C. 20402.

1000
HOME DETAILS

1000

HOME DETAILS

A COMPLETE BOOK OF INSPIRING IDEAS TO IMPROVE HOME DECORATION

Editor: Francesc Zamora Mola

FIREFLY BOOKS

A FIREFLY BOOK

Published by Firefly Books Ltd. 2013

First printing

Publisher Cataloging-in-Publication Data (U.S.)

A CIP record for this title is available from the Library of Congress

Library and Archives Canada Cataloguing in Publication

A CIP record for this title is available from Library and Archives Canada

Published in the United States by
Firefly Books (U.S.) Inc.
P.O. Box 1338, Ellicott Station
Buffalo, New York 14205

Published in Canada by
Firefly Books Ltd.
50 Staples Avenue, Unit 1
Richmond Hill, Ontario L4B 0A7

Cover design: Erin R. Holmes/Soplari Design

Printed in China

Developed by
LOFT Publications
c/ Domènech, 7-9, 2º 1ª
08012 Barcelona, Spain
www.loftpublications.com

For Loft:
Editorial coordinator: Claudia Martínez Alonso
Editorial assistant: Ana Marques
Art director: Mireia Casanovas Soley
Editor: Francesc Zamora Mola
Text: Alejandra Muñoz Solano, Àlex Sánchez Vidiella, Irene Vidal Oliveras, Manel Gutiérrez (@mgutico)
Layout: Cristina Simó Perales, Sara Abril Abajo

INTRODUCTION

From the kitchen where we start our busy days to relaxing bedrooms and bathrooms, we want each space to reflect our personality. Outdoor spaces are extensions of our homes and therefore, the same rules should apply. The same depth of thought must be put into every one of these spaces. We certainly want our rooms to look stunning, but also utilitarian. Form and function in decorating are equally important, and every room should accommodate the ways the occupants live, entertain, work and relax. Pulling all the components together can be arduous, but it can also be very rewarding.

When it comes to decorating, everything counts, down to the last detail. It is a work in progress, and so a home is actually never "finished." It evolves over time reflecting trends, lifestyle and our own personal tastes. A good way to start out is with questions about function, mood and personality, the three main design considerations.

Before taking any action, put some thought into who will be using a particular room: adults, children, both? How will it function: as a place for entertaining, as a working area, as a retreat for relaxation? Some questions should be room specific. For instance, how many cooks use the kitchen? Or how many members of a family share a bathroom? Once you've ascertained how a room should function, focus on how you want it to feel and what sort of mood you wish to create: cheerful, relaxing, dramatic? There is nothing better than vibrant colors to create a cheerful room where the sun seems to always shine. On the other hand, a neutral color palette tends to suit calm personalities. Using eye-catching furnishings sparingly or mixed with diverse styles can achieve a dramatic modern look.

Beyond a well-planned selection of furniture — which will probably constitute a major part of your budget — accessories, artwork, window treatments and linens will complement and bring in the final touches, reflecting your personality. Are you attracted to vintage style? Traditional, rustic cottage, French country, contemporary, eclectic? Each decorating style comes with its own characteristics and can fit in any room of the house, whether it's the living and dining room, the kitchen, the bedroom or the bathroom.

Vintage style showcases items of the past, some of which you can repurpose by transforming them into fresh home accents. Traditional styles are made up of classic furnishings often in formal arrangements. The key is to achieve a traditional style without looking dated. Rustic cottage is practical and comfortable, with soft colors and natural materials. It provides a space with a casual character whether it is a seaside retreat, a mountain refuge or a penthouse apartment in the city. Floral patterns, antique furnishings and gilded accents are characteristics of French country. With its casual elegance and homey comfort, this style pays homage to the south of France. More than just a palette of neutral colors and clean lines, modern style seeks a balance between sleek open spaces and comfort, avoiding an excess of accessories.

Regardless of style, each room should be looked at with specific attention. The living room is probably the most lived-in room of a home and might present a bit of a challenge since it often incorporates a dining area, and sometimes even a workspace. A sofa, some chairs, oversized floor pillows for lounging and several side tables can fashion a comfortable living room. Small gestures such as extra pillows, flower arrangements and scented candles create instant ambience.

The kitchen is more than just a cooking and eating place. If space allows for an island, it can be a nucleus for socializing. It needs to be, nonetheless, a functional utilitarian room with tough materials, good lighting, integrated appliances and cabinetry with convenient features.

While the living area and the kitchen are spaces suitable for socializing, the bedroom is a private space. It is a room where one can express their most personal tastes. Decorating a bedroom for kids is fun, but can be intimidating, while a master suite with a bathroom invites a luxurious treatment.

If your bathroom is frequented by the whole family, it's more important than ever to plan carefully. Along with choosing the proper materials, you'll want plenty of storage for towels and supplies.

When designing an outdoor space, it should be looked at in the same way as an interior room. By paying the same attention to detail as you would when decorating your home, you will create a seamless transition between interior and exterior, so that the style feels unified throughout the home.

Whether you are redecorating or moving into an empty new home, and regardless of the mood you want to create and the style you are inspired by, you can achieve an amazing one-of-a-kind look that reflects your personality. Get inspired! Put together color schemes using paints, wallpapers and fabrics from the wide variety of materials and finishes available. Get ideas on how to arrange furniture and how to use decorating accessories for every room of your home.

0001 Straight lines and curves applied in appropriate proportions stand out in a living room with balanced character. If plain surfaces and angles predominate on the sofa and armchairs, their best accessories are a spare table and round cushions, and a pouf instead of a stool.

0002 The lively tones in these sofas are common in the Italian Adrenalina brand, which expresses the essence of contemporary life in its designs without abandoning comfort. There is no need to fear bright shapes and colors if we want to offer a good dose of originality.

0003 Just as the living room furniture distribution is crucial, we also have to take into account the balance of weights. In this case, a solid and sturdy sofa is balanced by the accessories — a table and an armchair with a sleek, austere style of relative lightness. (Arketipo)

0004 An armchair with simple lines, upholstered in leather and with a chromed steel base, is very suitable for building a minimalist and frank style, as well as being both comfortable and ergonomic. (Domus by Arketipo)

0005 A living room atmosphere can be renewed without too much investment. Throw pillows are an essential detail on a sofa and can be changed at whim. These pleasant fabrics give a new life to the quilted back classical sofa.

0006 Poufs, footrests and ottomans are all ideal for obtaining additional space in a living room in a very practical way. With a pouf, the imprecise roundness and the lightness of the filling are features that make adaptability its best quality.

0007 A living room is an ideal space in which to create a reading nook. Making use of natural lighting as much as possible, use a low, wide armchair with a high reclining back. This is perfectly complemented with a matching side table.

0001

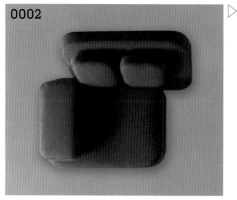

0002

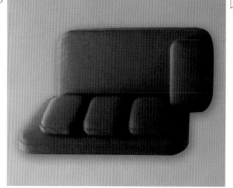

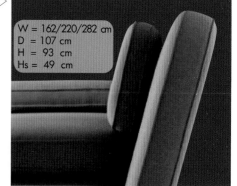

W = 162/220/282 cm
D = 107 cm
H = 93 cm
Hs = 49 cm

0003

0004

0005

0006

0007

0008 Absolute white is a tempting color option because of its freshness, purity and brightness. It is also a demanding and powerful color, since every touch of color in accent pieces captures attention.

0009 Unexpected materials and bright colors are a perfect combination if we are looking to avoid monotony and surprise ourselves every day. In this case, the wall pattern and chair's originality bring an undeniable vitality to the living room.

0010 This curule seat adds some colonial flair to this living room. The delicately carved floral detail echoes the floral patterns of the pillows on the couch. Although not particularly comfortable to sit on for a long time, a curule seat makes a good accent piece.

0011 In this rural living room two groups of color can be appreciated: the deep terracotta tones of the fabric on the furniture harmonize with the floor and contrast with the wall's wood, the curtain and the light-toned carpet. Thus a cozy, comfortable and casual environment is created.

0008

0009

0010

0011

0012

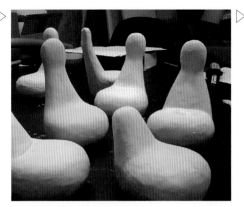

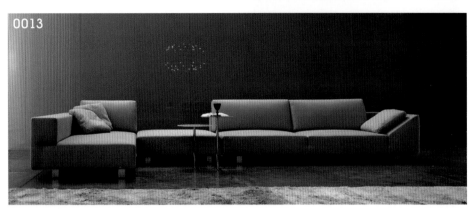

0013

0014

0012 Oppo (the armchair) and Puppa (the hassock) are two designs that give a lot of personality to a room thanks to their wide range of colors and their varying configurations: one armchair only, with an accessory bedside table and footrest ... (Puppa and Oppo by Blå Station)

0013 If we have a large space available in the house's common areas, the sofa's dimensions can be taken to the limits of magnificence: a very wide sofa in several positions, with or without a back, different sized cushions and a multiplicity of uses. (Arketipo)

0014 The space underneath the stairs is commonly used as a wardrobe, pantry or even as a powder room for guests. In some cases it is possible to make the most of this protected corner to create a warm and cozy place to relax, with a built-in sofa.

0015 The thread-bare look of some materials can be charming. A leather sofa's shabby, worn-out leather, with its history and use on display, is the center of this living room's rural and naked style.

0016 Unexpected details needn't be exclusive to daring and alternative design choices. In this relaxed family living room, a mirror in the armchair's arms is a pleasant surprise.

0017 Armless armchairs offer a lavish feel: the back is wider, the seat is deeper and the upholstery is thick and extremely fluffy. In this case, a neutral color makes the legs stand out slightly, reminiscent of 1950s style.

0018 Animal leather patterns have come back into fashion. For a chic and modern style, vibrant colors like this royal purple are daring when combined with a black and white zebra-patterned carpet.

0015

0016

0017

0018

0019

0020

0021

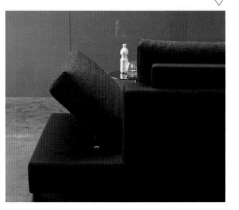

0019 The combination of black and white is striking. It has a chic, urban look and is never old-fashioned. In a living room, glossy materials like this sofa's metallic base, amplify the sophistication of the contrast of black and white.

0020 Where technology and comfort meet, this sofa's cushions can be adjusted on different axes and inclinations to suit those seated. (Arquetipo)

0021 It is very easy to make use of a living room corner with charm and grace. These window-seat cushions can go with an aromatherapy set, a vase of flowers or a book that invites us to enjoy it with natural light.

0022 Some sofas' accessory units include central divans or heightened footrests that can be used instead of a central table, since their size and height are adapted to sitting, lying down, resting feet or placing a tray of food.

0023 The arrangement of the seating in a living room is an important consideration. In this case, natural light floods the sofa from the back, and a separate seating area has been created with the placement of swiveling armchairs and side tables over a warm and delicate carpet. (Arketipo)

0024 This design has been conceived as a modular structure in which two elements, a pouf and a glossy stack of shelves, can join together with the sofa in different positions. The freedom and mobility of the set lets the space be renewed and adjusted, eliminating all restrictions. (Peanut B by Bonaldo)

0025 The genius of good design can be seen in the successful transformation of this deck chair from relaxed and informal, to an elegant and sophisticated piece, through a careful selection of materials and the refinement of composition lines. (Arketipo)

0026 The combination of two settees illuminated by a single light source creates an alternative reading and meeting corner, to the traditional group of sofa and side table. In this case, this arrangement takes advantage of natural light and a wall with attractive motifs.

0027 Red velvet is a symbol of exuberant and sensual luxury. A cherry chaise lounge is theatrical, dramatic and mischievous all at the same time. This type of furniture remains a classic with its silky tactility and winding shapes, just like the bold color.

0022

0023

0024

0025

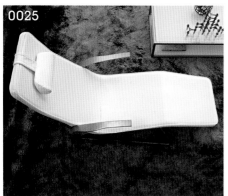

0027

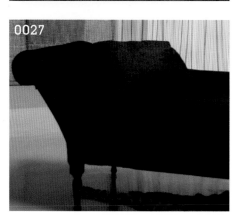

0026

0028 It is essential to get sofas and armchairs of the best design in terms of comfort and durability. Poufs, stools and ottomans, offer more play and plasticity as occasional and decorative seating.

0029 The grid that constitutes this chair brings a fresh feel to the living room because it reminds us of the wicker and rattan furniture used in gardens and terraces. A feeling of warmth can be achieved with the addition of a blanket and a leather or light-colored cushion.

0030 Consider complementing a neutral-toned living room with multi-colored and brightly patterned fabric. With their cheerful combination of flowers and stripes, these floor pillows evoke a playful and casual feel.

0031 Simple geometric shapes reveal good craftwork while maintaining their pure nature. A wooden stool offers a spot of warmth in this cold-floored space and represents the organic world, in addition to being practical and long lasting.

0028

0029

0030

0031

0032

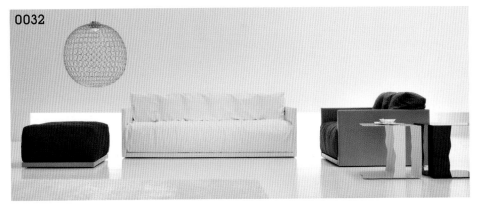

0033

0034

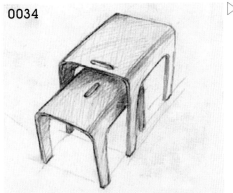

0035

0032 An effective way to achieve a minimalist feel in the living room, is to distribute color to each piece of furniture, and maintain a single neutral tone on the walls. In this way, the areas of color are restricted in an orderly and measured way.

0033 In addition to the high collar and fluffy filling, this seat's upholstery contributes to its comfort. A wide-striped fabric gives the armchair presence and invites relaxation. The small details of a few pops of red in the painting, the pattern on the cushion and in the wood's mahogany tone are subtle but impactful.

0034 A key element to this molded wood stool's design, is a wide space between the top and the legs. This allows it to be versatile in its functions: stool or spare table, it can be combined in its three sizes and stacked when not in use. (Bimbo by Blå Station)

0035 The matte sand tones of the upholstery and the table contrast nicely with the shiny copper finish of the lamp. In addition to the range of colors and finishes, adding a side table the same height as the sofa helps create a feeling of stability and sense of homogeny.

0036 An isolated seat will not look out of place in a living room if we consider the context that the shape, tonality and finish suggests. A chair that evokes antique dining rooms with a tall straight embellished back and refined upholstery, looks marvelous against a backdrop of classic books and encyclopedias.

0037 Seats with simple arms and medium backs can easily be placed in any space in the house, in order to obtain additional seating.

0038 The Muuto Brand reinterprets traditional Nordic design by putting a twist on everyday objects. This sofa has a steel base, but a wooden frame. The dark color stands out in a predominantly white living room with excellent lighting. (Anderssen & Voll for Muuto)

0039 Smaller homes can benefit from multi-functional creations like this pleasant settee: untie the laces found on the back, and the seat is transformed into a floor-level futon and a stool with storage space. (Tutumo by Kaori Shiina for Bonaldo)

0040 This sofa's flattened shape is the structural base of an original modular system that allows the angle of the seat back to change. In this way, different positions can be adopted on the same sofa. (Arketipo)

0041 The high-quality of the fabrics and fillings used in this furniture allows the original design to materialize as it was conceived. For this reason, each armchair has specific technical requirements, whether covered in cloth or leather, or filled with feather goose down or polyurethane foam. (Minotti)

0042 When graced with a striking architectural element, such as this floating staircase, a home's beauty can be enhanced with the careful placement of an artistic item, such as a sculpture, a suitably sized mirror, a group of candles, a leafy plant or a seat of contemporary design on the landing or under the stairs.

0043 The choice of colors for the living room can be posed as a superposition of alternate plans. In this case, two colors follow one another, the green and the white, to create a feeling of depth.

0044 The charm of a piece of furniture's finish and detail can lay in their imperfection or wear. Furnishings that do not hide the years of their use provide great personality in a living room.

0042

0043

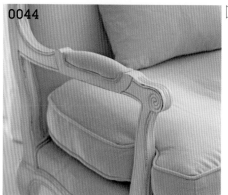

0044

0046

0047

0045 The windows and spectacular view offer a sublime background to the dominant white in this room, complemented by subtle touches of black and metal. The delicately cushioned and smooth-lined sofas are in keeping with the carpet and curtains' ethereal feeling.

0046 This light chair embodies modern elegance and innovative design. The angles and slope of the back guarantee comfort, and with targeted lighting, interesting shadows can be cast on the surrounding space.

0047 The combination of different styles gives rise to a space with its own personality: an armchair's rustic and rural feel with its smooth material and lines, warms up the industrial sideboard with straight lines and metallic luster.

0048 A great way to update and revive an inherited or secondhand armchair is to reupholster it in a daring color that contrasts greatly with the wood. In this example, the bright blue of the armchair leather parallels the colors in the tile.

0049 For a traditional style we can opt for a flawless combination: classic furniture and a Persian rug. The fabric's saturated colors and abstract motifs correspond to the baroque ornamental engraving and the dark, brilliant and ornate wood.

0050 Antique furniture can adapt to be used in a contemporary space if we dare to experiment. Taking into consideration the pattern that the sofa dictates, incorporate subtle and original details, like reused materials and a touch of color.

0051

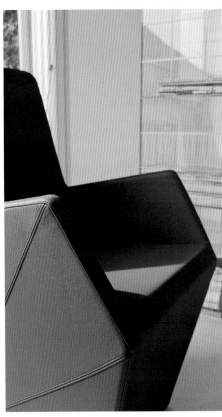

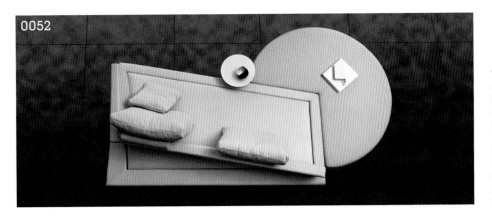

0051 The sculptural character of this chair incorporates natural details into a prism design that projects dynamism. The polyurethane foam smooths the geometric lines and offers us an armchair that we can also pull up to the dining room table.

0052 This avant-garde design is striking but it can give the impression of impracticality for the necessities of everyday life. However, in addition to being original, this sofa's unconventional geometry has been designed for providing comfort and versatility.

0053 This seat has an external structure made of ash wood which functions as a protective barrier for the user: the back's extension around the sides creates an isolated space that conserves heat and provides greater privacy and comfort. (Koja by Blå Station)

0054 The optimal armchair design should incorporate a wide support for the head, an inclined back and of course, a footrest. In this example, the black leather is elegant and is highlighted by the colored carpet.

0055 On the coldest days, furniture that has been upholstered in warm and textural materials can make optimal use of the heat that an adjacent fireplace provides. These ideal chairs for this warm corner in front of the hearth are low, with wide back and inclining seat.

0053

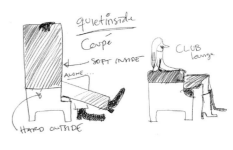

0054

0055

0056 This armchair's design is suggestive of past eras with a high back, and angles and edges that are slightly dropped. The metallic base gives lightness and modernity to the solid volume. (Coley by Minotti)

0057 In spite of blacks inherent elegance and distinction, it is not easy to incorporate into a home's interior. A way to make it work in a living room is to make the most of the natural shine of the finish of the leather or wood the furniture is made of, and complement it with transparent and reflective elements.

0058 Traditionally shaped sofas can establish a sobriety in a living room that can be tempered with carefully chosen upholstery, curtains, wall decorations and other more versatile and transitory accessories, like vases and cushions.

0059

0060

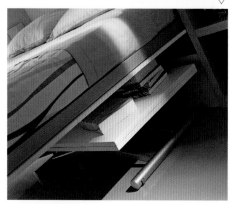

0061

0062

0063

0064

0059 Wall systems that combine stacks of shelves with open or closed compartments for storage or display, can incorporate the rest of the living room's furniture as well, taking maximum advantage of the available space.

0060 This design in particular allows a small living room to be converted into a guest room. In addition to the structure's design, it is important to choose a type of fabric for the sofa bed and the pouf that has a neutral motif, which is as functional in the communal space as in the private one.

0061 L-shaped sofas, with their modular or extended arm supports and incorporated chaise lounges, are suitable for homes of variable affluence, and easily serve both needs of an individual, as well as larger groups of people.

0062 Storage space incorporated into a sofa could not be more useful, especially when the sofa can also be folded out into a bed. It is a convenient place for storing pillows, sheets and blankets, ready to be used at any given time.

0063 The balance between elegance and comfort in a living room does not only depend on the sofa's shape and upholstery. Other accessories, like cushions and carpets, offer opportunities to create a stunning, yet cozy, intimate space.

0064 Swivel armchairs can be ideal in the living room, especially when their design aims to achieve the highest levels of comfort through the use of mechanisms for regulating angle and height, as well as adapting their resistance according to their user's weight and current position.

0065 Varied tactile qualities and strong colors are key to the décor of this living room. Contrasting colors have been chosen for the sofa and carpet, in silky and textured materials, that stand out amongst the accessories and white furniture scattered here and there.

0065

0066 A couple of occasional tables side by side can house all those things you want to have close at hand. They provide surface space for lamps, books, candles and drinks.

0067 There are a lot of ways you can use pallets and turn them into something creative and useful. This is an extremely simple coffee table that was made with a recycled pallet and casters.

0068 What can we do with a pallet? Even though they are not made of good quality wood, pallets can make for an interesting piece of furniture if you are looking for a rustic style.

0069 This is another example of a pallet's versatile use. This one, turned into a coffee table, provides the living room with an industrial touch. It harmonizes with the fireplace mantle and contrasts with the rug and the blankets on the sofa.

0070 Salvaged wood often has a beautiful aged grain and varied colors that imbue a piece of furniture with a rich patina and a lot of character.

0071

0072

0073

0071 The several small tables in this living room ensure that there is adequate room for drinks and can even be used as additional seating when necessary.

0072 This stunning coffee table is only a couple of shipping pallets and a can of paint away. In this case, stacking two white painted pallets brings the table to a more useful height.

0073 Repurposing old suitcases and trunks allow for many creative combinations: Whether singled-out to shine as a focal piece or stacked to form small tables or room accents, these items once used for traveling are a popular decorating trick.

0074 The form of this low coffee table seems to be inspired by pallet design. The table is made more practical by replacing the widely-spaced boards with a solid surface.

0075 An ottoman or upholstered bench can be used as an occasional table if it is firm enough. Have it match the sofa or curtains for a unified décor, while making good use of a versatile piece of furniture.

0076 Wood is still the material of choice in furniture making. In this case, a side table combines a modern design with the natural look of untreated wood.

0077 Tray tables are inspired by low Moroccan tea tables. This type of table is versatile, functional, movable and takes up very little space. Depending on the space available, you can set up a pair combining different colors and sizes.

0078

0079

0080

0081

0078 The use of recycled materials in furniture making is a popular design trend. Made of salvaged pieces of wood in different sizes and finishes, this coffee table and stool are unique pieces that add special character to the space they are used in.

0079 In most cases, trunks are tall enough to serve as a coffee table. Moreover, they can make for additional storage.

0080 Inspired by Moroccan tray tables, the design of this side table features folding legs and a removable top. Excellent as accent furniture, it comes in handy as a place to set down a drink at a party and can easily be put away.

0081 While the occasional table is not a dominating piece of furniture, its style needs to fit with that of the room it is used in. This wood and steel table can be a perfect accessory in classically styled rooms.

0082 The simple design of this table will complement any décor: interior or exterior, rustic or modern. The reclaimed wood top and the steel frame give the table a sturdy quality.

0083 Yellow is a daring color, however, it can give the room a dynamic or relaxing feel depending on its hue and the amount it is used. A pair of small yellow tables will give a pleasant and sophisticated touch, and even more so if they accompany dark colored furniture.

0084 A small folding table at one end of a sofa provides an ideal solution to a room of limited space and creates a casual sitting area.

0085 A matching table and stool made of recycled wood with a steel frame complement the rustic look of the kitchen. The combination creates an industrial, loft-like atmosphere.

0082

0083

0084

0085

0086

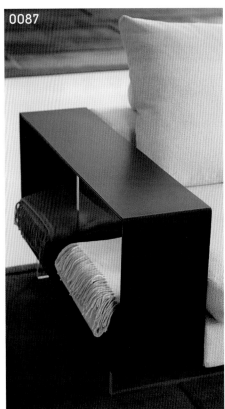

0087

0088

0086 This brushed steel three-legged occasional table is an interpretation of the popular wood version. It features a round top with a riveted edge that gives the piece an interesting industrial look. The overall design transcends periods and styles, becoming a one-of-a-kind piece.

0087 This side table – part of the sofa design – serves two purposes: it is an armrest and it doubles as a storage unit where you can keep books, blankets or anything you want to have close at hand when you are sitting on the sofa.

0088 New trends in furniture design have encouraged designers to think out of the box and produce unique furniture pieces using recycled parts of other items. For instance, this hand-made table has bicycle wheels.

0089 An ottoman or a pouf is a versatile piece of furniture. It can double as a footrest or an impromptu table. They also offer a fun way to add color, pattern and texture to a space.

0090 This small low table fits nicely in the simple interior that has a strong connection with the outside. The design of the table is plain just like the room, whose décor seems to focus on geometric forms. The spherical lampshade adds contrast both in shape and color.

0091 Set up a pane of glass on trestles for an improvised table instead of an ordinary piece of furniture. It is easy and budget-friendly!

0092 This coffee table is actually composed of two parts that are similar in shape but differ in height and color. Their flexible designs allow for many combinations.

0093 Tray tables can be used in many different ways. This characteristic has more relevance if, in addition, the tray includes handles that facilitate its handling.

0094

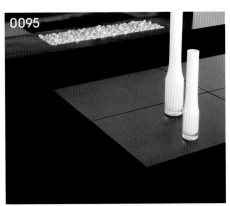

0095

0096

0097

0094 A wooden coffee table with a glass top is the focal point of this classically styled sitting area. Its light and airy design has a transparent element that helps to open up the look of the room.

0095 Although black and white is a minimalist choice for a contemporary living room, pairing these two colors with a third will intensify the contrast. The proportions in the use of the different shades should be so that one is the general color and the other two are accent colors.

0096 Rustic interior decoration is characterized by carved or turned items such as this low turned-leg table, which in combination with the animal hide emphasizes the desired effect.

0097 Bring in a vintage piece of furniture to start arranging your retro looking living room! This side table with tapered legs dictates the overall design of the room.

0098 The beauty of this coffee table lies in the inter-play of smooth curvy lines and sharp edges. White is a good choice to bring a cool and airy feel to a room.

0099 This round metal side table, with a shelf to stack magazines or any other items, is ideal for rooms with space limitations. The brushed finish harmonizes with the black leather armchair.

0100 Minimal and lightweight, this plastic side table is suitable for interior or exterior use. Combined with a retro-looking couch and a brightly colored rug, the design of the table adds to the fresh clean feel of the living room.

0101 The use of polymer in the production of furniture offers great advantages. The result is durable and func-tional items, available in an unlimited range of shapes and colors.

0102 This table is modeled after a typical Moroccan tray table. This simplified interpretation features a wooden frame characterized by its straight lines and a powder-coated steel tray.

0103

0104

0105

0103 Pierantonio Bonacina's Lario table features chrome steel legs and a mirrored top framed by a wicker band, which allows the table to be used as a tray.

0104 Side tables are very useful because of the minimal space they take up. Normally located against the wall, lamps and decorating items can be displayed on them.

0105 The Bresson coffee table by Minotti is available in two shapes: circular and square. The elegant laser cut forms and black and nickel finishes give the tables an elegant and unique appearance.

0106 This luxury design is distinguished by materials of optimum quality and a made-to-measure functionality. This furniture frame is rigid but its inner arrangement can be personalized according to the interests of the user. It has been devised to house the latest entertainment and multimedia technologies. (Alivar's Off-shore System)

0107 For a hanging shelf stack, the type of wall determines the appropriate style. The roughness of the stone and concrete are complemented by a small, primarily decorative, simple, single-ledged stack of shelves, enhanced by rustic materials, like roughly sanded wood.

0108 The four geometric figures of this shelving unit produce a rhythm of patterns that transform an often static and normal piece of furniture into one of dynamic, original aesthetics and variable functionality.

0109 Bookshelves and other objects that are not built into the wall can have other functions in addition to organization and display, like this tall bookcase that has an incorporated lamp.

0110 These floating shelves are simple with clean lines, and make great use of space in the smaller living room. Furthermore, they support all types of objects and blend well with the existing walls and windows, without clashing with other furniture or obstructing the entry of natural light.

0111 This modular system has been made up from several four-sided units with varying divisions inside that give rise to multiple combinations. Available in three different modules, these structures can be used horizontally, vertically or joined together.

0106

0107

0108

0109

0110

0111

0112

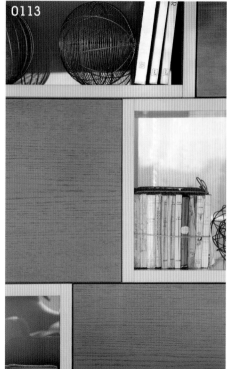

0113

0114

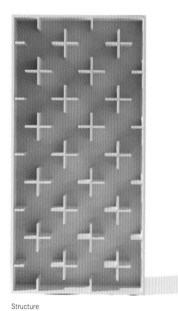

Structure

  White

  Grey-beige

0115

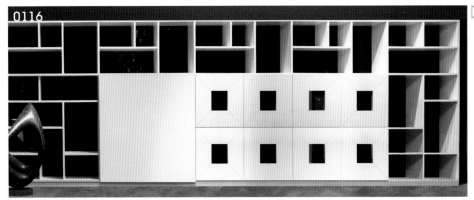

0112 Modular libraries allow as many of their components to be assembled together as are desired. This open modular design creates a visual effect if it is placed in front of a colored wall and can also separate spaces without obstructing general vision or isolating the rooms completely. (Ciacci Kreaty Cover)

0113 Shelving units often don't have doors. In this case though, some modules are closed while others are left open, giving the option of concealing less decorative objects. There is also the visual impact of the combination of different wood tones for the structure and for the doors.

0114 This shelving unit's design has the distinction of being able to house books of different heights. The crosses can carry less capacity than a normal bookshelf, but all sizes of books fit, besides being an attractive and very light arrangement thanks to the voids created by the composition of the structure. (Archetype Target)

0115 The installation of glass doors protects and frames the decorative elements placed inside a niche. In this case, the striking color of the doors guides the eye toward the sculptures that it shelters.

0116 Besana's Concerto bookcase is a modular composition of open shelves and cabinets. Housing books and displaying objects can transcend the ordinary and become creative when the bookcase has an eye-catching arrangement.

0117 Integrating removable desks onto the shelving unit is a way of taking advantage of the space and the furniture's functionality. A variety of inner compartments allows for the organization and availability of necessary objects in the working area.

0118 Bookshelves that have widely spaced shelves are great for displaying objects of different sizes and purpose. The wide design and the honey tone of the wood complement its basic lines.

0119 Light colors and smooth textures help to keep this built-in from appearing over-designed. The photographs and other objects placed in the shelves become the focal point when they rest on a white shelf.

0120 Using a limited color palette on the walls, the built-in and the sofa allows the displayed objects and other decorative elements in this living room, like the colors and prints on the throw pillows, to shine.

0121 Sequence is a modular shelving system designed by Patricia Urquiola for Molteni&C. Its geometric design embraces concepts of symmetry and asymmetry through the free positioning of dividers in solid or punctured steel.

0119

0120

0121

0122

0123

0124

0125

0122 Several small niches of the same size in a wall can create a focal point. They are part of a final composition that can include decorative items enhanced with spotlights, for instance.

0123 In this piece of furniture, enclosed storage is alternated with open storage, intended for decorative display. The smooth honey wood of the structural modules is combined with easy opening flap doors in taupe.

0124 A period chair adds a relaxing feel to an interior space with white-washed walls. The niche gives an indication of the massive construction of the wall, which contrasts with the delicate wicker caning on the chair's back.

0125 Shelving space below a pass-through can be used for displaying any kind of object, but also can come in handy as a bar between the kitchen and the living area, where guests can gather for drinks and snacks, while chatting with the cook.

0126

0127

0128

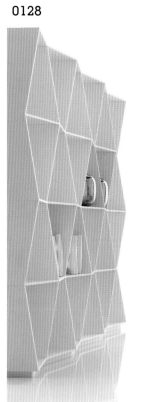

0129

0130

0131

0132

0126 This refinished antique bookcase gets a new life in a home among items of other periods including an Art Deco desk, a modern area rug and contemporary photographic artwork. It is all tied together with a neutral color palette: dark stained wood flooring and ceiling beams and off-white walls.

0127 Built-in shelves are easy to integrate in the décor of a room since they are part of the architecture. The front of the shelves can either be flush with the face of the wall and not alter the shape of the room or can project into the space, creating a focal point.

0128 These libraries are made of acrylic stone, a composite, biodegradable material of great strength and durability. Its quality and appearance remain unaltered by the passage of time because it is a waterproof material, neither absorbent nor porous. (Alivar's Wavy)

0129 You can create storage space with built-ins in the underused nooks of a room. They can serve as ledges for displaying artwork as an alternative to hanging pictures from the wall, or they can serve as a console table behind a couch.

0130 The Pass system is representative of Molteni&C's experience in the multimedia furnishing sector. This wall-mounted unit, available in various configurations, has colored glass doors that allow remote control signals to pass through.

0131 More decorative than utilitarian, these shelves would not stand the weight of books or heavy items, but adorned with a few objects they can make a great room divider. When using shelves in this way, keep in mind that if the unit is taller than 6 feet, one of its sides needs to be attached to a wall.

0132 Although generally made for displaying china, a built-in cabinet can provide a handy display space for tableware, books and knickknacks. A good advantage of built-ins is that they offer storage space without taking up floor area.

0133 Sideboards in a dining room can serve several functions: from the display of vases with flowers, pictures, mirrors and other decorative accessories, to more practical uses like storing linens or china.

0134 The use of color integrates several of this desk's components. In this case, the upper part of the wall is white while the lower part almost merges with the tonality of the table. The accessories and colors show prominently thanks to the delineation of the space.

0135 The originality of this item of furniture is rooted in its similarity with homemade do-it-yourself craftwork. The repurposed filing boxes as drawers and the choice of pastel shades transmit this feeling.

0136 Small details, like an antique lock or silver-plated knobs on the wide drawers, give a delicate touch to a high, robust and large capacity item of furniture that can hold all the tableware, adornments and works of art for the table.

0137 A console table can break up a large space and separate it into different functions, for instance a living room and a dining room. A nice console table can also hide the back of a sofa, which are often plain and not particularly attractive.

0138 Rustic French design gives a stylized quality to this side table. The large hinges and bolts are a special touch to this piece, that in addition to its interesting height has generous space for storage.

0139 An inventive hutch above the sideboard, in the same quality and style of wood, is not only functional, it also marks out areas in a lively colored wall that frame the objects that are on display in it.

0140 The open spaces in the wooden and iron or steel items of furniture make them lighter and more pleasant. This dining room allows us to appreciate the floor's texture and sideboard design, just like the change of direction, horizontal or vertical, in the grain of the wood.

0133

0136

0134

0135

0137

0138

0139

0140

0141 Using a combination of different styles is an interesting decor choice. In this example, classically designed furniture with very wavy lines, stylized and curved legs, ornate applications and an elegant light tone contrast nicely with the wicker seat.

0142 A dark-stained wood chest of drawers from the first half of the 20th century integrates nicely into a room with a ceramic tile floor and natural stone walls. Regardless of the style and size, remember that you'll have a chest for a long time and you might want to move it around, so choose wisely.

0143 A very ornate heavy wooden item of furniture is an excellent accessory for formal and distinguished spaces: the wood's dark color contrasts with the red accents, and the carving gives it a delicate yet imposing presence.

0144 This green apple sideboard echoes the elegant lines of an 18th-century Genovese style chest. Bold colors and the high-gloss lacquer finish combined with antique-inspired furnishings, add some zest to a modern interior.

0145

0146

0147

▽

0148

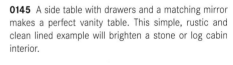

0149

0150

0145 A side table with drawers and a matching mirror makes a perfect vanity table. This simple, rustic and clean lined example will brighten a stone or log cabin interior.

0146 This trunk is an exceptional accent piece that lends old-world style to a home. A trunk can be used as a table, but depending on its condition and how attractive the exterior is, it can stand on its own. It can also be used as a bench, while providing additional storage space.

0147 Aesthetic details are printed onto the metallic structured furniture, and small wheels allow its movement and functional character, defining a very modern and practical industrial style

0148 This table's simple and basic structure doesn't demand attention and allows the texture of the wooden floor and qualitites of the stone wall to be appreciated.

0149 The white finish, simple forms and straightforward functionality are the main features of Scandinavian furniture design, and combine very well with basic accessories of the same color.

0150 The light color of the accessories — boxes and candles — stands out amid the harmonious and matte color range shared by the wall, floor and furniture.

0151

0152

0153

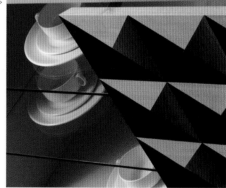

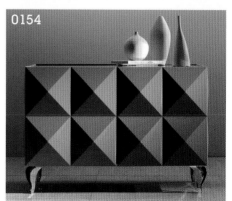

0154

0155

0156

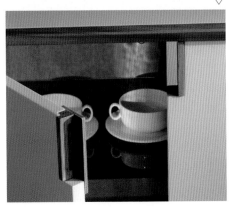

0157

0151 A console table can complete a seating area, adding storage and display space. Lamps make good decoration items on a console table, but you must think of how you are going to deal with unsightly dangling cords.

0152 Fratelli Spinelli is an Italian furniture company known for its transformable systems composed of modular entertainment centers that can be turned into convenient bedroom furniture, including a bed. The daytime compositions are completed with a TV console and plenty of storage.

0153 This Italian design's sliding doors are a marriage of a mastery of handicraft and avant-garde design. The decorative pattern's triangular edges fully accentuate the wood's qualities. (Artex de Besana)

0154 With a wooden base and chromed metal legs, this sideboard's body is notable because the pyramidal form of its modules reflects different light intensities on each face. (Prisma de Besana)

0155 Sobriety and exquisiteness are embodied in the compact and sturdy structure of this furniture, fabricated with a shiny lacquered material for the doors and the drawers, and with walnut wood in the details.

0156 A beautiful console table such as this 17th-century walnut piece makes an elegant focal point in this large room with a high ceiling. Highly decorative items like this should be allowed to shine on their own, and not be crowded by other furniture.

0157 The special design of some sideboards is better appreciated if we use them as space dividers – in halls, dining rooms or living rooms – instead of setting them against the wall. In this way, their fronts and corners can be appreciated by all.

0158 Patterned curtains enliven large rooms. The floral pattern of the curtains and the throw pillows harmonize with the blue-green color of the walls and floor, and animates the room.

0159 Roller blinds are a practical and efficient solution to control the amount of light that comes into a room.

0160 Large windows, balcony doors and bedroom windows are parts of the room that, just like an upholstered piece of furniture, offer the chance to dress up a room, while framing the views to the outside.

0161 Curtains perform important functions in a room, filtering light and providing privacy. This makes them an important decorative element and consequently, it is important to include them in the room design.

0162 Tasseled tiebacks are an elegant way of keeping draperies secured to one side. They come in a wide range of designs and are a nice detail.

0163 Due to their low opacity, sheer fabrics let enough light enter a space without sacrificing privacy.

0164 Curtains don't have to be boring, quite the opposite. They can be used in any kind of setting, whether modern, classical or rustic.

0165 Glass screens are an optimum decorative and functional solution to separate a space without building walls, with the added advantage of allowing light to travel through.

0166 Vertical blinds respond to lighting needs and privacy. Especially recommended for large windows or patio doors, the pivoting system that controls the position of the blinds filters light as needed.

0167 Matching drapes and throw pillows create a well-balanced appearance and are a great touch.

0160

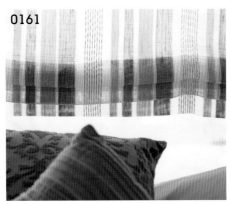

0161

0162

0163

0164

0165

0167

0166

0168 Fireplaces go unused at certain times of the year. One way of taking advantage of a fireplace in warmer seasons is to place stones and candles with harmonious textures and colors on the inside.

0169 The structure of this fireplace and chimney are reminiscent of the roof and frieze's classical style. These clean lines are mirrored in the geometric design of the colorful carpet.

0170 This fireplace is the focal point of this dining room. The floral relief and spotless white finish provide elegance to this classically styled fireplace that relies on modern technology.

0171 Books look very nice in the firebox when it is not in use. Other options include flowers, leaves and dry branches, decorative logs, mirrors, photographs, etc.

0168

0169

0170

0171

0172

0173

0174

0175

0172 Prefabricated wood-burning stoves can be added to any room in the house and they are made to the measure. They are most efficient because they produce the largest quantity of heat for the least amount of energy. The elevated body and trap-doors eliminate annoyances like smoke and ash.

0173 The structure and arrangement of the fireplace can serve as an invitation for a reinvigorating rest. Elevated upon a rise, this fireplace makes for a perfect welcoming and personal reading corner, in this rural home.

0174 Freestanding modern fireplaces provide a spacious and light feeling in a room, given that they are not a heavy element anchored to the floor and wall, but are instead suspended delicately from their chimney. In an environment where bland colors and light browns preside, the ergonomic form and dark material make this fireplace a showpiece.

0175 Brick and stone are materials that guarantee longevity for a fireplace, since they do not crack or split at high temperatures. The casually stacked wood and soot on the mantle gives a warm and cozy feel to the dining room.

0176 The biomass fuel that is used in pellet stoves can be stored externally, or is sometimes located in a hopper that is usually in the upper part of the stove. It is possible to put fragrances and essential oils into the deposit to create an aromatherapy effect throughout house.

0177 The pellet heaters have got an automatic function system that allows us to program the fire's duration, strength and temperature. In this way a constant and controlled temperature is maintained in all of the house's environments.

0178 Modern fireplaces perfectly balance the age-old tradition of the hearth as center of the home, with technology and innovative design. In this case, the frame has nickel steel cladding and the woodshed and fire screen are built in.

0180

0181

0179 An ideal solution for enhanced heat distribution is to choose a double-sided firepflace. The fire functions at the same time as a boundary and transition between the different rooms of the house, which take advantage of the flames' heat in equal measure.

0180 Gas stoves and fireplaces offer two essential advantages for a stressful and busy life: on the one hand they offer the highest efficiency; and on the other hand, they eliminate complications like cleaning ash, and the purchase and the storage of firewood or any other fuel.

0181 With the metal box chimney's modern design built-in, the firewood's combustion is fully exploited and we can appreciate the pleasant contrast between the metal and wood. The stack of logs in a very vertical space gives a special touch to the set.

0182

0183

0184

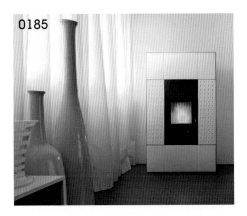

0182 One of the highlights of having a fireplace, and lighting a fire is the color, shape, scent and pleasant texture of firewood. When piled tidily firewood looks good in urban and refined environments.

0183 The face of this fireplace has a steel frame coated with bronze powder; the aesthetic can be adapted to different housing styles, from a modern loft to a cozy rural home.

0184 Storing your firewood indoors needn't be an eyesore, and in fact can have real appeal. Stacked neatly in a built-in or freestanding shelf, or under a nearby bench, it can be a striking decorative element.

0185 The new MCZ range offers both pellet and traditional woodburning stoves. This design's simple and clean lines are made possible due to detachable handles that can be put away when not being used.

0186 While classical designs make the most of the surround facing as a shelf, contemporary designs often have no mantel, and the facing is flush or only slightly raised from the wall. In this contemporary example, the ceramic surround facing extends horizontally along the wall, echoing the width of the firebox. Ceramics are some of the most interesting materials to use in surround facing, because they allow for creative decorative details and are available in several colors.

0187 The proximity of flammable objects such as carpets and books is not an obstacle for enjoying the fireplace, because the modern designs provide safety tools like security doors, ledges and brass or marble edgings to avoid accidents.

0188 Wallpaper is a simple and budget-friendly way to renew the look of a room. The texture of this wall resembles cracked clay. It emphasizes the fireplace and enhances the framed artwork.

0189 The antiqued gold embossed finish of this texturally based wallpaper provides the living room with a touch of luxury.

0190 Nature motifs can be found in many wallpaper designs. In this case, elegant mossy tones create a patina that serves as a rich backdrop to an Asian antique.

0191 The choice of materials imparts style as much as accessories. The renaissance touch and the deep ornamental relief in this ceiling define in great measure this space's style.

0192 These hand-painted ceramics are handcrafted masterpieces that enrich the space. The traditional design in deep blue and yellow above the varnished white are dynamic.

0193 These flagstones are made of pigmented cement and offer countless geometric floral models, with reliefs and drawings that imitate antique or modern mosaics. Some manufacturers offer a personalized design service by means of which the colors can be chosen.

0194 The combination of opposite styles – classic and modern – is materialized in this space. The wall's classic aura with frescoes and the mirror's carved frame contrasts the chair's modern design.

0195 A mural with palace motifs are appropriate for a room of great distinction and elegance, in which other elements, like the ceiling, the curtains and the lamps, have to coexist aesthetically.

0196 Rustic elements, like stone walls, have become a star tendency in the decoration of interiors. In this way warmth is achieved in spaces where tradition and modernity cohabit. In this living room, the Sagar stove stands out, made of steel and powder-coated in black.

0197 This damask pattern is created with the repeated image of a Damascus plant. The silvery sheen of this pistachio version harmonizes with the chrome light fixture and chair.

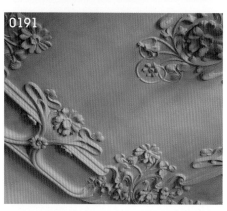

0194

0195

0196

0197

0198

0199

0200

0201

0202

0203

0204

0205

0198 Inspired by the dandelion, this original print combines audacious colors and black outlines. This popular design is applied to wallpaper and upholstery fabrics.

0199 The most important characteristic of this rug is the effortless combination of a modern aesthetic with impeccable handicraft. It is designed and made to last, embracing the natural beauty of the material.

0200 The décor of this living room harmoniously combines the different materials of the table's tempered glass, the various textures of the leather sofa and the interesting weave of the rug.

0201 The modern and geometric fireplace and acrylic furniture blend amicably with the organic nature of the wicker furniture and lush foliage in this living room.

0202 The design of this wallpaper is inspired by vintage Indian silk saris. The golden and washed-out burgundy stripes are printed using a photogravure technique.

0203 A fireplace set into a stone-clad wall has a clean modern look in this living room. This steel fireplace surround incorporates storage for firewood.

0204 The design of this living room spotlights the mixture of materials. The oak stool, the wool and silk rug, the painted sideboard and the concrete walls are a well-balanced combination.

0205 Audacious urban spaces allow for the stark combination of white and black because they carry the impression of modernity and distinction at the same time. In this case, the pattern on the wall is the primary focus and, therefore, the furnishings and accessories are subdued in their lines and textures.

0206 An eclectic atmosphere can be easily achieved through the careful selection of a few key elements, like motley printed wallpaper and elaborate candelabras adorned with hanging glass crystals.

0207 These spheres, embellished with seeds and silver pellets are placed in a golden bowl on a wooden table, and result in a harmonious arrangement of layers that combine natural and metallic elements.

0208 There is a certain honor in not concealing the passage of time and allowing the age of the material to be show with grace and dignity. These accessories boast an ennobling aged effect in the silverware's rust and the lamp's worn-out base.

0209 A critical consideration in floral arrangements is the relationship between the type of flowers and the vessel that contains them. In this case, springy and rounded flowers rest inside the spherical vase that, in addition, leaves the stems in view.

0210 Fabrics can radically transform spaces through texture and color's expressive capacity. In this case the natural fibers and brown smoke tone of the throw pillows with a brightly colored accent, transmit a rustic and homely feeling.

0206

0207

0208

0209

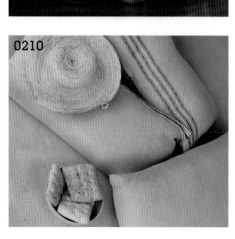
0210

0211

0212

0213

0214

0211 In a modern room, antique objects are intriguing without exception. This considerably sized urn with its weathered patina looks like a vestige from other times and gives an air of respectability to the living room's modern design.

0212 When an object is repurposed, its qualities can be strengthened in its new application. This wooden carving that may have been on the lintel of an entrance hall or an adornment on a piece of furniture, now decorates a wall in harmony with the range of the other accessories' colors.

0213 Some isolated accessories are subtly reminiscent of times past. These zoomorphic candlesticks and the sculpture of an angelic baby above the sideboard combine well with the antique furniture and the brown and cream-toned palette.

0214 Another way to play with sizes is progression: the union of three identical accessories of growing dimensions — small, medium and large — is a configuration for decorative accessories that can be placed on living room furniture.

0215 A birdcage converted into a vase for a dried leaf arrangment is a good example of how to exploit the latent versatility of all types of objects. Separated from its context and used for functions that are not its own, the accessory is remarkable for its originality.

0216 A way of creating balance when decorating is to play with the size of comparable objects. A large bowl paired with smaller bowls similar in shape and color is an example of how to achieve a clean style with uniform lines and shapes.

0217 Excellent results can be achieved when a monochromatic scheme is applied to a room's heavier elements, with the addition of some details in a contrasting color that combine well with the base tone, but stand out. In this living room, the accessories in blue envigorate the space.

0215

0216

0217

0218

0219

0220

0221

0218 These simple forms are enriched by the contrast of the materials. We can protect a candle with a glass cloche that is reminiscent of a butter dish. Its cylindrical form is mirrored by the height of the small round and deep toned wooden table.

0219 The matte finish of the rug, and the glossy finish of the leather pillows juxtapose the natural texture of the base material against the fine texture of the processed product.

0220 This living room's accessories create a dynamic feeling. Aside from the cohesive color palette, the circular incisions in the bottles on the table are echoed in the hypnotizing effect of the picture's concentric circles, creating a feeling of movement.

0221 When we choose a style for our living room, we have to pay attention to each element in order to achieve a coherent atmosphere. In this case a modern and urban style has been complemented by the high contrast black and white chevron-patterned rug.

0222 To creatively and economically decorate a wall, opt for photographs. You can frame them in any style that suits your decor aesthetic.

0223 Wall decoration with photographs is very common. For a touch of originality, establish a visual relationship between the type of image and the frame, like aged black and white photos in a thick wooden antiqued frame.

0224 Made of wood, or wrapped in leather or fabric, trunks fulfill their primary purpose of storing clothes and other objects. In the living room they come in handy for the storage of throws, extra pillows and the like, while serving as a striking coffee table.

0225

0226

0227

0228

0229

0225 While frames are a typical and more lasting way of displaying photographs and artwork, other more creative options exist that allow us to easily change out photos, post cards and even notes that we want have close by.

0226 In a living room where light and pastel tones dominate, use accessories to accent the room. In addition to jars with flowers, other options are airtight transparent containers with sand, herbs or spices.

0227 Wall mounted magazine racks allow us to organize and display books, magazines and other printed materials. Important considerations are the type of wall the rack is being mounted on, as well as the capacity of the unit. Many are metallic, easy to clean and durable.

0228 Candles in a living room create a warm and intimate atmosphere. Even if they remain unlit, a candle's color, texture and shape turn it into a lasting and practical accessory. Furthermore, candlescapes can be created with the addition of candelabras and other accessories like shells, mirrors and flowers.

0229 The orchid is one of the most appreciated flowers in interior decoration because of the range of striking colors they come in, to the uniqueness of its shape. When incorporating an orchid into your interior design, try recreating the plant's natural conditions, taking into account lighting and moisture.

0230 To visually expand a living room and enhance the quality of the light, use a mirror. Reflection transforms a room. Make sure that the frame works with the decorating style of the room.

0231 If the tones that dominate a room are black and white, choose accents that go well with both but that bring some zest to the room, such as the sparkling crystal chandelier and ornately framed mirror in this example.

0232 The abundance of squares in different functional objects are a focal point in this living room. The geometry emphasizes with the material's raw yet elegant character; the cushion's soft, warm leather contrasts with the cold and smooth reflective quality of the mirrors.

0230

0231

0232

0233

0234

0235

0236

0233 Metal and glass pieces make excellent décor items in living rooms of muted and dark tones. Sheen, just like transparency and reflection, produce an interesting visual effect of color and light.

0234 A living room is a space that allows a greater combination of styles and cultures. These large vases with floral and calligraphic decorations recall ancient civilizations with their exotic and aged feel.

0235 This mirror reflects the ceiling's moldings, adding visual interest to the room. The mirror also brightens up the room by reflecting light.

0236 As an alternative to a traditional rectangular mirror, this composition of several round mirrors reflects the exterior in an unusual and geometric way. The disorganized configuration is balanced with the classic style of the furniture and walls.

0237 Hanging ornaments from tree branches seems like something we would do in children's rooms, but it is perfectly feasible in living rooms as demonstrated in this example.

0238 In a living room with rural or garden style furniture, a throw pillow in striped fabric is ideal. For a bit of playfulness, and to vary the look, vary the direction of the fabric's lines, with some vertical and others horizontal.

0239 Cheerful, casual and vibrantly colored, these cushions bring dynamism to this living room. Classic tartan patterns are reinvented with brilliant color combinations. Of course, if you opt for patterned cushions, choose a solid cloth for the sofa.

0237

0238

0239

0240

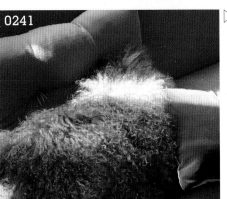

0241

0240 Moroccan or Turkish style textiles feature intricate and multicolored embroidery. Choose one design, or mix different ones for a more exuberant and exotic ambience.

0241 Furry blankets and throw pillows add an irresistably tactile element to a room, and in combination with the warmth they provide, makes them perfect to cuddle up in.

0242 Don't be afraid of choosing a multitude of different patterns, textures and motifs in the fabrics and textiles used in a living room. Provided they complement each other, and the general decor of the room, it won't necessarily overwhelm.

0243 A great way to ensure that mixed fabrics can work together, is to maintain a chromatic or style relationship. In this case, the color and graphic image on one of the pillows harmonizes well with the furry blanket of similar tones.

0244 The charm of neutral tones can add even more value as a decorative element with the addition of texture. A touch of color is always welcome, and even more so if it comes accompanied by a rich texture.

0245 A luxe environment has been created in this rural setting with the choice of fabrics similar in tone, weight and texture for the rug and upholstered furnishings.

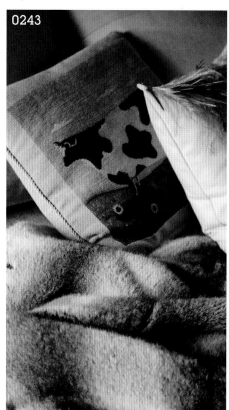

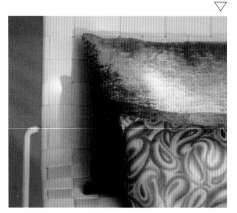

0246

0247

0248

0249

0246 White and neutral tones combine very well with natural materials like wood and handcrafted fabrics. A monochromatic palette, for all of the living room's decorations and accessories — lamps, candles, flowers and cushions — creates a balanced and harmonious atmosphere.

0247 Large vases can be placed on the floor of the living room, in the foyer and hallways. Made of ceramic, metal or acrylic, these vessels can hold flowers and ornamental leaves.

0248 Lime green and pink are usually used together in children's rooms or at parties because of the cheerful combination of colors. This color palette in a living room is, without a doubt, a successful attempt to fill the room with energy.

0249 Colorful pillows add a touch of color to an otherwise bland sofa. Changing out throw pillows are the easiest but most impactful way to restyle the atmosphere of a room.

0250

0251

0252

0253

0254

0255

0256

0250 When an animal motif is used in a children's room, farm animals are the most common choice. In living rooms, others prevail. Flowers, birds, butterflies, elk, deer, and other wild, Nordic and African savannah animals are common.

0251 Monochromatic color schemes convey serenity. Start with the main color and add some color variations in the accessories and décor objects.

0252 The embroidered and quilted fabrics in these pillows create an interesting texture and are pleasant to the touch.

0253 Textiles with smooth color patterns and muted drawings are ideal for living rooms decorated in a French country style, in which white dominates and is combined with light and pastel shades. Accessorize with rustic furnishings, such as trunks, ceramic jars, chests and natural fabrics, to further cement the look.

0254 Embroidered pillows with floral designs and pastel colors are a good trick for decorating a "shabby chic" style room. Use them in spaces that mix antique and modern elements to establish an elegant and welcoming atmosphere.

0255 When combining cushions of different fabrics, take into consideration texture, color and pattern. Use this trick to add a colorful touch to your living space.

0256 To brighten a living room and add an artistic flair, use pillows with graphic patterns.

0257 The harmonious and minimalist design of this Rhythm light fixture (designed by Arik Levy for Vibia) has multiple configurations thanks to a pivoting system allowing the undulating movement of its "ribs."

0258 Nigel Coates' Angel Falls for Terzani is an original sculptural light. Suspended from a large LED lighting fixture, crystal angels seem to be in dancing in the air. A dramatic piece like this can be an accent in a room decorated with ornate Victorian elements, or can stand alone as the centerpiece of a room.

0259 For a special touch, and to enliven a plain white wall, a brightly colored lamp like this one is a great solution. Composed of a metallic frame with an elastic, removable and washable cover in many choices of color, it can be a wall, ceiling or hanging lamp. (Muse de Axo Light)

0257

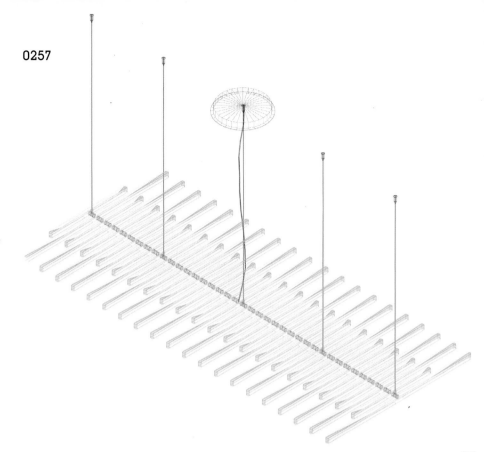

0258

0260 In dining rooms with high ceilings, the most effective chandelier will be large and dramatic. In this case, a light fixture with hanging lights provides the space with the necessary light and adds a decorative touch.

0261 The combination of hand-worked wire, crystal drops, and lace cover give this light fixture a kitschy feel and gives a casual and relaxed touch to the living room.

0262 This is a new version of the Bubi lamp designed in 2001 and launched in the market by Pandul. The original shape was inspired by the designer's grandchild's sombrero. The cover has a chrome finish and the differently colored cables create a playful atmosphere.

0263 This hanging lamp stands out for its original cluster shape with cylindrical shades. Despite the number of bulbs, the amount of light is surprisingly not excessive, as it is filtered through the rice paper shades.

0260

0261

0262

0263

0264

0266

0265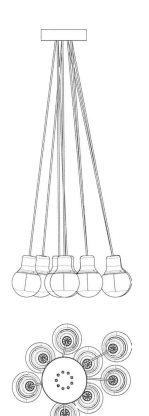

0267

0264 This hanging fixture's uniqueness comes from its ingenious arrangement. Identical lamps of different diameters fit inside each other like in "Matryoshkas" or, Russian nesting dolls.

0265 The unusual but striking large black sockets gives this fixture an exceptional and timeless quality.

0266 In libraries and offices where focused light is required, spotlights are the ideal solution. In this case, these low-energy LED lights are adjustable, with the ability to direct light wherever needed.

0267 Despite this low-energy table lamp's thin shape, it provides sufficient light with an LED tube with a high efficiency heat dissipator. The design is distinctly minimalist and has high functionality. The light is suspended by two fine, adjustable cables.

0268 This chandelier is the room's main feature, not only for its magnitude, but also for the combination of textures in the arm's ornate weathered metal, the pleated shades and the glass and crystal that reflect the color of the walls.

0269 A chandelier-type fixture has grandiosity and elaborate design that bestow elegance upon a rustic space — in this case, the rough brick ceiling. The melted wax effect and light bulb's resemblance to a flame shape recall these lamps medieval origin.

0270 These chandeliers provide a solemn elegance and serve as an ideal complement in classic living rooms, with friezes and ornaments on their ceilings. The hanging adornments' transparent material sparkles at different angles in the light's reflection.

0268

0269

0270

0271

0272

0273

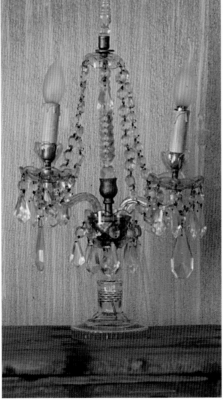

0271 With the aim of transforming a space through the small details, the combination of shades of different sizes and colors on this classic chandelier provides color and a contemporary and personal touch to a classic piece.

0272 To create a warm and familiar atmosphere, avoid typical matching light fixtures and choose different lamps or chandeliers for each area of the living and dining rooms. This creates small lit environments with exceptional lamps, and plays with two disparate styles.

0273 Crystal drops are an element of chandelier design that recall the refinement and pomp of a palace. They can adapt to different applications in the home, adorning table lamps and ceiling-mounted fixtures.

0274 A wall-mounted light fixture, placed high on the wall, draws the eyes upward. This method of enlarging the sense of space in a room works exceptionally well in a dining room.

0275 Metal is an interesting material for lamp shades, as it offers several colors, like brass or nickel, and finishes, such as shiny, matte or aged. In this example, an ornamental design has been cut out of the smooth copper surface, allowing light to filter outward, as well as down.

0276 The VP1 Flowerpot light, designed by Verment Panton in 1964, is characterized by the simplicity of its lines. It has become a classic design thanks to its distinguishable form.

0277 The configuration of this ceiling lamp is dramatic and eyecatching. The light bulbs on each of the triangular faces of the metallic icosahedron emit a direct light that, like the lighting in an actors dressing room, provide an urban, cabaret touch.

0274

0275

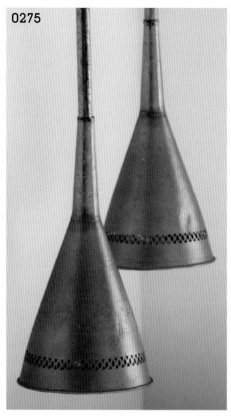

0276

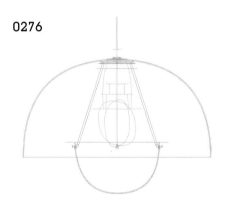

0277

0278

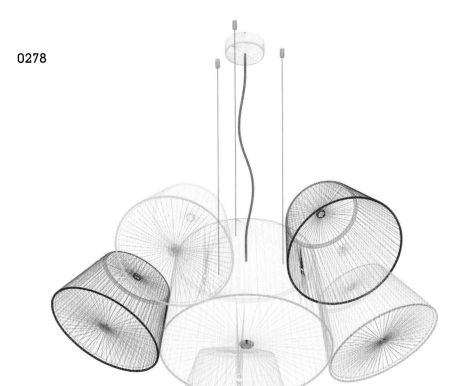

0279

▽

0278 Marset's Tam Tam lamps are characterized by repetition, and by the archetypical shades that cover a number of lights shining in different directions.

0279 The ceiling lamp is one of the most pivotal elements in establishing a room's general style, as its position has a significant visual impact. The choice of a fixture with a distinctive aesthetic is decisive and governs the space.

0280 In a living room with a double-height ceiling and wooden saddle beams, the gaze is naturally directed upward. In these rooms it is convenient to choose a lamp that meshes with the style both in the living and dining rooms.

0281 These fixtures have been designed to create a cozy environment around a table. The seams are folded outward around the edge of each panel that shape the screens' modular box. (Hood light fixture for Ateljé Lyktan)

0280

0281

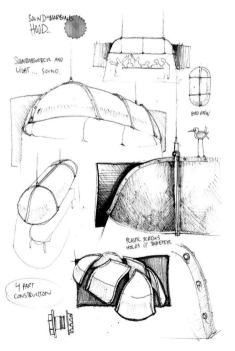

0282

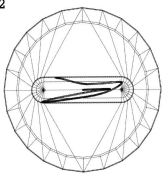

0283

0284

0282 With a shape inspired by machinery, these ceiling lamps for the dining room are made of blown glass. The bulky thickness causes a pleasant shade of light and the wide mouth is ideal for long tables. (Size de Belux)

0283 Increasing reliance on technology can result in a greater appreciation for the calm sense of well-being that is associated with nature. There is a particular appeal to handcrafted objects and the activities that create them. The presence of a hand knitted lampshade imbues this room with warmth.

0284 The white lampshades in this dining room, together with white walls and curtains, contribute to the quality of the light in the room. It also allows the wooden ceiling and beams to stand out, and their textures are better appreciated.

0285 We can obtain a subtle harmony between several key pieces of a room: the ceiling lamps radiate a bright but transparent color and share tones with the accessories, all over a light, neutral canvas.

0286 La Belle is a lamp that emits a pleasant, diffuse light, providing an enjoyable atmosphere. A white polyethylene drum and a transparent diffuser combines to create a light fixture that is not likely to go unnoticed.

0285

0286

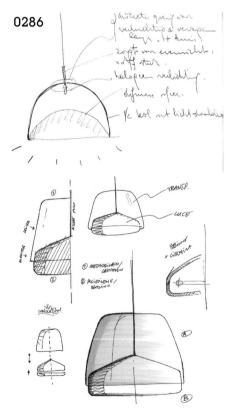

0287

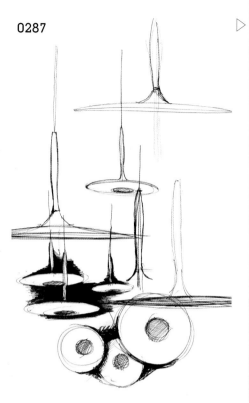

0288

0287 This light fixture belonging to Targetti's Decanter collection, is an exclusive design with a distinctive touch: its sculptural shape. Even when not lit, it serves a decorative element that adds drama to a living or dining room.

0288 To increase the amount of light in a room, consider a cluster of light fixtures, instead of a single one. Manufacturers usually offer sets of ceiling lamps that share the same design and vary in some features, like the color, size and height.

0289 Louis Poulsen's PH Snowball is a light without a harsh glare. The design stands out for its sculptural qualities.

0290 The extraordinary organic shape of this NLC lamp resembles a jellyfish, and the lacquer finish gives the fixture a futuristic appearance. With no doubt, it stands out in any space for its sculptural qualities.

0289

0290

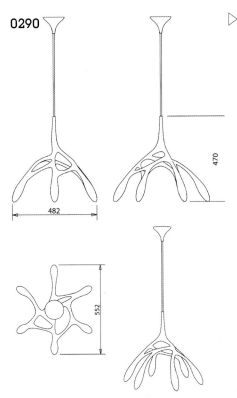

482

470

552

0291

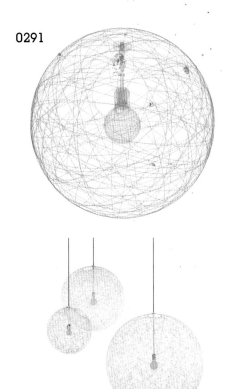

0292

0293

0291 The lacelike look of this light and airy fixture is an interesting foil for this contemporary living room. Made of fiberglass and sealed in epoxy resin, it has an ornateness to it that is not in discord with the simple and clean lines that dominate the room.

0292 Even simple materials and combinations can have a lot of impact in a room. The dark-toned chickenwire screen provides interesting visual contrast against the light center shade.

0293 Aside from the eclecticism of combining accessories of different styles in one room, the clashing of differing styles in a single accessory, as in this lamp, can be compelling and impactful. The refined crystal drops combine with the roughly textured fabric, and hand tooled wire edging into a singularly captivating piece.

0294 An almost identical tone in the wood of the table, wall and lamp functions to harmonize the dining room space and, together with the white walls, make the accessories — chairs, a bookshelf, a pitcher and some bowls — stand out with their lively colors.

0295 The translucent fabric covering this dining room light emits soft, ethereal lighting, which is incongruent with the the dramatic and irregular peaks, curves and slopes that are created by the underlying metal structure.

0296 Louis Poulsen's Snowball is designed to prevent glare. Its geometry ensures that all the lighting surfaces receive light at an identical angle. It provides uniform lighting above the dining room table, where it is most often used.

0294

0295

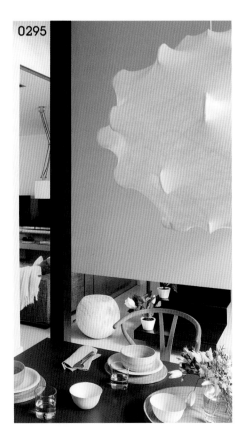

0296

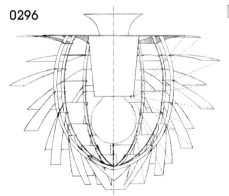

0297

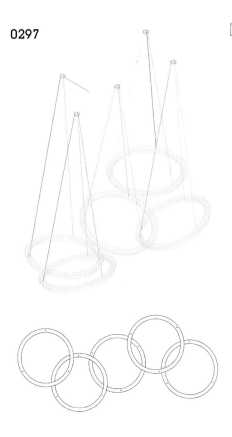

0298

0297 Circular Halo is a hanging lamp with several circular pieces, which create subtle environments, bathed in a magic light. Finished in white lacquer, this lamp was designed by Martín Azúa for Vibia.

0298 Luis Eslava studio designed Agatha, this wood veneer lamp. It is also called "optimist lamp" because of its "petals." Its form provides warmth and a whimsical touch to the dining room.

0299 A methacrylate satin structure covered in a screen of strips can be reinvented in a number of ways; as a suspension lamp, table lamp or two or three leveled standing lamp, because it is modular and stackable. (Bailaora de Metalarte)

0300 This ceiling-mounted lamp designed by Miguel Herranz for LZF stands out for its spectacular organic and dynamic shape. Made of thin wood strips, it provides an interesting interplay of light and shadow.

0299

0300

0301

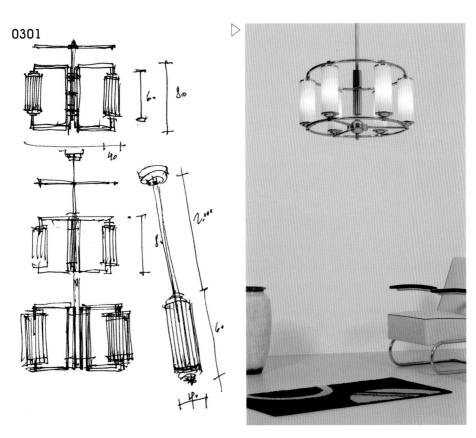

0302

0303

0301 In fifties-sixties style retro living or dining rooms, this hanging lamp design offers a dim, pleasant and comfortable light. This "revival" style is made up of six cylindrical lights distributed symmetrically on a chrome steel base.

0302 The understated but inventive elegance of the Wish lamp from Brazilian designer Fernando Prado for Lumini has become an icon in the lighting design world.

0303 In 2008 Serge Cornelissen designed the LUMO lamp for Steng. It is suspended by two stainless steel cables that allow the adjustment of the height and the tilting angle, and the design lends itself to the use of many of them, depending on the amount of lighting required.

0304 The lighting in this dining room is a study of contrasts. First, there is the combination of an up-lit light box, and two pendulum lights that direct light downward. Within the pendulum lights themselves, there is an opaque inner layer of blown glass inside a perfectly translucent outer layer. The resulting light fixture is unique and remarkable piece.

0305 The fixtures in this room are made of cellular plastic, which means that although it appears solid, the plastic is filled with tiny micropores. This allows the lamp to emit a brighter light, and the geometry of the shape is reflected in the furniture and even in the panes of the windows.

0306 The "Ogle" pendant lamp is a design of the Swedish trio Form Us With Love. The light of the LED bulbs in this dramatic fixture are directable, due to the hidden system in the upper part of the base. The design of this fixture allows it to be used in many variations. It can illuminate a large area as a table light, or a small area as a focus light or spotlight, depending on where the beams of light are aimed. It can also be used as a single unit, or in clusters.

0304

0305

0306

0307

0308

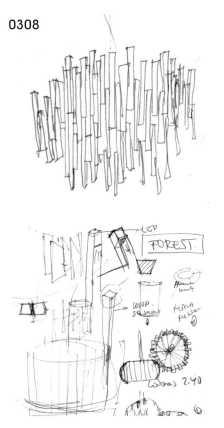

0309

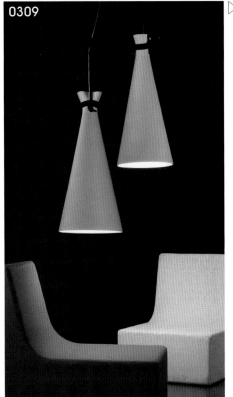

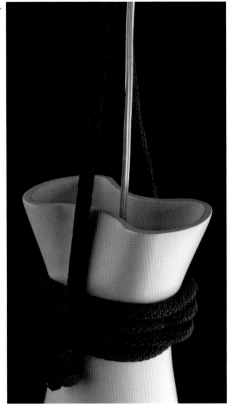

0307 This ceiling light operates under the functional principle of indirect ambient lighting but with a modern structure: the carefree placement of rigid circular plates is reminiscent of the petals of a flower.

0308 Inspired by the silhouettes of trees in a forest, Héctor Serrano designed the lamp, "Woods." The light is surrounded by rectangular pieces of birch suspended irregularly from clear plastic filament. It dims the light and imbues the room with the warm colors of the wood.

0309 The "Campanella" model, designed by Herme Spanish Ciscar and Monica Garcia is made by hand and revolves around the theme of mountaineering. The idea was to transform rough stone into a beautiful object and suspend it from the ceiling with rope and a climbers knot.

0310 This unique and eyecatching LED floor lamp is an up-lighter, but it also radiates a diffuse colored light. The LED are partially enclosed by a matte white body, within which lies a glass diffuser that modulates the colors.

0311 The dim, romantic light of candles is a great option in keeping with the rustic and warm spaces. Traditional and common materials, such as wrought iron, used in a modern way, revitalize this accessory.

0312 Office desk lamps are usually metal, as the material lends itself well to the construction that allows for the precise direction of light. This design uses a warm wood instead and a light shade more suitable for a living room that is also in line with the colors of the furniture.

0313 The musical motif of these lamps add character and whimsy to the warmth of this space, complemented with other details like the support that mimics a melting candle and their unique placement on the frame of the mirror.

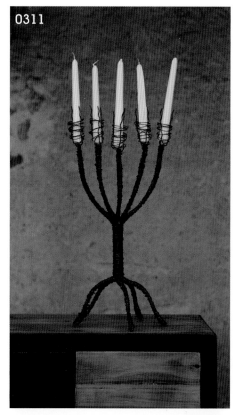

0314

0315

0316

0317

0314 This contemporary design uses directional technology, high-quality materials and agile structures that merge industrial knowledge, with aesthetic delight.

0315 Dynamism and a brilliant metallic quality combine in an ultramodern design that simulates a Mikado game – the traditional wooden stick game with colored points – suspended in the air.

0316 Some areas of this house, like the foyer, the hallways or the L-shaped corners, require special lighting. In this case, a luminous disk in the wall has an impressive presence: its shape and power look like a sun and are in line with the tribal adornments on the shelves.

0317 The "Code" by Trizo21 spotlight allows for an infinite number of configurations. The rounded corners make this light fixture elegant and stylish.

0318 Lamps with jointed structures fulfill an important function as auxiliary lights because they can be directed so that light can reach pointed corners, illuminate specific areas with great precision and direct attention towards decorative details.

0319 "Funiculi" was originally designed in 1979 by Lluis Porqueras. Its pure design and its cable car-like mechanism make this floor lamp a classic for living rooms.

0320 In a space that benefits from a lot of natural light, a standing lamp with a white and generously sized shade favors the ideal distribution of light and has a large reach without being obtrusive.

0318

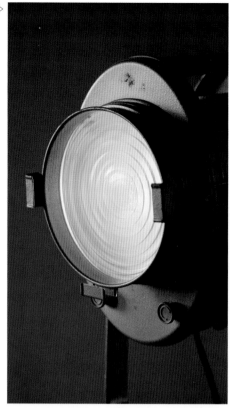

0319

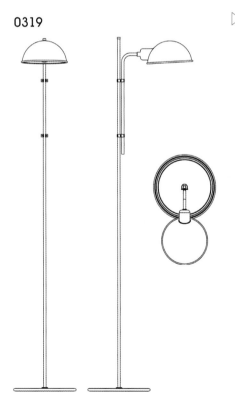

0320

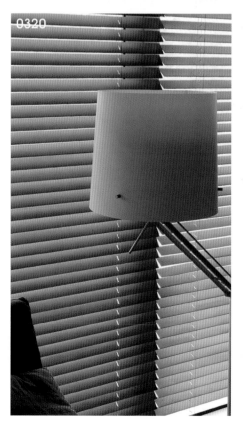

0321

0322

0323

0324

0321 The distribution of light sources is one of the main aspects to take into account in a living room's interior design. Table lamps that cast light of generous intensity and spread are ideal for lighting corners and crannies that natural light cannot reach.

0322 Clarity is a quality that we associate with good lighting and therefore, table lamps made of transparent and white materials are those with the best functionality. Additionally, these same qualities won't saturate and overwhelm the atmosphere.

0323 Designed by Ferdi Giardini, Nerolia is a table lamp that radiates a diffuse light thanks to the translucent glass, but also diffuses aromatic scents. The beautiful amber cones are made of Murano glass.

0324 The combination of black, red and white creates an impressive contrast that strengthens the shapes of the objects to the maximum. In this case, the table's straight lines and the curious shape of the lamp stand out against the daring red background.

0325

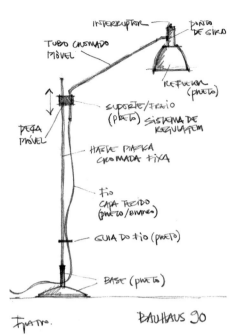

INTERRUPTOR
PONTO DE GIRO
TUBO CROMADO MÓVEL
REFLETOR (preto)
SUPORTE/FRAIO (preto) SISTEMA DE REGULAGEM
PEÇA MÓVEL
HASTE PRETA CROMADA FIXA
fio CAPA TECIDO (preto/branco)
GUIA DO fio (preto)
BASE (preto)

Quatro.   BAUHAUS 90

0326

0327

0328

0329

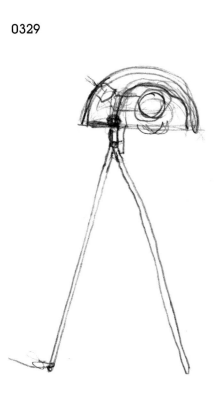

0330

0325 This lamp was designed to celebrate the 90th anniversary of the Bauhaus School of Design. Bauhaus 90 has a height-adjustable system that eliminates the use of locks or screws.

0326 As though in the corner of an antique shop, this table houses classic books, a crystal paperweight and inkwell, a magnifying glass and a lamp that brings to mind an apothecary that, all together, give a vintage air to the living room.

0327 Table lamps allow for the targeted lighting of a specific area without being visually disruptive, while adding warmth to the atmosphere. In this case, the curved line of the support that connects the base to the light bulb gives rise to a clear and dynamic design.

0328 Some standing lamps have an advantage over others if their design makes it easy to change the direction of the light with ease. In this way, different atmospheric lighting options can be obtained from the same lamp depending on the needs of the situation.

0329 Circles and triangles are key shapes in the "Random" lamp. Hans Sandgren Jakobsen has created a clean design in which each detail is justified. The base has a triangular form that ensures stability.

0330 One way of amplifying a home's artificial interior light is to aim them towards a mirror. In this way, the spotlights are reflected, made less intense and duplicate their luminescent capacity.

0331 In this example, a standing lamp completes the living room's corner without occupying too much space, as well as accomplishing the important function of illuminating a specific area. It is ideal for reading and other tasks that require a brighter light.

0331

0332 This table's modest technology makes the extendable wings that increase its size almost invisible and they unfold with a single rapid movement. The innovative base attracts a lot of attention and frees all the space under the table to facilitate mobility. (Prora de Bonaldo)

0333 The "Emmei" brand, characterized by designing elegant furniture adapted to contemporary living rooms, has created the Arcanto table. This extendable table has a black-tinted tempered glass top and legs made of extruded aluminum.

0334 Rustic does not necessarily clash with elegance. In this example of the modern trend, that consists of mixing restored or antique tables with contemporary furniture, the table stands out for its characteristic appearance and its practicality.

0335 This table is constructed of an aluminum frame that holds the legs and the glass surface, which is available in greater or lesser opacity. In contrast with the heaviness of wood, a table of this material gives a feeling of lightness and freshness. (Layer de Bonaldo)

0336 In a neutral space it is a good idea to add a touch of color to an unexpected place, like on dining room table legs. Traditional materials, like steel, wood and glass, are combined in an avant-guard style that changes according to the point of view. (Big foot de Bonaldo)

0335

0336

0337 Designed by Enrico Franzolini for Jesse, the "Lord Milady" table is an example of elegance in furniture. It is characterized by its apparent lightweight appearance, the softness of its edges and the curvature of its legs. Built of oak, it is a table that, aesthetics aside, is very functional.

0338 Reflecting and increasing natural light and the illusion of more space are the main benefits of having a mirror in the dining room area. These effects can be doubled if the table top is made of bright, smooth reflective materials. (Montenapoleone de Emmemobili)

0339 When the dining room is adjacent to the kitchen, a pleasing affect is achieved if the furniture matches, as in this case, in which the dining room table maintains the minimalist and contemporary style of the kitchen. (Elle de César)

0337

0338

0339

0340

0341

0340 Emmei's "Segno" table is ideal for large living and dining rooms. The tempered glass top reflects the light, which helps to brighten the expanse of the space. Worth noting are the legs, which are wrapped in white, quilted leather.

0341 Notio is a piece of furniture with a sculptural quality designed as a showpiece, that occupies a place of honor in a room.

0342 On occasion, it is necessary to add a touch of color to minimalist spaces where white dominates. The table with the transparent orange top gives this living room with a playful character.

0343 This table's design confers a rural and homely style on the dining room because of the gingham pattern on its surface. This pattern, which is typical of a picnic tablecloth, is created by colored stripes that cross perpendicularly to form a square. (Fabian de Kitsuné and e 15)

0344 In addition to its great size, the outward angle of this table's legs, and the base's crossed support beams make it appear forceful, firm and static. However, the functionality of this dining room table can be changed into a desk, for example, with the addition of a powerful floor lamp with great lighting capacity. (Clark de Rodolfo Dordoni for Minotti)

0342

0343

0344

0345

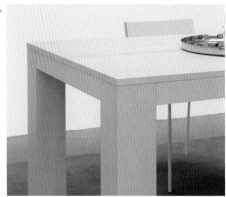

0346

0347

0345 This table designed for e15 follows in the company's tradition of working with natural materials such as wood. Its archetypical shape makes the table a particularly adaptable piece to any living room, and to most diverse lifestyles.

0346 Multiple dining room options are achievable when the table is modular. In addition to the extension that allow it to increase in size, the base position is adjustable. By rotating and folding the parts, they can be combined in myriad different configurations depending on the needs of the occasion. (Isaac de e15)

0347 Wood is the most suitable material for living and dining room tables. Current design tendencies are to highlight, as opposed to mask, the material's texture. In this case, the grain of the wood is left exposed as its own decorative element.

0348 This table's rectangular surface parallels the chromed steel crosspiece in the base, and that, combined with the high quality oak wood it is constructed of, gives the table a sculptural quality. (Dylan de Casamilano).

0349 This table has been constructed of materials that were chosen for their durability under daily use, with a reinforced glass tabletop and varnished aluminum base, and all without sacrificing an elegant and dynamic design. (Diapason de Kreaty Ciacci)

0350 In a predominantly white space, black elements are prominent. In this dining room, the stunning dark oak table is emphasized and only the chair legs stand out dramatically, and cream upholstery almost disappears. (Ettore de Jesse)

0351 A slight, minimalistic dining room table is optimum in smaller spaces. Available in black and platinum white, its curved lines, rounded corners and flat legs are ideal for a futuristic loft. (Slim de Meneghello Paolelli para Kreaty)

0352 The tables designed by Doimo are characterized by the juxtaposition of diverse materials in a harmonious way. Natural wood is paired with polycarbonate; glass is used alongside polyamide. For example, this rectangular table combines curved glass legs with stainless steel tabletop support.

0348

0349

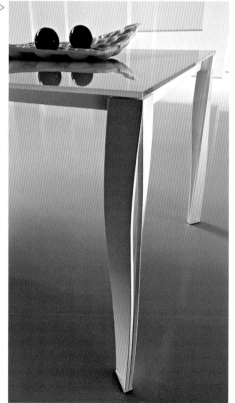

0350

0351

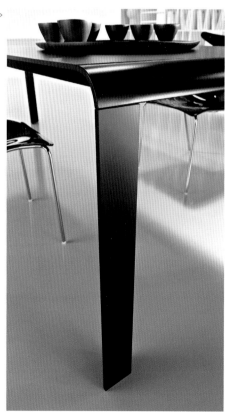

0352

0353 The chairs straight modern lines conform to the ebony table top's linear quality, but they are in dynamic contrast with the ornate table base. In addition to the distinction between the geometric and organic shapes, the dissimiliarty of the materials' textures and sheen — the shine of the ebony, the leather chairs, the lacquered steel, the base's matte wood — is provocative. (Fratino de Bertelé)

0354 For a minimalist environment, stripping a dining room down to its essential requirements can be visually compelling. This simple dining room table has been built with walnut tree wooden beams attached to steel legs. (Anton de e 15)

0355 The "Canaletto" table was designed by Emaf Progetti in 2009. Its substantial construction of solid wood gives it an almost medieval appearance, which complements the ornate chandelier, but is foiled by the contemporary design of the chairs.

0356 Thanks to its durability, flexibility and beauty, wood is the perfect material for the fabrication of tables of all types. These characteristics allow such novel designs as this table's top made of staggered wood boards with their edges cut at 45˚.

0353

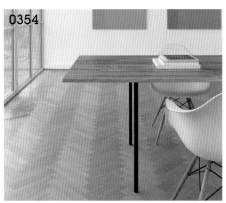

0354

0356

0355

0357

0359

0357 This sophisticated and stately dining room is the product of several elements, that impart a sense of lustre. The highly textured deep-pile black area rug is the only piece in the room without shine, and contrasts the hanging light fixture of shiny twisted strips of black glass and the majestic table, whose shiny metallic ornate legs are topped with an ultra-light glass table top. (London de Modà)

0358 Stately tables with moderate curves are striking, especially when finished in a gold lacquer, which enhances their beauty with contemporary textures and high quality materials. (New York de Modà)

0359 The "Orion" table, designed by Ronen Joseph for Pierantonio Bonacina, features a brushed stainless steel structure and a polyethylene top. Its color and finish is similar to that of many of the elements of the room (the steel framed windows, the light glossy floor) allowing the chairs and accent pieces to be the focus.

0360 Glass and wood are two of the most used materials for the construction of furniture. In this example, the contemporary design is exemplified in the warm organic wooden base that is highlighted by the cool glass tabletop.

0361 As the dining room table is usually in the center of the room, why not make it even more overt by choosing one in a bright color and a luminous material? The lively lime color makes the plants and vegetables that are around the dining room's natural green stand out. With a chrome base and clear glass top, the table has an equally commanding presence, that is not minimized by the strong accent colors in the room. (Athene de Modà)

0362

0362 Made of reflective material and with an embellished shape, this oval table is reminiscent of an old fashioned mirror. The organic lines and reflective quality contribute to the polished and refined ambience of the room.

0363 Wenge wood is one the darkest, hardest and most resistant woods in the world. Although it is very difficult to work with, it is ideal for home furniture, especially for pieces that are subject to direct and continuous use like the ones in a dining room. It is so durable, that it is often used for staircases which this table is reminiscent of. (Palermo de Emmemobili)

0364 This table's rounded glass top lets us appreciate the base that has been constructed from hand crafted wooden strips into a braided and curved structure, which doesn't need additional pieces or joints for support. (Nastro de Emmemobili)

0365 Philipp Mainzer designed this table following classical furniture tradition. This table's perfect and balanced proportions make it an outstanding furnishing that irradiates solidity and elegance.

0366

0367

▷

0368

0366 The variety of combinations of materials in the design of dining room tables is limitless. In this example, the chromed steel base, reminiscent of a flower or fountain, is covered in white leather to match the chairs.

0367 This table is remarkable for the sculptural character of the steel legs that endows the space with elegance. The top is made of glass, relieving some of the weight of the base.

0368 Walnut is the most appreciated wood for interior furniture because it can be comfortably worked into small or large boards. The dark grained tone draws beautiful patterns and allows designs, like this table's elliptical base together with chromed metal in the base, to shine. (Sestante de Besana)

0369 An interesting reinterpretation of classical tastes, this arrangement of refined furniture over more risky choices like transparent gauze curtains, a high-pile thread carpet and modern chandelier, still manages to appear cohesive. (Emiliano de Bertelé)

0370 This table's assertive geometry unleashes dynamic movement. The base consists of triangular sides that revolve around the eye of a spiral. A material composed of a base of polyester and acrylic resins loaded with pigmented minerals lends itself well to a design of this kind. (Elica de Zanotta)

0371 The typical support on four-legged support for the dining room table has been replaced by several chromed steel columns arranged like trees in a forest that supports this table's glass tabletop, which can be round or rectangular and is fixed to the steel. (Mille de Bonaldo).

0372 Blues and green tones remind us of nature, of the seaside and the forest. The freshness of these colors is made even more inviting when it comes in different textures, opacities and shades.

0373 In addition to the customary flower jars, we can bring other natural elements to the table, such as wide tree leaves, pineapples, small branches, seeds and wild fruits, and complement their vibrant colors with the dishes and the tablecloth.

0374 Traditional accessories and fabrics for the table have a versatility and strength that we can take advantage of. If two people are dining, it is a great idea to place a table runner in order to generate a feeling of closeness and affinity.

0375 A touch of spontaneity is welcome even in sober and formal dining rooms. In this example, the different sized candles, the leaf accents, using placemats at some seats and not in others, putting the vases in unexpected places, using different sized glassware and mismatched china still all work together for a elegant look.

0376 Dining room tables are used for so many more activities than just at mealtimes. The elements that denote a "dining room" removed and replaced, renewed, combined and transformed as many times as you like, to achieve any functionality you desire.

0372

0373

0374

0375

0376

0377

0378

0379

0380

0381

0382

0377 Placemats, coasters or bread baskets made of natural fibers, and bowls, glasses or plant pots made of roughly finished clay, give the table a handcrafted touch and combine very well with other cloth, paper or plastic accessories that we usually dress a table with.

0378 Just as we can opt for lively colors and textures for the table, so too can we choose tones of white to obtain a clean and refined style. The brown wooden tabletop and the candelabra's base make the white of the wall, chairs and crockery stand out, while the crystal and glass lighten the space.

0379 Decorative tableware such as plates, cutlery and glassware, as well as trays, fruit bowls, teapots and cocktail accessories, can be complemented with candles, vases and a specific lighting.

0380 A connection between the dining and living room is easy to achieve if you decorate with complementary colors and patterns. In this case a deep creamy color dominates the furniture and walls, and unusual accessories have been chosen in a flowery pattern that echoes the real flowers in the same color range.

0381 A table acquires a distinct personality when the type of motifs, patterns or fabrics on the tablecloth, placemats, cloth napkins and dining room seat cushions are varied. The designs can be rural or refined, according to their patterns and colors.

0382 A substantial tablecloth imparts a homey feeling, as well as reducing the unpleasant sounds of clashing plates and cutlery. There are numerous options in tablecloth materials that make for practical tableware maintenance: machine washable, reversible, heat resistant, waterproof, etc.

0383 The "Ciacci Kreaty Diva Chair" designed by Gino Carollo is an original chair with a dynamic design that calls to mind a racetrack. Made of polycarbonate, the Diva chair is available in various colors.

0384 The "Hans" chair by e15 ensures comfort with its combination of a clean and softly curved wood seat and back. Supported by a thin steel frame these chairs seem to float in the air.

0385 The Wishbone chair is unique among chairs with armrests. Its wonderful design features a wraparound back, which allows for good support. Its design was inspired by classic portraits of Danish merchants seated in Ming Dynasty chairs.

0386 The "Houdini" chair by e15 is an example of quality and precision in woodwork technology, gracefully combining aesthetics with ergonomics.

0387 The "Houdini" chair model offers great versatility. The armchair version features a steam-curved wood back. The chair is available in different finishes: oak or walnut, clear or colored lacquer, and can even be upholstered upon request.

0388 This set of weathered metal chairs contributes to an industrial look. The red finish softens the coldness of the metal while the wood table brings in a warm touch.

0383

0384

0385

0386

0387

0388

0389 People don't normally think of plastic when they're furnishing their homes, but this mindset has begun to change. Plastic furniture can add a modern and cheerful feel to any room of your house, even though plastic furniture is generally used outdoors.

0390 The Sensei Biba chair by Jesse has a minimalist and dynamic aesthetic. Its unique design has a perfectly molded seat, which is ergonomically suited for maximum comfort, which is supported by a chrome-plated frame.

0391 The unusual dull gray distressed finish on this matching table and chair provides a modern and casual accent in a room dominated by white.

0389

0390

0391

0392

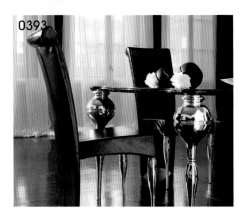

0393

0394

0392 Upholstered chairs are a common choice around the dining table. The fabric can match the design of the wallpaper and of the drapes for a uniform décor.

0393 A mixture of materials and styles also has a place in chair design. The "Lolita" chair by Noir-Italy combines upholstery of black leather with chrome legs. The result is an elegant and classically inspired chair.

0394 Plastic is not a noble material. It does, however, allow for the manufacture of products that fit any style, including spaces filled with period furnishings.

0395

0396

0397

0398

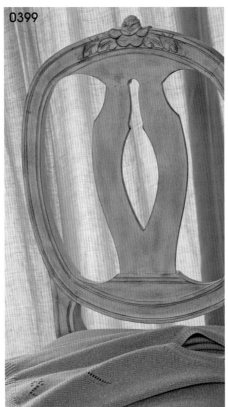

0399

0400

0395 For a compelling twist on classical style, simply keep the bones and use eye-catching fabrics with abstract prints, and high gloss metallic lacquer instead of natural wood. (Remix by Modà)

0396 Chairs, like any other piece of furniture, contribute to defining the style of a room. A wooden chair with simple lines and upholstered seat fits well in a rustic environment.

0397 A classically styled chair acquires a different life when unconventional fabrics are used, and when the wooden parts are finished in aggressive colors. (Dolcevita by Modà)

0398 The choice of chairs depends on the space available and on the room style. Keep in mind that a chair with armrests takes up more space than those without, but they are more comfortable.

0399 The medallion back and the carved wood legs and armrests are characteristic of some antique chairs. This chair finds new life with a new distressed finish and new upholstery that fits in a casual but stylish room.

0400 This is another example of a classical chair design reinterpreted to achieve a contemporary look. The shape is simplified and ornament is limited to a minimum to emphasize form and color.

0401 In this kitchen the doors, cabinets and drawers have a glossy, lacquered finish. They act as the main decorative element in the room and create a minimalist, contemporary and elegant atmosphere.

0402 A simple sideboard can be quite versatile. Its surface can serve as a table, while its shelves allow glassware to be displayed and ready for use. In this kitchen, glasses and wicker baskets are artfully presented on the lower shelves of a sideboard.

0403 A glass cabinet like this not only stores kitchen products, it also gives them added character. These bottles, protected and emphasized by the glass, become the room's prominent decorative element.

0404 Open shelves near a kitchen island are certainly convenient. Shallow shelves are great to display jars of herbs and spices. They can be nice to look at and you can quickly spot the one you need!

0405 The easiest way to create a sparse and minimalist kitchen is to opt for white cabinetry with colorful accent pieces. These bursts of color will pop in a white kitchen, adding contrast and interest to the room.

0406 This kitchen shows how the concepts of symmetry and asymmetry can be played with in order to organize storage units. The parallelism between the cooking surfaces on both sides of the stove is complemented by the diminutive, wall-mounted shelving unit.

0407 Along with basic cooking utensils, you can also display potted plants on your kitchen shelves. Not only do they give color and life to the room, they will also help absorb any unfavorable smells. And don't forget the clock, essential for checking cooking times and a key element in any kitchen.

0408 This Tecnocucina design is based in symmetry. The cabinets, arranged symmetrically around the sink, are reflected in the glossy floor and give off a surreal and modern feel.

0401

0402

0403

0404

0405

0406

0407

0408

0409 Who said that the kitchen is only for cooking and eating? The intimate and comfortable atmosphere of this room makes it the ideal place to read, study and relax. This inviting environment was created by adding some books and artwork among the jars of spices.

0410 Labeling drawers by their contents shows how organization and decoration can go hand in hand. This simple detail, together with the rounded shape and the pale tone of the drawers, provide the kitchen with a daring and futuristic character.

0411 The orange cabinetry in this monochromatic kitchen has great visual impact. The color of the cabinets is echoed throughout the accent pieces, such as the hanging oven mitts.

0412 These wooden shelves store many decorative items as well as dishes that see daily use. The plates, teacups and glasses that sprinkle the shelves make the kitchen an inviting and homey space in which one can feel at ease.

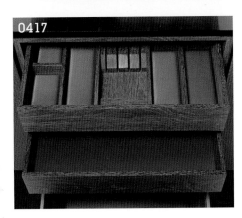

0413 If there is an element that defines this kitchen, it is its shine. The cabinets, the steel surfaces and the floor all are highly reflective. The combination of materials and colors enhances the sensation of coldness and purity.

0414 Using a curtain instead of a cabinet door is an economical and original solution. It can also be used in addition to a cupboard door, if you wish to display the door only at select times. Furthermore, this added touch brings color to a room and harmonizes with other fabrics that are present, like window curtains or tea towels.

0415 If you dream of a really elegant and chic kitchen, overcome your fear of the color black. A trick for not overwhelming the room with darkness is to keep the main elements (for example the cabinets) black, and leave small details in lighter colors to create an effective contrast.

0416 In a kitchen's design, storage units can play a central role if their bold color predominates throughout the room. This kitchen's blue tone exudes liveliness and serenity, combining perfectly with the wood and stainless steel.

0417 Equipped with sophisticated gliding mechanisms, these drawers allow for optimal accessibility and feature refined details. Their chestnut wood harmonizes with the black countertop.

0418 This L-shaped countertop provides a great additional storage space and, at the same time, offers a surface that can function as a countertop on which to cook and eat and, why not, as a work and study area as well.

0419 These space-efficient cabinets create a modern and distinct atmosphere. Installing only one wall of cabinets allows you to have a more minimalist kitchen and, on the other hand, the colors and lines become the main decorative element in the room.

0420 In this case it is the cabinets that stand out in the kitchen environment. In contrast with the black-and-white striped walls, their solid color and glossy finish draws attention.

0421 This drawer, belonging to the Casale model by Rational, has wooden separators that prevent the plates from moving. Smoked oak wood is the perfect choice for giving character to a kitchen and creating a modern country home atmosphere.

0422 The storage modules in this kitchen are distributed in a "U" shape, acting as the kitchen's work surfaces. In an open space, this structure creates the feeling of seclusion that the walls do not bring and separates the cooking area from the rest of the room.

0423 Tecnocucina architects design spacious and open kitchens that are connected to the living room. Under the premise of uniting functionality and innovation with design and aesthetics, they have converted this space into a modern, elegant and exciting sanctuary.

0424 Behind these pocket doors designed by Armani, everything but the fridge and freezer are hidden. With bronze paneling and a plaited texture, these doors create a sober and linear style that is extremely sophisticated.

0425 In this space tones of black and white predominate, with the exception of the lone wooden countertop. The scale's most intense color is found in the cabinet with the chrome base.

0426 At times a simple feature, such as this unique handle, is capable of turning a piece of furniture into one of the room's defining elements. Achieving an original kitchen can be as easy as looking after small details and finishes.

0427 Laminate, which has always been perceived as a high-quality, resistant and superior product, has been reinvented by Tecnocucina in the Graphos model. This kitchen is aimed at a consumer with refined taste in search of style and rigor.

0428 Designed as part of an affordable architecture project, G.One cabinets don't have visible handles and their lightly rounded corners soften the set's effect. Its style is reminiscent of the 1950s and 1960s, yet it is compatible with smartphones.

0425

0426

0428

0427

0429

0430

0431

0429 It is always easier to have an organized kitchen, in which the exact whereabouts of each pan and dish are known. Even though their exterior is simple, the inside of these cabinets is compartmentalized so that each item occupies its own place.

0430 Cutting-edge appliances, adjoined at the center of the wall, are completely surrounded by kitchen cabinets. This wall unit adds to the elegant contrast of black and steel, giving the kitchen a museum feel.

0431 In a small kitchen, look for ways to take advantage of all available space. This drawer is a good example – despite being situated in a corner, its diagonal opening mechanism allows you to gain storage space.

0432 A practical and homey way of storing dish towels is to install removable baskets. The texture of these wicker baskets brings a handcrafted, rustic and also modern look to this kitchen designed by Rational.

0433 A very practical way to store food is to install a gliding column unit with interior shelves. Accessibility to the content is paramount, so ensure that the shelves' depth and storage capacity is taken full advantage of.

0434 Drawers have a greater capacity than cabinets and offer more accessible storage because they allow complete access to all their contents without the need to reposition items at the front.

0435

0436

0435 Drawers can contain many different internal organizers to optimize their storage space. There are inner compartments for storing pot lids and separators for organizing contents and for ordering tableware by size.

0436 In an L- or U-shaped kitchen, it helps to find solutions that take advantage of corner spaces. This cabinet with a lacquered silk finish opens to reveal removable trays that allow easy access to their contents.

0437 The outward simplicity of this kitchen does not extend into the interior of its cabinetry. At first perceived as a sparse and minimalist space, upon opening any cabinet one finds the true character of this room.

0438 Inspired by the architecture of Giuseppe Terragni, the design of this unit pays utmost attention to detail. Dividers allow every type of cutlery and kitchen utensil to occupy its own place, creating a design that is both practical and sleek.

0439 For the Dada brand, the kitchen is the heart of the house. Given this, a kitchen must not only reflect our personal style, it must fuse design with functionality. In this kitchen two qualities stand out: organization and rationality.

0440 Designed by Dante Bonuccelli, in this kitchen each utensil has its own place. It is a perfect example of how multiple forms of storage can be combined in a single space, such as shelves of various sizes, cabinets and compartmentalized units.

0437

0438

0439

0440

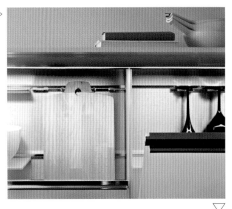

0441 Elegant and practical, each of this kitchen's details is designed to keep kitchenware in order. Having some drawers just below the stovetop can be a practical solution for keeping all your kitchen needs at hand.

0442 Tivalí, designed by Dante Bonuccelli, is built into the framework of the room. The folding doors collapse into the surrounding walls to leave the working area open. The inner surfaces are made of stainless steel, while the doors are made of white lacquer with a glossy finish.

0443 Tivalí also includes a set of matching doors, such as those for the fridge and the cabinets that have adjustable shelves and drawers. This well-planned homogeneity, together with the glossy finish of the surfaces, provides the kitchen with a minimalist aesthetic.

0444 For avant-garde design, the starting point is order: the optimal organization of this Mobalco model takes into consideration the kitchen equipment and tools necessary for every culinary endeavor.

0445 In this kitchen inspired by the architecture of Le Corbusier, recycling is easier than ever. Some rectangular buckets, made to the measure of their drawers, conveniently allow for the separation of waste. This is what it is all about: making life easier for people with every little detail.

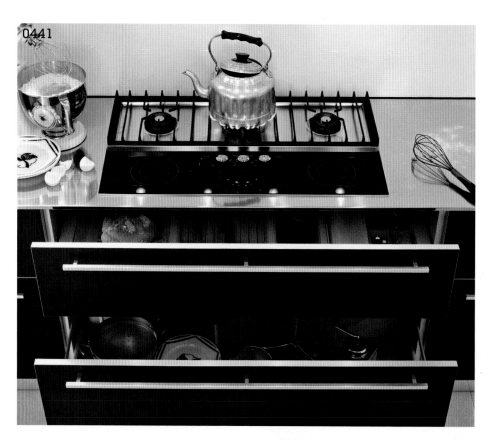

0441

0442

0443

0444

0445

0446

0447

0448

0449

0450

0451

0446 Mobalco's Organica is a design that is both environmentally friendly and constructed with superior-quality materials. The distribution of its appliances across a wide kitchen creates distinct areas and allows for multiple users to perform tasks simultaneously.

0447 Wall-mounted cabinets with doors that open vertically are both sensible and stylish. They maximize your storage space above the counter and add a subtle, modern touch to the room's design.

0448 Would you like to be able to hide or display the contents of your kitchen cabinets according to the occasion? This system of adjustable shelf coverings allows both options. The contents become more decorative when the cover is lowered and they are on display; lifting the cover, on the other hand, convieniently conceals the contents.

0449 In order to create a more refined, elegant and minimalist kitchen, it helps not to have superfluous items in view. Installing a compartment like this can help to keep utensils in an orderly manner and achieve a zen kitchen.

0450 If your kitchen is small, it is not impossible to create a minimalist atmosphere. Choosing appliances on a smaller scale allows you to save space, and well-ordered cabinets can do wonders for maximizing limited storage space.

0451 These American walnut doors hide more than they seem. To take advantage of a corner space, a swiveling cabinet has been installed that illustrates Charles Eames' phrase, who this kitchen is inspired by: "The details are not details. The details are the design."

0452 This island is made up of two areas differentiated by function: the cooking area, crowned by the range hood, and the countertop, which is both a food preparation surface and bar. A pale gray tone extends the length of the island, visually uniting the two areas.

0453 A simple way to create a breakfast bar is to place a raised countertop with a pair of stools on one end of an island. This elevated surface is ideal for quick meals and transitions the kitchen into the dining room.

0454 Although this island is diminutive and its functions may seem limited, one end can easily be set up as a breakfast bar. In small kitchens, islands help to make the most of all available space and can also offer an improvised office when we need it.

0455 One way to enhance the functionality of an island is to integrate kitchen appliances into it. It is likely that gas and electricity will need to be installed, so it is wise to rely on the help of a professional.

0452

0453

0454

0455

0456 In a spacious kitchen, a large island can be divided into working areas (sink, cooking surface and countertop, for example) to allow various people to use it at the same time. In this way, the island is converted into an accessible and comfortable place in which to gather and prepare meals.

0457 This model by G.One is functional and formal in its simpicity. The island's shape, a Schiffini design, creates an uninterrupted surface that widens in order to accommodate a small dining area.

0458 An island is just a piece of furniture in the middle of a kitchen, but given its versatility, it is one of the kitchen's most used spaces. This island illustrates how we can take full advantage of this piece of furniture by adding compartments, working areas and a good countertop on which to enjoy food.

0456

0457

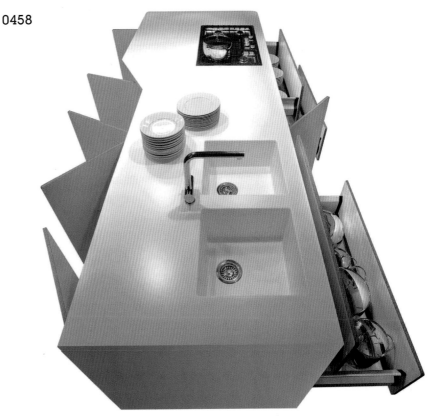

0458

0459

0460

0461

0462

0459 The kitchen island does not necessarily have to match the rest of the kitchen's cabinetry. It is a focal point in its own right and so it makes perfect sense to have an island that stands out in shape, color and surface material.

0460 Why not convert an island into the kitchen's center of attention? Instead of coating it with light colors to reduce its visual weight, we can use dark and heavy materials so that it stands out. Covered with supplies of different shapes and colors, it becomes an extraordinary storage piece.

0461 Positioned between the open kitchen and the dining room, this tall table can also function as an island. Accompanied by three pairs of stools, it is a place to gather for a meal. Used as a surface for storing kitchenware or for preparing meals, however, it is a functional and elegant island.

0462 The Vivo chimney, from the MCZ Brand, enhances the rustic yet sophisticated mood created by this dark island. Its glossy surface reflects the flames from the fireplace, providing a much-needed refuge from the chaos of daily life.

0463

0464

0465

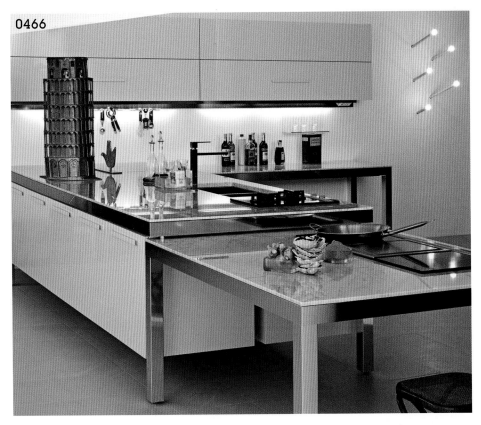

0466

0467

0468

0463 Even though this is a kitchen, the island has a distinct office or dining room table feel to it. This elegant piece of furniture transforms the room's atmosphere and gives it a new meaning. It is certainly the most dominant feature in the room.

0464 The generous size of this Aero island, by Mobalco, is supported by small, metal legs. As its name indicates, it almost appears to float. Rosewood is used in both the island and the cabinet doors, unifying the overall space and giving it elegance.

0465 To get the most out of an island, drawers, shelves and cabinets can be installed. In this way, you gain storage space and you have everything necessary for eating and cooking together in the same space.

0466 This L-shaped countertop is made up of different units and levels that help divide the space according to function. The modern lighting, sink fixtures and accessories complete the look of this sleek and minimalist kitchen.

0467 An island's countertop must be suitable for a variety of uses, so it helps if its surface is durable. In this case, however, a more aesthetic than functional style has been chosen: although the wood is delicate, it gives the island a modern and timeless touch.

0468 These two intersecting islands are made of different materials: Calacatta marble and wood. When combined, the islands provide four very different areas: the food preparation area, the cooking area, the dining area and a multipurpose surface.

0469

0470

0471

0472

0473

CHOICE BLEND
TUDOR
TEA
Earl Grey
Net. Weight 8 oz 227g
Especially blended for and imported by
Ferd. Andersen & CO. Established 1885

0469 It is not difficult to create a welcoming and intimate atmosphere, in which you can sit and enjoy a coffee while you read the newspaper. The combination of the Dandy table and the Party stools, designed by O&G, creates this retreat in the middle of any house.

0470 You can create a breakfast area by mounting a bar against the wall and adding a pair of barstools. The optimum depth of a bar is 18 inches (45 cm), and its height oscillates between 35 and 41 inches (90-105 cm). The length will depend on the space available: at 59 inches (1.5 m), two adults can fit comfortably.

0471 The O&G Ping Pong console table can be placed in any corner of the house to create an intimate and versatile atmosphere. Discrete and functional, it creates the perfect place both to work and to share an informal meal. You can combine the table with Relax foldable chairs, designed by O&G.

0472 If you have an island available, you can use one of its ends as a breakfast bar. Some placemats and barstools are all that you need to turn one section of the island into a dining space.

0473 Removed from the clamor of the kitchen, this table placed by a hallway wall offers a calm refuge in a space we would not expect to find one. It also demonstrates that, when referring to what is known as a "breakfast bar," bigger does not necessarily mean better.

0474 In this house, the dining room is found in the kitchen. A small wooden table and a pair of chairs located in one end of the room are a practical solution for making the absolute most of the kitchen space and having at hand everything necessary to set the table.

0475 If you have a kitchen that opens into a dining room, one option is to place a table between the two spaces. Small and discrete, this table is in harmony with the other furnishings in the room and effectively separates the two spaces.

0474

0475

0476 The Bridge kitchen countertop by Armani/Dada has grey oak finishes, and stainless steel and waterproof technical fabric covered with glass plaques that emphasize the room's minimalist and functional design.

0477 To counteract the birchwood's warm finish, a very thin white acid glass countertop can be set up. Although the thick surfaces transmit modernity, thin countertops are more economical.

0478 Black and white are at opposite ends of the color spectrum but work very well together. This contrast of colors gives the kitchen elegance. The space's central piece, the countertop, is in grey, the palette's intermediate color.

0479 Wooden countertops are beautiful and natural, but the porous nature of wood is problematic; it is a delicate material, easily stained and scratched. The coutertops are available in a wide range of colors and can offer a modern or rustic appearance.

0480 Stainless steel countertops, frequently used in restaurants, are resistant to acids and heat and are very hygienic. They are ideal for giving a modern, functional atmosphere to a kitchen; the only inconvenience is their high price.

0476

0477

0478

0479

0480

0481

0482

0483

0484

0481 The rustic atmosphere of this kitchen is provided by the wood and stone walls and floors. The countertop in stainless steel balances the effect by providing space and functionality. Stainless steel is easy to clean but scratches easily.

0482 This office design displays an interesting idea: two storage areas sunk into the countertop so that spices and dressings can always be available.

0483 Porphyry is a resistant non-slippery material, long-lasting and cheap to maintain. Beautiful, elegant and sober, this brushed brown porphyry countertop is 3 inches (8 cm) thick and matches perfectly with César Yara's personality (the designer of this kitchen).

0484 This is a Laminam ceramic slate countertop. Thin and light, it is only 0.3 inches (7 mm) thick and is created by layering fiberglass between two 0.1-inch (3 mm) sheets of slate. Its dark and somewhat dull color contrasts well with the cupboards' vibrant red.

0485 In a small space like this, the countertop can double as a breakfast bar. Remember that the depth must be a minimum of 12 inches (30 cm) to be comfortable for users. If the ceiling is high enough, you can place a shelf above the space in order to provide more storage.

0486 A food hatch with a pocket door prevents food smells from wafting into the dining room. By closing the door, you can also define two separate spaces.

0487 Exactly the same color as the kitchen and living room, this hatch connects both spaces visually and lets light and air circulate. Furthermore, the plant and mirror placed at both ends of the food hatch turn it into the heart of the room.

0488 Installing a food hatch can be as simple as placing a piece of furniture in front of a door. It also allows for strategic placement of dishes when serving food.

0489 In this kitchen, the wall opening is decorative rather than practial: the kitchen is presented as a picture, framed by the opening. And the shelf is a convenient place to add small details that give a touch of color to a room in which white dominates.

0490

0491

0493

0492

0494

0490 An extractor hood is an important electrical appliance since it eliminates smoke, smells and heat produced when cooking. For a glass-ceramic hob it is recommended that hoods are placed 22 inches (55 cm) from the cooktop, covering the area completely.

0491 An elegant wine chiller is found in the Bridge kitchen. It is closed by a plaited textured glass pocket door with borders and anodized aluminum handles. The inside, like the structure, has sucupira wood laminates.

0492 Having a TV monitor in the kitchen can be handy; you can prepare a meal while following the instructions from your favorite cooking show! A ceiling-mounted TV screen is practical since it does not take up valuable counter space.

0493 Stainless steel appliances are a popular choice and can be paired with any color scheme. Bold or dark colors are not a problem since stainless steel reflects light.

0494 A built-in microwave and oven on the wall offers advantages: it saves space and lets you keep the kitchen tidier; it makes a feauture of the electrical appliances and draws attention to their decorative appeal.

0495 A shiny stainless steel suspended hood, from the Elica brand, reveals vibrant color on the inside surface: available in turquoise and red, this splash of color contrasts stunningly with the neutrally colored kitchen.

0496 Range hoods don't have to be utilitarian kitchen devices that blend into the background. Elica's Platinum model is a sleek stainless steel model that reflects the design of the cooktop below; together they become the center of this kitchen design.

0497 Elica's Wave model, made of stainless steel, includes halogen atmosphere lighting. It not only lights up the working area but also illuminates the surrounding area.

0498 Compartmentalizing the island helps to organize the working areas: the sink has been separated from the range with a glass panel that gives this area a ping-pong table appearance.

0499

0500

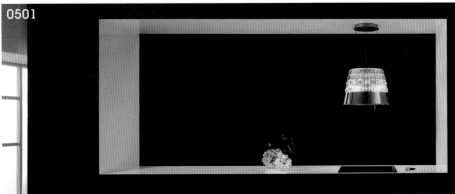

0501

0499 Stainless steel is the favorite material for manufacturing design hoods. It gives an aura of modernity to the kitchen and is highly resistant to corrosion, but it is easily stained with fingerprints and can scratch easily. Therefore, it helps to choose a hood with an anti-scratch system.

0500 This stainless steel and glass wall hood is an elegant example of Cube lighting. Enveloped by the opaque-toned glass, the light gives the kitchen a surreal halo. This Elica design is clean, delicate and ethereal.

0501 Made of stainless steel and glass, this Victoria model gives off sparkles of light that refract and divide into colors. More like a lamp than a hood, it is a technological jewel that inspires our day-to-day life and transcends the principle of mere utility.

0502 Vogue Black Leather combines functionality with the beauty of exclusive materials: stainless steel and black leather. The model, which looks like an architectural piece in miniature, has a particulary high-suction capacity, especially suitable for large kitchens.

0503 Suspended above the kitchen's peninsula, Grace is a white glass and stainless steel hood designed by Elica. The white echoes the peninsula's countertop and contrasts with the vertical surfaces' dark tones.

0502

0503

0504 Elica's Space model is fitted out with the EDS3 system, which allows it to work so silently that it cannot be heard at low speeds. It represents an over 35% reduction to acoustic pollution compared to traditional hoods, and it doesn't reduce the suction capacity.

0505 This hood's height and shape allow an uncommon usage: it takes advantage of the surface as one more storage area. This electric device is suspended as a swing above the kitchen island and offers us more space.

0506 Designed for Elica by David Lewis, the Bogart model presents pure geometric shapes for light to play on. The inclined surface that crosses over the glass hood is the highlight of this special accessory.

0507 The Stone Gallery hood is equipped with LED technology, guaranteeing ideal lighting for the cooking area. Extremely ecological, the LEDs last up to ten times longer than traditional lamps and allows up to 90% savings on electrical energy.

0508 Despite the advantages of glass ceramic hob and induction plates, traditional kitchen lovers still prefer gas. Having the ranges in line is a very practical solution that allows you to cook several dishes at a time.

0509 More than a hood, Elica's Legend model looks like a sculpture suspended in the air. It includes a perimeter suction system and five halogen bulbs. Available in shining stainless steel and glass, this revolutionary circle is absolutely eye-catching.

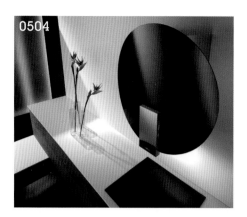

0510

0511

0512

0513

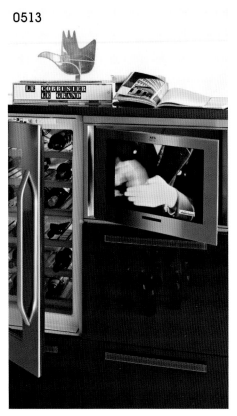

0514

0510 Kora, designed by Tecnocucina, is a kitchen with oak finishes. The electrical devices are disguised by the wood. The cooking and oven areas have the darkest tones, standing out visually and telling us about the inhabitants' tastes.

0511 The Nuvola kitchen, by Dada, presents original electrical devices: a wine cooler, an oven and a fridge with a quick freeze option and refrigerate function. All made with stainless steel, they take advantage of the island's smaller space.

0512 Designed by César Yara, this sink can be hidden beneath the sliding glass white acid countertops. Upon closing, these are fused with the peninsula's countertop, made of the same material, widening the kitchen's working area.

0513 Screens are a ubiquitous part of our lives and this invasion is also reflected in the kitchen. With technological advances, it is possible to set up a television screen on a cupboard door or a microwave door.

0514 In order to choose a fridge and freezer, we have to take into account how many people live in the house. If it is a large family, it is helpful to have these functions separated. If you are looking for a non-conventional kitchen, an option is to hide them in one of the kitchen cupboards.

0515 The taps set up on the wall offer a solution for those sinks that don't include a place to install the taps. This old-fashioned polished brass tap gives the room a retro touch and suits the rural kitchen atmosphere.

0516 If it is a double sink, it is important to set up a revolving tap which rotates 180° and aims the water towards both sinks. This double handle tap model has also got buttons for opening and closing the water flow.

0517 An ecological solution that single-handle taps offer nowadays is called "always open cold." We tend to leave the handle in a central position, which represents a waste of energy; with this solution only cold water comes out when we open the tap.

0518 In a very personal environment, it is worth considering choosing a tap that has a design matching the room's style. It is best not to think about the tap individually but consider it in relation to the rest of the kitchen design.

0519 Removable taps allow the water stream range to increase, and are ideal for washing vegetables, rinsing dinner surfaces, washing the sink or reaching any difficult-to-access area. After using them, we only have to put them back in their original position.

0515

0516

0517

0518

0519

0520

0521

0522

0523

0520 Given the mixing taps' ease of opening, they can almost always be opened to the limit. To avoid this waste of water, a mechanism has been invented to open it in two phases, with an intermediate limit that offers enough flow for habitual uses, which reduces water consumption by 50%.

0521 Given the wide range of kitchen taps available, it is best to consider the way the kitchen will be used. If you cook a lot, install a high pipe tap which is handy for filling large pots and pans.

0522 The stainless steel sink and tap represent an elegant contrast to this butter-colored silk-lacquered kitchen designed by César Yara. The geometrical shapes of the tap enhance the space's tidy and functional nature.

0523 Due to their simplicity and aesthetic appeal, single-handle taps are more and more common. They offer an advantage that we have to consider with regard to double-handle taps: they are a lot more efficient and conserve water.

0524 When choosing the kitchen tap, we have to take into account the house's style. In this space you can see how the tap matches the room's stylistic line: white, rounded and modern, it enhances the kitchen design.

0525 Single- or double-handle taps? That is the first question that we usually formulate when we have to choose a tap. A double-handled tap allows us to adjust the temperature and water flow in the most accurate way, but it is more difficult to set up, because usually it means making three holes in the sink.

0526 Although commercial kitchen taps are manufactured for these kinds of facilities (restaurants, schools, hospitals, hotels, etc.), they can also be used in domestic settings. Although they are more expensive, they are designed to endure daily use and will last longer.

0524

0525

0526

0527

0528

0529

0530

0527 Wood reminds us of nature and is the ideal finish if you want a warm atmosphere. In this rustic-style kitchen, wood has been used for the countertop and shelves as well as in the small details.

0528 A final decorative detail could be a tile frieze along the walls, in a pattern and color that match the rest of the elements, tying everything together nicely.

0529 This Yara kitchen combines the warmth of Yellow Pine Trufa wood (the low cupboard doors) with colder materials like the brown aluminum of the the handles or the countertop and back wall's ceramic Laminam slate.

0530 The 4-inch (10 cm) thick countertop is made of Calacatta marble and leaves the pot and pan drawer edge in sight. This employs a servo-drive system, allowing the drawer to open with a slight pressure from any point on the unit's front.

0531 Bold colors add energy to any room, including kitchens. Kitchens used to be functional spaces as opposed to living rooms which were for socializing. As the line between these uses blurs, colors become more important, making the kitchen more inviting.

0532 If you want to give your kitchen a bar atmosphere, you can paint one of the walls black and fill it with signs and writing related to the space. With this simple idea, the place acquires a livelier character.

0533

0534

0533 This Nuvola kitchen, designed by Luca Meda for Dada, presents an attractive contrast between the cupboard's brilliant white lacquer, the Grigio Carnico marble of the countertops (1.5-inch/4 cm thick) and the sink, electrical appliances and handles' stainless steel.

0534 If you have a kitchen with natural light, stainless steel is a good choice of material for the countertops. It reflects the light and gives off a sparkling and smooth texture. In addition, these qualities make it perfect for a minimalist atmosphere.

0535

0536

0537

0538

0539

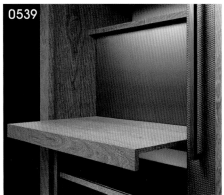

0540

0535 Wood is grained, natural and warm, the opposite of lacquer's smooth, artificial and cold appearance. This kitchen highlights the contrasts and emphasizes the human activities that take place in this room.

0536 The Rational brand's Atmos kitchen is made of cherry tree melamine. This material presents a wide variety of colors and textures; it is resistant and prevents the spread of microorganisms, so it is ideal for aseptic environments.

0537 Mixing materials and textures is not easy, but can provide a colorful and sensitive richness to an environment. The mixture of pale tones enhances light and visual width and gives the space intimate warmth.

0538 The shining lacquered finish gives the kitchen a modern, technological and sophisticated look. In this space, the combination of white and black creates an elegant contrast. To counteract the lacquer's smoothness, you may want to introduce some wooden surfaces, adding a warmth that a purely laquered finish does not have.

0539 In this piece colors and textures are mixed. The fold-out counter's sucupira wood combines with the base and handle's bronze color. In contrast with the wood's grained texture and smooth base, the foldable door displays a plaited texture.

0540 Designed by César Yara, this kitchen shines thanks to the brushed finish that has been given to the countertop and back wall's stainless steel. To achieve this finish they use soft abrasives, which create a reflective and shining effect over the metal.

0541 In this room's lighting, the lighting structure itself is what stands out. A spider ceiling lamp hangs over the central surface and spotlights emerge as though they were its legs, claiming the spotlight as the main decorative objective in the room.

0542 The central table area has to be a welcoming communal center, and light helps to define this atmosphere. The most appropriate type of lighting for this effect is a hanging or ceiling lamp that focuses on the table and creates a halo of intimacy around it.

0543 This kitchen island is lit up by two light bulbs that direct light towards the objects found below and project shadows onto the floor. You have to make sure that the shadows do not fall directly on the work surfaces because they could interfere with the activities taking place on the island.

0544 In this kitchen, a combination of fitted lamps or bull's eyes provides the ambient or general lighting. Strung along the ceiling they feature an exterior wall lamp that controls the light and directs it towards different points in the room.

0545 In the kitchen's working areas we need detailed lighting which gives enough light to enable food preparation. These adjustable wall lamps project light downwards and project sufficient lighting onto the countertop and board.

0546 When placing a ceiling lamp, it is very important to calculate the height at which it is located in order to avoid obstructing sightlines between the diners. Practical and versatile, the adjustable height hanging lamps offer a solution to this problem.

0547 The lighting that this wall lamp produces is mostly decorative: its function is aesthetic rather than practical. Since this is not a working area, it is an appropriate light for emphasizing select details; in the case of this kitchen, it is a plate that we particularly like.

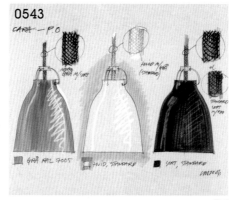

0545

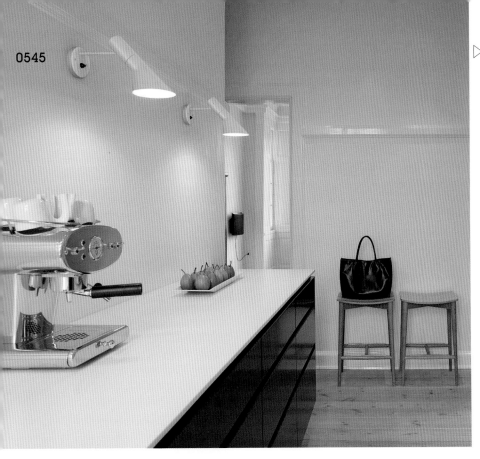

0546

0547

0548

0549

0550

0551

0552

0554

0556

0553

0555

0548 It is not only the choice and arrangement of furniture that matters in a kitchen design: the practical nature of the electrical appliances needs to be considered, and the utensils should be carefully chosen since they are often left in sight and capture attention more than countertops and cupboards.

0549 It is not difficult to give a kitchen a vintage look. It is often enough to choose a functional object that has some outstanding feature. In this case, it is a set of antique weigh scales that gives the room a retro focus.

0550 A drawer is not the only storage place for cutlery. Zinc buckets represent an original way of storing it in plain sight. This detail shows how changing up what we are accustomed to can become a decorative idea.

0551 The candles form part of the decorative lighting so, more than a source of light, they are used for aesthetic value. The three lively colored and hindu-inspired lanterns that we find in the thin shelf above the sink give the kitchen an oriental atmosphere.

0552 This wine lover's kitchen shows how the combination of elements can be played with to create a unique and harmonious atmosphere that reflects personal tastes. The wine labels combine beautifully with the tea towels.

0553 In this kitchen details are paramount: the hanger, the tablemat, the wicker drawer, the glass jar for the rice. Ultimately it is the small details that convert a room into a personal space and tell us about the people that live there.

0554 The kitchen is an ideal place in which to install a slate wall. Amusing and useful at the same time, both children and adults can enjoy its whimsy. It can be used for drawing, writing inspiring verses or noting the most prosaic shopping list.

0555 What hanger can be more appropriate for the kitchen than one in which the hooks are the cutlery? It may be a small thing, but it's a detail that helps to define the room's essence and highlight the kitchen's identity.

0556 This kitchen sink is organized in a rational way: the sliding door surfaces allow for draining, storing vegetables and food preparation. It is an example of how small details can unite aesthetics and functionality.

0557 When designing a custom headboard, you can make the most of it by creating alcoves in both sides of the bed and using hollows as decorative shelves. In this room, the headboard and plaster alcoves fuse with the wall, emanating calm because of their uniform white treatment.

0558 A headboard can combine the greatest elegance with maximum versatility. This beautiful piece of wooden furniture, with its cloth stripes that match the cushions, also acts as a headrest and a ledge for functional and decorative objects.

0559 A floor to ceiling curtain made of heavy fabric serves as a divider between the walk-in closet and the bed. Although not a headboard per se, it does mark the head of the bed aesthetically.

0560 A white line extends from the bed's structure and marks out a section of the wall to suggest a headboard. This technique is at once non-traditional and incredibly chic.

0561 Designed by Gino Carollo, the Giotto bed is based on a single line that extends upward to form the headboard. The surface is suspended upon a circular base, which can be fixed or rotating. This aerodynamic and imaginative design bestows a sort of New York atmosphere upon the room.

0562 If you choose a bed whose structure already includes the headboard, make sure that the combination follows the same decorative line as the surroundings. Smooth and dynamic, these rounded shapes look good in any environment.

0563 An original way to tackle the installation of a bed's headboard is with a concrete wall, like this half-height wall with a distinct finish to that of the actual wall, whose ledge is also used as a bedside table.

0564 If you do not have enough space available for placing bedside tables, you can set up a narrow one-piece headboard, made of chipboard or MDF, with a niche on each side that functions as a shelf.

0557

0560

0558

0559

0561

0562

0563

0564

0565 Configured upon rails, the bunk beds, bedside table and small stack of shelves enjoy maximum mobility and give the bedroom a wide possibility of combinations. Also, the rails allow you to stack the beds during the day and optimize room space.

0566 In smaller spaces, using furniture on wheels helps to make the maximum use of available space. In a wide room like this one, the arrangement of the pieces can be changed up at will to accomodate the distinct purposes the room serves at different times throughout the day.

0567 The headboard is not only a practical, essential element of bedroom design, rather it can also serve as the main decorative piece. Consider the atmosphere you want to create and choose one that helps you to transmit it. Installing some matching bedside tables may also enhance the chosen atmosphere.

0568 A simple and sober dark wooden structure constitutes a functional and sophisticated headboard. This material, of elegant and traditional appearance, combines with any type of decoration and does not require great maintenance.

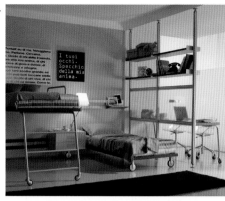

0569

0570

0571

0572

0569 This bedroom plays with the combination of friezes in multiple forms. The wall, made of decorative tiles, plays with the bedspread, and the wooden headboard draws another frieze on the ceramic wall with its shape. This jumbled design gives the room a rococo look.

0570 If the bedroom wall is an incredible design feature unto itself, if it has some qualities that give the space personality, it is not necessary to attach a headboard. Simply allow the wall to convey its full impact.

0571 This smooth, spongy quilted headboard seems to invite you to dream. The depth of the dark blue color and blandness of its texture conveys ultimate relaxation.

0572 Even though headboards serve a functional purpose (protecting the head and maintaining the bedclothes in place), often they have a purely decorative role. An original and easy way to create a headboard is to install a curtain bar and hang cushions on it.

0573 Some bedrooms benefit from a very utilitarian, simple approach to headboard design, such as this plain white rectangle configuration.

0574 In small bedrooms, the headboard's thickness can pose a problem. Consider sourcing and sizing a section of thin wood that will give a classy and warm touch, without having to take up much space.

0575 A practical solution for resolving the headboard issue is to place a lengthy cushion against a wooden rail. The cushion cover can be switched seasonally or whenever a new look is desired.

0576 If you want to give a cheerful and youthful appearance to a bedroom, decorate the headboard in a playful pattern. A practical solution is to place adhesive vinyls, but you can also choose a ready-patterned headboard.

0577 A neutral colored upholstered headboard goes very well with the other furniture and, more importantly, with any style. It is not only the perfect choice if you want to create a classic atmosphere with a distinguished mark, but also for obtaining a chic and sophisticated atmosphere.

0573

0574

0575

0576

0577

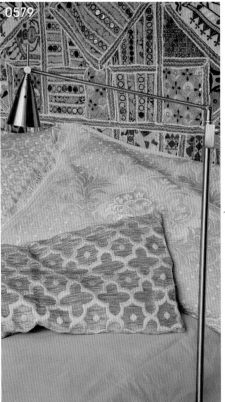

0578 Developed by Cia International in collaboration with the designer Giuseppe Viganò, this bed displays a headboard formed by three colored stripes that match the bedclothes. A vivid colored headrest will transmit energy and dynamism, and is ideal for a children's bedroom.

0579 If you want to crown your bed with a headboard but you do not have many resources available, a practical and cheap solution is to place a tapestry on the wall. An oriental-style patchwork, for example, will give life and color to the atmosphere and will fill you with energy when you get up.

0580 Installed in one of the rooms of the prestigious Hilton Athens, this COCO-MAT bed has an innovative ergonomic base. Hand-made and constructed of beech wood slats and rubber strips, it offers an isometric support, maximum elasticity and perfect ventilation.

0581 Even though it is more conventional, there is no need to place the bed's headboard in contact with a wall. A bed placed in the center of the room leaves the walls free for elements such as stacks of shelves, helping to optimize the space and bringing a surprising and inspiring touch to the bedroom.

0582 Headboard design today is trending toward taller and taller, but consider a modest, proportional look such as in this space.

0583 In cases where the bed is placed against a feature wall clad in vibrant wallpaper, consider forgoing an actual headboard.

0584 Instead of one headboard, it seems that there are three. The bed's structure, elevated upon the wall, stands out above the wooden headboard, which is framed by the white wall in turn. This triple set of textures and contrasts gives the room a Russian doll effect.

0581

0582

0583

0584

0585

0586

0587

0585 In order to create a minimalist atmosphere, opt for a simple headboard: light, thin, white and, if possible, of low height. Sometimes the simplest bedroom is the ideal one.

0586 To create an appropriate resting atmosphere, it is helpful to use natural materials (especially for the bed and headboard) and to situate electronic devices away from the bed.

0587 If you have a house with an attic, what could be better than using it as a bedroom? In this case, consider placing the bed backing on to the rest of the house and build a small wall that separates the two spaces. The same medium height wall will function as a headboard.

0588 Various theories exist about which direction the bed should face in order to facilitate rest. Here, the bed is situated between the window and the mirror, to make best use of natural light.

0589 This colonial style bed is a Bertelé design. Constructed of ebony and forged iron (used in the columns and the canopy), this piece recalls the elegance of the colonial era and becomes the focal point of the room.

0590 In the case of building a concrete headboard or taking advantage of a master beam as a headrest, there is no reason to limit it to covering the width of the bed; it can extend along the entire wall. In this way, a feeling of dynamism and functionality is obtained.

0591 Honey, designed by Arik Levy, is a bed composed of one thin line, upholstered with fabric or with leather. For the designer, the challenge was to create a bed of minimal design, conformable to different spaces, easy to install and of simple, modern and elegant proportions.

0588

0589

0590

0591

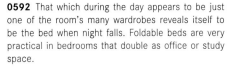

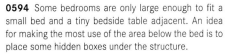

0592 That which during the day appears to be just one of the room's many wardrobes reveals itself to be the bed when night falls. Foldable beds are very practical in bedrooms that double as office or study space.

0593 Choose a simple, utilitarian headboard such as this plain white shelf when a busy, eclectic approach is taken with the rest of the bedroom decoration.

0594 Some bedrooms are only large enough to fit a small bed and a tiny bedside table adjacent. An idea for making the most use of the area below the bed is to place some hidden boxes under the structure.

0595 Installing the bed below the window is an ideal decision for a room completely dedicated to rest. In this way, the morning light lets you read in bed without having to get up. By night, a lovely fireplace provides the heat and lighting that by day is provided by the window.

0596 Designed by Stefano Gallizioli, the Elysee Classic bed structure is upholstered with a removable fabric cover. The sumptuous texture and curved lines create a welcoming atmosphere in the bedroom.

0597 A velvet touch in the bedroom gives it a stroke of sophistication. Smooth in texture and appearance, it expresses warmth and exudes elegance. Use this material on the headboard to achieve a luxurious environment.

0598 Renoir, a bed by Noir, is completely upholstered in smooth hide. The small legs can be made of chromed or gilded steel. Its smooth shapes and its proximity to the floor invite lying down and enjoying its comfort.

0599 Zanotta's Caracalla bed boasts brushed steel legs. The padded headboard and base are upholstered with polyurethane or polyester fibers. The leather cover is non-removable.

0600 The most characteristic aspect of this bed by Noir is its similarity to a chaise longue. Its white-ice tone is in keeping with the rest of the room, and its gigantic rounded chaise longue structure gives the room a French salon look.

0601 White leather for a bed? Why not? In the bedroom, white serves to convey relaxation and enhance rest, making it a logical choice. The curvy design enhances the calming effect.

0597

0598

0599

0600

0601

0602

0603

0604

0605

0606

0607

0602 A bench at the foot of the bed offers both a place to sit and storage for linen. It also adds a special touch to the bedroom's look. Both the Flint bed and the bench are designed by Rodolfo Dordoni for Minotti.

0603 This design forgoes a headboard in favor of including a small laptop desk adjacent to the bed, in a practical and aesthetically pleasing manner.

0604 Although it is not essential, a chair can be of great use in the bedroom. It can be used to create a reading area or can make for an improvised nightstand.

0605 More than just a decorative accent, a bench at the foot of the bed provides for seating and storage. Available in any style and finish, whether upholstered or wooden, it can help finish off your bedroom's look.

0606 Any corner of the room can be used as a work area. The space created by this glass table with eye-catching legs is complemented by a shelf and a table lamp to provide a comfortable work environment.

0607 The small desk in this bedroom could easily be transformed into a dressing table if a beautiful mirror were to be placed above it.

0608 Given their diminuitive size, nightstands are the ideal piece for adding a touch of color to the room. Before choosing a color, analyze the room's palette and consider what tone can complement and emphasize the dominant range.

0609 This small antique style cupboard has greater versatility than the typical bedside table. The piece boasts a spacious interior, and its surface is the ideal place on which to place a reading lamp and some books.

0610 Creating a bedside table from antique style wooden boxes is not only an ecological solution, it also gives the room an original touch. The boxes can stack up until they achieve the desired height, and they can be painted and decorated. The result is eclectic chic at its best.

0611 In some cases, the bed's own structure has a built-in bedside table on each side. This option represents a saving of space and homogenizes the decoration, but, on the other hand, it does not allow the small table to be the contrast that enriches the room's style.

0612 Through the paint effects, moldings and ornamental details of the matching headboard and side table a maritime theme is created. This theme is enhanced by many of the room's accessories.

0613 If the bedroom is classically styled, opt for a traditional bedside table design. In addition to presenting an aesthetic complement to the room, its shelves add storage capacity.

0614 A simple white cube, a sort of dice whose numbers are missing, can function perfectly as a bedside table in a chic environment. In this bedroom, the geometric shapes help acheive the desired sophistication.

0615 Bedside tables can be the unexpected detail with which to create an original atmosphere, because just about any object with a flat surface can be used.

0608

0609

0610

0611

0612

0613

0614

0615

0616 To take advantage of the space below the window, you can position a narrow chest of drawers. It is a way of distributing storage areas to lighten the wardrobe's content and to keep frequently needed items at hand.

0617 In this warm bedroom, a wooden chest with grilled doors substitutes as a bedside table, combining multiple uses into one beautiful, practical piece.

0618 Here two stacked suitcases have been used as a sort of bedside table. They display patterns that cheer the room up and offer two useful spaces: the interiors and the top surface. It is an original idea that helps to settle the problem of selecting side tables for low-to-the-ground beds.

0619 In addition to being decorative and functional for a bedroom, a chest of drawers is at much at home in the dining room, living room or kitchen, so that it could be used in a different room in the future, once a change in style is desired.

0620 A piece of furniture with a multitude of drawers lets space be compartmentalized and contents organized in a simple way. This industrial looking chest of drawers emphasizes space division through the use of different colors for the drawers.

0621 When a bedroom contains multiple elements that each have a distinct personality, with multiple textures and styles, make sure to view a prospective piece, such as this side table, in situ before finalizing the purchase, to ensure the elements cohere well.

0622 Add some wheels to any furniture and you will get maximum versatility. Bedside tables with wheels are extremely practical: you can move them closer to the bed in order to reach something or to clean easily underneath.

0623 In a minimalist space, consider including a low, light-colored wooden table with geometric lines. The grained texture provides a nature-inspired element in the heart of the room.

0616

0617

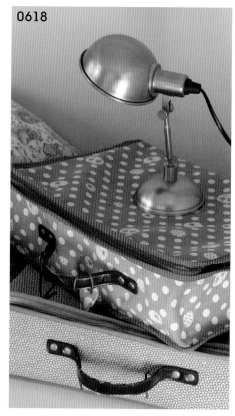

0618

0619

0620

0621

0622

0623

0624 If you don't mind renouncing the functionality of a shelved bedside table for the sake of an artistic statement in your bedroom, a surprising idea is to substitute it with a dramatic piece of art, such as this sculpture. And if the upper surface is flat as in this example, you can at least place a lamp upon it.

0625 If the area is so reduced that there is no room for placing a table on each side of the bed, there are several objects that can exercise a similar function. A small stool, for example, allows for basic objects on its surface.

0626 Wood conveys warmth, a very appropriate quality for a bedroom. Any furniture can be made of wood: the bed's structure, the bedside table, even the lamp! Organic and pleasant, this material will help to create a welcoming atmosphere in which to give oneself over to sleep.

0624

0625

0626

0627

0628

0629

0630

0627 If you like leaving things in view, you can consider substituting the typical bedside table for a long shelf. The total storage space will be less than that of a piece of furniture with drawers or various shelves, but keeping only the basic items will be sufficient and these will function as decorative elements.

0628 A small table slightly taller than the bed is of the appropriate height for placing a reading lamp that allows you to read comfortably.

0629 To protect a wooden table top from scratches and stains, an option is to place a glass laminate upon the table top. In this way you will be able to leave a glass of water on the bedside table without worrying about it damaging the material.

0630 If you have no storage problems, you can consider the option of placing a decorative rather than functional bedside table. This small and slender table top with a bureau style is the ideal surface on which to place elements that give the room life.

0631

0632

0633

0634

0635

0636

0637

0631 Even though reaching its surface from the bed is nearly impossible, a column of various drawers means a functional and versatile way of taking advantage of the space.

0632 One of the bedroom's main furnishings, the bedside table, becomes your ally for managing to give the atmosphere a determined style. In this case, the small vintage table enhances the room's welcoming and intimate environment.

0633 This cream colored piece of furniture without handles creates a space with a classic look, turning a simple chest into a sort of dreamy dressing table when combined with the vintage mirror.

0634 There are pieces of furniture that tred the line between table and chair, between shelf and sculpture. Versatile and apt for any space, they can exercise infinite functions. If we place them in a bedroom, they can be used as a decorative and mobile bedside table.

0635 Designed by Bertelé Mobili, this chest of drawers is handpainted and boasts pearl handles. Inspired by the 18th-century Venetian style, this work of art is appropriate for highlighting an environment's refined character.

0636 The Harvey chest of drawers has a dark brown wooden base, drawers with a shining lacquered finish and sophisticated black nickel details. Designed by Rudolph Dordoni for Minotti, its volume evokes Scandinavian chests of drawers from the 1970s.

0637 The pouf is an ideal accessory for a low bed or futon. In addition to being mobile and looking good in any room, if you place it at the side of the futon it can be used as a bedside table. Also, this comfortable seat enhances the elegant style of the bedroom's Asian look.

0638 In addition to making good use of space, an advantage of a pull-out wardrobe is comfort. The fact that the wardrobe, including its bars, shelves and other storage systems, can be pulled out facilitates the organization of the contents and provides easy access.

0639 Relatively little space is needed to include a dressing room. Between a wooden door and some opaque glass windows, a narrow area is hidden while including many storage options. Besides facilitating the arrangement of clothes, this area is wide enough to get dressed in.

0640 If the closet's interior is critical, the outside is no less important. The doors are the ideal surface to give the bedroom a decorative touch, or, as in this case, a youthful look. Apply an adhesive vinyl to change the appearance of an otherwise neutral closet.

0641 Designed by Besana, the Domino wardrobe owes its name to its upholstered black leather doors that look like domino pieces. Attractive and playful, this voluminous wardrobe has sliding doors.

0642 Before choosing a wardrobe, there is a decision you have to make. Do you want it with or without doors? If the content needs heavy organization, the best option is the doorless wardrobe, even though it has a disadvantage: dust. The visual effect of a doorless wardrobe is, however, stunning.

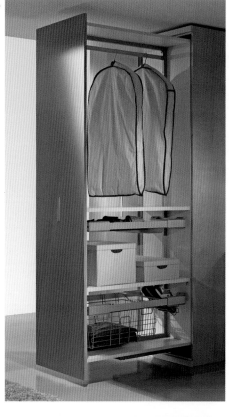

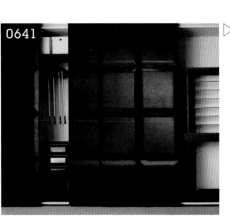

0642

0643

0644

0645

0646

0647

0648

0649

0650

0643 If you only have one wardrobe, its inner distribution needs to be calculated with precision and provide for different types of storage. You will need vertical areas for hanging garments like trousers and dresses, and horizontal spaces like shelves or drawers, in order to store clothes that can be folded.

0644 In order to be able to change the arrangement according to varying needs over time, adjustable wardrobe shelves are recommended. Another aspect you need to take into account when setting up the shelves is the kind of garments you are going to store on these shelves for better organization.

0645 One of the most important qualities in a wardrobe is its versatility. This sideboard by Cia International is a good example of functionality both for its structure and its organization. Symmetrical and easily movable, it is adapted to any corner of the bedroom.

0646 Designed by Jesse, the original Plurimo wardrobe suits a variety of contemporary lifestyles. With a composite versatility that ensures maximum flexibility, the Breeze doors are made of lacquered brushed pinewood.

0647 The Flou wardrobe presents six options of polished glass doors with bronze printing, an elegant and tasteful addition to any contemporary bedroom.

0648 Storage, designed by Piero Lissoni in collaboration with Porro, is a modular system that allows for the display of stored items. Its beautiful design dresses up a room.

0649 The most important item in a bedroom is the bed, and so we need to prevent the wardrobe from usurping its prominence. These discrete doors, although tastefully decorative, hide the storage area without attracting undue attention.

0650 The Dossier DC290M wardrobe's doors, designed by Pinuccio Borgonovo for Former, feature an interesting system of movement: they fold, pivot and finally slide back, offering complete access to the interior.

0651 These spotlights that hang from the ceiling like golden bells demonstrate that often the function of a lamp is not simply to light up a room, but also to contribute to the creation of the desired ambiance. The matt golden finish and the way the fixture emits light add to this room's décor.

0652 During the night, this floor lamp emits full spectrum lighting, which is known as the type of lighting that best mimics the natural qualities of daylight.

0653 General lighting is insufficient for carrying out some activities in the bedroom. It is necessary to set up other light sources to reinforce ambient lighting and to be able to read comfortably.

0654 To read in bed, lighting must not be glaring. It should not cast shadows on the book either. A lamp with a diffuser on the bedside table is the best option because it provides good reading lighting.

0655 The EC 400 table lamp consists of a thin copper body that oscillates above a square nickel base. A single 1-watt LED diode emits a diffused beam over a fairly wide area. The lamp was designed by Enzo Catellani design for Catellani &Smith.

0656 This wall-mounted swing-arm light fixture is absolutely ideal for bedroom lighting. This design is extremely versatile and since it is wall-mounted, the bedside table is clear for other items.

0657 In this bedroom with black walls, the common nightstand lamp has been replaced with a decorative hanging light fixture. It provides enough lighting for the bed area, and since it does not produce any glare, it makes for the perfect reading lamp.

0658 On this low bedside table, the lamp emits indirect and smooth lighting to promote relaxation. Its minimalist design fits nicely next to a decorative African mask. As for colors, the contrast between black and white is softened by the light.

0651

0652

0653

0654

0655
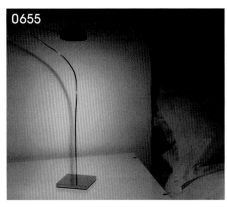

0656

0657

0658

0659 Before you choose bedroom lamps, think about what type of lighting you need and what your priorities are. If reading is not an essential activity in this room, a lamp on the headboard side will mainly be decorative and provide ambient lighting.

0660 Lov is a round shaped wall lamp with a matt white aluminum structure. Designed by Nahtrang Disseny for LEDS-C4, this reading light fixture has two 4-volt and one 3-volt LEDs.

0661 Pleg is a folding wall-mounted lamp made of wood veneer forming a shell. This design from Yonoh studio for LZF Lamps won the Red Dot Design Award 2012.

0662 This Tobias Grau design was baptized with a poetic name: Falling Star. As a shooting star, this wall lamp offers a playful approach to light. Thanks to the LED technology it emits an intense, adjustable, low consumption light.

0663 Designed by R&S Cornelissen for Lucente, Amrak is an aluminum cone shape wall lamp. When directing the light downward, this spotlight draws attention toward the bedside table and highlights its presence inside the bedroom.

0659

0660

0661

0662

0663

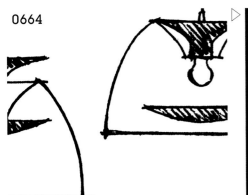

0664

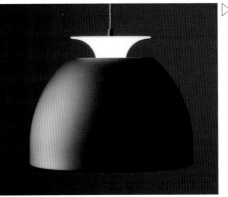

0665

0666

0667

0664 The great advantage of the Bossinha lamp, designed by Fernando Prado for Lumini, is that it allows light intensity to change by moving the shade up and down. Also, this hanging aluminum lamp includes a cover that provides efficient anti-glare control.

0665 Designed by Javier Herrero for LZF Lamps, the Raindrop lamp owes its name to its shape: it looks like a delicate drop of water that creates a warm and inviting atmosphere. Light emanates from a glass globe and shines through the lampshade made of wood veneer.

0666 A bedroom needs two types of lighting: general lighting and task lighting. This convenient wall-mounted LED diode can almost go unnoticed when tucked into its case during the day.

0667 Scar-LED 1FDS by Trizo21 is a subtle wall-mounted lamp that provides sufficient light for reading without disturbing the surroundings. The flexible tube adds a decorative touch to the lamp and allows light to be directed toward the desired direction.

0668

0669

0670

0671

0672

0673

0674

0668 A bright red paper lantern adds a note of color during the day and creates an intimate atmosphere at nighttime.

0669 This chandelier that hangs above the bedside table adds a twist to the otherwise conventional bedroom decoration and turns the bedside table into a focal point. Due to its location, this eye-catching accessory produces an effect of asymmetry and dynamism.

0670 In this bedroom, a floor lamp was chosen to provide lighting to the headboard side as an alternative to a table lamp. The main advantage of this type of lamp is its mobility: independent and versatile, it can move and adapt to the rearrangement of furniture.

0671 If you have space problems, you can resolve the lighting with a wall-mounted swing-arm light fixture. You will be able to set it up either on the wall, headboard, or on a shelf, and you will be able to adjust the light to avoid glare.

0672 This bedroom's dreamlike character can be enhanced by means of lighting. Use fantasy ceiling lamps, with nature and fairy tale inspired shapes to highlight the atmosphere. The shades screen the light and provide the fixture with a magical look.

0673 Even though the main function of a light fixture is, needless to say, to light up a room, its use does not have to end there. One original and at the same time decorative idea, for example, consists of using the leg of the lamp to hang jewelry.

0674 LED reading lights with flexible arms combine design and functionality. With a simple and modern aesthetic, they can be directed to where light is needed. Furthermore, LED lights have a significantly low environmental impact over incandescent lights.

0675 The bedroom has to have an atmosphere that promotes proper rest and relaxation regardless of the style. Consider how different materials can bring balance and texture to your room.

0676 Today there are infinite options of lamp designs available, so try to complement the room's style.

0675

0676

0677 Play with bold colors against neutral shades to make the bed the focal point in the bedroom. The strong contrast produces a dynamic effect that does not necessarily conflict with the desired restful atmosphere.

0678 Matching pillows is recommended to achieve a clean look. The turquoise pillow and the stripped blue, brown and gold stand out from the white bedspread and bring an elegant feel to the room.

0679 There are designs that make a favorite accessory out of pillows. These items have the capacity to soften a room: here the pattern, pale colors and soft textures combile to create a feminine and romantic style.

0680 To achieve this artful, inspiring look, try to combine colors and textures in a unique way: the smoothness of the velvet contrasts with the saturation of the colors.

0681 Linen offers the flexibility that furniture cannot provide. Experiment with your favorite colors! You can always go back to a more neutral look, but you don't want to miss the chance to explore and create something new.

0682 If you want to personalize children's rooms so that they have a more playful look, be creative with the pillows. Even though they are white, the shapes and the stitching are original.

0677

0679

0678

0680

0681

0682

0683 Cushions can change a room's character completely. By combining colors and textures you can achieve a distinct atmosphere, reflecting your true personality.

0684 In designing a color scheme, you may want to start with the color on the wall as the main color and play with bedding to bring in accent colors.

0685 The easiest way to give your bedroom a new look is to change the bedding. It is an economical and practical change, but its effect is very noticeable. With a simple color and pattern variation, the bedroom will look completely different.

0686 If your bedspread has a particularly busy, colorful pattern and unusual texture, such as this example, consider choosing a more subdued, neutral color for the walls.

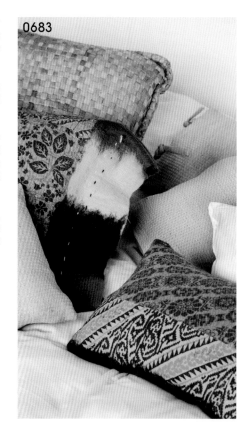
0683

0684

0685

0686

0687

0688

0689

0690

0687 Ambrosia is a collection of metallic fabric tones: silver, bronze, and rust. Designed by Gancedo, the elegant palette of colors and the metallic singular effect give the bedroom a sophisticated look.

0688 In this bed, texture and colors combine to transmit a welcoming atmosphere and an aura of intimacy throughout the bedroom. Textiles including linen and cotton in warm colors make the bed a place of rest, while the calligraphic typography completes the composition.

0689 If you want a bed that awakens tactile sensations, concentrate on textures. The woven pattern on the cushion and the thick linen bedspread and headboard help acheive this tactile feature.

0690 Another decorative advantage that linen offers is the possibility of adapting to seasonal changes. Fall and winter call for deep earthy colors and heavy weaves, while spring and summer call for cool shades and lighter fabrics.

0691 The Jaipur collection by Gancedo is a reinterpretation of the "toile de Jouy." This pattern features landscapes and figures on a soft-colored background.

0692 In order to create a homogenous décor, stick to the same range of colors used on the walls and curtains. Use similar shades for the headboard, the bedspread and the pillows.

0693 To give the bedroom a unique character, you can use a pattern that imitates an animal skin. Animal prints provide the room with a focal point, while adding an exotic touch.

0691

0692

0693

0694

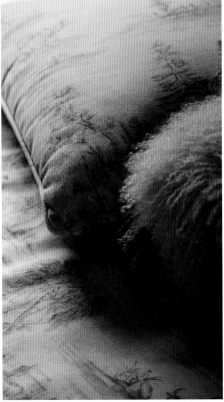

0695

0696

0694 Sometimes we don't need a striking color to enliven a bedroom. The material might just do the trick. A furry pillow, for example, stands out, bringing visual and tactile interest.

0695 The layering of blankets and bedspreads brings the room an attractive combination of textures and tones.

0696 A pillow with different designs on each of its sides is the epitome of versatility. Change it around according to your state of mind to instantly change the décor of your bedroom.

0697

0698

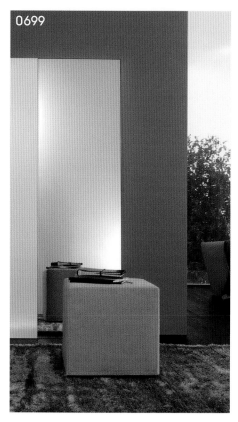

0699

0700

0701

0702

0703

0704

0705

0697 If space allows, a dressing table and desk add flexibility and functionality to the bedroom. The options are infinite!

0698 A bookshelf serves not only as a necessary piece of furniture if you need to include a study area inside the bedroom, rather it can also be used for organizing the room.

0699 Poufs are one of the most versatile furnishings. Soft and springy, they make for comfortable seating. They can also be firm enough to be used as a low table. This elegant pouf is a design of Maximilian Momati for Jesse.

0700 Mirrors are a small space's great allies. The design of this ornate oval mirror seems to be inspired by some fairy tale and gives the room an imaginary look, while it visually expands the space.

0701 You can hang artwork above the headboard to reinforce the bed as the centerpiece in your bedroom.

0702 Wooden crates and boxes can come in handy to create an original side table that also serves for storing books and magazines. Left in their original state or painted, they are a clever and budget-friendly decorating idea.

0703 The dresser does not only fulfill a storage function, it can also be a key item to define a room's style. This black piece of furniture provides plenty of shelf and drawer space and adds an ethnic touch to the bedroom.

0704 If you are looking for a place to hang your collection of scarves or other clothing items, a simple and practical idea is to lean a ladder against a wall. It is without doubt a very creative storage solution.

0705 If you want to install a television in the bedroom, think carefully about the height at which you want it. TV screens come with wall brackets that allow you to mount the device on the wall and be tilted as needed for a better viewing angle.

0706 One of the accessories to take into account for decorating a crib is the cushions. Here the fabric's reddish, orange and yellow colors, combined in this girl's room, overflow with optimism and vitality. With these the generation of a stimulating atmosphere is achieved.

0707 Laser cutting is used to manufacture furniture. This technique is ideal for making personalized items such as this crib. Painted white, it easily integrates in the room, letting the bold decorations stand out.

0708 Wood brings warmth to the littlest ones' rooms. Its natural quality, even in themed designs, generates an ideal atmosphere for rest. Its combination with the headboard's cast iron and the mosquito net recreate a comfortable space with rural atmosphere.

0709 The overuse of white tones can give rise to cold and isolated atmospheres. You have to introduce tones and textures that contrast and break the room's uniformity, for example, the bed's accessories like teddy bears and the colorful striped bedspread.

0706

0707

0708

0709

0710 The orange colored monochromatic decoration confers an active, radiant and expressive character. Bunk beds can be the solution to space problems, since they accommodate children in a single bedroom, optimize the square footage and allow them to have a play area.

0711 This modern and slightly futuristic design includes a bed in the upper part and a desk in the lower part. This is a practical solution for children's bedrooms with little space. The bi-color design in red and black lends a sophisticated touch to the decoration.

0712 The rose color against a neutral tone is common in rooms designed for young girls. Together with the butterfly and fairy designs a calm and comfortable atmosphere is achieved, appropriate for this age bracket. The bed's accessories follow this theme.

0713 This whimsical mosquito net suspended above the bed makes the room into a really original space with a touch of chic. The cute side table matches the bed frame and includes a mobile tray as its tabletop.

0714 Today a wide variety of styles and shapes of nest beds exists: space saving ones, pull along ones, compact ones, ones with drawers, etc. This model includes storage underneath.

0715 This is a nest bed with the mattress base in the upper part and an area with sofas in the lower part. The ladder with drawers at back is another storage solution that takes advantage of the space. The pastel colors give the design vitality and a sense of fun.

0716 If a traditional bed and frame are preferred, it is best to situate it right into the corner of the room, perhaps under a window to take advantage of natural light, in order to save space in the rest of the room for furniture such as a table, chest or bookshelf.

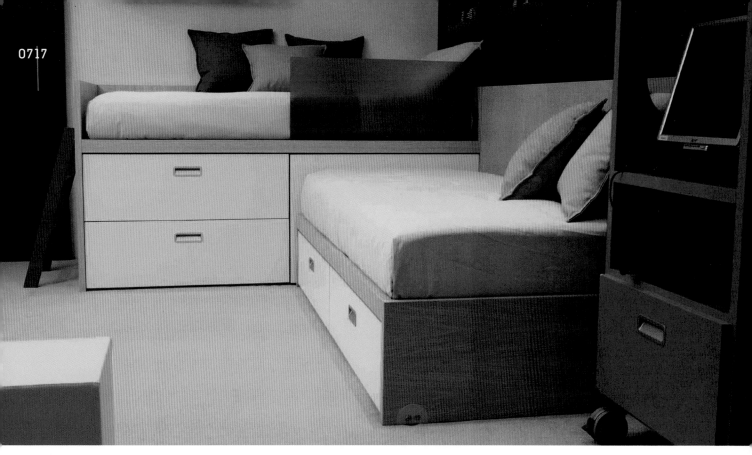

0717

0718

0719

0717 In contrast with complementary colors or in combination with primaries, green bestows a natural feel upon a room. It generates a relaxed atmosphere for children and produces an elegant look. This innovative bed design includes drawers underneath the mattress base, to accomodate extra storage.

0718 The rose color conveys romanticism and is ideal for a vibrant girls' space; this strong tone evokes fun and fantasy. The nest beds joined to the wall are a sure bet, since they include structures with different heights in which chests of drawers and wardrobes have been installed.

0719 The neutral tones of this design give the space great visual span, making it an excellent solution for small children's rooms.

0720 This pleasant piece of furniture designed by P'kolino combines a table and seat and is perfect for children. The design is simple, well balanced and functional, with ample space for paper, books and jigsaw puzzles, echoing the simplicity of the padded seat and storage area below.

0721 Stools are spare furniture that are easy to move and transform. They are an ideal accessory for rooms without a lot of space because they function as a seat or as a footrest. A stool built with different colored and textured fabrics creates an ideal atmosphere for playing and entertainment.

0722 Chests of drawers in children's desks offer the opportunity to give the room a touch of design and color. These pieces of spare furniture are ideal for keeping order, stimulating imagination and having everything at hand.

0723 This unique table and chair set by P'kolino combines fascinating shapes and lines with an overall streamlined look. The addition of a playful rug and fun accessories completes the design.

0724 For this playroom, whimsy and an incredible sense of fun were the inspiration for the unique and child-friendly design. The solid wood pieces combine nicely with the plastic-covered foam pieces, all of which are easy to clean.

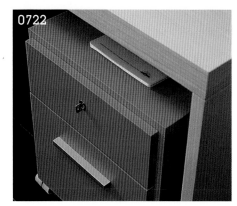

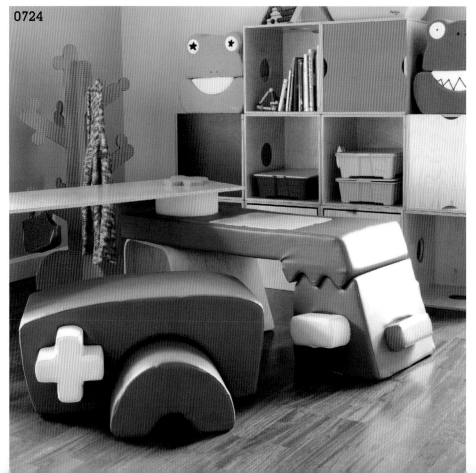

0725

0726

0727

0728

0729

0725 Dearkids produces beautiful custom desks that are perfectly adapted to the necessities of children's rooms. The dynamic and energetic character of the room's design is ideal for lively kids.

0726 A round table is ideal for preventing bumps and scrapes, with its lack of sharp corners. The rainbow striped carpet is perfect for adding a splash of color to this otherwise traditional design.

0727 Curvy, contemporary furnishings in a light wood tone lend a feeling of spaciousness to this simple, modern design.

0728 The pleasant color palette in this room is created through the mixing of plain wood, light yellow and natural green. Note the ample storage space and modern lines.

0729 This unit is constructed of ash wood that features a contrast between the cocoa, rose and fuchsia colors. It maximizes storage space while providing a comfortable and dynamic workspace.

0730 This attractive sliding door wardrobe is equipped with a large storage capacity chest and various drawers located on the inside. The overall effect is a compact and highly functional unit.

0731 Multifunctional furniture is the best ally for decorating a small children's room. The sliding drawers and trunks function as storage elements for keeping games and clothes. They are easy pieces of furniture to transform and situate in any corner.

0732 When the smallest children start getting dressed by themselves, built-in wardrobes with frame and curtain are a very practical option, as long as they are appropriate in height.

0733 Refurbished antique furniture gives a personal touch to any bedroom. The wood's natural and always elegant color is a classic style choice; the pieces of sturdy wood instill an authentic luxury so that the room's occupant feels comfortable.

0734 This wardrobe displays a pleasant tri-color combination that is repeated in the whole room's design. Vibrant color is one of the easiest ways to enliven a room.

0735 This lacquered wardrobe with four large sliding doors, in tones of yellow and orange, creates an interplay of contrasts underlined by horizontal lines. In the interior, the wardrobe is equipped with large capacity drawers and suspended clothes rack hangers. An ideal design for children.

0730

0731

0732

0733

0734

0735

0736 Wicker is characterized by its warmth, being a material of natural origin. Thus wicker baskets are a classic for baby room design, as well as a practical storage element.

0737 Shelves are a highly important element to maintain order. They can also double as decorative elements. In this case, some old treated and refurbished boxes are used as storage for games and books.

0738 These lacquered shelves with foldable doors are an effective resource for children's rooms. This system allows quick use and a perfect place for storing books and toys. In this case, a shade of saffron has been chosen as the ideal color for the space.

0739 The purpose of storage boxes may be utilitarian, but that's no reason to waste their potential as a decorative object. Wood is a resistant and very durable material and it is easy to paint and decorate to the child's taste.

0740 The storage in this nest bed is a great solution to the problem of tight spaces. Generally with nest beds, the storage spaces are located in the lower area, to allow easy access. The blue and green color scheme is soothing and restful.

0741 Dearkids' use of stairs with built-in storage stands out for its practicality and innovation. Elevated bed systems already maximize space by leaving the space underneath open for use, and in this case the additional utility of the piece is just outstanding.

0742 Among the many storage boxes on the market today, these metal ones stand out. They have a retro style and display very diverse colors. The lids can double as trays.

0743 The best solution for taking advantage of an alcove in the wall is the placement of stacks of shelves. The shelves help organize clutter and are useful for placing either toys or books. It is essential that they be placed at an appropriate height for children.

0736

0737

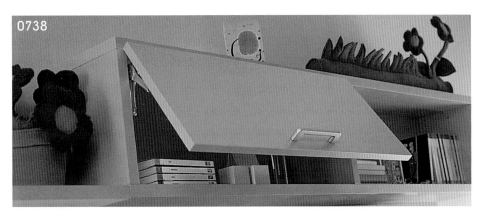

0738

0739

0740

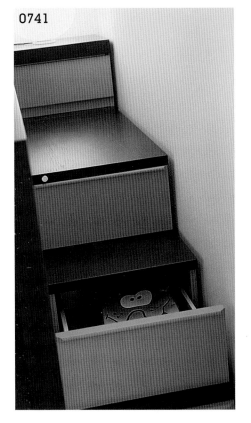

0741

0742

0743

0744 Creative solutions that make tidying the bedroom efficient and fun help encourage children to keep things in their place.

0745 Becoming familiar with the effects that different colors have on our moods will help in deciding what tones are most appropriate for children's rooms. Reds and oranges are inviting, stimulating and cheerful.

0746 Plush toys made of adorable animal shapes are ideal for decorating any room, and they let the smallest children play and stimulate their imagination.

0747 If space allows for a small wooden swing to be installed in a child's room, consider including this whimsical piece, but be sure to have it professionally installed following all safety regulations.

0744

0745

0746

0747

0748

0749

0750

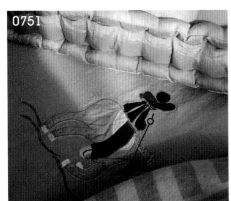

0751

0752

0748 The red and white theme evokes the joyfulness of childhood. Choosing a vibrant color scheme for both the bedspread and accessories is a bold move, but design for children is the time to make fun selections.

0749 In adult bedrooms, an excess of cushions seems too busy and over the top. But in design for children, there's no such thing as too many soft, fun cushions.

0750 Custom made children's cushions delight even the smallest kids. These accessories are useful and decorative, and allow the children to play and let their imaginations fly away with them.

0751 The color blue, in all its extensive chromatic range, transmits calm. It is the color of the infinite, of dreams, and evokes rest. When combined with other colors, such as this embroidered detailing, the effect is stunning.

0752 In this room the combination of the wall's rosy and cream tones, the bedclothes, the cushions and the accessories generate a perfect visual harmony. These colors may be a conventional choice for girls' rooms, but the effect is classic and fun.

0753 Lamps of white colored spherical shapes are a modern choice for any type of children's room. During the day they are very decorative and by night they create an effective atmospheric light. In general, these lamps are made out of polyethylene resin.

0754 Adjustable light fixtures, such as reading lamps, are ideal for placing above a desk. Care has to be taken with materials that are put within children's reach and to avoid the fluorescent tubes. These designs are flexible, functional and very original.

0755 Lanterns provide a fun lighting solution. This type of light, located in strategic points, allows you to attend to the child during the night without disturbing them. These minimalist style designs are easily transportable.

0756 The design of this lamp for desks or games tables emits the perfect amount of light to facilitate stimulation, learning and games.

0753

0754

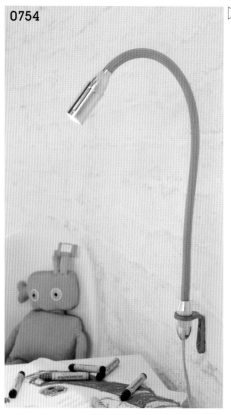

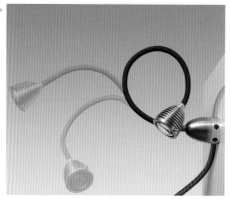

0755

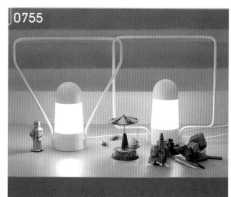

0756

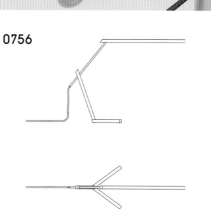

0757

0758

0757 Decorating kids' rooms with self-adhesive vinyl wall decorations brings life, color and imagination. It is an economical solution and takes children to a world of fantasy and fun. Tree and animal designs are the most successful for the décor of children's spaces.

0758 With a simple cord, like a clothes line, you can create a useful solution for hanging photos or artwork, or whatever the child considers most important. You have to take into account that the wall must be monochromatic in order not to overload the decoration.

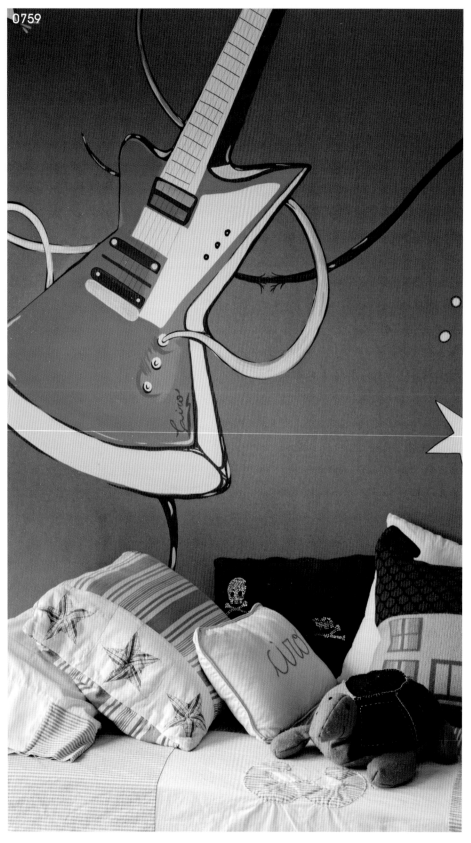

0759

0760

0761

0762

0763

0764

0765

0759 Murals give a very original touch to any children's room, filling them with fantasy and tenderness and allowing the children to give a free rein to their imagination and to their capacity for play. For example, with a guitar and some painted stars we reflect the child's dreamy personality in their surroundings.

0760 Decorative vinyls are very versatile and can often serve an educational purpose as well as decoration, such as a world map.

0761 Wall pegs bring the order and organization necessary in kids' rooms. Displaying pictures above the pegs brings a sense of fun to that corner of the room.

0762 In this case, a short clothes line on the wall is a very original and practical resource for showcasing personal items as a decorative element.

0763 The rustic style of this room is acheived by a simple picture frame and stack of shelves in combination with the room's traditional wood furniture.

0764 In babies' rooms it is very common to use the wall for placing photos of the first milestones in life. White multi-frames are a solution that, combined with the perfect wall color, can be highly effective.

0765 If toys and teddy bears are important elements that accompany children during their growth, hanging them on the wall facilitates the child having them at hand. Constructed of a simple cord, this version provides a touch of originality to the room's design.

0766 Ensuite bathrooms are no longer a luxury. Whether it is a new construction or a remodel, a modern home is becoming a versatile space where partitions are kept to a minimum. This often affects the layout of the bedroom, which can openly incorporate the bathroom.

0767 An open shower offers a whole range of possibilities: To start with, the flooring is continuous throughout with no level change. Since there are no enclosures, shower heads and other shower-related plumbing fixtures gain visual importance.

0768 The Arne ergonomic bathtub made of white titanic resin stands out for its sinuous shape that pays homage to the Egg chair designed by Arne Jacobsen in 1958 for the Radisson SAS hotel in Copenhagen.

0769 The Deque line of bath and spa faucet by Dornbracht is easily recognized by its flat, wide spout that spills a gentle rain-like flow of water. This severe design rounds off a minimalist bathroom design.

0770 Lavasca is an elegant bathtub in titanic resin conceived by Matteo Thun for Studio Rapsel. Elegant and sculptural, the Lavasca tub has paved its way to the Philadelphia Art Museum permanent contemporary design collection.

0766

0767

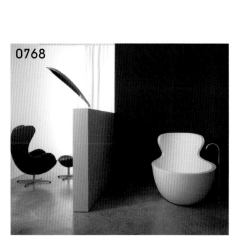

0768

0769

0770

0771 This bathtub and floor mount bath filler express a fusion between old and new in industrial design. The shape of the bathtub with its curvaceous form references the old slipper tub popular during the Victorian era. One end is raised and sloped to provide greater back support.

0772 This wall mounted shower head in brushed stainless steel designed by Studio Rapsel is a minimalist design choice that elegantly contrasts with the rich grain pattern of the wood panel.

0773 An overhead shower and hand shower combo has turned what was once a simple shower into pure luxury: the overhead shower releases a lavish spray of water that feels just like rain, while the hand shower fulfills more directed showering needs.

0771

0772

0773

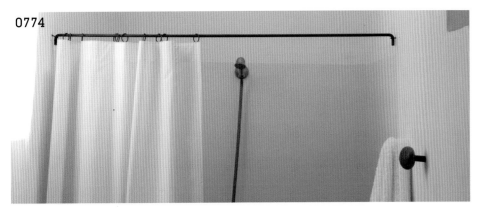

0774

0775

0776

0774 A limited color palette, straightforward lines and subtle detailing create an austere ambiance that transmits a sense of balance, serenity and harmony. Good natural lighting is the finishing touch that ties together a simple bathroom.

0775 This built-in bathtub is framed by a dark wood ledge, creating contrast with the white tub and walls and reinforcing the country style of the bathroom. The white river stones and the exposed ceiling beams introduce a natural touch in line with the style of the room.

0776 Concrete is a popular material, especially in contemporary home design. Its rich texture brings visual interest and creates a warm and inviting atmosphere or a cool and industrial look depending on the materials it is combined with.

0777

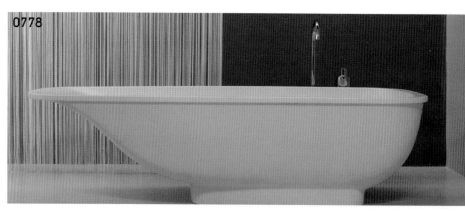

0778

0779

0780

0781

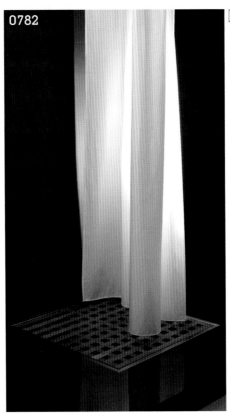

0782

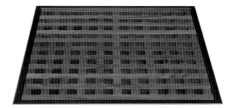

0783

0777 The first thought that might come to your mind when looking at this stainless steel bathtub may be that of coldness. In fact, stainless steel is the best material for a tub because it keeps the water warm the longest!

0778 KeaVasca is another modern interpretation of the slipper bathtub, which has an inclined back allowing for maximum comfort as you bathe the hours of stress away. Instead of claw feet, the bathtub has an integrated base giving the overall design a monolithic look.

0779 Designer Matteo Thun conceived this clever shower system that combines a spiraled curtain rail and shower head. Playful yet elegant, the Pluviae system creates a distinct circular space rather than the typical rectangular shower.

0780 Show off your style and make a design statement with plumbing fixtures and faucets. Oil-rubbed bronze fixtures are a popular choice thanks to the vintage trend and are a good match for your claw-foot tub.

0781 Studio Rapsel's Cobra wall-mounted shower is made of satin stainless steel. This unique contemporary shower system allows for a distinctive minimalist profile that meets the highest standards in bathroom design.

0782 The main advantage that a built-in shower tray offers is that it can be flush with the bathroom floor allowing for a continuous surface. The tray is made of genuine teak, a material containing a natural oil that repels water and keeps the wood from warping.

0783 A built-in concrete bathtub goes nicely with the rough plastered walls for a rustic country style. Natural materials and an abundance of textures evoke images of a seaside cottage.

0784 The rc40 sink unit by Burgbad is made of a material that matches the wall finish. It brings an architectural aesthetic to the design of this bathroom, diverging from traditional bathroom furnishings.

0785 This counter-mounted single-handle faucet designed around a sleek cylinder makes a refreshing statement in a bathroom where rich patina finishes dominate. Also, the curve of the spout relates to the soft shape of the vessel.

0786 In this innovative master bedroom, the vanity takes center stage. Sleek white cabinets form the vanity base, while the washbasins are seamlessly integrated into the design.

0787 The Crystalline line of basins by Alape is fabricated of enameled steel, which makes them very durable. The high gloss finish gives the pieces a certain lightness and delicacy. Standing or wall-mounted, the basins are accompanied by drawers.

0788 An architectural approach to bathroom design is achieved by introducing modules, whose variations accommodate solutions for almost any type of space and need.

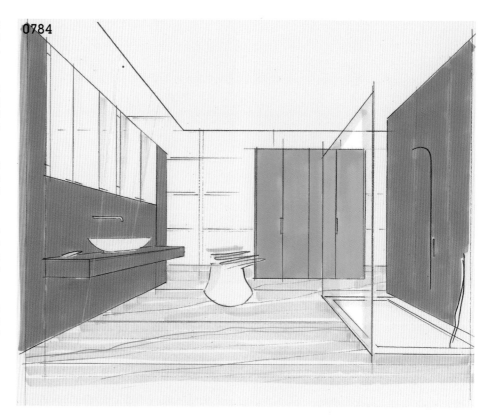

0786

0787

0788

0789 Carmen Barasona created this water inspired hotel bathroom design. The soft lines of the basins are suggestive of river stones, eroded over time by the continuous flow of running water.

0790 The wall-mounted washbasin adds to the airiness of the bathroom. All the plumbing fixtures are white and become an integral part of the bathroom design. In contrast, the movable storage cabinet and over the counter tray are of wood.

0791 This rounded surface-mounted ceramic washbasin recalls a polished pebble. It makes a minimalist statement lending a simplicity and serenity to the bathroom. This effect is reinforced by the soft gray tile on the walls and on the washbasin console.

0792

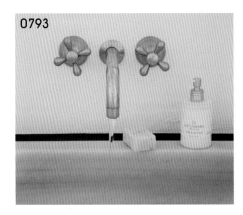

0793

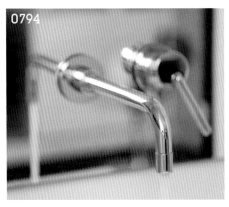

0794

0795

0792 A neutral color scheme was chosen to combine a salvaged marble basin and wood console table, creating a vintage look. In contrast, the contemporary fittings introduce a modern twist to the overall design.

0793 At first glance, this mismatched anodized steel spout and vintage style nickel handles seem like a strange combination. Nonetheless this mix picks up on the cool and warm shades of the marble sink.

0794 Upgrading a bathroom does not always require a total makeover, especially when there are budget constraints. You can achieve a different feel by simply replacing the faucets with some reasonably priced fixtures.

0795 Combining the traditional look of marble with a contemporary wall-mounted faucet gives this bathroom an up-to-date yet timeless design.

0796 Nothing makes guests feel more pampered than a stylish powder room. A block of rough marble for the basin, and an antique-cut crystal chandelier and oval mirror punch up a small room.

0797 A gilded recessed sink and copper faucet add character to this bathroom infused with a warm glow provided by the yellow tone of the walls. The faucet was mounted to one side due to the limited depth of the counter.

0798 Like regular concrete, fibered concrete can be shaped in any desired way, and can also be stained in a wide variety of colors to match the décor of a room.

0796

0797

0798

0799

0800

0801

0799 This antique marble sink is supported between two flanking ledges, leaving a space underneath for storage. This is a clever design that works with the rustic style of the room without compromising comfort and functionality.

0800 Accessorize the area around your washbasin according to the style of the room. For instance, antique silver vessels and perfume flasks were chosen to go with a marble wainscoat and mirror frame, and a sink with brass legs.

0801 Straight lines are dominant in this bathroom, including the tubular faucet spout. The contrasting stone wall behind the frameless mirror and polished finishes is visually striking.

0802 This rough block vessel, rustic and clean-lined, along with the sandy tones of the vanity and walls, would go perfectly in a simple beachside cabin.

0803 Portuguese architect Eduardo Souto de Moura is mostly known for his extraordinary buildings and his attention to materials and detail. The same attention is translated to the design of pieces such as this freestanding cylindrical washbasin in travertine.

0804 This stone vessel on a wood counter is displayed as an art object. Its sculptural quality is unmistakable.

0805 A freestanding vanity with a mirror sections off an area of the room. More than a functional item, it is an important design element that organizes the circulation around the room.

0806 The soft brushed finish of the faucet complements the Corian sink. This is an example of how high-tech products can create a warm, natural feel.

0802

0803

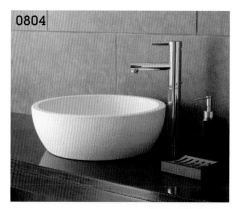

0804

0805

0806

0807

0808

0809

0810

0807 The Diva line by Burgbad is feminine and full of nostalgia for 1940s-style furniture. The washstand consists of an oval chest of drawers topped with a stone basin. This luxurious piece has golden feet and a drawer handle inlaid with Swarovski crystals.

0808 This bathroom design makes the most of a corner window, under which the bathtub is built. Bathrooms should be places to relax and enjoy rather than a utility room, and viewing windows help acheive this.

0809 The washbasin is an important feature of a bathroom. It may be distinctive and have a striking shape, but ultimately, it should be in harmony with the rest of the room's components.

0810 By providing a faucet-mounting hole on its wide flange, this ceramic basin avoids the hassle of drilling an additional hole in the countertop material.

0811 Whether ceramic, glass, metal, or stone, vessel basins rest perfectly flush atop the counter. Because of this, vessels are easier to replace as opposed to recessed washbasins and can often be showstoppers.

0812 A nice new faucet is sometimes enough to upgrade a bathroom. The arched spout and cross handles of this faucet create a vintage look combined with the plain white tile countertop and backsplash and the wood framed mirror.

0813 This octagonal washbasin featuring stepped sides evokes the style of grand eras past. In the context of a room where wood is the dominant material, the ceramic sink fits elegantly.

0814 A washbasin with an extra wide ledge on one side has a slightly elevated lip to prevent water dripping onto the floor. Its design works particularly well with the beveled subway tiles of the wall.

0811

0812

0813

0814

0815

0816

0817

0818

0815 For a clean and uncluttered décor, wall-mounted faucets are a good choice. Sleek and geometric forms with refined spouts and handles will give a bathroom a splash of style, especially when combined with a light color scheme.

0816 Avoid cluttering your bathroom countertops with toiletries other than soap and a hand towel. Instead consider displaying a simple decoration item such as this freshly picked sprig, to enhance the beauty of the materials used in the room.

0817 Add some texture when a bathroom is too cold and uninviting. Use fabrics such as silk, linen or wool to create a more natural, inviting and agreeable feeling, but avoid too much pattern as this would interfere with the clean look.

0818 A table console with a matching mirror, which was originally part of a bedroom set, is repurposed here to decorate a bathroom. The chipped paint finish is preserved for greater effect.

0819 Contemporary plumbing fixtures, rather than being perceived as cold and bare, should be conceived as fixtures with clean and smooth surfaces that appeal equally to men and women.

0820 Floor mounted tub fillers combine old-world craftsmanship and contemporary high-tech manufacturing. Decorative metal hoses, cross handles and porcelain handle buttons enhance a luxurious and pleasurable bathing experience.

0821 Since privacy is not really a concern when using a washbasin, it can be moved outside the bathroom as long as plumbing allows, for example into the bedroom or dressing room.

0822 A waterfall spout is commonly used as a bathtub filler for its relaxing waterfall flow. Nonetheless, they can be used to fill washbasins with the same calming effect.

0823 Dressing up the deck of an undermount bathtub is a simple way to make a design statement in a bathroom. Whether stone, ceramic or wood, it'll help frame the bathtub, making it the centerpiece of a room.

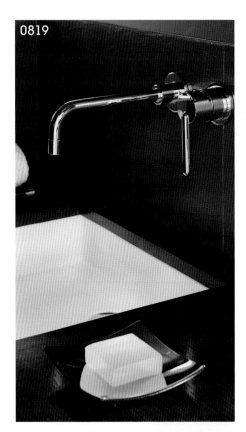

0819

0820

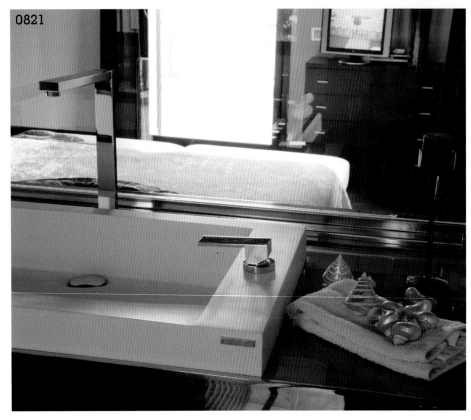

0821

0822

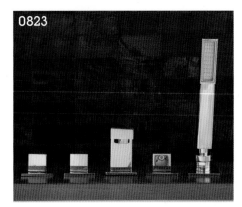

0823

0824

0825

0826

0827

0824 A surface-mounted washbasin adds a decorative note to a bathroom either on its own or combined with a wash top. While they are easier to install than recessed basins, surface-mounted sinks require more care.

0825 This simple geometric washbasin manufactured by Alape, for its Metaphor series of bathroom products, is conceived as a piece of furniture which combines functionality and décor. The glazed steel basin sits on a base of American oak.

0826 Wall-mounted faucets are perfect for vessel sinks. From traditional to modern, there are models to fit any style. These chrome cross handles and gooseneck spout tie together an ultra modern sink and a decorative framed mirror.

0827 This thick concrete shelf incorporates two sinks and makes an architectural statement. Hand-packing the concrete is a method that produces the attractive veining. A coat of polyaspartic is usually applied for protection against water penetration.

0828 A hand-carved stone washbasin can lend a custom look to your bathroom, providing durability and handcrafted beauty. While stone vessels are an expensive option, it is a good investment that will add value to your home.

0829 Try to keep your bathroom counter clutter free to let the material truly shine. Nonetheless, a few carefully chosen items can be used to complement the décor in favor of simplicity and casual elegance.

0830 This old, rough concrete trough equipped with copper spout and handles has an antique country style charm. Since concrete is unpredictable, every piece is unique.

0831 The beveled mirrors, a painted and distressed candle holder and a silver pitcher with dried flowers harmonize with the warm gray of the epoxy finished concrete bathroom countertop.

0832

0833

0834

0835

0836

0832 Leftover fabrics can be handy when you want to refurbish a vanity table. Turn this fabric into a skirt to disguise the underside of the sink or hide unsightly plumbing devices, while adding some charm to the room.

0833 A vanity area is built in an otherwise unusable corner of a room. This is a perfect opportunity to make a design statement, in this case with a particularly nice vessel mounted on a bespoke table.

0834 The sill of a window offers additional surface space behind a bathroom sink. Not exactly flush, the top of the sink is slightly higher than the windowsill. This facilitates the transition between materials.

0835 The counter and walls, which have the same finish, serve as backdrop for a fired ceramic vessel and a matching framed mirror with swing-arm wall lamp. The chrome faucet adds some sparkle and the decorating items bring in a touch of color.

0836 A long wood countertop unifies a vanity area with two vessels, which are accompanied by their respective faucets and ceiling-mounted rotating mirrors. The result is a very functional and airy space.

0837 A slender but strong profile vanity is the beautiful focal point of this bathroom. In this case, it is effectively displayed with a bold color on the walls around it. Scale back the rest of the elements so the overall design of the room isn't overwhelming.

0838 A vanity and matching wall cabinet make up a composition that plays with verticality and horizontality, solid and void, and balance and asymmetry.

0839 Various pieces of furniture were chosen to introduce a warm touch of wood in a room where white dominates. These furniture pieces provide the area around the trough washbasin with storage in a simple but functional composition.

0840 The depth of a counter or vanity doesn't need to be greater than the vessel sink that will go on top of it. This kind of washbasin only requires a small cut out into the support that serves as a drain hole.

0841 Material, texture and color are orchestrated to further articulate the design elements. Far from being dull, monochromatic color schemes in contrast with ultra modern stainless steel fixtures infuse your bathroom with a sophisticated touch.

0842 An interesting looking washbasin can play a major role in setting the tone of your bathroom. This glass washbasin is definitely an attention catcher, reflecting the colors and finishes of the tiles, mirror, fittings and the light.

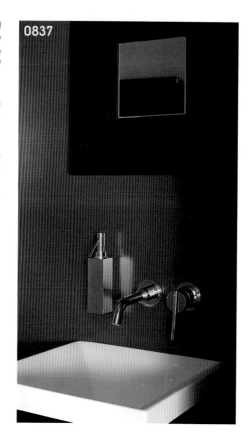

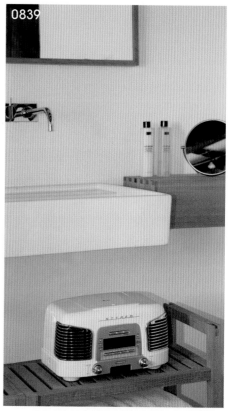

0843

0844

0845

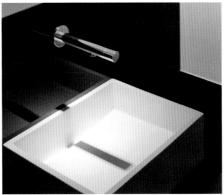

0846

0843 For a small bathroom, avoid bulky units. Instead go for space saving vanities that still offer plenty of storage room, while making a bathroom look larger.

0844 Tatoo is the name of this wall-mounted washbasin in Corian material, with stainless steel towel rail manufactured by Rapsel. Tatoo is the expression of the concept of flow and form reduced to its bare essentials, without neglecting functionality.

0845 Two sinks are very convenient in shared bathrooms, if space allows. Because there are two of them, they will have a greater impact on a bathroom. Lighting and accessories such as mirrors will double in size, and so will storage!

0846 This single lever chrome basin faucet stands out primarily for its aesthetic design, becoming the focus of any bathroom. Its enhanced functionality provides ease of use and greater accessibility.

0847 This mirror slides across the front of this cabinet above the sink. While it hides much of the cabinet, it does leave part of it exposed for easy access without having to maneuver around swinging doors.

0848 Burgbad's Culta mirror cabinet has a fully-mirrored front that lifts up and folds to reveal the interior of the cabinet. It also provides lighting, keeping the lines of a minimalist bathroom tidy.

0849 Burgbad's Solaire line of bathroom furnishings features a striking combination of colors and finishes that can liven up a bland room. The vanity has integrated towel bars, while the mirrored wall cabinet has incorporated lighting.

0850 The Sinea line by Burgbad features furnishings fully equipped with all the necessary accessories and storage possibilities. A shelf with integrated lighting above the mirrored front of the medicine cabinet provides excellent diffused lighting.

0851 In addition to fulfilling their obvious function, the side mirrors flanking the washbasin enhance the décor. Made out of vertical stripes, they create a playful visual effect and open up the space.

0852 Rapsel's Melting Chic line features bathroom furnishings in rosewood. The wall-mounted cabinet has a mirrored front and an open shelf for easy access. The rationalist design is reminiscent of Mondrian's Neo-Plasticism.

0853 This is a wall-mounted mirrored cabinet with hidden lateral shelves manufactured by Rapsel. The volumetric design of this product is enhanced by the material, which creates many reflections.

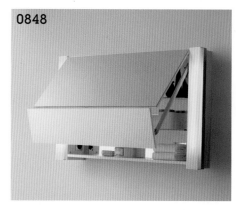

0854

0855

0856

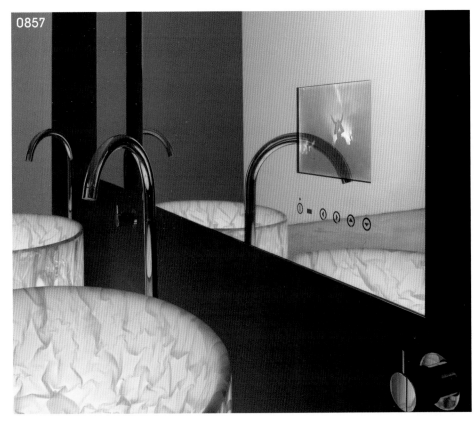

0857

0858

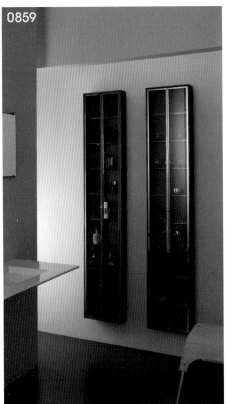

0859

0860

0854 An ornate mirror and light fixture add some detail to a simple bathroom and turn the vanity area into the focal point without altering the bones of the room. This allows the décor of the room to be changed as desired at any given moment.

0855 An alternative to the above-sink medicine cabinet is this wall-mounted column cabinet with a mirrored front. Clearly it doubles as a full-length mirror and can be used in the bedroom or the dressing room.

0856 This recessed cabinet fully integrates into the bathroom. Because of its location down low, it is not suitable for keeping prescriptions out of the reach of children, but it can certainly be used for toiletries.

0857 The Vista wall-mounted mirror manufactured by Rapsel has an LCD 8-inch (20 cm) TV with touch screen buttons, and connections to DVD and cable TV. Perfect for catching the morning news while getting ready for the day.

0858 This convenient cylindrical bathroom cabinet on casters has a top that can be used as a tray and can be wheeled wherever needed: by the shower, tub or washbasin.

0859 Two side column cabinets mark the entry to a bathroom. Their elegant look is an introduction to what comes next: a spacious room with furnishings characterized by clean lines.

0860 A right angle mirror is a pair of plane mirrors adjoined at right angle to each other. It is often used in bathrooms for wraparound reflections and because they make the room look larger and brighter.

0861 Small drawers are piled up to form a large storage unit. Perhaps not the most practical due to the number of drawers and their proportions, it is however suggestive of the Japanese step tansu cabinet and goes nicely with the wood ceiling beams.

0862 Utilitarian vanities feature integrated towel bars on their fronts, sides or both. These additions hold functionality without marring the look of the vanity they are attached to and avoid the necessity of having to mount pegs on the walls.

0863 A glass shelf and shower wall give this bathroom a clean look. The glass shelf keeps bathroom accessories within reach or provides a sleek way for displaying decorative items.

0864 The dark finish of the under counter cabinet imitates the low tiled wall of the bathtub and shower. Colors above the counter line are lighter. By doing this, all the visual weight is kept close to the floor, keeping the upper part airier.

0865 A custom vanity and shelves are the best option to keep a unified design in the bathroom. The sharp contrast with the white surfaces and the rich texture of the wood are the result of the attention to detail.

0861

0862

0863

0864

0865

0866 An open shelf under a vanity counter will come very handy for storage. It is in line with the clean look of the bathroom and camouflages the unsightly drain pipes of the vessels.

0867 Designing a modern bathroom with a vintage look takes careful planning and a bit of research. Priority is given to the major items: bathtub, shower, toilet and washbasin. Then come the accessories that will give the bathroom the desired look.

0868 A pair of traditional metal wall hooks with ceramic tips are the final touch to this unadorned yet functional bathroom. This is proof that there is no need to spend much to create a perfectly functional and visually pleasant space.

0869 If storage space in a bathroom is an issue, take advantage of wall space by hanging towels on a ladder drying rack. Available in many styles and finishes, you can also use a repainted old ladder, which will give you the chance to custom-design a unique piece.

0866
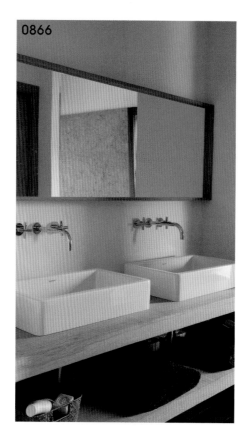

0867

0868

0869

0870 The shelf under the long vanity accentuates the horizontality in this bathroom. It also echoes the fact that the bathroom floor is raised above the rest of the dwelling. Further, this horizontality is emphasized by the rows of white fabric containers.

0871 The space under the washbasin is a tempting spot for storing bathroom toiletries, or anything that cannot go anywhere else due to lack of space. Keep your eyes peeled for an appropriate piece of furniture that also looks good in your bathroom.

0872

0873

0874

0875

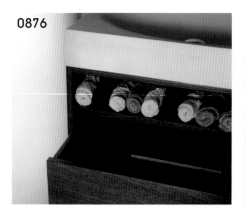

0876

0877

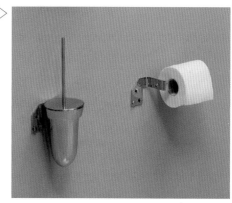

0878

0872 An otherwise bland bathroom is livened up with colorful accessories on the counter and a coat stand next to a light source, which makes the colors more vibrant. Also, the curvy lines of the coat stand contrast with the bathroom's linear style.

0873 A low cabinet under the sink fulfills the storage necessities of this open bathroom. Access to the valves is made easy. To hide the plumbing, two stainless steel towel bars are mounted on the front of the vanity.

0874 Vintage wire baskets are good to hold spare toilet paper rolls or any small items such as soap bars and lotions. They provide storage space and they are a great accent for the bathroom.

0875 Decorative stone and wood wall knob hooks add a natural accent to this bathroom. Rounded over time by rolling in the ocean, each stone is unique. Used in groups they have the quality of an art installation displayed on the wall.

0876 A combination of open shelf and drawer offers storage flexibility under the washbasin: An open shelf for easy access to hand towels and a drawer for toiletries to keep the area above the washbasin clutter-free.

0877 Toilets or washbasins in stainless steel are tempting, but this material can give a bathroom a cold, sterile feel when used in excess. Stainless steel accessories often acheive the right amount, providing a bathroom with a sleek look.

0878 Adding a towel bar to an existing vanity is easily done. Not only will this free up your countertop and walls, but in combination with other accessories including a toilet paper holder and hooks, they will round off your bathroom décor.

0879 The Butterfly chair, a classic designed by Jorge Ferrari-Hardoy in 1938, is popular for outdoor spaces. Its sturdy steel frame pairs nicely with fabric made from marine-grade acrylic, cotton or natural leather.

0880 Plastic outdoor furniture is waterproof, practical, durable and does not break the outdoor design budget. Powder-coated cast aluminum is a sturdier, yet still lightweight, alternative to plastic.

0881 A salvaged wood bench is transformed into a comfortable seat with the addition of cushions and pillows in varying patterns and colors. The bench brings a worldliness to the porch's decoration.

0882 Improvise a daybed by placing a large, firm cotton cushion directly on the ground. Complete the set with blankets and pillows of different sizes and patterns.

0883 When choosing throw pillows and fabrics to use on your porch, make sure they withstand UV rays, heat, water and inclement weather. Some suitable fabrics for outdoor use include various kinds of cotton, acrylic and other synthetic materials.

0884 You can make your outdoor space cozier with a daybed. Whether it is made of cast iron, wood or wicker, this hybrid piece of furniture works in many ways and was used by ancient Greek, Roman and Chinese cultures.

0885 This casual dining room with stone walls is light and airy. It opens up to a secluded patio furnished with lounge chairs and casual accessories, adding to the rustic charm of this country house.

0886 Folding metal furniture is ideal because it is compact, portable and versatile, allowing us to effortlessly change the mood of a space at a moment's notice.

0879

0880

0881

0882

0883

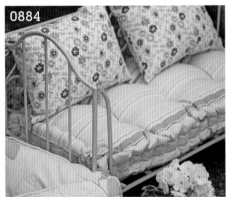

0884

0886

0885

0887 Treated natural wood is a suitable choice for a deck, but mixed materials are a perfectly acceptable alternative. A wide range of natural wood finishes and color options are available on the market, as well as outdoor furniture sets that are are designed specifically to combine well with wood.

0888 Eames' molded plastic RAR rocking chair adds a sophisticated feeling to any indoor or outdoor space. The curved edge of its seat reduces the pressure on the back of your thighs, making this a very comfortable seat.

0889 Powder-coated steel furniture is a good choice for everyday outdoor use, which requires durability and long-lasting beauty. Powder-coated finishes resist scratches and corrosion, making them ideal for all weather conditions.

0890 Weathered wood can be unsightly when it is not intentional, but if this is the look you are hoping to achieve, then weathered patinas can provide a rustic charm and complement any outdoor setting.

0887

0888

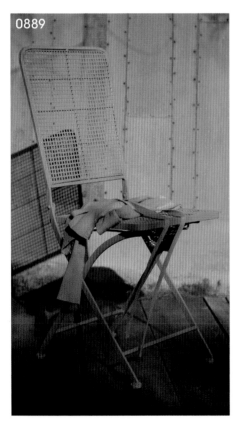

0889

0890

0891

0892

0894

0893

0891 A weathered blue-gray finish on wicker furniture and accessories is ideal for creating a nautical theme. The look is cool and relaxed, perfect for a beachside home.

0892 A clean, breezy and casual nautical style can be achieved by painting old wood furniture and accessories. Shades of white, green, blue and gray are always good choices. For a decorative touch, add pillows with matching fabrics and patterns.

0893 Wicker furniture is a popular choice for outdoor spaces as it creates a relaxed atmosphere, especially with cushioned seats. As far as style goes, choose whatever matches your home décor: classic, country or modern.

0894 Wrought iron furniture brings a touch of old-fashioned charm to your patio. In this daybed, the rigidity of the wrought iron is softened by its cushion and pillows in ocean-inspired tones.

0895 Rustic wicker and natural wood furniture are ideal for furnishing your casual beach house or your rustic cottage in the mountains.

0896 This iron chair has a woven plastic seat that is available in a range of colors. Its creative design is a modern interpretation of the traditional corded rope chair, which was made popular in the 1940s by furniture designer Hans Wegner.

0897 Canvas is heavy fabric woven from cotton, linen, hemp, jute or polyester. It is a good choice when resistance and durability are necessities in order to withstand varying weather conditions.

0898 Wicker is made of willow, reed or rattan. Being a natural material, it integrates well into casual, outdoor environments. It can also be stained or painted to add flair to your garden, patio or terrace.

0899 Portable furniture is ideal for a picnic or an afternoon tea outdoors because it is lightweight and easy to transport. Maneuverability is key, so any piece of furniture should fold to fit in the trunk of a car.

0895

0896

0897

0898

0899

0900

0901

0902

0903

0900 This version of the original Adirondack armchair, designed by Thomas Lee in 1903, maintains the main features of its predecessor: an angled back made from wooden boards and wide armrests that provide casual comfort. This piece of furniture is perfect for a cottage setting.

0901 This Tartaruga gazebo has a wooden structure and a white canvas covering to protect loungers from the sun. Enjoying a nice meal or drinks on a warm summer's day is made all the more enjoyable in this stylish gazebo.

0902 Nested side tables are usually sold in groups of two or three and come in handy for entertaining. They can be arranged in many ways, together or separately, and may even double as additional seats!

0903 This spacious, wooden gazebo serves as an outdoor room, with cushioned benches, side tables and planters — all under the protection of an awning to make the most of outdoor living.

0904 A gazebo is always a nice addition to a garden or backyard. Not only is it well-suited for entertaining friends and family throughout the year, it is an ideal hideaway space to enjoy a good book.

0905 This gray polyethylene sofa for Gervasoni's InOut collection is a take on the traditional wing chair. In an unusual twist, the wings on this chair extend all the way to the armrests. This modern interpretation, however, serves the same purpose as its predecessor, which is to provide protection from drafts.

0906 Designed especially for outdoor use, this daybed for Gervasoni's InOut collection is made of a woven polyethylene base and a polyurethane mattress.

0907 Cane and bamboo can be converted into sturdy and unique furniture, suitable for both traditional and contemporary designs.

0908

0909

0908 The chairs and tables in this Le Terrazze set can be configured in many different ways to suit the surrounding environment. These images show how natural wood furniture can be incorporated seamlessly into poolside settings.

0909 The design of the Adirondack chair offers a versatility that continues to meet modern design challenges. Many designers have adapted its classic form to contemporary settings. These teak lounge chairs by Gervasoni have adjustable backs and cushions that are available in various colors.

0910 The undulating shape of these cotton lounge chairs and side tables by Myyour are inspired by nature. Made of ABS translucent Plexiglas and painted metal, these pieces look like delicate leaves.

0911 Zoe, manufactured by Myyour, is an ergonomic lounge chair with an adjustable back that allows you to enjoy it in both a reclined and upright position. It comes in three finishes: embossed print, glossy paint or faux leather.

0912 A wooden pergola with a rectractable awning and screens on two sides creates a protected outdoor room. Just like any other room in your home, this space should convey personality through well-selected furniture, accessories and lighting.

0913 These lounge chairs by Tartaruga are protected from the sun, which means that there is no need for an umbrella. The result is a perfect example of "form follows function" made beautiful.

0914

0915

0916

0917

0914 Vintage, wrought iron furniture is a hot commodity for handicraft enthusiasts. They prefer the sturdiness and artistry that this material offers over similar products in cast aluminum that are much lighter and cheaper, but less charming.

0915 Resin wicker is used mainly for outdoor patio furniture. Unlike natural wicker or rattan, resin wicker is resistant against UV radiation and mildew and is therefore more durable.

0916 This Gervasoni line of armchairs, sofas and coffee tables in teak are ideal for a shady space brimming with vegetation. This line's simple design appears to be inspired by the Arts and Crafts movement.

0917 The casual canopy over this teak sofa will make a terrific addition to your garden or backyard. Light-filtering sheer fabric can be pulled around the sofa to create an airy, whimsical atmosphere.

Lounge furniture   265

0918

0919

0920

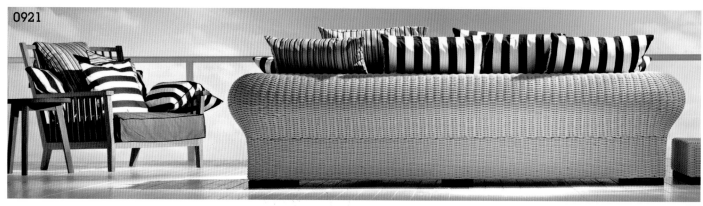

0921

0922

0923

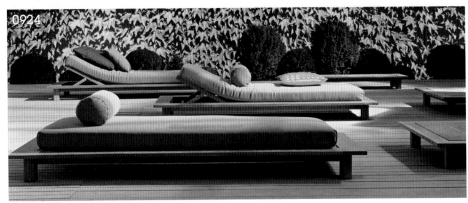

0924

0925

0918 This sofa is deep enough that it can be used as a daybed. The extra pillows reduce the depth to that of a standard sofa, while bringing color and texture to the ensemble. Because of its slim frame, the sofa does not look bulky.

0919 The Cubetto sofa from Novo has a blockboard frame finished in different veneers. Because of its size, it will take center stage in a large living room or on a porch, well protected from the elements.

0920 This deep blue and crisp white outdoor furniture set looks bright and airy, embodying a chic Greek island vibe. Whitewashed walls and sparkling azure waters would make for a perfect backdrop.

0921 Blue and white striped fabrics add a nautical touch to your outdoor space. The wooden frame of this armchair interrupts the color scheme without transforming the overall atmosphere of the space.

0922 Gervasoni's refreshing version of the garden armchair has a malacca frame woven with white polyethylene, which creates an elegant Mediterranean style.

0923 Garden furniture can create a strong impact on the atmosphere of your outdoor event. To host a successful party, make sure you have some elegant yet comfortable outdoor furniture. You can make things interesting by assembling a variety of seats.

0924 Gervasoni's teak lounge chair has an adjustable slat back and roll cushion to combine style and function, bringing comfortable elegance to your outdoor patio, pool area or garden.

0925 The Sundance chair from Tonon is made of white polyethylene and is suitable for outdoor and indoor use. A sophisticated manufacturing process that uses rotational molding allows for the production of these high-quality, hollow and seamless objects.

0926 A well-protected porch can be the perfect setting for a casual summer dining area, reserving the dining room for formal events. If space allows, you may even have your special outdoor china displayed in a cabinet or sideboard.

0927 Chair decoration is usually overlooked, but with the right accessories you can transform a nondescript folding chair into a design statement for any type of event.

0928 A large, heavy table can remain as a permanent piece of furniture on your porch, while chairs and benches can be set up only when needed. In addition to freeing up much-needed space, this will allow the table to have multiple functions throughout the year.

0929 There are many ways to create attractive dining sets. One of them is to combine mismatched chairs and tables, lending visual texture to your outdoor space.

0930 A small, folding side table is a practical addition to any large gathering. Use it to serve snacks and drinks during a party, to hold serving dishes before a meal or to set aside used dishes while guests are still at the table.

0931 Foldable tables and chairs are very convenient for casual al fresco dining: they are easy to set up and just as easy to take down.

0932 A casual and eclectic selection of outdoor furniture on shady patios or gardens creates inviting places to linger on hot summer days. This seemingly effortless style is the signature characteristic of country decorating.

0933 Folding completely flat, the popular bistro table and chairs are certainly practical, especially when limited space is an issue.

0934 This solid and sturdy dining set goes well with any décor. It also contrasts nicely with this light, foldable, powder-coated table and chair, which in the occasion of a large gathering can come in handy as an additional surface.

0926

0927

0928

0929

0930

0931

0932

0933

0934

0935 The clean and geometric design of this table, bench and chairs combine with the rustic materials of the porch, creating a unique contrast within this outdoor space.

0936 Practical and lightweight, folding metal furniture in different colors add some punch to your patio, backyard or terrace. For a refined look, combine with pillows and table sets in matching tones and patterns.

0937

0938

0939

0940

0937 Leaving wood untreated is rarely a consideration. Nonetheless, untreated wooden furniture integrates effectively into natural settings when paired with the right accessories.

0938 This stylish cast aluminum table with a tempered glass top and matching mesh chairs are perfect for summer days by the pool. Mesh chairs offer superior ventilation and therefore are a good choice for lounging on hot days.

0939 This table is made of zinc-plated iron with a Carrara marble tabletop. The silvery blue finish of the structure and its slim top provide a handsome contrast to the ivy-covered wall.

0940 A tumbled marble floor, brick walls, high ceilings and a large wooden door grace this entryway. This elegant setting, however, seems to overpower the diminutive dining table and chairs. When selecting furniture, ensure they harmonize with the style and the materials of the room in which they will be located.

0941

0942

0943

0944

0941 These built-in planters along a stone wall double as a long bench with a back rest. Pillows provide added comfort and touches of color.

0942 A ceramic border in blue, white and gold set into the terracotta flooring marks out a space for tables and chairs while leaving an accessible route around the pool.

0943 Similar to folding metal patio furniture, this line of table and chairs by Le Terrazze is practical by design. Wood adds a natural feel and a sturdiness without loosing the lightweight character so common in folding furniture.

0944 A large terrace may feel cold and unwelcoming before it is furnished and landscaped with planters and flower pots. To bring down the scale, a good idea is to divide the terrace into different areas. This image shows how different areas can be framed with canopies and plant urns.

0945 Le Terrazze proposes a line of dining tables and chairs that combines the modern and urban character of aluminum and glass with the warmth of wood and synthetic wicker.

0946 Add a special touch to untreated wood furniture to bring out the beauty of this natural material. A matching table runner and chair cushions in a muted brown color don't compete with the color and texture of the wood.

0947 This dining area is open to the garden while at the same time it occupies its own space. These separate areas are created by the cast iron structure of the canopy and the difference in the ground's material.

0948 This glass pitcher and cup add a little whimsy to the dining table with patterns that reflect the light in different ways. Their green tones echo the lush vegetation of the surroundings.

0949 Get inspired by the bright, sunny colors in your garden when you set your table for an outdoor meal. Decoration can be formal or casual, depending on the occasion and on the guests.

0950 Seasons are a good theme to use when decorating your table. In this image, earth tones, natural materials and small clusters of walnuts celebrate the fall, and leave behind bold, sunny colors that are more associated with warmer months.

0951 This practical picnic tray with handles and compartments helps keep everything in order: glasses, plates, silverware and even wine bottles.

0952 A tablecloth will hide a table that is not up to snuff and adds a touch of elegance to a special occasion. When your table is in good condition, however, you can forego a tablecloth and simply opt for placemats. They can easily be changed to reflect the season.

0953 If you are running low on ideas for table settings, look somewhere outside the ordinary: organic-shaped plates and bowls with delicate patterns.

0954

0955

0956

0957

0954 A white orchid in a square vase and a glass jar with a lid accent this chic table. The white and yellow colors of the orchid harmonize with the white-washed walls and blue chairs and windows.

0955 From simple groupings of flowers to elaborate floral arrangements, decorating with flowers will bring a fresh touch of color and energy to your table. Paying attention to details will make your tabletop very personal.

0956 Impress your guests with creative table settings for a brunch outdoors. Start with a design theme that is either casual or elegant, floral or striped, and apply it to all the items on the table.

0957 A picnic on a warm, sunny day is an excellent idea to celebrate the height of spring. Heavy fabrics, muted colors and drab tableware give way to brightly colored plastic glasses, pillows, blankets and wicker trays.

0958 This simple and functional floor lamp looks like a modern take on a hanging paper lamp. It emits a soft glow that adds ambiance to the room and makes a perfect reading lamp when positioned next to a chair.

0959 Look for knickknacks around your house and garden to create new objects, such as this lampshade with pebbles and salvaged glass decorations that once were part of a chandelier. All the pieces are tied to a thick wire spiral that is attached to a light cord wrapped in burlap fabric.

0960 If your porch is your favorite spot to read and write, find a task light that will suit the décor of this quiet area and will invite you to relax with a good book, or with a notebook and pen.

0961 Don't these lights look like artwork that artist Eva Hesse could have done? This unique and highly creative group of pear-shaped resin light fixtures is an example of the blurred line between design and art.

0962 Use unexpected materials like wire mesh and a sheet of wood veneer to create a unique and inexpensive ceiling light fixture. Of course, do not forget some basic light hardware!

0963 This fabulous handcrafted Moroccan-style lantern exudes elegance. Perfect for entry halls and porches, it adds an exotic touch with its elaborate star-shaped patterns and colored glass.

0964 Decorative lanterns come in many styles, colors and finishes. They are a popular item for outdoor decoration and add enchantment to summer evenings, whether ceiling or wall mounted, or simply set on the floor or on a piece of furniture.

0965 These outdoor floor lamps with white polyethylene shades make for delightful evenings out in the garden or by the pool. Their design goes well with the sinuous shape of the lounge chairs and the round side tables.

0958

0959

0960

0961

0962

0963

0964

0965

0966

0967

0968

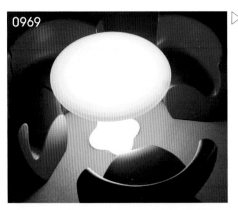

0969

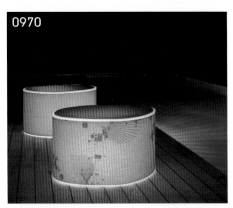

0970

0971

0966 The Tulip XL outdoor lights by Myyour are both decorative and functional. The glowing tulips catch everyone's attention whether they are placed individually or set in groups as if they were growing out of a planter.

0967 The glowing lamp in this staged sitting area is not particularly suitable for outdoor use. However, worthy of note is the very clever effect achieved to simulate a sunset.

0968 In addition to providing general lighting, some ornamental light fixtures can highlight specific areas of your outdoor space. They can either take center stage or help demarcate boundaries and paths.

0969 Elsewhere we have seen a light fixture inspired by the sun, whereas this is one light design that looks more like the moon. In fact, it is one of the various items in this outdoor space that contributes to a circular theme.

0970 There is a growing number of designers interested in illuminated furniture. Functional as a bench and occasional table, this piece is also a light fixture with a fiberglass structure.

0971 The generous proportions of these polyethylene armchairs from the InOut collection by Gervasoni are perfect for relaxing outdoors in. A cover is available that can change the look of the chair completely.

0972 Plants add character to an outdoor space in the same way that architectural details can make a design statement. Focusing on subtle color and textural changes, cacti and succulents can embellish barren walls and demarcate paths.

0973 Cacti and succulents are perfect for xeriscaping. They look their best when various types are grouped together in a lively mix. The color and the shape of the different species can be used to create patterns.

0974 Mustard yellow, burned orange and creamy white combined with dusky purple or International Klein Blue are evocative of Southern European and Mediterranean rural villages. In this case, the deep purplish-blue is used as an accent color to balance out a warm color scheme.

0975 Although burlap is a rough fabric, it makes attractive pillows, especially if the original printing is displayed. But you can do much more to decorate your home inexpensively with burlap bags besides using them as pillowcases, such as for tablecloths, runners, placemats, ottomans and lampshades.

0976 Transform your old furniture or a piece that you might have found in a secondhand furniture shop into something fresh and creative. Furniture makeovers can be as simple as an easy paint job, some cheerful prints or clever cut-outs.

0977 Country decorating is casual, cozy and all about comfort. Rustic finds have a place in your cabin: heavy iron, rusty metal, weathered wood and mirrors can be repurposed in innovative ways. Keep your mind open to the possibilities and experiment.

0978 Silver accessories and gray felt pillows combine well with this white sideboard and stool, creating a sharp contrast with the aged wood flooring and weathered wall.

0979 Heavy cotton fabrics are suitable for outdoor use, but generally need to be protected from the elements. Their natural feel is accompanied by the vintage look of recycled wooden boxes, which can be used as tables.

0972

0973

0974

0975

0976

0977

0978

0979

0980 These all-white pieces of furniture and accessories add some zing to a weathered porch. A few decorative elements like flowers, a tarnished silver candle lantern and an off-white wool blanket soften the contrast.

0981 Old wicker-covered wine jugs and rusted metal urns are common decorative accents in cottage gardens. Lush vegetation and a seemingly unintentional placement of objects are key.

0982 Decorate your terrace with succulents in glass vases that are filled with colored sand for a simple and affordable decoration. Play around with varying arrangements, mixing different types of plants, sizes and colors.

0983 To decorate your countryside cabin, use colors that pay homage to the natural surroundings, like displaying a vintage basket full of freshly picked wild flowers. Modern items are not off limits. In fact, they can bring a sophisticated touch without looking out of place.

0984

0985

0986

0987

0984 Table centerpieces do not necessarily have to be grand. It all depends, of course, on the occasion. A casual yet elegant look can be achieved with a wildflower arrangement that echoes the natural surroundings.

0985 There's nothing better than a piece of wooden furniture to enhance the beauty of a natural backdrop. To keep wood furniture in good condition outdoors, soak it in oil a few times a year. This will help to keep the moisture out and protect it from the sun and wind as well.

0986 Woolen felt stones come in different sizes and shapes, just like the real thing. They can be used for seating and add a playful touch to playrooms. Not limited to indoor use, outdoor felt stones are treated with resin.

0987 Beach-themed decorations bring a calm and refreshing feel into your garden, whether you live in a tropical island or by the wild ocean of some northern country. Decorate with shells, driftwood and pebbles along with weathered and distressed finishes.

0988 Use colorful planters to liven up your garden. They are also great for breaking up an outdoor space into themed areas where planters are matched with plants according to color. You can also play with different heights to create attractive designs.

0989 Make your outdoor space as comfortable as your living room. A selection of casual and portable furniture and accessories is an easy way to create a cozy corner in the garden.

0990 A group of molded plastic armchairs and side tables counterbalances the rectangular shape of the pool. Their muted color harmonizes with the silvery green grasses, while the pillows and bright green decorations add refreshing touches.

0991 Cut flowers placed in a pitcher on your desk by the window are cheerful. Match the tones of your flower arrangement with the color accents of the room and you'll have another element of décor!

0992 There are so many ways of recycling clutter to make fantastic decorative accents! Additionally, it's a good hobby to pick up. You decide how much time and effort you want to invest in your repurposing projects.

0993 Group vases of different sizes together for a greater effect and fill with plants, cut flowers or simply let them shine on their own. Keep in mind that bold patterns and saturated colors add visual weight and should therefore be used sparingly.

0994 Molded plastic outdoor furniture has many benefits: it is easy to clean, durable and lightweight. It is suitable if you have a big patio or backyard, but on the other hand, if your space is limited, you might not want to make this kind of investment, in which case simply opt for foldable furniture.

0995

0996

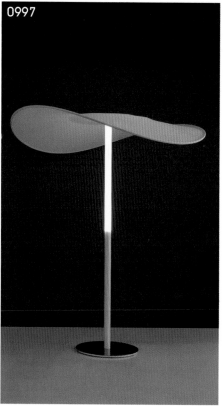

0997

▷

0995 Transform your patio into an outdoor room where you can relax surrounded by plants. Just be patient: you are doing more than furnishing a room. Gardening is a work in progress that generally gets better every year. That is the beauty of it!

0996 Unless the patterns are subdued, avoid mixing more than three in one space. They do not have to be similarly themed. For instance, the curtain with a lighthouse design is combined with a solid, light-colored blanket with a blue fringe and thin-striped chair cushions and pillows.

0997 PO'light by jmferrero is the most sought-after item for hot days. At dusk it turns into a night umbrella with a light mast. With its integrated table, it becomes a pleasant gathering place for a small group.

0998 Copper accents add earthiness to this display. Even though the vases are a different color and material, they seem to blend easily with the ivy-covered wall thanks to their embossed surfaces. In fact, the result is quite homogeneous and very well balanced.

0999 Mixing fabrics, especially patterns, in one single space is not an easy task. Even in an open area, there is a risk of overdoing it. To start with, find a fabric you really like and work around it. You may choose from a selection of similar colors and patterns, which can be of different scales.

1000 Create an outdoor room with fabric as if it were a room in your house. The bushes and trees are the walls, and the lawn is the floor. Chairs and tables can be arranged the way you would arrange an indoor space, with pillows and accessories completing the look.

0001, 0004, 0005, 0007, 0008, 0009, 0010, 0014, 0015, 0016, 0017, 0018, 0021, 0022, 0026, 0028, 0029, 0030, 0031, 0033, 0034, 0035, 0036, 0037, 0042, 0043, 0045, 0046, 0047, 0048, 0049, 0050, 0056, 0066, 0067, 0068, 0069, 0070, 0071, 0072, 0073, 0074, 0075, 0076, 0077, 0078, 0080, 0081, 0082, 0083, 0084, 0085, 0086, 0087, 0088, 0089, 0090, 0091, 0092, 0093, 0094, 0095, 0096, 0097, 0098, 0099, 0100, 0101, 0102, 0104, 107, 0108, 0109, 0111, 0114, 0115, 0117, 0119, 0120, 0122, 123, 124, 125, 0127, 0129, 0131, 0132, 0133, 0134, 0135, 0136, 0138, 0139, 0140, 0141, 0142, 0143, 0145, 0146, 0147, 0148, 0149, 0150, 0159, 0160, 0161, 0162, 0163, 0164, 0165, 0166, 0168, 0169, 0170, 0171, 0172, 0173, 00174, 0175, 0181, 0191, 0192, 0193, 0195, 0205, 0206, 0207, 0208, 0209, 0210, 0211, 0212, 0213, 0214, 0215, 0216, 0218, 0219, 0220, 0222, 0223, 0224, 0225, 0226, 0227, 0228, 0229, 0232, 0234, 0237, 0238, 0240, 0241, 0242, 0243, 0244, 0246, 0247, 0248, 0249, 0250, 0251, 0252, 0253, 0254, 0255, 0256, 0261, 0268, 0269, 0270, 0271, 0272, 0273, 0274, 0275, 0277, 0279, 0280, 0283, 0284, 0285, 0292, 0293, 0294, 0295, 0307, 0311, 0312, 0313, 0315, 0316, 0318, 0320, 0321, 0322, 0324, 0326, 0327, 0328, 0330, 0331, 0334, 0342, 0347, 0356, 0372, 0373, 0374, 0375, 0376, 0377, 0378, 0379, 0380, 0381, 0382, 0385, 0388, 0389, 0391, 0394, 0396, 0398, 0399, 0402, 0403, 0404, 0405, 0406, 0407, 0409, 0410, 0411, 0412, 0415, 0416, 0453, 0454, 0459, 0460, 0467, 0473, 0474, 0478, 0479, 0480, 0481, 0482, 0485, 0486, 0487, 0488, 0489, 0490, 0492, 0493, 0494, 0515, 0516, 0517, 0518, 0519, 0520, 0521, 0523, 0524, 0525, 0526, 0527, 0528, 0531, 0532, 0534, 0537, 0541, 0542, 0548, 0549, 0550, 0551, 0552, 0553, 0554, 0555, 0557, 0558, 0560, 0562, 0563, 0564, 0567, 0568, 0569, 0570, 0571, 0572, 0573, 0574, 0575, 0577, 0579, 0581, 0582, 0584, 0585, 0586, 0587, 0588, 0590, 0593, 0594, 0603, 0604, 0605, 0606, 0607, 0608, 0609, 0610, 0611, 0612, 0613, 0614, 0615, 0616, 0617, 0618, 0619, 0620, 0621, 0622, 0623, 0624, 0625, 0626, 0627, 0628, 0629, 0630, 0631, 0632, 0633, 0634, 0637, 0649, 0651, 0653, 0654, 0656, 0657, 0659, 0668, 0669, 0670, 0671, 0672, 0673, 0674, 0675, 0676, 0677, 0678, 0679, 0680, 0681, 0682, 0683, 0684, 0685, 0686, 0688, 0689, 0690, 0693, 0694, 0695, 0696, 0697, 0700, 0701, 0702, 0703, 0704, 0706, 0708, 0709, 0712, 0713, 0716, 0721, 0723, 0726, 0731, 0732, 0733, 0736, 0737, 0739, 0742, 0743, 0746, 0747, 0748, 0749, 0750, 0751, 0752, 0758, 0759, 0760, 0761, 0762, 0763, 0764, 0765, 0774, 0776, 0780, 0783, 0785, 0790, 0791, 0792, 0793, 0794, 0795, 0796, 0797, 0798, 0799, 0801, 0802, 0804, 0805, 0806, 0808, 0809, 0810, 0811, 0812, 0813, 0814, 0815, 0816, 0817, 0818, 0819, 0820, 0821, 0822, 0823, 0824, 0826, 0827, 0828, 0829, 0830, 0831, 0832, 0833, 0834, 0836, 0839, 0840, 0842, 0845, 0846, 0850, 0853, 0855, 0859, 0860, 0861, 0862, 0863, 0864, 0865, 0866, 0867, 0868, 0869, 0870, 0871, 0872, 0873, 0874, 0875, 0876, 0878, 0879, 0880, 0881, 0882, 0884, 0885, 0886, 0887,

0888, 0889, 0890, 0891, 0892, 0893, 0894, 0895, 0896, 0897, 0898, 0899, 0900, 0902, 0914, 0926, 0927, 0928, 0929, 0930, 0931, 0932, 0933, 0934, 0935, 0936, 0937, 0938, 0946, 0948, 0949, 0950, 0951, 0952, 0953, 0956, 0957, 0959, 0960, 0962, 0963, 0964, 0974, 0975, 0976, 0977, 0978, 0979, 0980, 0981, 0982, 0983, 0984, 0985, 0986, 0987, 0989, 0991, 0992
© José Luis Hausmann
www.hausmannfotografia.com

0002
© Adrenalina
www.adrenalina.it

0003, 0004, 0011, 0013, 0020, 0023, 0024, 0040, 0052, 0058, 0063, 0113, 0233
© Arketipo
www.arketipo.com

0004 (0001)

0005 (0001)

0006, 0112, 0314
© Busnelli
www.busnelli.it

0007 (0001)

0008 (0001)

0009 (0001)

0010 (0001)

0011 (0003)

0012, 0033, 0053
© Blå Station
www.blastation.com

0013 (0003)

0014 (0001)

0015 (0001)

0016 (0001)

0017 (0001)

0018 (0001)

0019
© Divani&Divani
www.divaniedivani.it

0020 (0003)

0021 (0001)

0022 (0001)

0023 (0003)

0024 (0003)

0025 0031, 0039, 0051, 0332, 0335, 0336, 0371, 0561
© Bonaldo
www.bonaldo.it

0026 (0001)

0027 0110, 0348
© Casamilano
www.casamilanohome.com

0028 (0001)

0029 (0001)

0030 (0001)

0031 (0001)

0032 (0001)

0033 (0012)

0034 (0001)

0035 (0001)

0036 (0001)

0037 (0001)

0038
© Muuto
www.muuto.com

0039 (0025)

0040 (0003)

0041, 0055, 0064, 0105, 0151, 0344, 0602, 0636
© Minotti
www.minotti.com

0042 (0001)

0043 (0001)

0044, 0106, 0128
© Alivar
www.alivar.com

0045 (0001)

0046 (0001)

0047 (0001)

0048 (0001)

0049 (0001)

0050 (0001)

0051 (0025)

0052 (0003)

0053 (0012)

0054, 0262
© Carl Hansen & Son
http://www.carlhansen.com

0055 (0041)

0056 (0001)

0057 0278, 0319, 0546, 0666
© Marset
www.marset.com

0058 (0003)

0059, 0060, 0062, 0152, 0592, 0638
© Spinelli
www.fratellispinelli.it

0060 (0059)

0061, 0103, 0359
© Pierantonio Bonacina
www.pierantoniobonacina.it

0062 (0059)

0063 (0003)

0064 (0041)

0065, 0144, 0230, 0357, 0358, 0361, 0395, 0397, 0597
© Modà
www.modacollection.it

0066 (0001)

0067 (0001)

0068 (0001)

0069 (0001)

0070 (0001)

0071 (0001)

0072 (0001)

0073 (0001)

0074 (0001)

0075 (0001)

0076 (0001)

0077 (0001)

0078 (0001)

0079 (0001)

0080 (0001)

0081 (0001)

0082 (0001)

0083 (0001)

0084 (0001)

0085 (0001)

0086 (0001)

0087 (0001)

0088 (0001)

0089 (0001)

0090 (0001)

0091 (0001)

0092 (0001)

0093 (0001)

0094 (0001)

0095 (0001)

0096 (0001)

0097 (0001)

0098 (0001)

0099 (0001)

0100 (0001)

0101 (0001)

0102 (0001)

0103 (0061)

0104 (0001)

0105 (0041)

0106 (0044)

0107, 0116, 0153, 0154, 0155, 0368, 0641
© Besana
http://www.besana.it

0108 (0001)

0109 (0001)

0110 (0027)

0111 (0001)

0112 (0006)

0113 (0003)

0114 (0001)

0115 (0001)

0116 (0107)

0117 (0001)

0118
© AR.PA. Mobili
www.arpamobili.it

0119 (0001)

0120 (0001)

0121, 0130, 0591,
© Molteni&C
www.molteni.it

0122 (0001)

0123 (0001)

0124 (0001)

0125 (0001)

0126, 0156, 0353, 0589, 0635
© Mobili Bertelè
www.bertelemobili.it

0127 (0001)

0128 (0044)

0129 (0001)

0130 (0121)

0131 (0001)

0132 (0001)

0133 (0001)

0134 (0001)

0135 (0001)

0136 (0001)

0137, 0775, 0836, 0954
Herdade da Malhadinha
www.malhadinhanova.pt

0138 (0001)

0139 (0001)

0140 (0001)

0141 (0001)

0142 (0001)

0143 (0001)

0144 (0065)

0145 (0001)

0146 (0001)

0147 (0001)

0148 (0001)

0149 (0001)

0150 (0001)

0151 (0041)

0152 (0059)

0153 (0116)

0154 (0116)

0155 (0116)

0156 (0126)

0157, 0236
© Creazioni
www.stile-creazioni.com

0158, 0167, 0188, 0189, 0190, 0197, 0198,
0202, 0392, 0687, 0691, 0692, 0996, 0999,
1000
© Gancedo
www.gancedo.com

0159 (0001)

0160 (0001)

0161 (0001)

0162 (0001)

0163 (0001)

0164 (0001)

0165 (0001)

0166 (0001)

0167 (0158)

0168 (0001)

0169 (0001)

0170 (0001)

0171 (0001)

0172 (0001)

0173 (0001)

0174 (0001)

0175 (0001)

0176
© Harman Stoves
www.harmanstoves.com

0177, 0178, 0179, 0180, 0182, 0183, 0184,
0185, 0186, 0187, 0196, 0201, 0203, 0462,
0595, 0995
© MCZ spa
www.mcz.it

0178 (0177)

0179 (0177)

0180 (0177)

0181 (0001)

0182 (0177)

0183 (0177)

0184 (0177)

0185 (0177)

0186 (0177)

0187 (0177)

0188 (0158)

0189 (0158)

0190 (0158)

0191 (0001)

0192 (0001)

0193 (0001)

0194, 0310,
© Nemo Cassina
www.nemo.cassina.it

0195 (0001)

0196 (0177)

0197 (0158)

0198 (0158)

0199, 0204, 0239, 0343, 0345, 0346, 0354,
0365, 0384, 0386, 0387
© e15
www.e15.com

0200, 0352
© Doimo Idea
www.doimoidea.it

0201 (0177)

0202 (0158)

0203 (0177)

0204 (0199)

0205 (0001)

0206 (0001)

0207 (0001)

0208 (0001)

0209 (0001)

0210 (0001)

0211 (0001)

0212 (0001)

0213 (0001)

0214 (0001)

0215 (0001)

0216 (0001)

0217, 0281, 0305, 0306
© Ateljé Lyktan
www.atelje-lyktan.se

0218 (0001)

0219 (0001)

0220 (0001)

0221, 0351, 0383
© Ciacci Kreaty
http://www.ciacci.com

0222 (0001)

0223 (0001)

0224 (0001)

0225 (0001)

0226 (0001)

0227 (0001)

0228 (0001)

0229 (0001)

0230 (0065)

0231, 0235, 0393, 0400, 0598, 0600, 0601,
0700
© Noir
www.noir-italia.com

0232 (0001)

0233 (0003)

0234 (0001)

0235 (0231)

0236 (0157)

0237 (0001)

0238 (0001)

0239 (0199)

0240 (0001)

0241 (0001)

0242 (0001)

0243 (0001)

0244 (0001)

0245, 0580, 0583, 0883
© Coco-Mat
www.coco-mat.com

0246 (0001)

0247 (0001)

0248 (0001)

0249 (0001)

0250 (0001)

0251 (0001)

0252 (0001)

0253 (0001)

0254 (0001)

0255 (0001)

0256 (0001)

0257, 0297, 0652
© Vibia
www.vibia.com

0258
© Terzani
www.terzani.com

0259
© Axo Light
www.axolight.it

0260, 0655
© Catellani & Smith
www.catellanismith.com

0261 (0001)

0262 (0054)

0263, 0267, 0303,
© Steng Licht
www.steng.de

0264, 0289, 0296, 0545, 0958
© Louis Poulsen
www.louispoulsen.com

0265, 0276
© &Tradition
www.andtradition.com

0266
Occhio
www.occhio.de

0267 (0263)

0268 (0001)

0269 (0001)

0270 (0001)

0271 (0001)

0272 (0001)

0273 (0001)

0274 (0001)

0275 (0001)

0276 (0265)

0277 (0001)

0278 (0057)

0279 (0001)

0280 (0001)

0281 (0217)

0282
© Belux
www.belux.com

0283 (0001)

0284 (0001)

0285 (0001)

0286, 0970
© Prandina
www.prandina.it

0287
© Targetti
www.targetti.com

0288
© Atelier Areti
www.atelierareti.com

0289 (0264)

0290
© Next Lighting
www.nextlighting.com

0291
© Moooi
www.moooi.com

0292 (0001)

0293 (0001)

0294 (0001)

0295 (0001)

0296 (0264)

0297 (0257)

0298, 300, 0661, 0665
© LZF
www.lzf-lamps.com

0299, 0309
© Metalarte
http://www.metalarte.com

0300 (0298)

0301
Zeitlos Berlin
www.zeitlos-berlin.de

0302, 0304, 0325, 0547, 0658, 0664
© Lumini
www.lumini.com.br

0303 (0263)

0304 (0302)

0305 (0217)

0306 (0217)

0307 (0001)

0308
© Arturo Álvarez
www.arturo-alvarez.com

0309 (0299)

0310 (0194)

0311 (0001)

0312 (0001)

0313 (0001)

0314 (0006)

0315 (0001)

0316 (0001)

0317, 0544, 0667, 0845
© Trizo21
www.trizo21.com

0318 (0001)

0319 (0057)

0320 (0001)

0321 (0001)

0322 (0001)

0323
© Dluce
www.dluce.com

0324 (0001)

0325 (0302)

0326 (0001)

0327 (0001)

0328 (0001)

0329, 0543
© Light Years
www.lightyears.dk

0330 (0001)

0331 (0001)

0332 (0025)

0333, 0338, 0340, 0341, 0362, 0366
© Emmei
http://emmei.co.uk

0334 (0001)

0335 (0025, 599)

0336 (0025)

0337, 0350, 0390, 0596, 0646, 0699
© Jesse
www.jesse.it

0338 (0333)

0339, 0401, 0436, 0456, 0463, 0468, 0477,
0483, 0484, 0512, 0522, 0529, 0530, 0540
© Cesar
www.cesar.it

0340 (0333)

0341 (0333)

0342 (0001)

0343 (0199)

0344 (0041)

0345 (0199)

0346 (0199)

0347 (0001)

0348 (0027)

0349
© Elegance
www.elegancecy.com

0350 (0337)

0351 (0221)

0352 (0200)

0353 (0126)

0354 (0199)

0355, 0367, 0370, 0599
© Zanotta
www.zanotta.it

0356 (0001)

0357 (0065)

0358 (0065)

0359 (0061)

0360, 0660
© Leds-C4
www.leds-c4.com

0361 (0065)

0362 (0333)

0363, 0364
© Emmemobili
www.emmemobili.it

0364 (0363)

0365 (0199)

0366 (0333)

0367 (0355)

0368 (0107)

0369
© Oluce
www.oluce.com

0370 (0355)

0371 (0025)

0372 (0001)

0373 (0001)

0374 (0001)

0375 (0001)

0376 (0001)

0377 (0001)

0378 (0001)

0379 (0001)

0380 (0001)

0381 (0001)

0382 (0001)

0383 (0221)

0384 (0199)

0385 (0001)

0386 (0199)

0387 (0199)

0388 (0001)

0389 (0001)

0390 (0337)

0391 (0001)

0392 (0158)

0393 (0231)

0394 (0001)

0395 (0065)

0396 (0001)

0397 (0065)

0398 (0001)

0399 (0001)

0400 (0231)

0401 (0339)

0402 (0001)

0403 (0001)

0404 (0001)

0405 (0001)

0406 (0001)

0407 (0001)

0408, 0413, 0415, 0418, 0420, 0422, 0423,
0425, 0426, 0427, 0429, 0430, 0431, 0437,
0449, 0450, 0452, 0455, 0465, 0505, 0510,
0514, 0535, 0538
© Tecnocucina
www.tecnocucina.it

0409 (0001)

0410 (0001)

0411 (0001)

0412 (0001)

0413 (0408)

0414 (0001)

0415 (0408)

0416 (0001)

0417, 0424, 0438, 0439, 0440, 0441, 0442,
0443, 0445, 0447, 0448, 0451, 0466, 0476,
0491, 0498, 0508, 0511, 0513, 0533, 0539,
0556
© Dada
www.dadaweb.it

0418 (0408)

0419
© Bsweden
www.bsweden.com

0420 (0408)

0421, 0432, 0433, 0434, 0435, 0536
© Rational
www.rational-kitchens.com

0422 (0408)

0423 (0408)

0424 (0417)

0425 (0408)

0426 (0408)

0427 (408)

0428, 0457, 0458,
© Schiffini
www.schiffini.com

0429 (0408)

0430 (0408)

0431 (0408)

0432 (0421)

0433 (0421)

0434 (0421)

0435 (0421)

0436 (0339)

0437 (0408)

0438 (0417)

0439 (0417)

0440 (0417)

0441 (0417)

0442 (0417)

0443 (0417)

0444, 0446, 0464
© Mobalco
www.mobalco.com

0445 (0417)

0446 (0444)

0447 (0417)

0448 (0417)

0449 (0408)

0450 (0408)

0451 (0417)

0452 (0408)

0453 (0001)

0454 (0001)

0455 (0408)

0456 (0339)

0457 (0428)

0458 (0428)

0459 (0001)

0460 (0001)

0461
© Molo Design
http://molodesign.com

0462 (0177)

0463 (0339)

0464 (0444)

0465 (0408)

0466 (0417)

0467 (0001)

0468 (0339)

0469, 0470, 0471, 0472, 0475
© O&G
www.olivoegodeassi.it

0470 (0469)

0471 (0469)

0472 (0469)

0473 (0001)

0474 (0001)

0475 (0469)

0476 (0417)

0477 (0339)

0478 (0001)

0479 (0001)

0480 (0001)

0481 (0001)

0482 (0001)

0483 (0339)

0484 (0339)

0485 (0001)

0486 (0001)

0487 (0001)

0488 (0001)

0489 (0001)

0490 (0001)

0491 (0417)

0492 (0001)

0493 (0001)

0494 (0001)

0495, 0496, 0497, 0499, 0500, 0501, 0502, 0503, 0504, 0506, 0507, 0509
© Elica
www.elica.com

0496 (0495)

0497 (0495)

0498 (0417)

0499 (0495)

0500 (0495)

0501 (0495)

0502 (0495)

0503 (0495)

0504 (0495)

0505 (0408)

0506 (0495)

0507 (0495)

0508 (0417)

0509 (0495)

0510 (0408)

0511 (0417)

0512 (0339)

0513 (0417)

0514 (0408)

0515 (0001)

0516 (0001)

0517 (0001)

0518 (0001)

0519 (0001)

0520 (0001)

0521 (0001)

0522 (0339)

0523 (0001)

0524 (0001)

0525 (0001)

0526 (0001)

0527 (0001)

0528 (0001)

0529 (0339)

0530 (0339)

0531 (0001)

0532 (0001)

0533 (0417)

0534 (0001)

0535 (0408)

0536 (0421)

0537 (0001)

0538 (0408)

0539 (0417)

0540 (0339)

0541 (0001)

0542 (0001)

0543 (0329)

0544 (0317)

0545 (0264)

0546 (0057)

0547 (0302)

0548 (0001)

0549 (0001)

0550 (0001)

0551 (0001)

0552 (0001)

0553 (0001)

0554 (0001)

0555 (0001)

0556 (0417)

0557 (0001)

0558 (0001)

0559
© Iñaki Bergara
www.bergaraphoto.com

0560 (0001)

0561 (0025)

0562 (0001)

0563 (0001)

0564 (0001)

0565, 0566, 0576, 0578, 0640, 0643, 0644, 0645, 0698, 0705
© Cia International
www.ciainternational.it

0566 (0565)

0567 (0001)

0568 (0001)

0569 (0001)

0570 (0001)

0571 (0001)

0572 (0001)

0573 (0001)

0574 (0001)

0575 (0001)

0576 (0565)

0577 (0001)

0578 (0565)

0579 (0001)

0580 (0245)

0581 (0001)

0582 (0001)

0583 (0245)

0584 (0001)

0585 (0001)

0586 (0001)

0587 (0001)

0588 (0001)

0589 (0126)

0590 (0001)

0591 (0121)

0592 (0059)

0593 (0001)

0594 (0001)

0595 (0177)

0596 (0337)

0597 (0065)

0598 (0231)

0599 (0355)

0600 (0231)

0601 (0231)

0602 (0041)

0603 (0001)

0604 (0001)

0605 (0001)

0606 (0001)

0607 (0001)

0608 (0001)

0609 (0001)

0610 (0001)

0611 (0001)

0612 (0001)

0613 (0001)

0614 (0001)

0615 (0001)

0616 (0001)

0617 (0001)

0618 (0001)

0619 (0001)

0620 (0001)

0621 (0001)

0622 (0001)

0623 (0001)

0624 (0001)

0625 (0001)

0626 (0001)

0627 (0001)

0628 (0001)

0629 (0001)

0630 (0001)

0631 (0001)

0632 (0001)

0633 (0001)

0634 (0001)

0635 (0126)

0636 (0041)

0637 (0001)

0638 (0059)

0639, 0784, 0786, 0788, 0807, 0838, 0844, 0848, 0849, 0850, 0855, 0858, 0859
© Burgbad
http://burgbad.de

0640 (0565)

0641 (0107)

0642
© Lema
www.lemamobili.com

0643 (0565)

0644 (0565)

0645 (0565)

0646 (0337)

0647
© Flou
www.flou.it

0648
© Porro
www.porro.com

0649 (0001)

0650
© Former
www.former.it

0651 (0001)

0652 (0257)

0653 (0001)

0654 (0001)

0655 (0260)

0656 (0001)

0657 (0001)

0658 (0302)

0659 (0001)

0660 (0360)

0661 (0298)

0662
© Tobias Grau
www.tobias-grau.com

0663, 0965
© Lucente
www.lucente.eu

0664 (0302)

0665 (0298)

0666 (0057)

0667 (0317)

0668 (0001)

0669 (0001)

0670 (0001)

0671 (0001)

0672 (0001)

0673 (0001)

0674 (0001)

0675 (0001)

0676 (0001)

0677 (0001)

0678 (0001)

0679 (0001)

0680 (0001)

0681 (0001)

0682 (0001)

0683 (0001)

0684 (0001)

0685 (0001)

0686 (0001)

0687 (0158)

0688 (0001)

0689 (0001)

0690 (0001)

0691 (0158)

0692 (0158)

0693 (0001)

0694 (0001)

0695 (0001)

0696 (0001)

0697 (0001)

0698 (0565)

0699 (0337)

0700 (0231)

0701 (0001)

0702 (0001)

0703 (0001)

0704 (0001)

0705 (0565)

0706 (0001)

0707
© RES4
http://re4a.com

0708 (0001)

0709 (0001)

0710, 0711, 0714, 0715, 0717, 0718, 0719, 0722, 0725, 0727, 0728, 0729, 0730, 0734, 0735, 0738, 0740, 0741, 0745
© Dearkids
www.dearkids.it

0711 (0710)

0712 (0001)

0713 (0001)

0714 (0710)

0715 (0710)

0716 (0001)

0717 (0710)

0718 (0710)

0719 (0710)

0720, 0724
© P'kolino
www.pkolino.com

0721 (0001)

0722 (0710)

0723 (0001)

0724 (0720)

0725 (0710)

0726 (0001)

0727 (0710)

0728 (0710)

0729 (0710)

0730 (0710)

0731 (0001)

0732 (0001)

0733 (0001)

0734 (0710)

0735 (0710)

0736 (0001)

0737 (0001)

0738 (0710)

0739 (0001)

0740 (0710)

0741 (0710)

0742 (0001)

0743 (0001)

0744
© Kinderräume
www.kinderraeume.com

0745 (0710)

0746 (0001)

0747 (0001)

0748 (0001)

0749 (0001)

0750 (0001)

0751 (0001)

0752 (0001)

0753
Slide
http://slidedesign.it

0754
© Less n more
www.less-n-more.com

0755, 0756
© Vertigo Bird
www.vertigo-bird.com

0756 (0755)

0757
© Carretero Design
www.carreterodesign.com

0758 (0001)

0759 (0001)

0760 (0001)

0761 (0001)

0762 (0001)

0763 (0001)

0764 (0001)

0765 (0001)

0766, 0771, 0773, 0863
© Hansgrohe International
www.hansgrohe-int.com

0767, 0789
© Barasona
http://barasona.com

0768, 770, 0772, 0777, 0778, 0779, 0781, 0782, 0803, 0852, 0853, 0857, 0877
© Rapsel
www.rapsel.it

0769
© Dornbracht
www.dornbracht.com

0770 (0768)

0771 (0766)

0772 (0768)

0773 (0766)

0774 (0001)

0775 (0137)

0776 (0001)

0777 (0768)

0778 (0768)

0779 (0768)

0780 (0001)

0781 (0768)

0782 (0768)

0783 (0001)

0784 (0639)

0785 (0001)

0786 (0639)

0787, 0825
© Alape
www.alape.com

0788 (0639)

0789 (0767)

0790 (0001)

0791 (0001)

0792 (0001)

0793 (0001)

0794 (0001)

0795 (0001)

0796 (0001)

0797 (0001)

0798 (0001)

0799 (0001)

0800
© Autoban
www.autoban212.com

0801 (0001)

0802 (0001)

0803 (0768)

0804 (0001)

0805 (0001)

0806 (0001)

0807 (0639)

0808 (0001)

0809 (0001)

0810 (0001)

0811 (0001)

0812 (0001)

0813 (0001)

0814 (0001)

0815 (0001)

0816 (0001)

0817 (0001)

0818 (0001)

0819 (0001)

0820 (0001)

0821 (0001)

0822 (0001)

0823 (0001)

0824 (0001)

0825 (0787)

0826 (0001)

0827 (0001)

0828 (0001)

0829 (0001)

0830 (0001)

0831 (0001)

0832 (0001)

0833 (0001)

0834 (0001)

0835 (0001)

0836 (0137)

0837 (0001)

0838 (0639)

0839 (0001)

0840 (0001)

0841 (0001)

0842
© Tervhivatal
www.tervhivatal.hu

0843 (0001)

0844 (0639)

0845 (0317)

0846 (0001)

0847 (0001)

0848 (0639)

0849 (0639)

0850 (0639)

0851 (0001)

0852 (0768)

0853 (0768)

0854 (0001)

0855 (0639)

0856 (0001)

0857 (0768)

0858 (0639)

0859 (0639)

0860 (0001)

0861 (0001)

0862 (0001)

0863 (0766)

0864 (0001)

0865 (0001)

0866 (0001)

0867 (0001)

0868 (0001)

0869 (0001)

0870 (0001)

0871 (0001)

0872 (0001)

0873 (0001)

0874 (0001)

0875 (0001)

0876 (0001)

0877 (0768)

0878 (0001)

0879 (0001)

0880 (0001)

0881 (0001)

0882 (0001)

0883 (0245)

0884 (0001)

0885 (0001)

0886 (0001)

0887 (0001)

0888 (0001)

0889 (0001)

0890 (0001)

0891 (0001)

0892 (0001)

0893 (0001)

0894 (0001)

0895 (0001)

0896 (0001)

0897 (0001)

0898 (0001)

0899 (0001)

0900 (0001)

0901, 0903, 0904, 0908, 0912, 0913, 0915,
0940, 0941, 0942, 0943, 0944, 0945, 0947,
0955, 0961, 0988
© Pircher
www.pircher.eu

0902 (0001)

0903 (0901)

0904 (0901)

0905, 0906, 0907, 0909, 0916, 0917, 0918,
0920, 0921, 0922, 0923, 0924, 0939, 0971,
0990, 0993, 0994, 0998
© Gervasoni
www.gervasoni1882.it

0906 (0905)

0907 (0905)

0908 (0901)

0909 (0905)

0910, 0911, 0966, 0968, 0969
© Myyour
www.myyour.eu/it

0911 (0910)

0912 (0901)

0913 (0901)

0914 (0001)

0915 (0901)

0916 (0905)

0917 (0905)

0918 (0905)

0919
© Novo Design
www.novoitalia.it

0920 (0905)

0921 (0905)

0922 (0905)

0923 (0905)

0924 (0905)

0925
© Tonon
www.tononitalia.com

0926 (0001)

0927 (0001)

0928 (0001)

0929 (0001)

0930 (0001)

0931 (0001)

0932 (0001)

0933 (0001)

0934 (0001)

0935 (0001)

0936 (0001)

0937 (0001)

0938 (0001)

0939 (0905)

0940 (0901)

0941 (0901)

0942 (0901)

0943 (0901)

0944 (0901)

0945 (0901)

0946 (0001)

0947 (0901)

0948 (0001)

0949 (0001)

0950 (0001)

0951 (0001)

0952 (0001)

0953 (0001)

0954 (0137)

0955 (0901)

0956 (0001)

0957 (0001)

0958 (0264)

0959 (0001)

0960 (0001)

0961 (0901)

0962 (0001)

0963 (0001)

0964 (0001)

0965 (0663)

0966 (0910)

0967
© Royal Botania
www.royalbotania.com

0968 (0910)

0969 (0910)

0970 (0286)

0971 (0905)

0972, 0973
© Shades of Green Landscape Architecture
www.shadesofgreenla.com

0973 (0972)

0974 (0001)

0975 (0001)

0976 (0001)

0977 (0001)

0978 (0001)

0979 (0001)

0980 (0001)

0981 (0001)

0982 (0001)

0983 (0001)

0984 (0001)

0985 (0001)

0986 (0001)

0987 (0001)

0988 (0901)

0989 (0001)

0990 (0905)

0991 (0001)

0992 (0001)

0993 (0905)

0994 (0905)

0995 (0177)

0996 (0158)

0997
© Punt Mobles
www.puntmobles.com

0998 (0905)

0999 (0158)

1000 (0158)